Computers in Manufacturing

**How to understand Metalworking's newest tools ...
and their use to improve output**

By the editors of American Machinist

American Machinist
McGraw-Hill Publications Company
New York

I

LIBRARY OF CONGRESS CATALOGING IN PUBLICATION DATA
Main entry under title:

Computers in Manufacturing

Selected articles, mostly from the past 3 years, from the American Machinist.
Includes bibliographical references and index.
1.   Production management—Data processing.
2.   Production engineering—Data processing.

I.   American Machinist
TS155.C59   1983   670'.285'4   83-8798
ISBN 0-07-001548-1
ISBN 0-07-001549-X (soft)

Computers in Manufacturing

1234567890

The editor of this book is William M. Stocker Jr.
Cover design and page layout by Arthur Finkelstein.

Table
of
Contents

2218406

Preface

In a few industries, production can be carried out as a continuous, orderly procedure, but, for most industries (those that manufacture individual parts and then assemble them into products), production is more likely to be a mad scramble of expediters working with shortage lists to try to push needed parts to the right place at the right time.

Computers are beginning to change that. With the aid of the computer, all the steps from design through to shipping can be integrated in a way that minimizes the time wasted between operations and the delays caused when parts aren't completed on schedule.

Computers were first introduced into manufacturing, as in other types of businesses, to handle payroll and accounting. These are fairly standardized operations for which packaged programs are readily available. Quite early in the process, however, a few far-seeing individuals began to realize that computers could accomplish much more in a company's engineering and manufacturing operations than in accounting.

As computers began to be used for inventory control, production scheduling, machine control, process operation, materials handling, and assembly, "islands of automation" began to develop in many companies. In other companies, computers were also used for engineering calculations and product testing. More recently, the development of interactive graphics/systems has enabled computers to be applied to drafting and then to actual design, initially for electrical work and later for mechanical work.

The popular term for these activities is CAD/CAM, meaning "Computer-Aided Design/Computer-Aided Manufacturing." The use of the two terms reflects the fact that most manufacturing industries operate with a number of computerized islands that are proving difficult to fit together into a single system. The goal is a single system for all the information processing in the company's activities, and the term being used to describe this is *CIM*, meaning Computer-Integrated Manufacturing.

When difficulties have arisen in applying computers to manufacturing, it has usually been because manufacturing managers, who knew less about computers than they should, turned the problems over to computer specialists, who knew less about the real requirements of the manufacturing application than they thought they did.

From the earliest steps in applying computers to any of the manufacturing operations, the editors of *American Machinist* have been regularly reporting on the activities taking place "at the leading edge of change." All of the material in this book represents the fruits of that reporting, most of it having appeared in the pages of the magazine in the last three years.

The book starts with a primer on computers and a broad view of how they are being applied in manufacturing today. Following chapters go into more detail on the use of computer graphics in design, applications in manufacturing planning and control, the recent development of simulation systems as a manufacturing tool, and the methods available to justify the use of computers in manufacturing. These are followed by descriptions of specific successful applications. The book concludes with a review of the activities in applying computers to manufacturing in Western Europe, Eastern Europe, and Japan . . . scenarios worth watching.

Most of the content of this book is the work of ten editors on the *American Machinist* staff: Ben C. Brosheer, Nancy Brooke Freeman, Robert L. Hatschek, Joseph Jablonowski, Lori Kapner, John M. Martin, Susan Qualtrough, George H. Schaffer, John A. Vaccari, and John T. Winship. The staff was further reinforced by input from McGraw-Hill World News correspondents Margaret Drossel, Robert Neff, and Naoaki Usui; plus a great deal of work by Art Director Arthur Finkelstein. George H. Schaffer's contribution to this compendium on computers deserves special note for its depth and diversity.

Contributors from industry and academia, for whose ideas and efforts we are most appreciative, are credited on the pages they have written. These people are pioneers, logging their adventures into an exciting new world of manufacturing capability.

Together, these editors and contributors have created a truly laudable contribution to understanding the role of the computer in manufacturing operations, especially in metalworking. Within this spectrum, they cover, clearly and concisely, information and ideas that will be useful to the people in industry who must comprehend this technology as well as to students and others who need to learn manufacturing from a new perspective.

The effective application of computers to the integration of manufacturing operations provides the best hope today for substantial gains in industrial productivity. Because each individual company has unique requirements, simple packaged programs rarely can do the job. This book is designed to help manufacturing specialists and computer specialists bridge the gap between their two worlds to effectively apply computers to the integration of manufacturing operations. As many of the applications in this book demonstrate, it can be done.

Anderson Ashburn
Editor, American Machinist

New York
April 1983

CHAPTER I

An Introduction to Computers

Computers in Manufacturing

Although computers are becoming one of industry's most useful tools, they are still feared and misunderstood. This primer for manufacturing engineers should help remove the mystery.

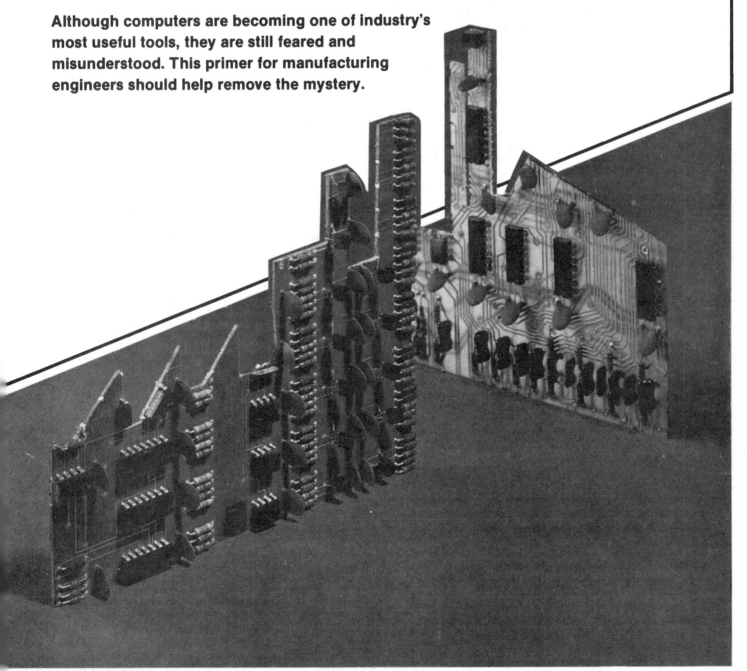

Computers in manufacturing

IN A RELATIVELY short time, the computer has become one of the basic and ubiquitous tools of our industrial society. To claim ignorance of its constant involvement in our everyday life bespeaks a naiveté bordering on folly; to resist utilizing its many-faceted services in the manufacturing arena is an invitation to economic disaster.

And yet computers are very much misunderstood and feared. "If anything can go wrong it will," states Murphy's Law. To which O'Brien adds, "When a computer is involved, Murphy must be taken as an optimist." True, but that's to the credit of the computer. If it weren't so slavish in performing its assigned task, it would not be capable of compounding errors—most often caused by faulty programming or bad data—with such ferocity. "Garbage in, garbage out" is the computer's rejoinder to both Murphy and O'Brien.

Contrary to popular notion, computers are indeed extremely reliable and willing servants—rather than ornery masters intent on screwing up the works. And they are not as stupid as we would like to pretend: they can be taught to reason—provided we establish the rules. In fact, computers are universally recognized as industry's most powerful and effective tool for improving productivity—the single most important concern of every manufacturing manager.

Perhaps the most readily discernible computer applications in manufacturing have been in the area of numerically controlled machine tools. From its very inception, NC has involved the use of computer assistance for program development. Direct numerical control (DNC)—in which one computer feeds data to a group of NC machines as needed—and, more recently, computer numerical control (CNC)—which uses a dedicated computer within a numerical-control system—bring the computer into more-direct contact with the machine tool.

Elsewhere in the manufacturing environment, computers are also active in manufacturing engineering, materials management, machine monitoring, scheduling and production control, and management-information systems. Without necessarily planning it that way, many companies are finding themselves deeply involved in some aspect of computer-aided manufacturing (CAM), which has been defined as the effective utilization of computer technology in the management, control, and operations of a manufacturing facility through either direct or indirect computer interface with the physical and human resources of the company.

Computer-aided design (CAD) ranges from the use of computers to perform isolated calculations to the ability of a system to compile a bill of materials. Designs can now be created on interactive graphic computer terminals, which place a vast data base at the designer's fingertip and, at the same time, force the use of established technology. The result can often be translated directly into such manufacturing instructions as NC machining tapes.

Order out of chaos

In a larger sense, it is predicted that the computer will help make order out of manufacturing, which has been aptly described as a kind of organized chaos. Most manufacturing control has really been just a matter of solving one crisis after another using the most expedient solution available at the time. The computer can change all that.

Consider, if you will, that all of manufacturing can readily be reduced to a series of data transformations. Data, or information, are generated from the concept in a person's mind and move through a whole series of transformations to the creation of the final product. Each data transformation (from drawing to operations sheet, for example) meets the need of a particular activity and may result in a new output format. But the end product of the design/manufacturing cycle is, in fact, the exact embodiment of the data with which the entire process started.

In essence, the various data transformations can be boiled down to the reiteration of three basic and relatively simple tasks: collect information, reach a judgment or decision, and disseminate an order—all tasks eminently suited to the computer's capabilities. The first and last of these tasks are clearly pure data-handling functions, the very task that computers excel in.

Decision-making functions do not require moral judgments or abstract reasoning but, rather, are based either on well-established rules and principles or, more often, on experience. A computer can be taught the rules or made to remember the experience. Herein is the computer at its pervasive best.

The result of such computer integration is a manufacturing environment structured as a series of computer-aided information services linked by a computer hierarchy to the various activity centers where the process of actual manufacturing takes place. And these processes themselves are increasingly controlled by computers and computer-like devices.

Dr Joseph Harrington Jr calls this kind of control and communications structure *computer-integrated manufac-*

ture, in his book of that name. "Sooner or later, the head of every manufacturing establishment must consider the subject of computer-integrated manufacturing procedures," writes Harrington. Sooner or later, every manufacturing manager must ask these questions:

- Is this the time for me to consider it?
- How extensively should I convert?
- How long will it take?
- Can I justify the cost?
- How will it affect what I now have?

Perhaps the biggest motivating factor leading to the increasing application of computers in manufacturing is the changing nature of industry, from a mass-production-oriented practice based on long model runs to a more batch-like operating scheme that can respond quickly and efficiently to the rapidly changing demands of the market place. Even such a paradigm of mass production as the automobile industry is sensitive to this change. As GM's "Pete" Estes put it recently, "since our industry's market has been turned topsy-turvy a couple of times since the oil embargo of 1973, one of management's goals is to provide more flexibility in our manufacturing operations. This can save money and speed up our response time when consumer demand does change."

One of the most valuable tools

Estes considers the computer "one of the most valuable tools we have." To provide the increasing flexibility he has in mind, GM manufacturing engineers are looking closely at the use of modular, integrated machining systems for some of their operations.

"A typical system would consist of a number of basic, numerically controlled machining centers supplied by a part-handling system—all under the control of a minicomputer, which would be tied to a larger, supervisory computer," says Estes. Such a system could be quickly programmed to do work on a number of different parts as long as they were all within its size range.

Although the use of computers in manufacturing now lags behind both data-processing and design uses at GM, an internal study predicts a 400% increase in manufacturing uses by 1982. Estes himself feels that, within ten years, computers will control about 90% of all the new machines in GM's manufacturing and assembly plants!

The major barrier to greater use of computer-related manufacturing, according to many manufacturers, has been the high cost involved. But that picture has changed dramatically over the years. Writing in a recent issue of

Scientific American, Robert N. Noyes, chairman of Intel Corp, states, "Today's microcomputer, at a cost of perhaps $300, has more computing capacity than the first large electronic computer, ENIAC. It is 20 times faster, has a larger memory, is thousands of times more reliable, consumes the power of a light bulb rather than that of a locomotive, occupies 1/30,000 the volume, and costs 1/10,000 as much. It is available by mail order or at your local hobby shop."

All that is undoubtedly true, but it does not necessarily mean that you can run your manufacturing facility with hobby-shop computers or that overall system costs are plummeting that rapidly. A more accurate picture is that you continuously get more computing power for your money and that, while the mainframe costs go down, the increasing use of more peripheral equipment coupled with the requirement to handle increasingly complex tasks tends to bring overall system costs back up. And, while hardware is becoming relatively inexpensive and very reliable, software development remains a time-consuming and expensive venture.

The real difficulty comes in justifying the installation of a computer. And, while some of the claims and educated guesses at the possible productivity increases are staggering, attempts to quantify them tend to be elusive: the influence of the computer in manufacturing is far too pervasive.

This point is well-expressed by Donald N. Smith and Lary Evans, who explore the subject of economic justification in depth in their recent book, *Management Standards for Computer & Numerical Control*: "When evaluating proposed investments in conventional machinery, many cost elements can be disregarded since they are equally affected by the competing alternatives. Often, such indirect costs as handling of materials, tooling, inspection, assembly, and inventory-related factors, vary little, regardless of which conventional machine is selected.

"However, once computer or numerical controls are considered as an investment possibility, indirect costs may change drastically, and the many factors previously ignored must be thoroughly examined." According to the authors, the investment dilemma regarding computer and numerical control produces two distinct consequences. "Many decision-makers simply feel overwhelmed by the many facets that must be evaluated and avoid the drudgery of an exhaustive analysis by rejecting outright the proposed investment. Some also pass up profitable cost reductions because their investment analysis was too cursory and overlooked the less obvious, but substantial indirect economies."

The other consequence of the investment dilemma results in simply authorizing the investment on the basis of good faith. When this faith proves unjustified, for whatever reason, and the expected economies do not materialize, all future computer applications become suspect; and an embargo against such investments may even be ordered. The unfortunate result of all these decisions is that technologically superior equipment is not utilized to the extent that is actually warranted.

Another barrier to manufacturing engineers in their application of computers is a basic lack of understanding. As Smith and Evans put it, "the complexity of computer-aided manufacturing technology has grown to a level such that even managers who progressed through engineering-related departments often do not fully understand the details of computer-aided manufacturing projects their subordinates propose."

Of course, an understanding of the intricacies of computer programming or the technology of solid-state electronics is not at all necessary for the wise use of computers. After all, we all learn to use the telephone effectively, and who of us has even a nodding acquaintance with the vast realm of computer-related technology that makes it all possible?

But ignorance breeds fear, and every manufacturing engineer should have at least some understanding of what goes on behind the terminals and CRTs, so that fear of the unknown does not prevent proper utilization. Only by understanding the beast, can manufacturing engineers bring their creative talents toward harnessing it to perform their increasingly difficult tasks. The fundamentals of computers are really not all that complicated; so let's take a look.

Some computer fundamentals

From the dawn of civilization, human beings have developed tools to lighten their burdens. Initially, tools primarily extended the power and usefulness of the human's physical attributes. The computer is unique in that it is a tool that helps extend the power of mental processes.

It started with the need to count. The first counting machines were pebbles or sea shells. The word "counter," meaning that store fixture that holds the cash register and separates customer and shopkeeper, derives from the fact that money was counted on tables designed with grooves in which beads could be moved to register a transaction. And, of course, we are all familiar with the abacus, a form of which was used until recently by Japanese bank clerks in their daily work.

The concept of numbers—those symbols that can represent anything we want, rather than having to represent the actual thing we count—was a major achievement in abstract thinking. But, for centuries, numbers were relegated to purely quantitative transactions. With the application, however, of a practical form of binary arithmetic and the development of symbolic logic—like Boolean algebra, in which reasoning is expressed in binary terms (true or false) that can be manipulated algebraically to give valid answers—the digital computer was born.

"Computer: a person who computes," according to the latest edition of the *American Heritage Dictionary of the English Language*. Or, alternatively: "A device that computes; especially an electronic machine that peforms high-speed mathematical or logic calculations or that assembles, stores, correlates, or otherwise processes and prints information derived from coded data in accordance with a predetermined program."

In other words, a computer is an information-handling machine. What makes it unique and so very useful is that it can execute instructions in a predetermined and self-directed manner. It does this by reading its instructions in the form of a program that it remembers by storing it in an internal memory. All subsequent data or instructions are then manipulated in accordance with this executive program. That means that the computer need not be reinstructed as the job it performs progresses and that it can, therefore, perform tasks of considerable complexity from start to finish without any operator intervention.

General-purpose digital computers can be used for a large variety of applications, because the program stored within the computer's memory can be changed. Rapid access to the stored program, as well as the ability to follow alternative program routes according to the computer-perceived results of a series of program steps (conditional branching), is what makes modern computers so versatile.

Computers speak binary

Regardless of the technology involved, digital computers depend on the ability to represent and manipulate symbols, commonly referred to as characters. In fact, all of the information that passes through a computer, including every instruction the computer executes, is in the form of numbers. A fundamental requirement for computers, therefore, is the ability to physically represent numbers and to perform operations on the numbers thus represented.

How can the computer best deal with and represent numbers? Computer systems, which are basically composed of electronic and electromechanical devices, can readily sense or establish one of two states—positive or negative current, magnetized or not magnetized, on or off, the presence or absence of a hole. The key to the computer's ability to deal with numbers, then, is a numbering system that can be represented as a bistate condition. And that's why the simplest number representation for computers is the binary system, in which only two symbols—a 1 and a 0—are required to represent any quantity.

What is simple for the computer, however, often seems perplexing to us, and, when computerniks start talking of

Binary representation of decimal values

Decimal value	Place values	Binary notation			
		8	4	2	1
0	=	0	0	0	0
1	=	0	0	0	1
2	=	0	0	1	0
3	=	0	0	1	1
4	=	0	1	0	0
5	=	0	1	0	1
6	=	0	1	1	0
7	=	0	1	1	1
8	=	1	0	0	0
9	=	1	0	0	1
10	=	1	0	1	0
11	=	1	0	1	1
12	=	1	1	0	0
13	=	1	1	0	1

binary bits or when the computer console blinks its binary memory location, it all starts to sound very complex. It really isn't as complicated as it sounds, though.

The binary numbering system follows the same set of rules as the numbering system with which we are all familiar: the decimal numbering system. The primary difference is in the number of distinct symbols, or digits, that exist within each: ten (0 through 9) for the decimal system, two (0 and 1) for the binary system.

To understand the binary system, remember first that all modern numbering systems are based on the principle of count and carry. You count in units until you run out of symbols; then you start all over again by "carrying" a 1 to the next place. For example, in the decimal system, each ascending digit is the result of increasing the value of the previous digit by 1:

```
 1    2..........5.................9
+1   +1........+1...............+1
 2    3          6                ?
```

What happens when the largest digit, nine, is increased by one? Most of us missed this concept when we learned math by rote. Nine plus one is not "ten"; when one is added to the largest digit, it results in an overflow condition. A zero is recorded in this digit position, and a one is carried over to the next highest digit position, where it becomes a carry-in, or is added into the new position:

```
carry   1
        09
       +01
        10
```

The concepts of overflow and carry-in establish the principle of positional value: the idea that the value of a number depends both on the symbol value and on the position of that symbol within the whole number. For example, in the decimal system, the digit 7 has a different value in each of the three numbers 127, 172, and 703. In the first number, the digit 7 has its original value 7; in the second, it has the value 70; and, in the last number, it has the value 700.

In effect, the positional values of the digits in the decimal system increase to the left of the decimal point in a series represented by the powers of ten: $10^n.....10^3, 10^2, 10^1, 10^0$, or N.....1000,

Notation comparison

Decimal	Binary	Octal
0	0	0
1	1	1
2	10	2
3	11	3
4	100	4
5	101	5
6	110	6
7	111	7
8	1000	10
9	1001	11
10	1010	12
11	1011	13
12	1100	14
13	1101	15

100, 10, 1. The total value of the decimal number is obtained by summing the products of each position value multiplied by the symbol values (0 through 9) in that position. For example:

$$652 = 6 \times 10^2 = 600$$
$$5 \times 10^1 = 50$$
$$2 \times 10^0 = \underline{2}$$
$$652$$

Another important concept in numbering systems is the use of the numeral zero to indicate a position within a number that has no units. Without that concept, there would be no difference in notation between, say, 302 and 32. The numeral zero fills the gap.

In the binary numbering system, the positional values of the digits increase to the left of the decimal point in a series represented by the powers of two: $2^n.....2^3, 2^2, 2^1, 2^0$ or N.....16, 8, 4, 2, 1. And, again, the total value of the binary number is obtained by summing the products of each position value multiplied by the symbol values (0 or 1) in that position. For example:

$$\text{binary number } 1011 = 1 \times 2^3 = 8$$
$$0 \times 2^2 = 0$$
$$1 \times 2^1 = 2$$
$$1 \times 2^0 = \underline{1}$$
$$11$$

Remember, a number is merely a convenient symbol used to represent a quantity, and a numbering system is just a means of representing quantities using a set of numbers. All modern numbering systems use the zero to indicate no units and other symbols to indicate quantities. The number of symbols used is called the base, or radix, of a numbering system. The positional values of the numbering system increase to the left of the decimal

Binary-coded decimal notation for the number 265,498

Decimal notation	2				6				5				4				9				8			
Binary notation	0	0	1	0	0	1	1	0	0	1	0	1	0	1	0	0	1	0	0	1	1	0	0	0
Place value	8	4	2	1	8	4	2	1	8	4	2	1	8	4	2	1	8	4	2	1	8	4	2	1

point in a series represented by the powers of the base.

In the binary system, the one that computers can best deal with internally, a group of four binary digits is required to express the decimal digits 0 through 9. (Incidentally, a *bi*nary dig*it* is called a *bit*, a term much bandied about in computerese.) In binary-coded decimal representation, each decimal position (and its value) is represented by a separate group of four bits. The number 30 would be written as 0011 (representing 3) followed by 0000 (representing 0). And the binary-coded decimal representation of the decimal number 265,498 would be 001001100101010010011000 (see accompanying table).

Binary needs shorthand

Now, that's quite a mouthful! Obviously, while the binary system is quite nice for computers, it is more than a little cumbersome for human use. It is very easy for humans to make errors in reading and writing quantities of large binary numbers; a long string of 1s and 0s cannot be effectively communicated from one individual to another. What is needed is some sort of shorthand system that will reduce all those 1s and 0s to something more manageable for computer programmers. There are actually two equally suitable alternatives: the octal (base-8) and the hexadecimal (base-16) numbering systems.

Because of their simple relationship to binary representation, numbers can be converted from one system to the other by simple inspection. For example, the octal system, which uses eight symbols (0 through 7) has a three-to-one relationship to the binary system; every three-bit group of a binary number can be represented by a single octal digit. If you memorize the binary equivalent for 0 through 7 and group a binary value into sets of three bits, conversion becomes relatively easy, and the octal system becomes a convenient shorthand notation. The hexadecimal system, which uses the symbols 0 though 9 and A through F, is simply another shorthand notation to express the bit pattern within a computer.

Now that you have some insight into the binary system, remember that it is used strictly as the internal language of the computer. As a manufacturing engineer, you can communicate with computers in the customary alphanumeric symbols, which the input device encodes into a binary-based code for computer handling. And, even more important, computers can be instructed by means of special English-like programming languages designed to suit a particular need.

But more about programming later. First, let's look at the general configuration of a typical computer.

Computers are all alike

Computer systems are composed of various physical devices, usually referred to as hardware; software is the various programs needed to operate the system. Basically, all computers—be they behemoths, minis, or micros—have the same functional configuration. They all need a means of communicating with the outside world, and this is accomplished with an input/output (I/O) interface that connects to and controls such peripheral devices as readers, printers, displays, and bulk-memory devices. The I/O interface also communicates with the appropriate process variables for other than data-processing computer applications.

Computers need to store information as they process it and, therefore, have internal storage capacity, often referred to as the main memory. Finally, but most important, computers must be able to process the information they acquire, and this is performed in the central processing unit (CPU), sometimes referred to as the mainframe of a system.

The CPU is really the heart of any computer. It supervises the entire computer system and performs the actual arithmetic and logic operations on data. Functionally, the CPU consists of two sections: control and arithmetic/logic.

The control section directs and coordinates all operations called for by instructions. It is an administrative or switching section, which receives information entering the computer and decides how and when to perform operations. For exam-

Basic computer structure

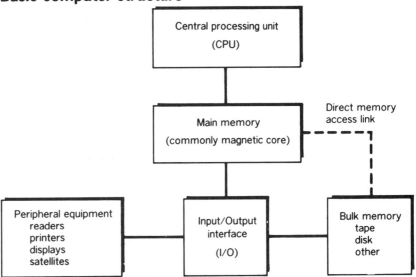

Typical central processing unit (CPU)

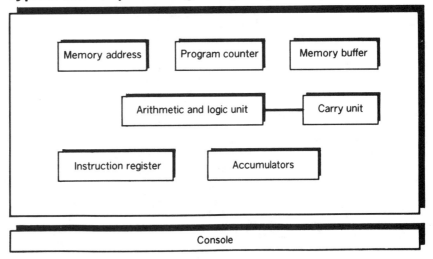

ple, it tells the arithmetic/logic unit what to do and where to get the necessary information. It knows when the arithmetic unit has completed a calculation and tells it what to do with the results and then what to do next. The control unit knows what to do by interpreting a set of instructions—the executive program—stored in the computer's main memory.

The arithmetic/logic unit performs the actual arithmetic and logic operations. For arithmetic, it calculates, shifts numbers, sets the algebraic sign of results, compares, rounds, and so on. The logic section performs the decision-making operations to change the sequence of instruction execution. It performs these operations by counting series of pulses or by the use of logic circuits.

Both the control unit and the arithmetic/logic unit use registers to perform their functions. Computer registers are devices capable of receiving information, holding it, and transferring it as directed by control circuits. They are commonly arrays of magnetic cores or transistors and are constructed to store a specific amount of data—usually one word. The output of a register is either data or a true/false result of a logic operation.

A word, in computer parlance, is a sequence of bits treated as a unit and capable of being stored in one computer location. It is the primary level at which bits are grouped and handled within any computer. Sometimes, computer specialists work with another group of bits called "bytes." This is a somewhat flexible term referring to a sequence of bits operated on as a unit but usually shorter than a word. Frequently, it is a submultiple of a word used with a particular system. To some, IBM in particular, a byte is an eight-bit data unit.

A large number of different word lengths (the number of bits per word) are in use, varying with the type and manufacturer of the computer. Many microcomputers use four-bit words, but eight-bit words are most common. Minicomputers use mostly 12- or 16-bit words, while large computers use 32- and even 64-bit word lengths. In order to determine the capacity of a computer or memory system, you need to know both the number of words that can be handled and the number of bits per word.

A typical central processor for a minicomputer may have the following functional units (see diagram):

- Program counter—holds the location (address) of the next instruction to be executed.
- Instruction register—holds a copy of the current instruction.
- Arithmetic/logic unit—does the number-crunching; where all the data manipulation takes place.
- Accumulators—provide easily accessible, limited-storage area for the temporary storage and manipulation of an operand (data to be operated on); often referred to as a scratch pad.
- Carry unit—provides an extension for the arithmetic and logic unit used to indicate overflow.
- Memory-address register—keeps track of latest address referenced.
- Memory-buffer register—contains the content of last address referenced.
- Console—includes switches for manipulating the various registers on a bit by bit basis.

Some memory minders

It is important to distinguish between the main memory of a computer and the bulk memory, sometimes referred to as storage, that is available to the computer. The main memory is physically located at the computer mainframe and is directly available to the CPU for its routine manipulation of data. It is the focal point of all data movement during processing and stores all instructions, necessary tables of reference data, and the blocks of actual data being processed at any time.

Bulk memory, on the other hand, is located in peripheral equipment and is

Magnetic-core storage: how it works

A magnetic core is a tiny ring of ferromagnetic material, a few hundredths of an inch in diameter. Cores are used as storage elements because a single core can be easily magnetized in a few milliseconds. And, unless deliberately changed, a core retains its magnetism indefinitely.

If cores are placed on a wire, like beads on a string, and a strong enough electrical current is sent through the wire, the cores become magnetized. The direction of the current determines the polarity of the cores. Reversing the direction of the current reverses the polarity of magnetization.

This ability to change polarity makes the core suitable as a binary storage element; its two magnetic states can be used to represent the binary digits, 0 or 1, which are used for storing computer information. Because any specific location of storage must be instantly accessible, the cores are arranged so that any combination of ones (1s) and zeros (0s) representing a character can be written magnetically or read back when needed.

To accomplish this selection, the cores are arranged on a grid of wires with two wires running through each core and at right angles to each other. If half the current needed to magnetize a core is sent through each of two core wires, only the core at the intersection of the ener-

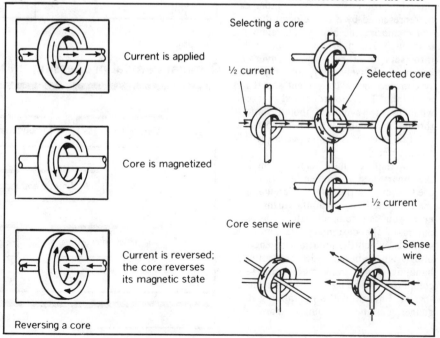

Current is applied

Core is magnetized

Current is reversed; the core reverses its magnetic state

Reversing a core

Selecting a core

½ current

Selected core

½ current

Core sense wire

Sense wire

not directly available to the CPU. The computer must bring data from such bulk memory into its main memory in order to operate with it. Usually this is done via the I/O interface, although some systems have so-called direct-memory-access (DMA) links for high-speed dumping of external memory directly into the computer's main memory. Bulk memory is used to file programs and other data to be transferred to the computer as needed for a particular operation.

High access speed—the time needed to retrieve any data within the memory—and the ability to alter the content are prime requirements for the main memory, because much of the data resides in it only temporarily and must be readily transferred in and out between it and other computer elements. That is why main memories are designed as random-access memories (RAMs); any individual bit can be accessed directly without the need to read through many other memory locations, as is necessary in serial-type memories, such as magnetic tape.

In most large computers and minicomputers, the main memory is made of magnetic cores—tiny donut-shaped ferromagnetic elements that store bits in terms of their magnetic state (see box below). Hence, main memories are often referred to as core storage, although

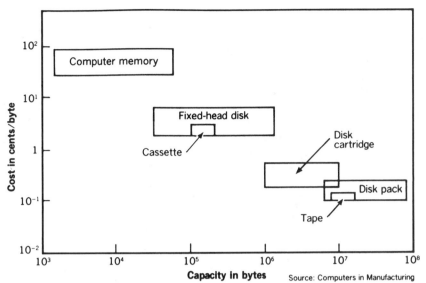

Storage cost and capacity vary for different peripherals. Byte equals 8 bits

microcomputers use semiconductor RAM chips as their main memories.

R/W, ROM, PROM, or other?

Because of the nature of the operation, the content of magnetic-core memories is destroyed during the normal reading cycle; therefore, the data must be replaced, or rewritten, into memory after it has been read. For this reason, the term read/write (R/W) memory is often applied to magnetic-core memories. More recently, this term has also been applied to any memory that allows data to be changed readily, as opposed to read-only memories (ROMs), in which data is permanently built in during manufacture.

ROMs are used for applications in which the program or data stored in

gized wires is magnetized. No other core on the grid is affected. By this principle, a large number of cores can be strung on

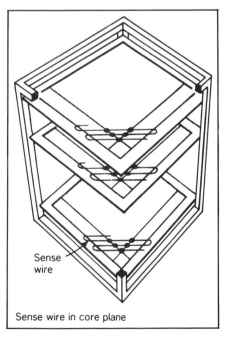

Sense wire in core plane

a screen of wires (usually called a core plane); yet any single core in the screen can be selected for storage or reading without affecting any other.

Once information is placed in core storage, some means must be devised to make it accessible; that is, to recall it when needed. It has been shown that a definite magnetic polarity can be set up in a core by the flow of current through a wire running through it. In a computer, the flow is actually not constant; it is sent through the wire as an electrical pulse, which is said to "flip" the core to a positive or negative state, depending on the direction of current flow.

If the magnetic state of the core is reversed by the pulse, the abrupt change, or flip, induces current in a third wire running through the center of the core. The signal through this sense wire can be detected to determine whether the core flipped, thus "reading" its magnetic state, which is, in turn, equivalent to the binary conditions 1 or 0.

Only one sense wire is needed for an entire core plane, because only one core at a time in any plane is tested for its

magnetic state. The wire is therefore strung through all the cores of the plane.

In other words, reading is accomplished by testing one core at a time for its magnetic state. But, since this testing is done by pulsing the core, the process, in effect, empties the memory: after reading, all the cores will be set to the same magnetic state. Readout is destructive because the process of reading a 1 resets the core to 0. Therefore, to retain data in storage, the computer must replace ones (1s) in those cores that had previously contained ones (1s). But cores that contained zeros (0s) must remain zeros (0s).

To reproduce ones (1s) as they should be, the computer tries to write back ones (1s) in all the locations previously read; at the same time, an inhibit pulse suppresses writing in cores that previously contained zeros (0s). The inhibit is sent through a fourth wire and, in effect, cancels out the writing pulse in one of the two wires used to magnetize the core. Like the sense wire, the inhibit wire also runs through every core in the plane.

Computers in manufacturing

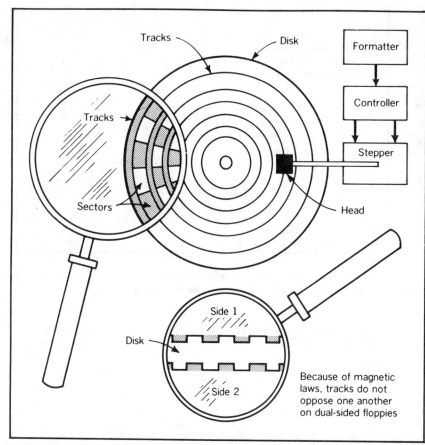

Tracks

Disk

Formatter

Controller

Stepper

Tracks

Sectors

Head

Side 1

Disk

Side 2

Because of magnetic laws, tracks do not oppose one another on dual-sided floppies

Floppy-disk recording scheme places data on a series of tracks with data grouped into sectors, each separated by identification and error-checking signals

them are not to be changed. A masking step fixes the bit pattern during manufacture of these semiconductor memories, which are frequently used to handle permanently assigned tasks, or microprograms, carried out by the computer.

Confusing matters a little are programmable ROMs, often called PROMs. A data pattern can be written (burned) into them at low speed. They consist of memory-array elements connected with fusible links, or junctions, or they consist of laser-severable islands on the semiconductor chip. One-time programming is effected by breaking the connections selectively, either by a high write current or under the heat of a laser beam.

Recently, there have been developed electrically alterable read-only memories (EAROMs), which can be rewritten many times with special techniques. They are technically R/W memories but have long write times and usually require a separate erase step, in which the entire memory chip is erased. Some are mass erased through a quartz window by ultraviolet rays.

Speed and capacity vary

All memories are essentially information storehouses. Their capacity and the rate at which information can be channeled into or out of them largely determine which memory is used for particular applications—main or bulk. Magnetic tape, drum (now mostly obsolete), or disk memories all use a magnetic element that moves relative to a recording head, with data recorded as magnetic blips in various tracks.

All of these memories can store large quantities of information at low cost and are available in many forms; some can store up to 10-billion bits; and all have the advantage of being nonvolatile, which means that they hold their data even when the power source fails. Their prime disadvantage is slow speed. For example, magnetic-tape memories can take anywhere from 0.1 to 100 seconds to retrieve just one piece of stored information. Magnetic disks and drums are faster—from 8 to 200 milliseconds—but they are still slow compared with other technologies, such as magnetic cores or semiconductors.

Recently, flexible-disk units, or diskettes, have been introduced to serve as low-cost, minisized RAMs, which have become a popular data-input medium for numerical-control systems as replacement for punched tape. Physically, flop-

pies—as they are also called—are flexible plastic disks, about the size and appearance of a 45-rpm record, coated with a ferromagnetic material. Data are recorded as magnetic pulses arranged in concentric circles and in pie-shaped sectors on either one or both sides of the ferromagnetically coated disk.

The major drawback to magnetic-core memories is their cost, which includes quite a bit of auxiliary circuitry needed to get at the stored information. For this reason, core memories are always rather limited in size compared with other storage devices, and efficient use of core memory is required to get the maximum power and efficiency out of a computer.

Semiconductor magic

Semiconductor, or integrated-circuit, memories store information in the form of simple electronic charges in small functional components on chips of silicon. A typical memory chip is less than a quarter-inch square and can contain as many as 16,000 bits of information. Information stored in the individual components is accessed by accompanying circuitry located on the same silicon chip. These are the little wonders that have spawned the microcomputer. Their main drawback is that they are volatile. But that can always be compensated for with backup battery power. And the latest chips require such low power that very small battery sources can ensure memory retention over long periods.

CCDs and bubbles

The latest developments in memory technology are charge-coupled devices (CCDs) and magnetic-bubble memories, both of which will become prevalent in future-generation computers. CCDs, invented at Bell Labs about six years ago, store information as packets of charge within a semiconductor chip. These charge packets are manipulated by voltages applied to a routing pattern inscribed on the chip's surface. The attendant circuitry required to store, move, and access the packets is contained on the same chip. CCDs can be manufactured with a large number of bits on a single chip; some, with capacities around 65,000 bits, are still in the developmental stages.

Magnetic-bubble technology, which actually predates CCDs, is based on the discovery (also at Bell Labs) that tiny magnetized bubble-like areas in the thin films of magnetic material could be controlled and ordered in a "digital" format much like that used by computers. The bubbles are generated, moved, and detected in a specially grown crystalline material. Bubble memories offer moderately fast data retrieval at reasonable cost, without losing information when circuit power is interrupted.

For example, bubble memory can access stored information in less than 2 milliseconds—slow by semiconductor standards but ten times faster than high-performance disk memories. Bubble memories hold the promise of high storage capacity—engineers at Bell Labs have already fabricated a 250,000-bit memory. They also use very little power and require few processing steps.

Programming trains the beast

Computers won't do a thing unless you tell them what to do, and that's what programming is all about. A program is a sequence of instructions that defines all the alternatives of operation to the computer, whether it is used for analysis, control, or a combination of the two.

The precise operation of a particular computer is dictated by its organization, often referred to as the architecture; the program instructions, or codes, necessary to run the computer are unique to its design. But, remember, computers understand only binary instructions, which are used both for their logical operations and for their arithmetic functions.

Such binary instructions are called *machine* language, the computer being referred to as "the machine," which is really what it is. Instructions in machine code are machine dependent and require special knowledge of the computer, if they are to be useful. This type of language is also known as *object* language. The *object code* can be immediately executed by the computer.

Because of its dependence on the use of long strings of binary digits and the programmer's intimate knowledge of the design intricacies of the computer, machine language is obviously a cumbersome way of communicating with a computer. But help is on the way.

Allied with machine languages are *assembly languages*, which are written in short symbolic codes—or mnemonic instructions. Instead of the binary instructions, a set of abbreviations is devised to closely resemble the meaning of the instruction. For example, the code "HLT" might replace the binary code 111100000010 to instruct a particular computer to cease operation.

But computers function only with their own machine language; any other language must be translated into machine-language terms before the computer can use it. Thus the example of "HLT" as a command in assembly language can be used by the computer only if there is some way to translate "HLT" into its binary-number equivalent. This is done with the use of a special *assembler*, a computer program (software) designed to translate the code into computer-understandable terms.

Assemblers, like the codes they work with, are designed for use on specific computers, and all such programs are, therefore, machine dependent. The symbolic assembly program is also called the *source program*, and the assembler translates source code into object code. Collectively, machine and assembly languages are known as *low-level* computer languages, because they are close to the fundamental operation of the computer.

By contrast, *high-level* languages are organized along the lines of ordinary speech and tend to be relatively machine independent. As with a low-level language, a high-level language must be translated into machine language by a special program within the computer before it can be put to use. Such a translating program is called either a *compiler*, which translates the entire program into machine language before execution by the computer system, or an *interpreter*, which translates each line of the program as it is being executed.

High-level languages for general problem-solving include FORTRAN (FORmula TRANSlator), which is particularly suitable for scientific and engineering com-

Flow chart for a simple control problem

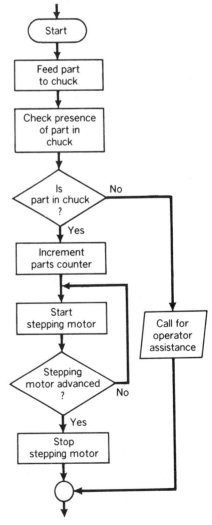

Some common flow-chart symbols

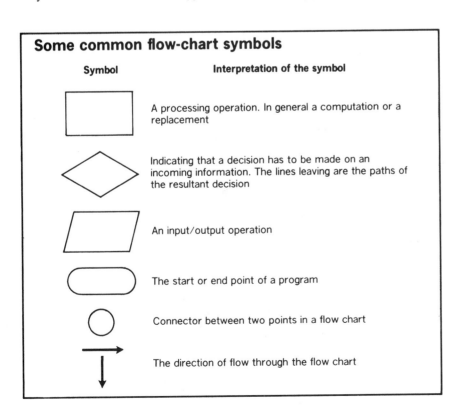

Symbol	Interpretation of the symbol
▭	A processing operation. In general a computation or a replacement
◇	Indicating that a decision has to be made on an incoming information. The lines leaving are the paths of the resultant decision
▱	An input/output operation
⬭	The start or end point of a program
◯	Connector between two points in a flow chart
→	The direction of flow through the flow chart

Computers in manufacturing

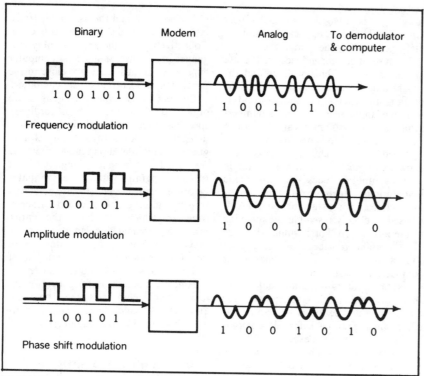

Binary   Modem   Analog   To demodulator & computer

1 0 0 1 0 1 0 → 1 0 0 1 0 1 0

Frequency modulation

1 0 0 1 0 1 → 1 0 0 1 0 1 0

Amplitude modulation

1 0 0 1 0 1 → 1 0 0 1 0 1 0

Phase shift modulation

Digital signals must be modulated for transmission over long distances when voice-grade lines are used. The three main modulation techniques used are illustrated

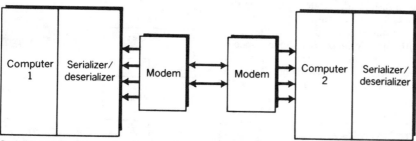

Computer 1 | Serializer/deserializer ↔ Modem ↔ Modem ↔ Computer 2 | Serializer/deserializer

Serial transmission requires hardware: a serializer/deserializer to arrange the data flow and a modulator/demodulator (modem) for transmission over voice-grade lines

Communication links

Type	Description	Characteristics
Serial asynchronous	1 bit at a time	Slow (600-1200 bps) but inexpensive
Serial synchronous	Block of data sent at regular intervals	Faster (4800 bps) but more expensive
Parallel	1 word at a time; number of lines equal bits/word plus control buses	Fastest (to 20,000 bps for twisted pairs; 500,000 bps for coaxial) but limited to private wires and over limited distance

puting, and COBOL (COmmon Business Oriented Language), which is tailored to commercial applications. One of the more widely used problem-oriented languages in manufacturing is APT (Automatically Programmed Tools), an English-like language that describes the part illustrated on an engineering drawing and takes the form of a sequence of statements that define the part geometry, cutter operations, and machine-tool capabilities.

When processed on an appropriate APT compiler program, which has been loaded into a computer, the APT statements are automatically converted into the X, Y, and Z coordinates of the successive tool-end positions (CL data) along the desired tool path. This represents the general solution to the programming problem, and additional processing (postprocessing) of these data generates the exact tape codes and format for a particular NC machine, or the part-program.

One thing to keep in mind about the various levels of programming is that the higher the level, the more power—or memory—is required by the computer. The various programs that convert English-like commands into computer-compatible form—assemblers, compilers, interpreters—must be stored in the computer's main memory.

Usually, compilers and interpreters occupy a significant amount of memory space. For example, a compiler for a minicomputer with 4096 words of memory can occupy about 2500 of these words, leaving less than half the memory for data and program storage. A low-level language, though longer and far more cumbersome to write, occupies only as much memory space as required for the job.

Programmers, particularly when programming in low-level languages, use flow charts to help them visualize the sequence of events to be handled by the computer program they are developing. The outstanding advantage of a flow chart is that it shows a great deal at a glance.

Computers must communicate

In order to be useful, computers must be able to receive and transmit data. The data stream between computers and peripheral equipment, with the processes they control and, in the case of distributed processing networks, with each other, can be organized in a parallel or a serial fashion.

In parallel transmission, all the bits constituting one word are transmitted simultaneously over a suitable number of parallel lines. That means that there must be at least as many lines as there are bits per word, plus some lines for control signals.

This is the fastest way of transmitting data, the only limiting factor being the maximum transmission rate of the sending device and the transmission capability of the transmission lines. Since all the bits of one word are transmitted in parallel, the word-transmission rate is equal to the bit rate possible with the cables. Maximum data-transfer rate is about 20,000 bits per second (bps) for twisted-wire lines.

Twisted-wire cables are the cheapest

to construct, but they are susceptible to crosstalk and interference pickup. These shortcomings are overcome with the use of coaxial cables, which can transfer data at up to 500,000 bps over a distance of 200 ft and are reliable and economically feasible for transmission to about 400 ft.

Serial for long distances

To reduce transmission costs over longer distances, serial data transmission is generally used. In serial transmission, the information contents of each word are converted into serial form before the word enters the transmission line, and, theoretically, only one line is needed to handle the entire data stream. But the data-transmission rate is obviously slower than with parallel transmission. Serial transmission can be asynchronous or synchronous.

In order for serial transmission to work, the sender and receiver must be synchronized so that the sequence of transmitted binary signals is properly ordered at the receiving end. In asynchronous transmission, the necessary synchronization signals are provided for each character, and the time interval between transmitted characters may vary; characters can be sent in close sequence or at longer time intervals.

With synchronous serial transmission, an entire block of characters is synchronized with one set of control signals. This provides greater transmission efficiency because fewer stop and start signals are required.

When data are transferred over long distances, voice-grade telephone lines are generally used. Such lines are not suitable for the transmission of digital data, and, therefore, it is necessary to convert the digital dc pulses originating with a computer or terminal equipment into analog—wavelike—signals acceptable for transmission over telephone lines. And, at the receiving end, the analog signal must again be converted into computer-, or terminal-, acceptable digital form.

Modems do the conversion

These conversions are handled by modulators/demodulators, or modems. Modems transmit data in spurts (asynchronous modems) or in steady streams (synchronous modems). Asynchronous modems are usually associated with keyboard-entry terminal devices, such as teletypewriters and CRT displays, in which the time between information segments (characters) is random. Synchronous modems are used with continuous data sources, such as card readers, paper- and magnetic-tape equipment, and computers, in which each character

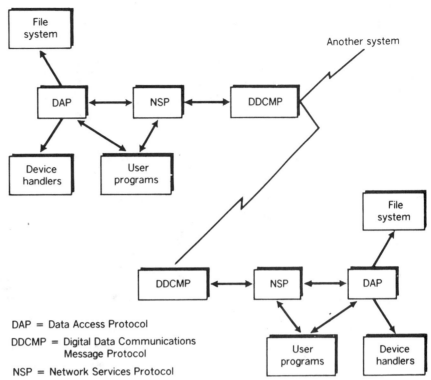

DAP = Data Access Protocol
DDCMP = Digital Data Communications Message Protocol
NSP = Network Services Protocol

Networks depend on appropriate communications protocols, such as Digital Equipment Corp's DECnet software, for efficient and accurate intercommunications

follows the preceding one at a fixed interval.

Modems may operate in three different modes: in the simplest mode, in which data are either transmitted or received; in the half-duplex mode, in which data can be both sent and received—but not simultaneously—similarly to an ordinary voice telephone conversation; and in the full-duplex mode, in which data can be simultaneously transmitted and received.

Several modulating schemes are used for serial data transmission, the most common being frequency modulation (FM), amplitude modulation (AM), and phase-shift modulation (PM). The choice depends on line characteristics and transmission-speed requirements.

An alternative to the modem is the acoustic coupler, a device that accepts a serial data stream from a data-processing device, modulates it in the audio spectrum, and produces the modulation as an audible tone. These are the devices that cradle an ordinary telephone handset and couple the acoustic energy directly into the mouthpiece at the sending end; at the receiving end, a similar device picks up the audible tones from a telephone earpiece and demodulates them to a serial data stream.

Building the hierarchy

In order to be cost-effective, computers must be fully utilized. But computers operate at high speeds, and, once the computer is programmed, the actual execution of a specific task may take only a very short time. For this reason, computers, other than those dedicated to a specific task, do not operate alone but, operate, instead, in a communications-oriented system, in which more than one task is performed by a centrally located computer served by a network of peripheral devices. These systems include several schemes:

- Message switching. A centrally located computer acts as an administrative message exchange between points of message origination and destination.
- Remote inquiry. Terminals capable of both sending and receiving information are used to achieve prompt attention by the CPU to the inquiring party.
- Remote batch processing. Programs as well as data on which these programs are to operate are entered into the central computer from a remote terminal, and processing is periodic rather then real-time.
- Remote computing. Distant users are equipped with on-line terminals to provide direct access to a central computer facility.
- Multiprogram execution and time-sharing. Several unrelated programs are executed simultaneously. In multiprogramming, although only one instruction at a time is being executed by it, the CPU works, in turn, on separate instructions

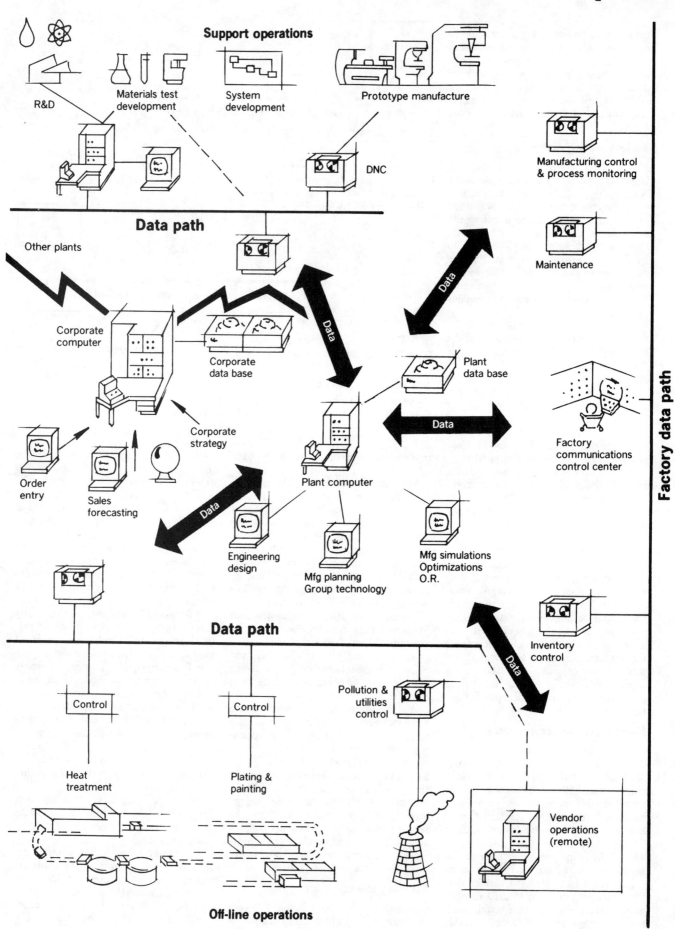

Support operations

R&D

Materials test development

System development

Prototype manufacture

DNC

Manufacturing control & process monitoring

Maintenance

Data path

Other plants

Corporate computer

Corporate data base

Corporate strategy

Order entry

Sales forecasting

Data

Data

Plant data base

Plant computer

Engineering design

Mfg planning Group technology

Mfg simulations Optimizations O.R.

Data

Factory communications control center

Inventory control

Data

Data path

Control

Control

Pollution & utilities control

Heat treatment

Plating & painting

Vendor operations (remote)

Off-line operations

Factory data path

in manufacturing

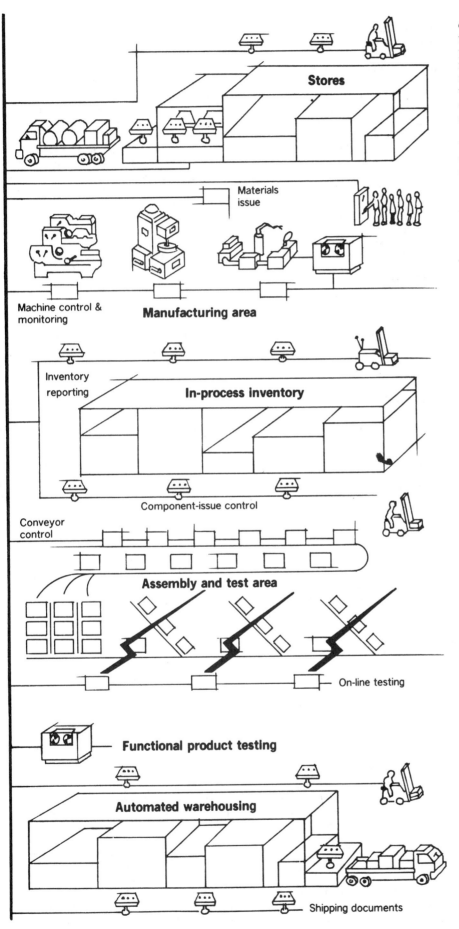

Factory data path

Stores

Materials issue

Machine control & monitoring

Manufacturing area

Inventory reporting

In-process inventory

Component-issue control

Conveyor control

Assembly and test area

On-line testing

Functional product testing

Automated warehousing

Shipping documents

of many programs based on some predetermined priority order. In effect, all programs appear to be running simultaneously. In time-sharing, specific segments of time are allocated to the various programs, in rotation, and the effect is that every user appears to have sole use of the computer.

Communications-oriented systems usually require supervisory programs, called operating systems, to handle the efficient allocation of the various resources. These make the various routing decisions based on availability. For example, six remote locations may call for the use of line printing, but the computer has capacity (main-memory locations) to handle only four. The operating system will deny two locations the use of line printing, based on the priority of the printing task. But the operating system also determines that there is some capacity left to run some less demanding program than printing and, therefore, will look for an appropriately scaled task within the system.

The networks are coming

More recently, the trend in industry is toward computer networks—an interconnected group of computers, some designated as processing systems and others as communications-control systems. The processing systems can be either host computers or remote computing systems.

The hosts in the network perform major computations, control data bases, and generally supervise operation of the network. They can share such resources as programs, data bases, and memory space.

Remote computing systems are local computing facilities with access to the host. They perform processing that would otherwise have to be done by the host, thereby relieving not only the communications load but also that portion of the processing that can be carried on closer to the point of action.

In a true network situation, the host processor and remote computing system can operate in a local mode under their own individual operating systems, can participate in network activity under the direction of a higher-level network supervisory program, or can do both.

The communications-control computers are devoted primarily to network-control functions, including line control, error checking, message formatting, message switching, and data concentration. Of course, a typical network would also include a wide variety of remote terminals and process-monitor/control interfaces to accommodate the various needs of the users.

All of this depends on the various

network elements' understanding each other with speed and perfection. What is needed for this understanding is a protocol—a formal set of conventions governing the format and timing of data exchanges among the communicating elements. For example, Digital Equipment Corp offers a set of software products called DECnet, which extend the various DEC operating systems so that they can be interconnected with each other to form computer networks. The major protocols with DECnet serve several functions:

■ Digital Data Communications Message Protocol (DDCMP) handles the link traffic control and error recovery within DECnet and can operate over full- and half-duplex facilities, using synchronous, asynchronous, and parallel facilities.

■ Network Services Protocol (NSP) handles management functions within DECnet, including the routing of messages between systems and the routing of messages within a given system.

■ Data Access Protocol (DAP) enables programs on one node (the end point of any branch of a network or a junction common to two or more branches of a network) of the network to utilize the I/O services available on other network nodes.

Computer-aided manufacturing

Computer-aided manufacturing (CAM) means different things to many people in different industries. For some, the term conjures up the ultimate automatic factory of the future; but, more realistically, CAM starts with the rational application of computers to handle specific tasks in the manufacturing cycle—anywhere from product design through manufacturing to distribution. Integration of these computer applications is coming, but the fact is that there is more CAM around, at various levels of sophistication and development, than you might think.

CAM makes cams

Take a relatively mundane operation like the manufacture of cams from old established physical masters. When Reece Corp built a new plant recently for its buttonhole-sewing machines, it decided to abandon the old copymilling methods for cam making and replace it with NC machines.

The existing masters had been developed for follower-type machines, for which the exact size of the master base circle is relatively unimportant; the

masters worked fine with the old machines, a simple mechanical adjustment taking care of the size variations. But NC machines require properly scaled tables of offsets.

That's where a computer comes in—a Digital Equipment PDP-8 minicomputer, which is part of a Brown & Sharpe Validator coordinate measuring machine. Reece uses the measuring system to digitize masters, establish the required scaling factor, execute the actual scaling calculations, and, finally, generate an NC tape for use on Boston Digital Corp BostoMatic NC milling machines.

The system is also used to generate an inspection tape for checking finished cams with the CMM. In effect, the Validator system is a digitizer, NC-tape-preparation unit, and inspection center all rolled into one. And the key to this versatility is the built-in minicomputer with its large library of appropriate computer programs, which include a series of standard measuring programs, on-the-fly contour measuring (digitizing), and V-FOCAL, an interactive high-level programming language used to develop such programs as the scaling program. In other words, the computer comes loaded with a program that permits manufacturing people to program the computer for their need in a language they can understand.

DNC: two approaches

To some, CAM means direct numerical control. DNC, as it was originally conceived, uses a centrally located host computer to develop part-programs, which are then transmitted to a subhost—the DNC controller—which stores them for accessing as needed. The DNC controller then sends the program data, on a real-time basis, to a number of machines assigned to it.

Such a DNC system has been in operation in the Casings Operation of GE's Evendale Manufacturing Operation since the early '70s (AM—Mar'76, p113). It has been so successful that a major new home-grown DNC program is now being implemented, to be fully operational on more than 100 machines by the end of June.

The new system is going into the Rotating Parts Operation, where there is a high concentration of NC machines; of around 300 work stations, 100 are NC machines. These NC machines are being retrofitted with a behind-the-tape-reader system served by a computer hierarchy with the corporate Honeywell 6000 at the top providing the overall data base and number-crunching.

An Interdata 732 minicomputer will serve as the master DNC computer to be shared among the 100 machines. Data

transfer is via Interdata 616 microcomputers (two machines per micro), which will buffer up to about 7½ ft of tape-equivalent data and will call for new data as its buffers empty. The AMEN (APT menu) computer-assisted part-programming system, developed for the original DNC system, is also operative on the Interdata system.

The system has been purposely designed with all off-the-shelf hardware, the only exception being the interface boards coupling each machine to the system. These were designed at Evendale and are manufactured at GE's NC Products Div in Waynesboro, Va. A main advantage to this off-the-shelf approach is that it will work with any mixed breed of NC systems. At Evendale, that involves mainly GE systems, but they range in vintage from early 100 Series to the latest 1050s.

An interesting first is the use of fully graphic CRT terminals at each operator station to supply information and descriptions relating to setup, part configuration, cuts to be made, and finished dimensions. They will be used by operators and supervisors and should completely eliminate all paperwork on the shop floor—another possible feature of computer-based systems. Ultimately, the DNC system will become a full-blown CAM setup with all 300 work stations tied to it for management-data reporting.

There are people who take a dimmer view of the DNC approach. In effect, all the NC machines in a DNC group time-share access to the data base resident at the DNC controller, and there is, therefore, a practical limit to the number of individual machines that can be connected before there are unacceptable delays in data transfer. A delay in data can cause dwell marks on the part being manufactured.

Even more catastrophic, a break in the communications link—be it because an errant forklift truck cut the line or because the computer is down—could put an end to all chipmaking.

The development of CNC, with its data-handling and storage capabilities, has, to a large extent, supplanted some of the original DNC concepts with new approaches. The latest wrinkle is now taking shape at Fairchild Republic Co (Farmingdale, NY), where a new machine shop is being tooled up for increased production of the A-10 military aircraft.

The machine-shop complex will consist of 30 machines, 26 with CNC systems by Vega Servo-Control Inc (Troy, Mich). The Vega III G controls, being retrofitted to a variety of government machines formerly on loan to other manufacturers, will accept CL-data (cutter-location) programs from floppy-disk data input. The CNC software includes postprocessing for the associated machine tool. All of the controls also feature full alphanumeric keyboards, CRT display, and a computer-communications interface.

Initially, the controls will operate in a stand-alone mode from floppy disks that have been prepared in a central NC-tape-preparation area from part-programs downloaded from the company's corporate computer that handles the APT processing. In effect, the floppies will merely replace the tape input of other CNCs.

But, because the floppies carry CL data and the system can communicate in straight binary form, it is also possible to download programs directly to them. Eventually, a Data General Corp (DEC) Eclipse minicomputer will form the DNC link and will be connected to the corporate host computer to receive part-programs, which will be stored on an associated disk file. When a machine operator calls for a new program, the Eclipse will transmit data to the floppy disk at the machine, where the old program will be erased and replaced with the new one.

In this way, part-programs will be transmitted to the individual machines during the machine-setup period, just prior to actual machining need. That provides plenty of time to handle even an occasional computer breakdown, which are invariably fixed in less time than it takes to change a machine over to running a different part. And, during actual machining, the system acts as a stand-alone system with the complete part-program resident on the floppy disk.

Fairchild's Paul Gitto, supervisor of machine planning and NC programming, believes that this non-real-time DNC concept provides all the benefits achievable by the more conventional real-time-DNC approach, with significant economies in computer utilization and without the drawbacks associated with dependence on the DNC computer for real-time data transmission. And he thinks each floppy disk should last for about a year under continuous use.

Managing information

All manufacturing processes are governed by an almost steady flow of information that must be received, stored, and recalled as required. As mentioned in the introduction to this report, the architecture of manufacturing today is best described as a series of activities connected in a network of information services. Each activity—be it inventory control, manufacturing, or distribu-

tion—requires access to information about the product and process, and each generates information that is then used for management control.

Over the years, companies have started to use computers to handle some of these individual monitoring functions. More recently, with the advent of distributed computer networks, factory data management is being integrated into hierarchical computer systems. Take International Harvester's Waukesha (Wis) foundry as an example.

The I-H foundry uses a high-rise storage area to hold mold cores for use on its automated core line. Each time a tote box of cores is moved in or out of one of the 567 slots in the seven-high multiple-aisle bin area, the forklift operator also enters its location, the core part number, and other pertinent information on a data-entry terminal tied to a Digital Equipment Corp PDP-11/40 computer located in a central data-management area. By interrogating the system via the terminal keyboard, the operator can get a printout giving the location and inventory status of any core or the content, by part number, of any bin.

A separate power-demand control system, running on the same mainframe, oversees the heating cycles of three Brown-Bovari induction furnaces used to melt the casting charges. Shedding furnaces according to a computer program that anticipates peak-power condition keeps demand charges for power to a minimum (AM—Feb.1'75,p50).

Production data have been collected by an IBM System 7 computer from IBM data-entry terminals located throughout the shop. A card-driven remote job-entry system, implemented on a DEC PDP-11/34, is then used to transmit batch data to an IBM 360 located at I-H's central computer facility in Hinsdale, Ill, for payroll generation, labor distribution, raw-material forecasting, and production planning for the Waukesha facility.

Recently, I-H installed a DEC DPM (Distributed Plant Managing) system to combine some of these functions into an integrated, interactive factory-data-management system with flexibility for future expansion and rearrangement.

The DPM concept combines on-line processing, real-time data acquisition, microprocessor control, distributed computing, and hierarchical computer systems—all integrated through a low-cost communications link, dubbed DEC-dataway. At the heart of the system are a series of industrial factory-data-management terminals and a communications protocol that allows real-time intercommunication among DPM subsystems via serial transmission along an ordinary pair of twisted wires. ∎

Glossary

All disciplines tend to develop their own special terminology, and the field of computers is no exception. In fact, computerese tends to be more fraught with jargon than most, because the rapid growth of the industry required the invention of terminology, which has been adopted, for the most part, from rather mundane English usage. Thus, words of simple meaning have rather specific connotations.

Computer Aided Manufacturing-International Inc (CAM-I), a consortium of industry, academe, and government that acts as a broker for CAM developments, has put together an excellent *Glossary of Computer Aided Manufacturing Terms* as an aid in creating a common communication base for computer-aided-manufacturing technology. It is designed to help the manufacturing user who has little formal contact with computer terminology to better understand and use CAM software systems. It will also aid the computer-system analyst in interfacing with and understanding manufacturing terminology. Excerpts (edited in some instances) from the 40-page Glossary available from CAM-I (611 Ryan Plaza Dr, Suite 1107, Arlington, Tex) are published here in the hope of furthering better communication among manufacturing engineers and others pursuing the ever increasing development of CAM systems.

Acoustic coupler. An electronic device that sends and receives digital data through a standard telephone handset. To transmit data, the digital signals are converted to audible tones that are acoustically coupled to a telephone handset. To receive data, the acoustically coupled audible signals are converted to digital signals.

Address. An identification—as represented by a name, label, or number—for a register, location in storage, or any other data source or destination, such as the location of a station in a communication network.

ASCII. American Standard Code for Information Interchange. The standard code, using a coded character set consisting of 7-bit coded characters (8 bits including parity bit), used for information interchange among data-processing systems, communication systems, and associated equipment. The ASCII set consists of control characters and graphic characters.

Assembly language. An operation language, composed of brief expressions, that is translated by an assembler into a machine language. The language result (object code) from the assembler is a character-for-character translated version of the original.

Asynchronous transmission. Transmission in which each information character is individually synchronized (usually by the use of start and stop elements).

Auxiliary storage. Storage that supplements main memory, such as disk, tape, drum, or virtual storage.

Background processing. The automatic execution of lower-priority programs when higher-priority programs are not using the system resources. Contrast with Foreground Processing.

Batch processing. Pertaining to the technique of executing a set of programs so that each is completed before the next program of the set is started.

Baud. A unit of signaling speed equal to the number of discrete conditions or signal events per second.

Binary code. A code that makes use of exactly two distinct characters, usually 0 and 1.

Binary-coded decimal notation (BCD). A positional notation in which the individual decimal digits expressing a number in decimal notation are each represented by a binary numeral.

Bit. A binary digit.

Block. (1) A set of things—such as words, characters, or digits—handled as a unit. (2) A collection of contiguous records recorded as a unit. Blocks are separated by clock gaps, and each block may contain one or more records. (3) A group of bits of binary digits, transmitted as a unit. An encoding procedure is generally applied to the group of bits or binary digits for error-control purposes. (4) A group of contiguous characters recorded as a unit.

Block length. The total number of records, words, or characters contained in one block.

Boolean operator. A logic operator each of whose operands and whose results have one of two values.

Broadband. Communication channel having a bandwidth greater than a voice-grade channel and is therefore capable of higher-speed data transmission.

Buffer. (1) A routine or device used to compensate for a difference in rate of flow of data or time of occurrence of events, when data are transmitted from one device to another. (2) A portion of storage used as a temporary holding area.

Byte. A sequence of adjacent binary digits operated upon as a unit and usually shorter than a word.

Canned cycle. A fixed function in hardware or software operations are performed in predetermined sequence and end in a return to the beginning.   [continued]

Computers in manufacturing

Central processing unit (CPU). A unit of a computer that includes circuits controlling the interpretation and execution of instructions.

Character set. An ordered set of unique representation called characters; e.g., the 26 letters of the English alphabet, 0 and 1 of the Boolean alphabet, the set of signals in the Morse-code alphabet, the 128 characters of the ASCII alphabet.

Check bit. A binary check digit; e.g., a parity bit.

Compile. To prepare a machine-language program from a computer program written in another programming language.

Computer network. A complex consisting of two or more interconnected computing units.

Computer numerical control (CNC). The use of a dedicated computer within a numerical-control unit with the capability of local data input. It may become part of a DNC system by direct link to a central computer.

Conversational mode. Communication between a terminal and the computer in which each entry from the terminal elicits a response from the computer and vice versa.

Core storage. See Magnetic core storage.

Data bank. A comprehensive collection of libraries of data; e.g., one line of an invoice may form an item, a complete invoice may form a record, a complete set of such records may form a file, the collection of inventory control files may form a library, and the libraries used by an organization are known as its data bank.

Data base. A collection of data fundamental to an enterprise. Composed of comprehensive files of information having predetermined structure and organization and suitable for communication, interpretation, or processing by humans or automatic means.

Data channel. An I/O bus that provides a path to transfer data between devices.

Data link. The communication lines, modems, and communication controls of all stations connected to the line, used in the transmission of information between two or more stations.

Data set. (1) An organized collection of information. (2) The major unit of data storage and retrieval in the operating system, consisting of a collection of data in one of several prescribed arrangements and described by control information to which the system has access.

Diagnostic routine. An action that facilitates device maintenance by detection and isolation of malfunctions or mistakes.

Direct numerical control (DNC). The use of a shared computer for distribution of part-program data via data lines to remote machine tools.

Distributed processing. A method of performing a data-processing task by performing the needed calculations in a distributed computing network. Performing simultaneous operations in several interconnected processors of a distributed computer network improves the efficiency of the data-processing task.

Executive. Same as Operating system.

Field. In a record, a specified area used for a particular category of data; e.g., a group of card columns used to represent a wage rate or a set of bit locations in a computer word used to express the address of the operand.

Flip-flop. A circuit or device containing active elements capable of assuming either one or two stable states at a given time.

Foreground processing. The automatic execution of programs designed to preempt the use of the computing facilities. Usually a real-time program. Contrast with Background processing.

Handshaking. Exchange of predetermined signals when a connection is established between two data sets.

Hard copy. A printed copy of machine output in a visually readable form; e.g., printed reports, listings, documents, summaries.

Hardware. Physical equipment, as opposed to the program or method of use; e.g., mechanical, magnetic, electrical, or electronic devices. Contrast with Software.

Hexadecimal. Pertaining to a number system with a base of 16; digits range from 0 through 9, then A through F.

Hollerith. A particular type of code or punched card using 12 rows per column and usually 80 columns per card.

Housekeeping. In data processing, those operations or routines that do not contribute directly to the solution of the problem but do contribute directly to the operation of the computer.

Illegal character. A character or combination of bits that is not valid according to some criteria.

Instruction set. The list of machine-language instructions that a computer can perform.

Interactive. Processing of data on a two-way basis and with human intervention providing redirection of processing in a predetermined manner.

Internal storage. Addressable storage directly controlled by the central processing unit of a digital computer. See also Main storage.

k. (1) An abbreviation for the prefix "kilo," meaning 1000 in decimal notation. (2) In data processing, k is used in defining memory locations to mean 1024 locations. For example, an 8k-capacity memory as 8 times 1024, or 8192 locations.

Line conditioning. The addition of equipment to a leased voice-grade channel to provide minimum values of line characteristics required for data transmission.

Load. In programming, to enter data into storage or working registers.

Logic instruction. An instruction that executes an operation defined in symbolic logic, such as AND, OR, NOR.

Machine language. A language that is used directly by a machine [computer].

Macro instruction. A source-language instruction equivalent to a specified sequence of machine instructions.

Magnetic-core storage. A storage device or system using a magnetic core for information storage.

Magnetic-disk storage. A storage device or system consisting of magnetically coated metal disks, on which data can be stored by selective magnetization of portions of the flat surface.

Magnetic-drum storage. A storage device or system using a magnetic drum on which data can be stored by selective magnetization of portions of the curved surface.

Magnetic-tape storage. A storage system that uses magnetic spots, representing bits, on coated plastic tape.

Main memory or main storage. (1) The general-purpose storage of a computer. Usually, main storage can be accessed directly by the operating registers. Contrast with Auxiliary storage. (2) All program-addressable storage from which instructions may be executed and from which data can be loaded directly into registers.

Microcomputer. A computer constructed with a microprocessor as the basic element.

Microprocessor. A basic element of a central processing unit, consisting of a single integrated circuit. A microprocessor has a limited instruction set that is usually expanded by microprogramming. A microprocessor requires additonal circuits to become a suitable central processing unit.

Microprogramming. A method of CPU operation in which each complete instruction starts the execution of a sequence of instructions, called micro instructions, which are generally at a more elementary level.

Modem. Modulator/demodulator. An electronic device that sends and receives digital data via telecommunication lines. To transmit data, the digital signals vary (modulate) an electronic signal coupled into the telecommunciation lines. To receive data, the electronic siganls are converted (demodulated) to digital data.

Nonvolatile storage. Storage that retains information when power is removed from the system.

Object program. A fully compiled or assembled program ready to be loaded into the computer.

Operating system (OS). Software that controls the execution of computer programs and may provide scheduling, debugging, input-output control, accounting, compilation, storage assignment, data management, and related service.

Overlay. The technique of repeatedly using the same blocks of internal storage during different stages of a problem. When one routine is no longer needed in storage, another routine can replace all or part of it.

Parity bit. A binary digit appended to an array of bits to make the sum of all the bits always odd or always even.

Parity check. (1) A check that tests whether the number of 1s or 0s in an array of binary digits is odd or even. (2) A check that tests whether the number of ones in a binary array is odd or even. If odd parity is used, an even number of 1s in the binary array indicates a parity failure; an odd number indicates that the binary array passes the parity check. If even parity is used, an odd number of 1s in the binary array indicates a failure of the parity check. A parity check is usually used with paper tapes used for numerical controls or computers, as well as in magnetic-tape systems and computer-memory systems.

Processor. In hardware, a data processor; for software, a computer program that includes the compiling, assembling, translating, and related functions for a specific programming language—COBOL processor, FORTRAN processor.

Protocol. The rules for controlling data communication between devices in computer systems or computer networks.

Real time. (1) Pertaining to the actual time during which a physical process transpires. (2) Pertaining to computation performed while the related physical process is taking place so that results of the computation can be used in guiding the physical process.

Register. A device capable of storing a specified amount of data, such as one word.

Remote access. Pertaining to communication with a data-processing facility by one or more stations distant from that facility.

Software. A set of programs, procedures, rules, and possibly associated documentation concerned with the operation and use of a computer system.

Software portability. Software easily installed in a variety of makes of computers and computer-hardware configurations.

Source language. A language that is an input to a given translation process.

Synchronous transmission. Transmission in which the sending and receiving instruments are operating continuously at substantially the same frequency and are maintained, by means of correction, in a desired phase relationship.

Time sharing. Participation, via terminals, in available computer time by multiple users. Characteristically, the response time is such that the computer seems dedicated to each user.

Virtual storage. Addressable space that appears to the user as real storage, from which instructions and data are mapped into real-storage locations. The size of virtual storage is limited by the addressing scheme of the computing system (or virtual machine) and by the amount of auxiliary storage available, rather than the actual number of real-storage locations.

Volatile storage. A storage device in which stored data are lost when the applied power is removed.

Acknowledgements

Many companies and associations have been very helpful with information and assistance in the preparation of this report. Of particular help were Data General Corp, Digital Equipment Corp, and IBM.

Further reading

Computers for Engineers, Bartow Hodge, McGraw-Hill Book Co, NY, 1969

Computer Integrated Manufacturing, Joseph Harrington Jr, Industrial Press Inc, NY, 1973

Computers in Manufacturing, Ulrich Rembold, Mahesh K. Seth, and Jeremy S. Weinstein, Marcel Dekker Inc, NY, 1977

Management Standards for Computer & Numerical Control, Donald N. Smith and Lary Evans, Industrial Development Div, Institute of Science and Technology, Univ of Michigan, 1977

The Successful Computer System, Joseph Orlicky, McGraw Hill Book Co, NY, 1969

ITEGRATED MANUFACTURING • DIRECT NUM

ONTROL • DATABASE • SIMULATION •

AL CONTROL • GROUP TECHNOLOGY • TIM

AD/CAM

ING • NET

ONTROL •

URING-RES

OMPUTER-

CESS PLA

SHOP-FLC

MANUFA

G • CAF

• VARIA

THE COMPUTER:
The Tool for Today

Manufacturing has entered a new age. As manufacturing managers face the demands of a rapidly changing, increasingly sophisticated, highly competitive world, a maturing computer technology is providing the right tool to help them meet those demands.

The computer is, after all, an information-handling machine, and manufacturing depends on the transformation of information—from a concept in the designer's mind through action at the machine tool into a finished product.

The application of this information-handling machine is changing the way manufacturing works. This issue of AMERICAN MACHINIST examines the hows and whys of these changes, their effects and their benefits. To begin with, here is the story about one company that has learned the power of this new tool. . .

ROCESS PLANNING • BATCH PROCESSING

MODELING • COMPUTER-AIDED ENGINEERIN

ATIONS NETWORKS • CLASSIFICATION ANE

ATABASE-MANAGEMENT SYSTEMS • GENEF

ESS PLANNING • COMPUTER NUMERICAL (

NC • 3D MODELING • DISTRIBUTED PROCE

THE COMPUTER AND JOHN DEERE

The right tool for the right job is the rule for computers at Deere

MANUFACTURING at Deere & Co depends on the computer. It is the tool that is considered absolutely necessary to ensure a competitive edge.

Several years ago, this world-renowned producer of farm and related equipment recognized that, of all the developments promising increased productivity and an improved competitive posture, the use of computer-based systems in design and manufacturing appears to offer the greatest prospect.

Today, fully committed to computer-integrated manufacturing, or CIM, Deere exemplifies the successful application of the computer to a complex and diverse manufacturing enterprise. For Deere, it's just a way of doing business.

This is not to say that it's a simple thing. The proper integration of computer-based systems is a monumental task, primarily because it involves the mastery of a new, rapidly changing technology that is often perceived as exotic and mysterious.

But Deere's efforts have been based on one fundamental, almost simplistic concept: the computer is simply a tool, not an end in itself.

"It is merely a tool to do all the things we have always wanted to do and to do them better—nothing more, nothing less," says James F. Lardner, vice president for manufacturing development and a chief motivator of the drive toward computer-integrated manufacturing at Deere. "Those who keep talking about the profundity of the computer in very intellectual terms are misunderstanding the challenge facing us. The real intellectual challenge is to use the computer as a tool to extend our capabilities beyond anything we have ever dreamed of.

"The danger is that we may act like

the sorcerer's apprentice: the temptation is to learn only half the spell!"

What Lardner means is that the user must master the computer, not vice versa. Such mastery requires commitment and education, and these are the essential elements of Deere's implementation of CIM. Its management, led by people like Lardner, has made sure that the spell is complete.

Behind Lardner's apparent dismissal of the complexity of the task is a very thorough analysis and clearly defined understanding of the computer's multifaceted role in the manufacturing scheme. That analysis led to the decision to plan from the top down but to implement from the bottom up.

The planning started with the realization, some six or seven years ago, that the many scattered but isolated computer applications within this decentralized company had more far-reaching implications than had generally been recognized and that there was a great potential for changing the entire structure of design and manufacturing. Fortuitously, the realization occurred during a period when Deere managers had access to the largest capital-spending budget in the company's history.

In the mid-70s, most people at Deere who were interested in the potential of the computer in support of design and manufacturing activities considered the applications strictly as extensions of existing capabilities. For example, computer-graphics systems were originally regarded as nothing more than the computerization of conventional drafting techniques.

But inherent in the drafting activity is the creation of a series of instructions for the many tasks required to produce the product, including inspection and verifi-

cation to ensure that the design intent has been met. Traditionally, this has resulted in the proliferation of many derivative drawing sets each aimed at a particular activity and claiming a single authority.

In reality, they turn out to be one individual's interpretation of the original and often end up like a book that has gone through several bad translations from its original language. Add to that the necessity of recording the many changes that occur in the natural course of manufacturing, and maintaining the database becomes a major problem.

Managing the data flow from what Lardner describes as "this cascade of derivative drawings" is probably one of the most complex aspects of any manufacturing operation.

It soon became clear that, regardless of the individualized approaches, many of the CAD/CAM applications at Deere were attempting to address some part of a common problem: the need for more accurate and timely information and control. "But, while we all seemed to be going in the same direction, we were surely going to end up like the Tower of Babel," notes Lardner.

And so a conscious decision was reached that the changing nature of the design and manufacturing functions, brought about by the introduction of computers, should be approached on a coordinated basis. There should be a set of goals, instead of a hit-or-miss process that depended almost entirely on the initiative of those who happened to become interested in a particular aspect of the CAD/CAM spectrum and who would then develop some small segment either in ignorance of or with indifference to activities elsewhere in the operation.

The idea was to develop a coordinated

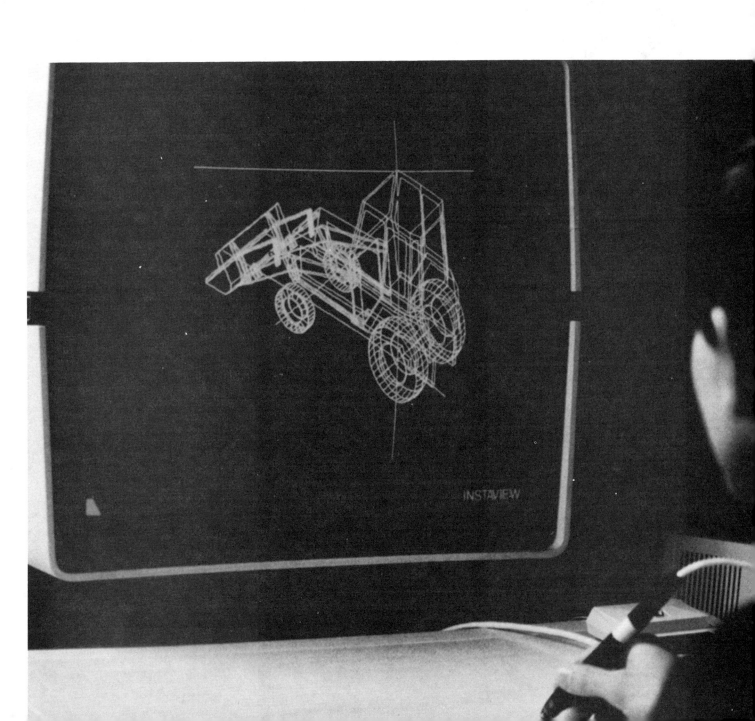

'It is merely a tool to do all the things we have always wanted to do and to do them better— nothing more, nothing less.'

James F. Lardner

plan without imposing restrictions. Arthur D. Little Inc was brought in as a consultant to help review the various computer-related developments within Deere, ranging from design through engineering and manufacturing to field testing of prototypes and finished products. As many as 200 Deere employees, at all levels, were actively engaged in this review.

The joint effort produced a general recommendation for an overall plan based on two concepts. First, each system should be classified and developed according to one of two categories: (1) systems that would form part of a corporatewide CAD/CAM system set and would therefore be developed in accordance with uniform corporate standards for software, hardware, and database structures; and (2) "stand-alone" local systems that are self-contained and whose data is not likely to be required for activities in other location within the operation.

Second, four fundamental computer-system building blocks should be created for computer-integrated manufacturing: (1) geometric modeling through the use of computer-graphics systems, to get the data set out of the designer's mind into a form that everyone can use; (2) group technology, to help identify manufacturing problems and opportunities; (3) computer-aided process planning, to help establish optimum manufacturing routings and processing steps; and (4) a system of computer-aided inspection and reporting, to close the loop between design intent and product performance.

Concurrent with the ADL study, Deere managers mounted an educational effort that culminated in an in-house conference titled "CAD/CAM, the Competitive Edge" and intended to reinforce the development of a common underlying philosophy. The introduction to the conference program stated the philosophy quite clearly: the success of CAD/CAM systems depends on a uniform corporate understanding of CAD/CAM technologies and of the use of such technologies to achieve "the competitive edge." The conference was carefully orchestrated to present a cohesive picture of where CAD/CAM technology was and where it was heading.

A formidable group of experts representing vendors, educators, and users was assembled to discuss the basic elements of CAD/CAM and to provide insight into the experiences of other major US and foreign manufacturing companies in introducing and exploiting CAD/CAM systems. Existing Deere programs were also reviewed, and a hands-on system display demonstrated key elements, the building blocks, of CAD/CAM integration: group

technology, geometric modeling, computer-aided process planning, NC graphics, and computer-aided inspection and reporting (CAIR, developed at Deere).

Representatives of General Electric were asked to address the problems of implementing a coordinated program in a decentralized company. Boeing was asked to participate because of its pioneering experience in such systems.

"We knew that not all their experiences were good," says Lardner. "They had struggled through many early hardships resulting from a lack of adequate computer languages, software, and well-developed concepts of database structures, and they therefore could point out some pitfalls."

Prof Walter Eversheim, executive director of the Laboratory for Machine Tools & Production Engineering at the Technical Univ of Aachen, was invited because his lab was very experienced in the classification and coding techniques of group technology and automated process planning. Prof Toshio Sata, of the faculty of engineering at the Univ of Tokyo, was there to shed some light on how the Japanese were approaching the integration of CAD/CAM.

General Motors had just been through the downsizing of its cars and was known to be moving very rapidly in the area of computer graphics and computer-aided engineering (CAE). "And GM was doing it under the stress of very tight schedules and very strong economic pressure," notes Lardner. The GM input was considered important.

Perhaps the greatest influence, however, at least according to Lardner, was a presentation by Dr Joseph Harrington Jr, who first coined the term *computer-integrated manufacturing* in his prophetic book of that title and who is a recognized expert in the field. "Harrington really has one of the better grasps of manufacturing and what CAD/CAM can do if we're only smart enough to make it happen," says Lardner.

The nature of manufacturing

Harrington claims that, to grasp the importance of computer-based systems to manufacturing, it is essential to understand two fundamentals about the nature of manufacturing itself, and he defines these clearly and simply. First, manufacturing, which begins with product design and ends with support and maintenance in the field, is a monolithic, indivisible function. It can be incredibly complex in its fine detail, but all of its components are so intricately connected that no part can be successfully considered in isolation.

The second fundamental defined by Harrington is that, diverse as the various parts of manufacturing may seem, there is a common thread running through all manufacturing activities: what we call manufacturing is, in the ultimate analysis, a series of data-processing operations. All manufacturing involves creating, sorting, transmitting, analyzing, and modifying data.

Therefore, everything done in manufacturing, whether in the physical act of material transformation or in planning and management, is part of a continuum of data processing. This data-processing activity provides the base to which all parts of manufacturing may be related, and it satisfies the intuitive belief in the monolithic character and singleness of the entity that the term *computer-integrated manufacturing* seeks to describe.

This view of manufacturing is not a theoretical abstraction, Lardner explains, but a reflection of manufacturing reality. "If this is the real nature of manufacturing," says Lardner, "two conclusions can be reached. One is that any technology that will make manufacturing more efficient must address all phases of manufacturing. The second is that the technology most likely to make manufacturing more efficient is the one that can make major improvements in the effectiveness of the data-processing task." Lardner firmly believes that US industry must turn more and more to computer technology to resolve the data-

management problems, and that is precisely the impetus behind Deere's commitment to CIM.

The ADL study also included three very significant specific recommendations: (1) establish an engineering-systems group that could champion the computer needs of the engineering community; (2) evaluate available computer-graphics systems and select one to become the standard for the corporation; and (3) embark on the development of a common-engineering-database system.

Engineers at Deere have always had access to the corporate mainframe computer system through time sharing. But those systems are developed and administered by the Corporate Computer Systems Div, whose orientation has been toward commercial application of computers; business applications, such as accounting and payroll systems, have long been fostered at Deere.

Traditionally, such business-oriented data-processing organizations have little appreciation of the immediacy of most engineering- and manufacturing-related needs or of the real-time nature of manufacturing. Systems development for manufacturing applications is difficult under those circumstances.

"The business group would typically put a request for development of an engineering system in a common queue of computer-system-development tasks,

and your turn might come up three years later," comments Don Manor, project manager in the relatively new Engineering Systems Dept. "By that time, you're probably involved in a whole new product-design/manufacturing phase, and you no longer need the system originally requested." As a result, a host of mini-computer-based systems had sprung up to address little parts of the CAD/CAM function, according to Manor.

Interestingly enough, the Engineering Systems Dept was constituted as one of five departments within the Corporate Computer Systems Div; the others are Computer Operations, Systems Planning & Administration, Database Management, and Commercial Systems. At Deere, the basic engineering functions—such as manufacturing engineering, product engineering, and research—first converge at the senior-vice-presidential level, and placing the systems group under any of those separate functions would make it suspect of bias.

"Putting us with the systems people theoretically eliminates that bias," notes Manor. "It puts us in the camp of what was once considered the enemy, the business-data-processing group." He reports that the engineering-systems people have developed an excellent rapport with the commercial-systems group. Now, however, Engineering Systems tends to be looked on as one of the computer-

Robocarrier carts automatically deliver materials from high-rise AS/RS to all areas of Hydraulics Div

Binoculars help supervisor survey FMS system and physically identify cart locations noted by computer

systems groups, and there are emerging signs of conflict between the new systems types and the operating personnel.

The survey of computer-graphics system has resulted in the installation of 12 Computervision Corp computer-graphics systems with a total of 63 terminals. Five of the systems are located at various facilities in Waterloo, Iowa; three are at the Dubuque, Iowa, works; and the remaining four are located in the Quad City area, including the Moline, Ill, corporate headquarters.

The systems are shared mostly by product engineering and manufacturing engineering. Primary use is currently allocated to product design, including conceptual work as well as design layout and engineering drafting; plant engineering and layout, including architectural design; and tool design, including inspection gages. Other uses are NC programming, which is just getting started; development of electrical schematics, including both product requirements and control requirements for machine tools and systems; foundry drafting; and a limited amount of electronics design.

The development of the corporate engineering-database system is one of the major projects tackled by the Engineering Systems Dept. "All the separate computer-aided functions have paid off

in the past," says Roscoe Pershing, manager of the department, "but we think that the greater payoff will come from the integration of all those systems through access to a common database." The idea is to create any geometry or associated data just once and then make it available to anyone with a terminal and proper authorization.

Although most people tend to think of such a database as a single entity, Pershing points out that, in reality, it is an integrated set of databases that appear to be one.

"All the relevant data exists somewhere today," he explains. "Some of it is in a notebook, some on paper or on drawings, some may be tucked in a drawer, and some of it is on a variety of computer systems. We have to manage that mixed bag of data sources in some way. What we are simply saying is that the management of that data would be far better and more efficient if it were all computer-compatible and integrated."

The master plan for such a database system calls for the individual database files to reside in a central library, adequately indexed and cross-referenced so that any user can access or temporarily transfer a particular file or group of files to a remote location for interaction with the data-processing function required by

a local activity. The database-management system also attends to security considerations and permits timely updating of all data in the various files.

That's the plan, but there are still some formidable hurdles to overcome.

"The biggest hurdle is that we are dealing with a wide variety of sources for hardware and software and there is no common way of interfacing all these disparate systems," says Pershing. "How you actually get interface 1 to match interface 2 is, in my mind, one of the biggest barriers, to CIM, and it is not being adequately addressed."

But then, database development is a long-range plan being implemented in a series of modules. The master plan is really only a philosophical guideline, not a hard plan, and the modular approach should allow sufficient interaction with the users to ensure success.

Some of the underlying conflict between the computer-systems people and the operating personnel centers mainly on the degree of integration of computer-based systems and how much interaction and data transfer there should be. It is a conflict over control and, to some degree, a conflict over turf.

The real fear, however, is that everybody will want to know everybody else's

business and, in the process, local initiative will be strangled: personnel, for example, wants to get a peek at what people are doing, the payroll department wants to get time and attendance figures, purchasing wants to tie MRP to production control, and soon a little stand-alone system gets hauled into the big corporate system.

Lardner believes that such an approach is wrong. "You should never take a system further away than you absolutely have to from the people that use it, even if it means putting an extra computer right there at their disposal." There should always be local control. As long as each department meets the master schedule, there is little reason to pass all the details of individual activities all the way up the information chain.

A big master-schedule system that spells out the results expected from each activity is good; trying to schedule all the activities down to the operator's level from one overall production-control system is absolutely wrong and self-defeating, according to Lardner. "Keeping the little stand-alone systems out of the grasp of the big systems is going to be increasingly difficult because, whether you like it or not, there's a Big Brother lurking inside everyone of us," he warns.

The operating people are keenly aware of this phenomenon and are on the constant lookout to prevent their stand-alone systems being co-opted or larger corporate systems' being foisted on them. "We don't always agree with all the concepts promulgated at headquarters," says Troy W. McAffee, manager of manufacturing engineering at the John Deere Component Works in Waterloo, Iowa.

Although he is an enthusiastic supporter of computer-based systems, he takes a cautious view of the overall-systems approach. "You have to be careful when you deal with systems people because they usually understand only systems, not the applications. And what you often get is a system that the user doesn't understand or even know how to operate and maintain."

McAffee agrees with the basic building blocks under development but doubts that they are all fully applicable in his operation. For example, he considers computer-aided process planning (CAPP) a controversial issue. "We're willing to be shown, but we want something that is cost-effective. I claim that you cannot really do generative process planning. Our situation is such that the families of parts you end up with are very small and you might as well stick to manual process planning."

He believes that process planning is one activity requiring heavy intervention by those with manufacturing-engineering experience and knowledge of available capacities.

"The point is, when it comes to computers, it's a matter of choosing the right tool for the right job. If that happens to be a personal computer, then that's what we use." In fact, he believes, the use of simple personal computers is an excellent way of educating people who may be afraid of larger, more complex systems. "It's a way to become familiar with computers. Progress to larger systems is then much easier," says McAffee. He considers many of the problems of engineers and the day-to-day activities of individual departments to be best handled with a small computer.

McAffee also suspects that the development of a big centralized engineering-database system may be overkill. "If we really need such a database, then the Pareto principle should apply with respect to both the number of parts included and the amount of information stored about each part.

[Vilfredo Pareta, an Italian sociologist and economist observed the phenomenon of "the vital few and the trivial many" as applied to the distribution of wealth. J.M. Juran identified its applicability to many fields, including manufacturing.]

"If you take those two scaling factors into account," says McAffee, "you have suddenly shrunk the information, and you no longer need such a large integrated system." What he is concerned about is that an iron-clad system will be handed down for his people to operate under without being able to change it as experience warrants.

An award-winning plant

Most recent publicity about Deere's accomplishments in the application of computers has focused on the relatively new Tractor Works in Waterloo, the first recipient of the annual LEAD award for "leadership in the application and development of computer-integrated manufacturing."

The award was granted by the Computer & Automated Systems Assn of the Society of Manufacturing Engineers (CASA/SME) last November.

Basically an assembly plant, the Tractor Works is a prime example of computer-aided materials handling—ensuring that the correct parts and components arrive at the right place on the assembly line at the right time. Computers provide complete control over the complex flow of materials within and among four buildings of the 48 acres under roof.

Seven automated storage and retrieval systems (AS/RS) and two automated transportation systems serve the mostly conventional tractor-assembly operations. Shop operations, storage, and transportation functions are controlled by nine separate minicomputers working under the coordinated supervision of a host computer handling overall production and inventory control.

But a broader picture of computer applications more illustrative of some of the emerging conflicts between the systems approach and the more pragmatic solutions often preferred by operating personnel is gained at the Component Works. Despite the conflicts, the managers of the Component Works fundamentally support many of the larger corporate systems. "We are full subscribers to the group-technology system, and, to my knowledge, we are probably the largest user of GT in the country or, for that matter, in the world," points out McAffee.

A unique opportunity to apply group technology on a large scale came when the new Tractor Works was formed, removing about 1½-million sq ft of manufacturing space from the Component Works and making it a prime target for rearrangement and capital improvement. "Who in the world ever had the opportunity to take a 4½-million-sq-ft factory and completely reorganize it?" exclaims McAffee with unbridled enthusiasm.

The first completed project of that

THE COMPUTER AND JOHN DEERE

rearrangement has been the creation of a new Hydraulics Div, with some 500 machines in approximately 533,400 sq ft of floor space designed, arranged, and operated through the application of a corporatewide GT system.

The John Deere Group Technology System (JD/GTS) has evolved under the watchful eye of Adel Zakaria, manager of manufacturing-engineering systems, who considers the system both a manufacturing philosophy and a powerful analytical tool. JD/GTS is an extension of the MICLASS system to include a great deal of process-related information. (MICLASS was originally developed by TNO, The Netherlands, and is now maintained, augmented, and marketed by Organization for Industrial Research, Waltham, Mass.)

Capturing the logic

The classification and coding scheme, involving a 37-digit code, was developed, in part, from responses of Deere process planners and manufacturing engineers to a questionnaire that elicited existing practice for typical work. Analysis of the responses captured the "logic" behind established practice, and a code was developed to reflect that logic.

There are four major areas at the Hydraulics Div facility: cast-iron machining, steel machining, assembly, and material storage. All of these are supported by smaller areas devoted to such critical functions as quality control, inspection, maintenance, and related plant-operation functions.

Using the many analysis features of the JD/GTS—some 25 different software programs can group parts according to type, manufactuing processes, historical demand, cost, etc—the Hydraulics Div was further subdivided into departments, each solely responsible for machining and assembling specific families of components.

Simply stated, this means that a part enters a department in an unfinished state and leaves that department only as a finished component ready for either final assembly or shipment. This concept eliminates costly materials handling, or cross-flows, between departments.

The analysis logic used involves the following steps.
■ Form part families by part code.
■ Combine families to form machine cells by part code and machine code.
■ Modify routing of parts within cells for optimum efficiency.
■ Combine cells to form departments by machine code.

The actual method of forming part families involves analysis of part codes, production flow, starting machine, production requirements, unique processes,

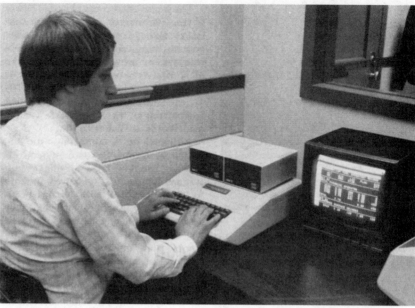

Apple II personal computer is the right tool for the tool-grinding department, where it is used to control inventory. As a result, inventory has been cut in half

Operator at head of FMS line (photo right) receives instructions for mounting parts on pallets of automated carts (foreground) after they pass through wash station

and chip-cutting vs non-chip-cutting activities.

The idea is to start out with a theoretical cell arrangement and then adjust it to practical reality by weighing cell arrangement against machine utilization within each cell. The cells, which are not necessarily in one physical location, are then combined to form departments.

The materials storage, inventory control, and materials-handling operations are all computerized and tightly integrated with a high-rise storage facility and an automated Robocarrier transport system supplied by Eaton-Kenway. The MRP-operated high-rise AS/RS towers 70 ft above ground level and provides space for 5500 material loads.

Fourteen driverless battery-operated Robocarriers, guided automatically by in-floor signal cable to predetermined pick-up or delivery stations, transport loads of up to 4000 lb between the AS/RS and all departments. A self-contained battery-monitoring feature of the Robocarriers automatically dispatches them to an automatic recharge station.

Recently, Zakaria added an "application" module to the JD/GTS to provide corporate managers as well as system users with a simple method of tracking the pattern of projects on which the system was used as an analytical tool. The aim is to obtain some insight into the resulting savings or improvements, and the program is strictly voluntary,

says Zakaria, not an attempt to play Big Brother.

After completing a project, the user is asked to input, through an interactive program, certain data describing briefly what the project was all about, the results, the saving achieved, who requested the project, and who did the work. The JD/GTS is available at any of the hundreds of multipurpose CRT terminals located throughout Deere facilities and used to access major systems.

The projects are classified according to 12 categories: part elimination or avoidance; material substitution; reference for design, process routing, tooling, or inspection; cost estimating; tooling elimination; machine-tool procurement; plant layout; materials handling; decisions regarding outside manufacturing; new technology; and other.

"This data is stored in an application database that we can access with the interactive program in the GT package," explains Zakaria. "For example, we can generate a distribution showing the number of projects by unit, application area, user, or any multiple combinations. We can also plot the pattern of use over time, and we can isolate applications of a given type. And, of course, we can generate reports reflecting this information."

The data generated by this application module is used to monitor results, trace patterns of use, share innovative ideas among users in different units of Deere,

24

and consult with selected users when it appears that the user was not aware of the full capabilities of the GT package.

"To date, we have had very good experience with the module," comments Zakaria. In fact, he reports that group technology is now so well accepted that users are beginning to question the need to prove its benefits. "And, incidentally," Zakaria points out, "we know that the majority—well over 50%—of the applications never even get reported."

At the other end of the computer-applications scale at the Component Works is a stand-alone personal-computer-based inventory-control system recently installed for the tool-grinding department. The basic objective was to improve scheduling of regrinding operations to reduce work in process (WIP) and, in turn, tool inventory overall. An Apple II personal computer, programmed by tool-grinding personnel with no prior computer experience, is doing the job.

Although the same number of tools are finished (about 13,000 per week), the overall inventory has been reduced from 32,000 to 16,000; the number of workers has been cut from 94 to 79. As of June '81, there was a 999.9% return on investment on the original $4635 expenditure. Obviously, the Apple has been the right tool for the right job.

Using a somewhat larger and more sophisticated stand-alone system, a Digi-

tal Equipment PDP 11/23, the area maintenance-shop operation at the Components Works has successfully combined the operations of three formerly separate shops into a much leaner, more efficient, and more responsive department. Although combining the operations eliminated many duplications and overlapping responsibilities, as well as reducing requirements for valuable floor space, it did promise to complicate the difficult and frustrating task of job tracking.

The DEC minicomputer was installed to aid planners and supervisors in prioritizing, tracking, and estimating jobs that come into the department. All work coming into the machine shop is received by a planner, who checks the job for necessary instructions and ensures that all required information is available. Typically, repair jobs are made from samples, and no specifications or drawings are available.

The planner establishes the routing for the job and enters the information into the computer system, thereby opening a maintenance work order (MWO). A hardcopy version of the MWO is generated on an associated printer. One copy of this MWO is given to the initiator of the work to help check on progress of the job. A second copy travels with the work until the order is closed out.

The operator assigned to a job is required to "log on" the computer. The remote job-entry terminal provides

prompting messages to ensure that all necessary information, such as clock number and machine ID, is properly entered. From then on, the computer keeps track of the job until it is finished and each operator has logged off.

"The computer gives us the ability to retrieve job information by selecting any one of many criteria," says Robert L. Osborn, manager of mechanical services. Information can be retrieved on the basis of machine number, department charged, tool number, or maintenance area. In addition, the performance of the department, by work station or operator, can be reviewed. The planner assigns a work difficulty—easy, medium, or hard—to each job at the planning stage. The computer continually compares the actual hours charged with the time estimate assigned to each difficulty category and updates those times. Consequently, the computer provides a real and valid backlog report, and any anomalies can be readily addressed.

The software for this shop-management system was written by Digital Equipment Corp (DEC) from functional specifications developed by a Deere project team composed mainly of the users. "We simply computerized what we had been trying to do by long-hand," remarks Russell L. Mattox, manager of process and tool engineering at the Component Works. The result is a neat, comfortable system that operators, supervi-

25

sors, and planners understand because they had a hand in putting it together. "If we imposed a production-control system from up top and then took it away, the operators and supervisors would cheer. But, if we tried to take this system out, I predict, we would have a riot on our hands," says Mattox.

On a totally different scale, the Component Works has a fully automated 12-machine FMS (flexible manufacturing system) to manufacture eight parts of a clutch-housing and transmission-case family. Supplied by Kearney & Trecker, the system has nine Modu-Line CNC machining centers, three two-axis Head Indexers, with 23 heads, and a towline materials-handling system with 45 pallets and 46 fixtures.

A DEC computer manages the entire FMS through a distributed-logic architecture operating at several levels. Part programs are downloaded to the CNC machines for non-real-time DNC operation, eliminating the need for a constant stream of data between the system computer and the machine computer. An intermediate level of control takes care of materials handling and is responsible for coordinating the movement of material through the manufacturing system.

Parts are mounted on cart-transported pallets according to instructions transmitted from the supervisory computer to a CRT terminal at the loading station. Before parts are loaded, each car/fixture unit passes through an automatic wash station to remove chips and other debris left by the manufacturing cycle.

The computer also dispatches tooling according to the expected tool life for each tool. As the cycle time logged for any particular tool reaches 90% of the intended tool life, the computer notifies the toolroom to prepare a new preset tool and deliver it to the appropriate FMS station. At 100% tool life, a beacon at the machine summons a roving setup person, who changes the tooling.

The supervisory computer can be used to generate a variety of pertinent reports, including tool-life data and production data, as well as such maintenance-related information as the accumulated length of track trave,ed by an individual cart or the total cycle time of any machine per shift.

All areas of manufacturing engineering have had an opportunity to use the corporate GMS (geometric-modeling system) via the Computervision computer-graphics system. One typical application is the design of pattern plates for the foundry operation. The Component Works includes one of the largest captive gray-iron foundries in the US.

Pattern-plate drawings are generated with library elements of standard plates and part geometry of patterns also stored in the system. An appropriate number of patterns is arranged on the pattern plate to obtain the best yield. The entire design/drafting procedure is performed on the computer-graphics screen. The operator then adds the gating system, puddle cavity, and sprue pin and calls up an automatic dimensioning routine to finish the drawing.

In some instances, the use of computers at the Components Works is almost imperceptible. A recently automated gear line is a good example. The line was established using GT to develop three different process lines. The actual installation is a turnkey job supplied by Liebherr GmbH. "After analyzing this operation, we decided it was not appropriate for actual computer-based process control," says Mattox. "But we did incorporate automated parts handling."

In fact, the line uses Allen-Bradley programmable controllers which are, after all, special-purpose industrial minicomputers, to control the flow of blanks to the various machining stations and to ensure that the buffer-storage area for each automated machine is adequately stocked. An automatic inspection station checks for running errors at the end of each line, and an annunciator panel, prompted by conditions reported by the PCs, summons an operator when a machine misses a cycle.

The right tool for the right job

The computer applications at Deere cover the entire spectrum, but, in each instance, it is a matter of using the right tool for the right job. What about the conflict between the systems approach and the stand-alone applications? "It seems to me that there are two distinct levels of computer applications," says McAffee. "At the operating level, we need autonomy and we need to keep the systems simple to allow people to use their own creativity. At another level, we need planning systems, such as master scheduling and GT. Those are appropriately run and managed in a host environment. These are two separate issues, and a lot of people haven't made that distinction yet." What he doesn't want is CIM for the sake of integration. What he wants is the computer as a tool.

How will the conflict be resolved? There's a feeling at the Component Works that pragmatism will win out in the end. "Suddenly, manufacturing engineers are beginning to get access to computers and are beginning to understand what computers can do," says Mattox. "They're bound to figure out how to apply them as effective manufacturing tools. That's a manufacturing engineer's job."

And, chimes in McAffee, "I really think that the manufacturing engineer owns the future. Any organization that neglects the health, well-being, and care of the manufacturing engineer is going to fall by the wayside because the future of any organization depends on manufacturing costs."

At Deere, the computer is the tool to help control these costs.

Operator assigned to repair job 'logs on' minicomputer system that helps track jobs and updates time estimates. Terminal provides prompting messages to prevent errors

THE COMPUTER AND MANUFACTURING

Quick reflexes and an integrated system are the keys to survival

THE COMPUTER is bringing manufacturing into the Information Age. This new tool, long a familiar one in business and management operations, is moving into the factory, and its advent is changing manufacturing as certainly as the steam engine changed it 100 years ago.

The basic metalworking processes are not likely to change fundamentally, but their organization and control definitely will.

In one respect, manufacturing could be said to be coming full circle. The first manufacturing was a cottage industry: the designer was also the manufacturer, conceiving and fabricating products one at a time. Eventually, the concept of the interchangeability of parts was developed, production was separated into specialized functions, and identical parts were produced thousands at a time.

Today, production is much more batch-oriented, and, although the designer and manufacturer may not become one again, the functions are being drawn close in the movement toward an integrated manufacturing system.

It is perhaps ironic that, at a time when the market demands a high degree of product diversification, the necessity for increasing productivity and reducing costs is driving manufacturing toward integration into a coherent system, a continuous process in which parts do not spend as much as 95% of production time being moved around or waiting to be worked on.

The computer is the key to each of these twin requirements. It is the only tool that can provide the quick reflexes, the flexibility and speed, to meet a diversified market. And it is the only tool that enables the detailed analysis and the accessibilty of accurate data necessary for the integration of the manufacturing system.

It may well be that, in the future, the computer may be essential to a company's survival. C.H. Link, former senior vice president and general manager of CAM-I Inc, puts it this way: "The computer 'have-nots' will be left behind and will become increasingly out of step in the Information Age. Many of today's businesses will fade away to be replaced by more-productive combinations."

Arthur R. Thomson, professor of manufacturing engineering, Cleveland State Univ, describes such more-productive combinations as "superquality, superproductivity plants. The goal, as I would see it, is to design and operate a plant that would produce 100% satisfactory parts with good productivity. People may say that such a goal is crazy, but we can develop turbines that are 98% efficient, and the struggle to reach 100% is bringing us fairly close to it. I think that we in manufacturing have settled for a lot less than we could really get."

A sophisticated, competitive world is requiring that manufacturing begin to settle for more, to become itself sophisticated. To meet competition, for example, a company will have to meet the somewhat conflicting demands for greater product diversification, higher quality, improved productivity, and lower prices.

The company that seeks to meet these demands will need a sophisticated tool, one that will allow it to respond quickly to customer needs while getting the most out of its manufacturing resources.

The computer is that tool.

Becoming a "superquality, superproductivity" plant requires the integration of an extremely complex system. This can be accomplished only when all elements of manufacturing—design, fabri-

cation and assembly, quality assurance, management, materials handling—are computer integrated, both individually and collectively.

Charles F. Carter, technical director of Cincinnati Milacron and president of SME, separates manufacturing into three phases: product design, planning for manufacturing, and the manufacturing itself. "The computer," he points out, "is revolutionizing all three phases."

In product design, for example, interactive computer-aided-design (CAD) systems allow the drawing and analysis tasks to be performed in a fraction of the time previously required and with greater accuracy. And programs for prototype testing and evaluation further speed the design process.

In manufacturing planning, computer-aided process planning permits the selection, from thousands of possible sequences and schedules, of the optimum process.

On the shop floor, distributed intelligence in the form of microprocessors controls machines, runs automated loading and unloading equipment, and collects data on current shop conditions.

But such isolated revolutions are not enough. "Installing a token robot here or a computer there," says Donald K. Grierson, senior vice president of General Electric Co's Industrial Electronics Group, "is like giving a Band-Aid to a guy who has been run over by a threshing machine. What is needed is a totally automated system, linked by common software from front door to back."

The benefits range throughout the system. Essentially, computer integration provides widely and instantaneously available, accurate information, improving communication between departments, permitting tighter control, and

Computer-integrated manufacturing

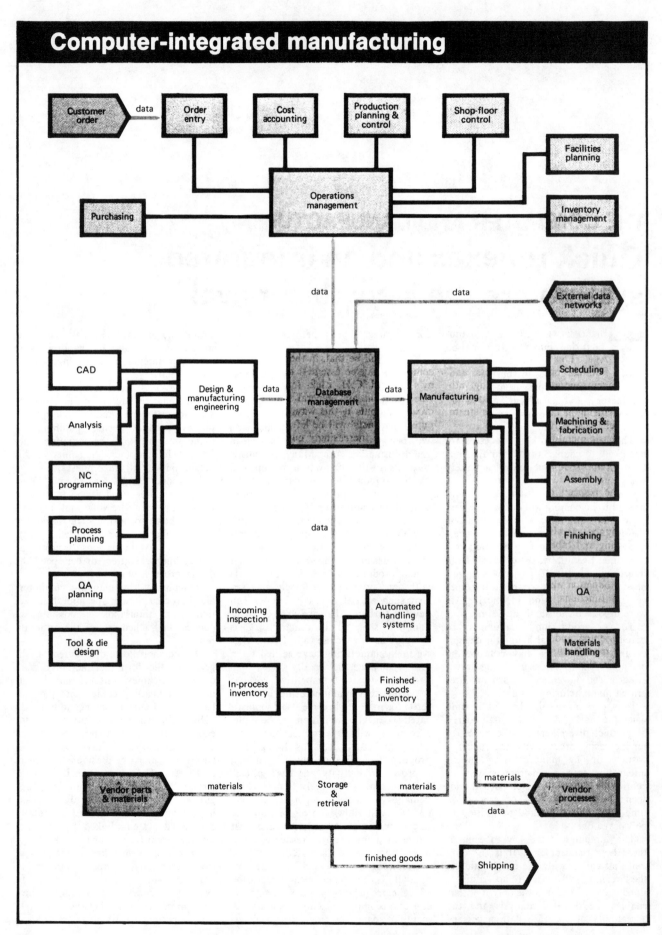

generally enhancing the overall quality and efficiency of the entire system.

Improved communication can mean, for example, designs that are more producible: "The NC programmer and the tool designer," says Jack Ulmer, chief of Design Technology, Research & Engineering for Boeing Military Airplane Co (BMAC), "have a chance to influence the designer, and vice versa."

Engineering changes, thus, can be reduced, and those that are required can be handled more efficiently. Not only does the computer permit them to be specified more quickly, but it also alerts subsequent users of the data to the fact that a change has been made.

Furthermore, the use of design data in NC programming means better NC tapes and, therefore, less rework and scrap.

Better data, better control

The instantaneous updating of production-control data permits better planning and more-effective scheduling. Expensive equipment, therefore, is used more productively, and parts move more efficiently through production, reducing work-in-process costs.

Product quality, too, can be improved. Not only are more-accurate designs produced, for example, but the use of design data by the quality-assurance department helps eliminate errors due to misunderstandings.

People are enabled to do their jobs better. By eliminating tedious calculations and paperwork—not to mention time wasted searching for information—the computer not only allows workers to be more productive but also frees them to do what only human beings can do: think creatively.

Boeing's Ulmer points out, too, that his company's experiment with an integrated team approach "heightens [workers'] sense of involvement and interdependence that has been lost in our more complex production environment."

Computer integration may also lure new people into manufacturing. Kingston-Warren Corp, for example, discovered that its computer-graphics system gave it an edge in a designer-scarce job market. "People are attracted to us because they want to work in a modern, technologically sophisticated environment," says Dr Victor Azzi, vice president and director of engineering.

Documenting the specific benefits of computer-integrated manufacturing is frequently hard to do: new installations in one area of the operation may produce effects in another far downstream. But some companies have identified just where improvements can be seen. GE's Computer Aided Engineering & Manufacturing Council, surveying more

than 300 organizations in 160 GE businesses, has determined the distribution of primary benefits of new CAD/CAM applications: 56% to productivity, 25% to quality, 17% to cycle time, and 2% to meeting contract requirements.

BMAC, says Ulmer, calculates a $2.8-million return on its investment in an experimental CAD/CAM program. Savings have been realized through such improvements as a reduction in engineering changes as a result of better drawing quality, a reduction in scrap and rework through improved control of NC tapes, elimination of duplicated effort, an improved reaction to changes, the integration of the handling of CAD/tool-design/NC data, and the cross-utilization of personnel.

Sikorsky Aircraft, according to Dr Kenneth M. Rose, manager of Air Vehicle Design & Development, figures that a designer at a terminal is, on the average, three times more productive than on a drawing board and, in some cases, as much as eight times more productive. Considering planned CAD-system acquisitions, the company expects to save 500,000 hr in design work during the period 1981-85.

In manufacturing engineering, Rose reports, CAD/CAM decreases tool-design, NC-programming, and planning times while speeding the response rate, which will eventually permit in-house staff to perform work that is currently being contracted out.

For smaller firms, too

And it's not just for the giants and the aerospace firms. For Setco Industries Inc, a 150-employee producer of machine-tool components, the speed of its computer-aided-engineering system has meant the difference between winning contracts and losing one. "In the five years that we've had the system," declares W.A. Ferguson, president and CEO, "we've doubled our sales. Estimating job costs by hand," he explains, "would take two or three days. On one particular job, a customer asked for a quote, and we were able to process the data in a matter of hours. We had the order before our competitor even had a chance to quote it."

The transition to computer-integrated manufacturing is, to say the least, not simple. "Basically, manufacturing is trying to move from a seat-of-the-pants and play-it-by-ear approach," says Milacron's Carter, "to a completely structured, computer-run system. Obviously, you can't just plug in a CAD terminal and let it go to work. You have to build up a database that will give the computer the information necessary to work with the particulars of your product lines."

Building up this database requires a real understanding of how the manufacturing process works, an understanding that is frequently lacking in the seat-of-the-pants operation and necessitates an in-depth analysis of the entire system.

Ironically, here the computer is both cause and aid: while creating the need for in-depth analysis of a multiplicity of complex operations, the computer is the only tool with which such analysis can logically be performed. And, too, such analysis in itself is beneficial, revealing the way the manufacturing process actually works and, therefore, can be organized and controlled.

Integration also "will force manufacturing to change the way in which it works," says Carter. "We no longer will have the freedom to customize data to fit our own jobs. Data must remain uniform throughout the operation. Each person who uses the data or adds to it will have to understand the needs of all others who use it. In short, we will have to get our various acts together."

Still a long way to go

Fully integrated manufacturing is not yet here. "Individual computer-aided functions provide greater speed and efficiency for individual tasks," Carter points out, "but we have a long way to go in assimilating the technology and applying it to every phase of our operations, which is the only way to derive the full benefit of the new technology."

The investment—in commitment as well as money, labor, and time—is enormous, but so are the potential benefits. And there may soon be no alternative.

Painful though the transition may be, any company that intends to survive in this increasingly sophisticated, highly competitive world will have to enter the Information Age. "I honestly believe," says William F. McAnirlin Jr, CAD/CAM-systems manager at Kingston-Warren, "that manufacturing companies not involved with computer systems have only two choices: get on board or get out of business."

The sections that follow are intended to help you stay in business. They cover the state of the art in currently and soon-to-be available hardware and software and their linkage into information networks; the changing role of the manufacturing engineer and education's response to the demands of this new world of manufacturing; management's responsibility in meeting the challenge of computer integration; government's and academia's participation in technology development; and what this all means to you and your company.

Welcome aboard!

THE TOOLS
Distributed microprocessors
put the computer where the action is

BACK SOME 35 YEARS AGO, when ENIAC, the first digital computer, was doing ballistics calculations for the Army at the then-incredible rate of 300 multiplications per second, few people had any inkling of how closely associated with physical work computers would get.

Early number-crunching machines were huge laboratory curiosities, fickle about operating voltages and ambient temperatures and destined, most people thought, never to leave the companionship of their white-coated attendants.

What happened along the way, of course, was a computer-manufacturing technique known as large-scale integration (LSI) and, more recently, very large-scale integration (VLSI). Photomasking advances, the development of the ability to refine high-purity substrates, and a host of other advances—including perhaps the most important one, the use of computers to design and control the steps in manufacturing other computer circuits—has brought about mind-boggling capabilities for the logic elements. From an oversimplified point of view, as the circuits got smaller, they got faster: the electrons had a shorter distance to go.

In the quest to put even more circuits on a microchip, the technology has progressed to the point where engineers, using such techniques as ion implantation, vacuum-chamber deposition, and sputtering are able to control etched circuit elements to an accuracy of plus or minus just a few molecules. (That may not be where the technology ends; research at a couple of universities and private companies is aimed at creating computational switches that not only approach the size of a molecule but are themselves molecules. One possible approach uses bioengineering to generate synthesized organic compounds that act as molecular switches.)

Subminiaturization is the reason that today's IBM 3081 computer can operate at 4.59-million multiplications per second, or 15,000 times faster than the ENIAC. It also enabled the design, slightly more than 10 years ago, of the first microprocessor, or computer-on-a-chip.

That first microprocessor, designed by Ted Hoff Jr at a new company named Intel, squeezed a central processing unit (CPU), a read-only memory (ROM), a random-access memory (RAM), and a shift register onto a single integrated circuit. At first, Intel did not realize what it had, and its marketing department, believing that the microprocessor would be sold only as a replacement for the minicomputer in certain applications, predicted that sales would peak at only a few thousand units per year. That initial estimate was off by several orders of magnitude.

Ubiquitous microprocessor

Today, there are microprocessors quite literally in everything from automobile carburetors, where they adjust gas/air ratios to compensate for changes in outside temperature and barometric pressure to permit maximum fuel economy while maintaining emissions standards and performance, to wristwatches, typewriters, and telephones.

Just as these more rugged integrated circuits are becoming part of ordinary consumer products, they are also becoming essential elements of computer-integrated manufacturing (CIM) by making the necessary conversions of information into action; in addition, they have the inherent capability to provide feedback information so necessary for controlling these activities.

In the shop, the ubiquitous micro is carving out two distinct roles for itself.

First, it can operate in a free-standing mode, forming the basis for control of a single machine, such as a grinder or a press brake. A microprocessor-controlled robot, for example, might calculate a straight-line trajectory between a pair of three-dimensionally defined points and then control movement in each of five axes directing the manipulator's gripper from one point to the other.

The second role for the shop-floor microprocessor has just as much significance. As a device for capturing data from the most basic steps in factory flow, sorting out significant pieces of information, and preparing them for use by supervisory controllers, microprocessors

---

Exponential growth
in semiconductors

Active devices per chip

Year	Devices
1970	100
1975	4,000
1980	100,000
1985	1,000,000

Cost of equivalent CPU and memory

Year	Cost
1970	50,000
1975	10,000
1980	1,000
1985	100

Speed-power product

Year	Picojoules
1970	400
1975	40
1980	2
1985	0.2

Source: Bradley Univ

and their associated sensors and actuators act as building blocks for control systems and the networks that link them together.

For either of these two roles, microprocessors themselves are becoming more powerful. The eight-bit CPUs—such as the popular Zilog Z-80—that juggle eight binary digits, or individual pieces of information, at a time already form the basis for many single-board computers. These, for a few hundred dollars, can provide on-site control over a series of variables. Newer, 16-bit processors, such as the Motorola 6800 extend capabilities considerably, and the coming generation of 32-bit-architecture micros, such as the Texas Instrument TMS320, promise to race along at 5-million instructions per second to offer high-precision data handling for such computation-intensive functions as digitally filtering analog signals, speech recognition, vision and high-resolution graphics and three-dimension-

---

Now hardware, too, is 'user-friendly'

If you've ever withdrawn cash from 24-hour banking machine, set up Space Invaders for two players, or entered a tool offset into CRT-equipped CNC, you have experienced "user-friendly software."

The term refers to the way the computer behind the machine is programmed to facilitate its use even by the uninitiated. A number of devices are used by the programmer: text messages on the scene prompt the user into selecting choices from a menu; those selections effectively "turn the page" to the next set of choices; each menu page allows a user to go back and correct mistakes; and entries that affect the outcome are verified before they are executed. Before long, the user has completed the transaction successfully and painlessly.

It's a far cry from the time when the computer user virtually had to be a programmer, when the user had to look up the code equivalents of many pieces of information before they could be input. Nowadays, most application software is user-friendly at least to some extent, and that trend has done wonders in getting computers accepted as everyday tools.

A more recent trend has been to design the physical part of the computerized tool, the so-called human/machine interface, to make the system easier to work with. The goal is to make the work station easier to use and more approachable.

Keyboards, especially the standard typewriter keyboard (called "qwerty," for the upper left-to-right character placement), are fine for text information. But they come up lacking for jobs like entering numbers, drawing graphics, or simply moving a blinking cursor around a CRT. Furthermore, their psychological association with secretarial work has led some shop-floor-terminal designers to substitute keyboards, often sealed under a membrane and offering little key "action," that are arranged in alphabetical order instead of the conventional qwerty setup.

Calculator-style keypads now routinely part of computer terminals speed the entry of numerals. Joysticks that convert analog X-Y movement via linear potentiometers into digital CRT coordinates for cursor positioning or drawing are also routine.

One popular hand tool for use with a CRT is the light pen. This instrument, attached by cable—sometimes using fiber optics—to the computer terminal, picks up light when it is held against the surface of the CRT screen. It signals this detection back to the computer's screen-printing circuitry, which is constantly scanning the CRT from left to right and top to bottom, refreshing the image, pixel by pixel. The circuit deliberately but invisibly flashes an erratic blinking to each pixel in succession, polling, as it were, the entire screen. By comparing the time (in milliseconds) that the light pen receives this coded pulse and the time within the scanning period it was transmitted to the screen, the computer can determine where on the screen that the pen is placed.

Team a light pen with a program that offers multiple choices, each preceded by a dot on the screen to which the pen is touched to indicate the choice, and you have a terminal at which the operator virtually never has to touch a keyboard.

The latest development along these lines is a transparent position sensor that conforms to the glass front of a CRT and lets an operator merely point to the desired selection. A finger's touch on the screen signals the continuous thin-film-coated sensor to transmit the coordinates of the touched point to the computer. Available for only a short time, the see-through touch sensors are already being incorporated into "executive decision-support" terminals and may well go a long way toward sidestepping many people's aversion to typewriter keyboards and, by extension, their avoidance of computers.

If holding a pen—or merely a finger—up to a CRT screen is awkward or potentially tiring for someone, like a design engineer, who must do it all day, the dedicated graphics tablet may be the answer. Typically a large, flat, drawing-board-like surface permanently marked with a graphics gridwork or alphanumeric or menu choices, the tablet is used with an electronic rather than optical pen, and it allows a worker to "write" in a comfortable position while viewing the product of the manipulations on a CRT.

Other kinds of user-friendly hardware offer even greater simplicity for the user but often at the expense of the amount of information that can be exchanged. Optical bar-code readers and inductance-sensing magnetic-tape-strip badge readers, for example, often restrict the format of information that can be acquired at that particular terminal. However, these devices—typically designed for shop-floor use or for exterior entry security—are probably among the most resistant to harsh industrial environments, and their input limitations may well be a blessing in disguise.

The enhancements often improve accuracy. For example, one MDI machine control soon to be introduced offers computer-synthesized speech that enunciates the name of button as it is pushed. Instead of a "bleep" as with some calculators, a "two" or "dee" or "ess," etc, is sounded when a numeral or letter is pushed. If a wrong button is pressed, the user knows it immediately, without even looking at the screen.

Voice recognition, the other side of the computer-speech coin, is a technology that is developing nicely, though not at the rapid rate that had been expected when it was introduced to numerical-control programming almost a decade ago. But, as computer-synthesized speech and computer recognition of human voice by comparison with prerecorded patterns enter into other, non-factory environments, the equipment costs will start coming down, making these human-oriented features even more accessible.

shape interpretation, and very high-performance controls applications.

A possible future alternative to large-capacity microprocessors is the "micro-mainframe," which can run several terminals at once through its capability to do multiprocessing. Its inventor, Intel Corp, which made the first microprocessor, hopes the new computer-on-a-chip will open up new applications, instead of just replacing more-costly mainframes and current microprocessors.

The tool on board the tool

Incorporating the microprocessor, the information-generating and -handling tool, into a piece of production machinery can yield some far-reaching results. On-board micros, dedicated to controlling the slide drives at each station of a Ford Motor Co transfer line for four-cylinder engine blocks, for example, led to other, productive changes in the design of the system. Programs that are burned into EPROMS (erasable, programmable read-only memories) associated with the micro CPUs eliminate the need

for limit switches on the Ingersoll-built line that Ford installed last year. But the feature also permits greater versatility of the servo systems, such as overlapping functions to shorten cycle times. Similarly controlled drives in the station-to-station transfer mechanism permit programmed acceleration and deceleration of the work, eliminating mechanical jolts that increase machine wear.

Ultra-high-speed spindles that cut aluminum structures for Boeing Commercial Airplane Co on a Turchan Cormil use microprocessors to perfectly center the magnetically levitated milling spindle. The S2M-built active magnetic spindle suspends the rotating member in a field between opposing electromagnets; sensed changes in the field tell the controlling processor that the spindle is moving out of alignment, and the field is instantaneously and adaptively altered to recenter the spindle.

Self-propelled materials-handling carts lugging workpieces between the individual machining cells in a flexible manufacturing system use microproces-

sors for steering. A bow-tie-shaped antenna slung beneath the carts electronically "sniffs out" a weak signal being broadcast from a wire implanted just below floor level. On-board circuitry seeks to constantly null the signal by steering the cart to maintain its position directly above the wire.

Transparent level of control

If we're moving toward a point where, as Gould Factory Automation Director Richard E. Morley puts it, every limit switch will use an inexpensive microprocessor, then that capacity also will open up additional possibilities. Not only will the limit switch be coupled to a localized controller hooked to a servo motor, but that controller will be able to communicate with a more generalized computer. The lowest-level microprocessors and localized controllers may well be invisible to the casual observer.

The design of the IRI robot from International Robomation/Intelligence is a good example. The machine uses pneumatic servo motors in each of its five

The saga of a part without a drawing

The first NC machines at Lamb Technicon's F. Jos Lamb Div. were put into use about 11 years ago. Today, about 10% of the machine tools in the company are NC (almost all CNC), and they do almost half of the machining done by the company.

The first Applicon CAD system was installed four years ago, and now about 25 design engineers are tightly scheduled on six graphics terminals (soon to be increased to eight).

The first true CAD/CAM part started production at Lamb not quite two years ago. The part, one that turns up frequently in transfer machines, is a probe box. Probe boxes mount a number of probes precisely positioned at holes drilled in the front plate. They are used to check the condition of the workpiece at different stations during the cycle.

Probe boxes are produced with three different mounting patterns for attaching to the transfer machine and have varying numbers, sizes, and locations of holes for probes.

When a machine designer requires a probe box, all these variables are specified and are stored in one of the 16 levels of the graphics-system memory. Jack Settimo, NC manager for Lamb, developed the procedures. "We wrote an interface program that interrogates that level of memory and extracts the

variables in a specific order, starting and ending with the part number. We use a cassette-tape recorder connecting the Applicon and the DECwriter to record these results, getting 100-150 drawing files on a single cassette."

This cassette goes by messenger from design engineering to manufacturing engineering, where it is loaded into a Tektronix programming system that extracts the data for a part, loads it into a postprocessor, creates an NC program to machine the probe box, and stores the data in disk memory. It is possible, of course, to run the NC program and display the cutter path on a CRT.

Probe boxes are machined at the Lamb plants in Dexter, Jackson, and Warren (all in Michigan), and the programs are transmitted by data line to the appropriate plant. Programs can be fed directly to the machine tools but are normally recorded on punched tape at each plant.

The first time the program was run, there was a hurried call from the plant reporting that the part was wrong: "One of the holes is missing." Sure enough, the hole was missing from the NC program. It was also missing from level 8 in the graphics system, though it was in the completed design. It turned out that one hole had somehow been

stored on a different memory level. "So we changed our interface program so that now it interrogates all memory levels," says Settimo.

Before this system was developed, drawings of the probe-box designs were created, and the boxes were produced on manual machines. At Lamb, Settimo is apparently the interface between engineering and manufacturing though he considers himself part of manufacturing. "But we are getting a lot closer together, beginning to program together," he says.

A DEC VAX 11-780 has been installed and, in a few months, should be linked directly to the Applicon system (manufacturing is already using it). When that happens, the data will move directly, and both the cassette tape and the messenger will be eliminated.

The next parts to get the CAD/CAM treatment will be drillheads, probably later this year. Then, in addition to NC tapes, Settimo will begin to produce inspection tapes from the same database.

Running down the different programming methods they've used in the past, Settimo says they are now writing most programs in BASIC, some in FORTRAN. "String manipulation is easier in BASIC," he says, "but subroutines are easier in FORTRAN."

revolute axes, and each motor has its own computer controller that encompasses up to 20 different control modes including acceleration, velocity, braking with a separate disk brake, deceleration, jogging, and load adapting. A single 16-bit microprocessor serves as an executive controller to the individual micros.

Transparent or not, microprocessors that boost the computing power of an electronic device not only enhance but extend the device's capabilities.

One of the recent developments in microprocessor-equipped programmable controllers, for example, is their use for motion control. PCS are, by definition, programmable, and, in the ten years since their general introduction as more-reliable replacements for electromechanical circuits, the ease with which they can change control logic—with the press of a few buttons instead of rewiring a relay panel—has made them grow in popularity. During the past two years, PC manufacturers have begun to offer their products configured to govern the movement of closed-loop servo systems.

The speed with which the microprocessor operates enables this capability. In a closed-loop system, an error signal is calculated by subtracting the digital feedback number from the command sent by the controller; the derived signal is then used to continuously correct for feeds, acceleration, and deceleration. In some cases, the time it takes to scan the memory within a programable controller exceeds the 10-msec-interval servicing requirement of a typical axis loop. Adding a microprocessor to the controller, as in the new G&L PC400, adds an interrupt capability that internally allows the function.

The user advantages include not only the lower cost typically associated with PCs but also the ability to program in simple ladder-diagram format. Again, the microprocessor is transparent.

Such internally decentralized processing within a single piece of control hardware blurs traditional distinctions between PCS, CNCS, MDIS, etc. Indeed, the newer single-axis electronic controls found on grinders and saws as well as the latest generation of robot controllers suggest, some say, an accelerating trend toward building individual controllers into production machine and eliminating the separate manufacturer of control hardware.

Internally decentralized control—as in the hierarchical NC that GE will introduce at IMTS-82—is also a microcosm of the information interchange in the factory of the future. DNC, for instance, no longer means "direct numerical control"; rather, the term has been redefined as "distributed numerical control," reflect-

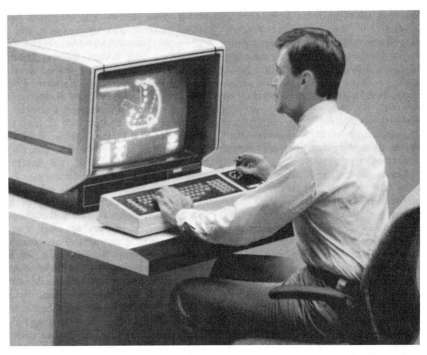

Full-color image, joystick movement of picture elements are features of the Megatek terminal hooked to a DEC VAX minicomputer in MDSI's new NC-programming station

ing the autonomy of each link in the chain.

Nor are motor actuators and stand-alone controls the only shop-environment elements in the computerized network that links the factory together. Increasingly, the sensors—tactile, vision, temperature, etc—that enable untended operations and computer-access terminals themselves are appearing next to or as part of the machine tool.

Tactile sensing can range all the way to a layer of viscoelastic material covering a semiconductor array that can sense objects the way the skin on a human hand does. But touch sensing need not be all that sophisticated to be useful in a production environment.

Probes, such as the one by Renishaw that was so much in evidence at the '80 International Machine Tool Show, provide the data for automatic toolsetting and the in-process gaging for determining tool offsets in lathes and other machines. Typically stored in a machining center's tool pocket, the probe is transferred to the spindle and connected electrically to the CNC. Machine datum positions on the various axes can be checked by bringing the probe's stylus into contact with the actual workpiece. The instant the stylus is deflected, an electrical circuit is broken, triggering a signal for recording inspection data.

Simple limit switches, potentiometers, and other systems that monitor air pressure provide binary signaling only and are useful, if a little crude. More-

complex devices are on the way, according to Prof Leon D. Harmon, of Case Western Reserve's Biomedical Engineering Dept, in a report to Robotics International's annual technical conference. The use of conductive elastomer in sandwiched layers is one avenue of exploration; another is nonpliable but high-temperature-resistant piezoresistive materials dubbed Pressistors.

Sensor feedback through sight

Harmon sees a third generation of robots emerging. If the first generation was characterized by fixed-program open-loop control and the second generation by adaptive systems with flexible programming, the third generation has sensory feedback. "The principal advances are in vision systems," he says.

Use of vision, of course, is not limited to robotics, but the two technologies seem to be moving closely together as the application of small videocameras to manipulator arms grows more common.

Closely related to other optical measuring systems, sophisticated vision systems give machines the important sensory feedback that is needed to operate autonomously from a central controller or a human operator. A machine with vision capability can correct for a misaligned seam to be welded, can reject a damaged part coming onto an assembly station, and can inspect a workpiece for completeness before permitting it to move away from the operation station.

Most vision systems use a binary

approach based on research initiated at Stanford Univ years ago. The microcomputer-based vision controller divides the TV-like image of an object into an array of points, then assigns each point a value above or below a threshold level somewhere along a gray scale. Depending on how well the threshold is selected, the computer divides the image into clusters of white and black two-dimensional shapes, then compares these silhouettes with stored representations.

Binary vision systems are not the only types that are potential solutions to the sensor-feedback problem. Others take different approaches to machine vision but are headed in similar directions: one software package processes gray-scale video information into "feature sets" and then recognizes patterns or dissimilar sets for verification or comparison; another, a three-dimension perception system, uses coded-light patterns for optical ranging.

Shop-floor-level sensors aren't limited to touch or sight. Arc-welding power systems like the ones available from CRC or Westinghouse measure the current flowing through the arc and can thus determine whether a welding machine is properly tracking a seam. Noncontact temperature sensors aimed at the cutting-tool/work interface provide information to adaptively control feeds and speeds at the machine.

In a totally integrated and computerized factory, these types of sensors not only control the local process but can also be interconnected to a supervisory factory controller.

Shop-floor terminals

While some factory-operation information that should be directed at a supervisory computer can be gleaned automatically from microprocessor-based sensors and localized controllers like PCs and CNCs, a good deal of it will always come from humans inputting data directly. Here, networks of shop-level computer terminals supply the interface.

A fairly typical installation of shop-floor terminals is the system at the City Auto Stamping Div of Sheller-Globe Corp, where 560 UAW members working on an incentive-pay system make stampings and accessories for automobiles and industrial equipment. A network of 128 work-station terminals installed on or near the factory's 65 presses and 93 welding/finishing stations has individual workers entering information directly into a Digital Equipment Co (DEC) minicomputer via Information Automation Inc terminals. The individual terminals mounted on the machines include production count-sensors that automatically

detect piece counts and compare the actual machine cycle time to standard.

Non-machine-linked terminals at City Auto Stamping accept manual input. The face of the small box-shaped terminal contains red and green status lights that indicate whether the machine is running, is down, or requires assistance. A button allows an operator to request assistance. And a piece counter displays the machine's production. The box also has a phone jack to call the central control or maintenance department.

Other shop-floor terminals offer less automation. Typically consisting of a membrane-enclosed keypad and perhaps a liquid-crystal display or small CRT, they require that an operator periodically enter data from the job ticket. Such information may include the job number, work-station number, an operator identification, and the operations that have been completed or are about to begin. In many cases, data entry is at least partially automated by the use of bar codes printed on job tickets that accompany the work around the shop floor.

Physically closer to the central computer that records information from the shop-floor terminals is a conventional data terminal. Typically consisting of a typewriter-style keyboard and a cathode ray tube (CRT) or printer or both to display text information line by line, computer terminals provide access to the processor and its associated memory.

Terminals: dumb and smart

In general, data terminals fall into one of two categories: "dumb" and "smart." Dumb terminals, with pricetags as low as several hundred dollars, are those that provide no computational capabilities or data storage of their own; to operate, they must be hooked up to and communicating with—"on-line to"—the host computer.

Terminals that do not rely on hosts 100% of their operating time are considered, on the other hand, smart, although there is no broad consensus about which features are basic. So-called smart terminals are able to conduct some computational operations, store data in an internal memory or buffer for manipulation during the time when they are off-line, change communication protocols to enable hook-up to a variety of host computers, etc. These features are usually enabled by a resident microprocessor.

Within a computer, data are organized into bytes, and eight-bit bytes are considered standard for most processors because a group of eight yes/no circuit switches can represent 256 unique number codes, more than enough for text characters, numbers, and special keyboard characters. But, although it is rea-

sonable to have eight data lines move from CPU to memory or to the input/output ports within a computer, eight-wire cables are prohibitive for long distances, both from a cost standpoint and because electrical noise would interfere.

Instead, the data are serialized, or converted into a continuous stream, prior to transmission. And, to transmit over telephone lines or broadcast media, data are converted to and from appropriate audio or other signals by processing devices called "modems" (for modulator/demodulator).

Windows to complex data

Terminals form the most visible portion of today's turnkey computer-graphics systems, but they are not the same keyboard and CRT combinations used for simple data access.

Interactive graphics terminals, with which designers can communicate with computers directly in terms of lines and drawings, put primary emphasis on the screen. Virtually all of these terminals use one of three types of video display: raster-scan, vector-refresh, and direct-view storage tube. All three produce images on a phosphor-coated screen in essentially the same way as a conventional television: by deflecting a beam of electrons aimed at the screen from an emitter at the rear of the glass tube. The way that beam is modulated accounts for the differences.

Direct-view storage tubes (DVSTs), in which the monochromatic track is stored directly on the screen rather than in computer memory, have dominated the computer-graphics market for the last ten years because of their superior resolution and large display capacity. Also, vector-refresh and plain raster screens were previously more expensive and were used where color was an absolute necessity.

Raster tubes more feasible

Recently, according to MSRA Inc, a research and consulting firm that has followed the CAD/CAM market for some years, as memory costs have declined precipitously, raster tubes have become economically feasible in lower-end monochromatic applications and offer higher response times, better dynamics, and better contrasts. The costs of monochromatic raster is now comparable to DVST, and it is quickly becoming standard on most turnkey systems as resolution improves.

A typical modern raster-scan screen might offer over 260,000 pixels arranged in 512 rows x 512 columns—more than enough resolution to eliminate the stair-step effect on diagonal lines of older, smaller-memory screens. A second rea-

The many systems that automate Grumman

Grumman Aerospace Corp's major thrust into interactive computer graphics dates back seven years to the advent of GEMS (Grumman Engineering and Manufacturing System), a 2D-CADAM-based program.

GEMS currently interfaces with Open Shop, an off-line batch and 115-terminal time-share system; RAVES (Rapid Aerospace Vehicle Evaluation System), an interactive computer-aided-design system for quick analysis of design feasibility, trade-offs, and cost/benefit relationships; and EIDS (End Item Definition System), a 500-terminal; alphanumeric part-identification and methodization system. GEMS provides "the picture"; EIDS outputs everything beyond the picture—bill-of-materials data, standard parts and finishes, drawings and parts lists, etc.

The picture is established by Design Engineering and recalled by downstream users, notably Manufacturing Engineering for tool design and NC programming and also Quality Assurance.

Since its implementation, GEMS has been used increasingly for aircraft design and manufacture. Gulfstream III, the latest version of the twin-engine business aircraft, provided a good example of the savings it can offer.

Of the 1043 design-engineering drawings required for the G-III, 218 were generated from the GEMS database. For the new wing, designers tapped the system for the company's "wing family of lines." Just one designer on a terminal was able to generate 45 drawings. Overall, using seven terminals, Design Engineering reduced total design time by 50% and drafting time by 7000 hr, or 10% vs traditional on-the-board practice. Manufacturing Engineering, using two terminals, pared tool-design time by 12% and programming time by 50%.

EIDS serves as a single source of drawing parts lists and related field-of-drawing information from a common database. It supports Design Engineering and Manufacturing Engineering by on-line teleprocessing stations

throughout the company's Bethpage complex and outlying plants, which range from several on Long Island to those in Milledgeville, Ga; Stuart, Fla; and El Segundo, Calif. Each teleprocessing station consists of a display terminal and keyboard and a printer for generating hard copy.

Grumman also uses a number of computer-aided production-planning and -control systems—systems within systems actually. Among them are MODS (Manufacturing Operational Data System), SMS (Schedule Management System), and CTS (Cost Tracking System).

MODS maintains updated information in memory from operation sheets, stockroom records, and work-order releases. At present, it accounts for some 700,000 parts by part number and tracks more than 400,000 transactions weekly, according to Sal Sakellarides, manager of Manufacturing Systems. The system, which includes 176 terminals, generates work orders in response to on-line requests, tracks orders through production, accounts for parts on hand, and stores up-to-the-minute inventory data.

SMS provides manufacturing plans based on shop capacity and short- and long-range scheduling requirements, prioritizing work orders at work centers accordingly. Should an unforeseen delay occur at a particular work center, the system can replan short-range parts scheduling, minimizing or eliminating delays at downstream work centers.

CTS provides continuous information on part cost by recording labor hours expended in parts production. This data also keeps track of employee attendance and labor hours and is simultaneously transmitted to Payroll for paycheck generation.

The multitude of systems Grumman has implemented since the '60s have been costly but cost-effective. No one knows the actual cost since it has been a building-block approach evolving over many years, but estimates start at $500-million.

The future calls for much greater use of all systems and further integration. All new aircraft design are now input to GEMS, EIDS, MODS, etc. The FSW (forward-swept-wing) aircraft, for which Grumman has recently contracted to build two prototypes, is a good example. Although the extent of the use of CAM cannot be estimated at this early date, the design will be 100% CAD.

Bob Sanderson, project engineer, Manufacturing Engineering, uses GEMS interactive graphics terminal for tool design

Computers create flat-part nests

One by one, specific manufacturing operations are becoming automated, and the development of nesting patterns is a typical example. Automation is permitting nesting patterns to be configured significantly faster and with greater utilization of material.

In 1980, Rohr Industries Inc implemented a system that ties together a Camsco computer system with a Trumpf CNC routing/drilling machine. In operation, an Auto-Trol unit digitizes part shapes from templets or mylar drawings, and computer software provides automatic, interactive nesting of the flat shapes.

Once the nest has been arranged, the data is transmitted to a floppy disk that runs the router. In this case, the 30,000 shapes stored in the computer are for aerospace components.

Grumman Aerospace Corp used a Camsco stand-alone computing system for digitizing about 20,000 master templets; the system incorporates a Hewlett-Packard computer. A terminal with a display processor is located at the station where construction of nested configurations is accomplished.

After patterns that cover an entire sheet are programmed, multiple sheets are stacked and routed simultaneously. The machine is a Trumpf BFZ3000, on which a ½-in.-thick stack of sheet stock is clamped to a reusable aluminum backplate and placed on the router bed.

The machine drills holes in select locations between parts and installs flush-head rivets to hold the sheets to the backing plate during routing.

System costs were justified by a projection of a $1.6-million saving over three years. This estimate takes into account the production of 1,580,000 pieces.

In the now-dated manual method, a stack of sheetmetal is mounted on a routing board, and a nesting pattern is produced by an operator who lays the templets down on a large sheet of brown paper and arranges them by hand for the best use of material.

This arrangement is then traced on the paper, which serves as a pattern for mounting the templets and stack of sheetmetal to the routing board.

Typically, the templets are prepared by digitizing undimensioned drawings, which are composed by the engineering department. Manufacturing Engineering then adds holddown tabs and other required details, and the actual routing process is done manually, with individual routing templets used as masters.

With this approach, 14-21 days may elapse between the engineering department's release and completion of the part, as opposed to a 1-hr flow time for any part with CAD/CAM.

Not only are time and waste reduced by automated nesting, but inventory can be cut as well, says Bob Peterson, CAD Operations Supervisor at Fiat-Allis. This manufacturer of heavy construction machinery is using its inventory faster and requires a lower number of different-size plates for its operations.

Before the company began using its Applicon system for nesting and flame cutting, plate utilization was about 70%; now the company estimates "80% and better" utilization.

son for acceptance of raster CRTs is their ability to use color.

The reason that semiconductor memory is dropping in price is the same VSLI technology that is affecting the cost of tiny CPUs.

Memory capacity is measured in kilobytes, each measuring 1024 (or 2^{10}) eight-bit words, or bytes. The techniques that are reducing the cost of microprocessor manufacturing also affect the associated ROMs and RAMs, so that today the 264-kilobyte RAM—etched onto a piece of pure silicon—is a commonly manufactured item, albeit still fairly expensive compared with previous-generation 64-kbyte varieties. Electron-beam etching and the development of other substrates, such as gallium arsenide, mean that the next step could raise that 264 figure to more than a million. With increased density, costs go down.

The same is true for data storage. Just as in the semiconductor field, suppliers of magnetic-disk storage devices are trying to advance the state of their art. Thin-film heads, plated disks, and vertical recording—where the magnetic impulses are aligned vertically through the recording media rather than longitudinally across it—promise to increase data density.

Off-line storage of data is important, even for today's most powerful mainframe computers, which contain thousands of individual chip boards. In present technology, storage usually means disks or bubble memories and, sometimes still, tape.

In flexible-disk (or "floppy-disk" or "diskette") drives, the storage medium is typically an 8- or 5¼-in.-dia disk whose storage capacity ranges from 100-kbytes to 1.6-Mbytes. Developments in the field have shown that an enhanced floppy can be made to hold as much as 10-Mbytes.

The same is true for hard-disk drives, either the removable-cartridge type or the Winchester sealed variety. Current densities range from 2.5-Mbytes for 14-in.-dia cartridges and 5-Mbytes for 5¼-in. Winchester types to the IBM 3380 and Storage Technology 8380's capacity of 2500-Mbytes, according to Tom Manuel, computers editor of *Electronics* magazine. A developmental hard-disk drive using thin-film disks with a ferrite head may offer 5000-Mbytes.

In bubble and charge-couple devices, which are nonvolatile memories that have applications for data storage, there is still a lot of developmental activity. The magnetic devices, particularly bubbles, are already used in NCs and other harsh-environment applications, and industry observers see a resurgence of interest for them in mainframe computers, potentially lowering costs.

McDonnell Douglas also uses a Trumpf router to cut nested shapes

THE SYSTEMS
Manufacturing runs on information, which is best handled by the computer

THE EMERGENCE of the computer as a dominant manufacturing tool started with a trickle of isolated applications that has evolved into islands of computer-based systems. Although the applications vary in scope and complexity, they feature a common characteristic: invariably, computers are used to provide more-accurate and more-timely information than is possible with present manual systems.

That should be no surprise because, after all, computers are basically information-handling machines and manufacturing basically involves a series of data transformations. Data, or information, is generated from the concepts in a person's mind and moves through a whole series of transformations to create the final product and support its maintenance in the field.

The basic information-handling tasks required during the life-cycle of a product are evolving into a series of computer-based systems that forms the basis for computer-integrated manufacturing. First in this interdependent chain of information systems is a means for capturing the information generated during the design process. Much of that information deals with geometric data that is readily transformed into a geometric model, a representation of shape and size in computer memory, through the use of computer-graphics systems. Such computer-aided design (CAD) is clearly taking over in the design of a product.

The geometric model can be used to generate fully dimensioned engineering drawings on automated drafting equipment, and, in fact, CAD was originally considered basically a means for automating the drafting processes. But the geometric model is also the key to a host of related design/engineering/manufac-

turing functions. Many of these can be performed concurrently, thereby greatly compressing the product-development cycle.

Some of these activities are now being called computer-aided engineering (CAE) and are intended to automate the entire mechancial product-development process, from conceptual design to manufacturing release through the application of appropriate software programs. General Electric Co and Structural Dynamics Research Corp (SDRC) recently formed a joint venture, called CAE International Inc, to fully exploit such computer-based analytical techniques, which SDRC has developed over the years.

Starting with the geometric model of a prototype, CAE uses the computer early in the design process to simulate performance of the proposed product. The model can be used for such analytical tasks as determining the surface area and mass properties of a part (volume, weight, center of gravity, moment of inertia). The model can be animated to simulate the kinematic action of complex mechanisms or to analyze such functional characteristics as vibration, noise, and service life. With some additional transformation, the geometric model can be converted into a finite-element model to help with stress analysis.

CAE slashes time and cost

According to Jason R. Lemon, chairman of the board and CEO of SDRC, the application of CAE has reduced costs by as much as 30% and shortened the design cycle by as much as 25%.

He cites an example. One of the keys to the Space Shuttle's success is its heat shield that permits the spacecraft to re-enter the earth's atmosphere without burning up like a meteor. The shield

consists of thousands of small ceramic tiles contoured to fit the surface of the shuttle. Before the initial voyage of the Columbia, the ability of those tiles to withstand the stresses and vibration of lift-off and re-entry was evaluated with CAE software developed by SDRC.

On a more down-to-earth level, CAE

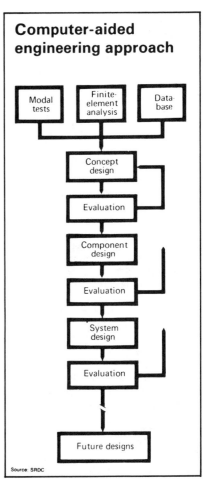

Computer-aided engineering approach

Modal tests

Finite-element analysis

Data-base

Concept design

Evaluation

Component design

Evaluation

System design

Evaluation

Future designs

Source: SRDC

has been used extensively by the automobile industry, particularly during the recent down-sizing programs, to reduce the product-development cycle while improving quality. General Motors produced the new Cadillac Seville design in 29 months, about a third less than the time usually required for new-model development, according to Lemon. At the same time, auto weight was reduced by 1000 lb.

More directly related to manufacturing, NC part programs are readily generated from geometric models with most of today's computer-graphics systems. The computer alone enhances the programmer's capability in a number of ways:

■ It provides calculation capability beyond that of the machine's NC system and removes from the programmer the burden of manual calculations and geometric constructions. Mirror-images; pattern generation, such as bolt-hole locations; pattern translation; and fairing of nonmathematically defined surfaces are all readily handled by computer routines.

■ Program reliability is enhanced because the programmer has fewer opportunities to make errors; diagnostics and prompting messages help ensure better programs.

■ The programmer's need for intimate knowledge of the idiosyncrasies of each NC machine and its specific coding requirements is greatly reduced because the computer typically uses a shop-oriented language.

■ The computer is not restricted to generating NC codes. It can also generate such other data as total machining time for a program and other management information.

Coupled with computer graphics, such computer-generated NC programs can then be verified by simulating the cutter action in a 3D representation. Ultimately, the geometric model can be used to generate the detailed process plans required to produce the part in a given facility, including the preparation of the necessary setup instructions and related sketches. By the same token, the geometric model can be used, in turn, to select or design and fabricate the fixtures and tooling required to fabricate the part; graphic representation of the planned cutter path can be used to prevent interferences between fixtures and tools.

To date, computer-graphics systems have typically used wire-frame graphic constructions, in which part shapes are represented with interconnecting line elements. Hidden-line-removal techniques reduce the jumble of resulting lines into recognizable representations of the object being modeled. Although such a model may appear like a solid, it really

MAGI solids-modeling approach uses a series of geometric primitives

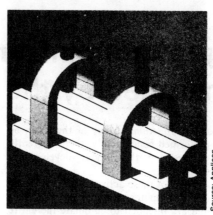

Source: Applicon

Primitives can be combined by logic operators to create realistic model

only defines the surface discontinuities, or the intersections of two or more surfaces, and therefore provides minimal information about the object. There is no information about the surface itself, and no distinction is made between the inside or the outside of an object. The advantage of these wire-frame models is that they occupy minimum computer memory and therefore can be handled economically and with relative speed. Also, in appearance, it has all the attributes of a conventional orthographic drawing or isometric.

NC programming often requires more knowledge about the surface of the part to be machined. Surface models can be created with computer-graphics techniques that involve the use of surface elements—such as planes, cylinders, surfaces of revolution—and of swept surfaces in which a geometric element, such as a line or curve, is moved along a defined path. More-complex, sculptured surfaces can be represented by a contiguous network of "patches," each a mathematical approximation of the equivalent surface element.

Surface models require more computer memory and are more time-consuming to handle than wire-frame models are. They provide considerably more information about an object than the wire-frame model but still lack informa-

tion about the solid nature of the object, and although mass properties can generally be calculated from such models, there is room for much ambiguity.

Solids modeling the trend

The advent of 32-bit minicomputers such as the Digital Equipment Corp VAX, has permitted the economical construction of solid models, which requires large memory and extensive data manipulation, and the trend in computer-graphics systems is to offer such capability. One of the earliest solids-modeling software packages, now used by Applicon and soon to be available on CADAM systems, is Synthavision, developed by Mathematical Applications Group Inc (MAGI). The system is interactive, has full color shade-picture capability, and has a drafting package that allows automatic hidden-line removal for the creation of multiple views and/or sections.

Synthavision represents a 3D structure in terms of solid geometric primitives. These primitives are the basic building blocks of the modeling software and may be combined via logic operators to create unions, differences, or intersections, A hollow pipe, for example, is merely the difference between two coaxial cylinders of unequal radii. In essence, models of this type are composed of a set of bounded volumes. They are unambiguous in the sense that any point in space can be determined to be either inside, outside, or on the surface of the model.

The modeling process, carried out interactively, amounts to defining the location, orientation, dimensions, and logical combinations of a set of solid geometric primitives. The ten basic primitives are box, wedge, convex polyhedron, sphere, ellipsoid, circular cone, elliptic cone, torus, and solid torus. More significant are three additional solids that can be constructed through boundary modeling, in which an arbitrary topology is operated on to produce a solid. These are the arbitrary slab, the solid of revolution, and the general-surface solid.

For example, an arbitrary-slab primitive can be created by first defining the topology of a part with conventional 2D graphic construction techniques and then translating the topology normal to its plane to generate a slab of arbitrary thickness. In the same manner, a solid of revolution is created by first establishing the surface contour and then rotating it about a line or cylinder. The general surface model uses a surface fitted to an arbitrary set of points for construction of a bounded model. All of these primitives are manipulated and combined to form the final solid model.

That model can then be presented in

3D shaded color pictures with true dimensional characteristics. Shading patterns are generated by "illuminating" the model mathematically from a point source and calculating the varying angles of reflection from each surface. This angle-of-reflection pattern is then translated into the varying shading amplitudes to produce a realistic 3D picture. The software also provides for translating and rotating the model, as well as for creating cross-sectional views, partial cut-away views, and exploded views.

GT is the glue

One of the most significant emerging information systems, sometimes referred to as the "glue" of computer-integrated manufacturing, is group technology (GT). It is a manufacturing philosophy, an organizational principle with far-reaching implications. The underlying principle is relatively simple and not particularly new: identify and bring together related or similar components and processes to take advantage of their similarities in design and/or manufacturing.

Forming families, or groups, of parts with similar characteristics from a design and/or manufacturing point of view reduces the number of unique tasks that must be dealt with. Some sort of grouping or standard practice has always been achieved on a subjective but hit-or-miss basis by the practiced designer or manufacturing engineer. Group technology uses well-structured classification-and-coding schemes and associated computer programs to exploit the sameness or similarity of parts, processes, and equipment. On the one hand, this avoids reinventing the wheel or duplicating engineering effort; on the other, it affords an opportunity to group similar parts and processes, thereby achieving economies of scale otherwise not possible in batch-type manufacturing.

The grouping principle can have a profound effect on virtually every aspect of the manufacturing cycle. This is particularly so in batch-manufacturing operations, which typically involve seemingly endless variations of parts and processes. By helping to identify select similarities, GT can provide considerable benefits for most of the functional areas in a manufacturing organization: product engineering, manufacturing engineering, production control, and procurement.

In product engineering, GT can help reduce part proliferation, encourage design standardization, provide manufacturing feedback, and help with cost estimating.

GT can help manufacturing engineering with process selection, tooling selection and grouping, machine procure-

Graphics system does electrical, mechanical design

A 3D color-graphics system installed in January by the Potter & Brumfield Div of AMF has greatly increased efficiency in the design of electrical/electronic printed-circuit boards (PCBs), such electromechanical components as solenoids and relays, and, from the manufacturing side, tools, fixtures, wave-soldering pallets, and various tooling aids. For about 25% of its annual production of new PCBs, the system is expected to save more than 11,000 labor hours, according to Harold D. Liepold, manager, Engineering Computer Graphics.

The current system, an Applicon AGS 895, is housed in two side-by-side rooms, one containing two interactive terminals, the other a DEC PDP 11/34A host computer, an Applicon 32 graphics computer, disk drive, plotter, system-control console, and disk- and tape-storage facilities.

In addition to hardware, 16 software packages were purchased with the AGS, including a 2D system for PCBs and a 3D system for mechanical design, says Gerald A. DiPalma, director of Solid-State Products. Other packages provide PCB schematics, printouts of network-list components, techniques for optimizing component placement (see photo) to reduce conductor density, and a check system for comparing finished PCBs with the schematics. There's also a postprocessor for generating paper tapes for a PCB NC drill-router and an NC axial inserter (which installs axially leaded components, such as resistors and capacitors), and for generating magnetic tapes for photoplotting line-art of the conductor path.

Early next year, a four-terminal VAX-based Applicon system will replace the AGS. Using the more powerful 32-bit DEC VAX processor, it will provide all the wire-frame-modeling functions of the present system plus solids-modeling capability and a more sophisticated database-management system. Although the terminals will be located in the room now housing the AGS terminals, a coaxial cable will enable extending the distance between terminals and host computer from the current 500 ft to 5000 ft, which would be in sight of the Princeton manufacturing plant. At present, however, there are no plans to wire-input machines. Hand delivery of tapes seems more economical for the foreseeable future.

One way P&B management justified the cost of the system was by calculating anticipated cost savings. For example, the design of a new 5- x 10-in. PCB containing 50 integrated circuits and 35 discrete components would take 115 hr manually and 30 hr by using CAD/CAM.

The cost of the entire system, hardware and software, using first the AGS and then the VAX-based, will come to about $750,000. Included in this cost is roughly $35,000 for the climate-controlled room that P&B had constructed.

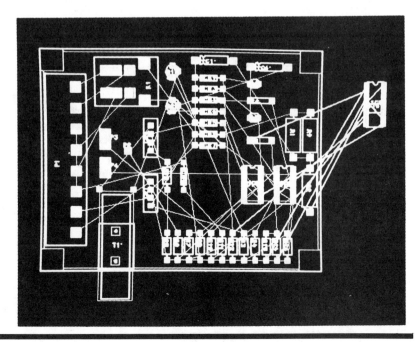

ment, facilities planning, materials flow, and materials handling. It can also help to bring newly available technology to the attention of planners by automatically including newly acquired applicable equipment or capabilities as processing alternatives.

In production, GT can reduce leadtimes, production delays, and setup times. It can also help with asset utilization, materials-handling decisions, and equipment selection to achieve appropriate quality levels.

Production control can use group technology for scheduling, stock accountability, expediting, and reducing work-in-process inventory. Buy-or-make decisions and the establishment of economic order quantities can also be handled through group technology. Ultimately, group technology can affect customer support by improving the handling of dealer inventory and by shortening delivery times.

All of these benefits are achieved by identifying and assessing a vast array of information, then retrieving and grouping designs, parts, or processes on the basis of select attributes. That task is best-handled by an information-handling machine like the computer.

One thing to bear in mind is that, although group technology implies the establishment of manufacturing cells to handle families of parts, those cells need not necessarily involve the physical rearrangement of a facility. Most of the benefits of GT can be realized through administrative means without such physical rearrangement.

Another important consideration is the amount of "up-front" work needed to establish the family groupings. Contrary to some popular opinion, every single part in a company's inventory need not be subjected to rigorous classification-

and-coding routines before the benefits of GT can be realized.

To begin with, no company manufactures a totally random array of unique parts. Each company makes what it does best, and that in itself reduces the range of physical as well as process variations. There really isn't that much variety to begin with, and an intelligent sampling approach can provide some significant data to help establish useful groupings. A representative random sampling of parts is usually sufficient to establish the full range of variation that can be expected.

For these reasons, it is probably best to start classification and coding with only those parts currently being released to the shop. The nature of most manufacturing is such that the number of new component shapes released begins to level out within a short time after a classification and coding system is implemented. Therefore, an increasingly high percentage of "new" part drawings can be retrieved easily from existing files. The same leveling-off effect has been observed for process plans issued to the shop.

Classification and coding are the key to group technology: parts, processes, and facilities must be classified according to appropriate characteristics, and then a meaningful code must be assigned to reflect those characteristics. Interactive computer programs effect classification through step-by-step prompting and interrogation, after which the computer program automatically assigns the proper code.

Other analytical programs then use the codes to assemble groupings according to selected characteristics. For example, all parts of a particular similar shape—say, shafts in a certain size range and with similar step and keyway char-

acteristics—are readily selected. Or the grouping may include material designations or process-related information.

The CODE system, offered by Manufacturing Data Systems Inc (MDSI), includes analytical retrieval routines to select families of parts from which a specific part could be made, parts into which a specified part could be made, and parts that are similar to a specified part. Similar analytical routines available with a GT system developed by Metcut Associates for the rotating-parts department of GE's Aircraft Engine Business Group have permitted better utilization of existing rotor-disk forgings from available stock.

The MICLASS system was originally developed by TNO, an independent government research and development organization of the Netherlands and is marketed as part of the group-technology services offered by Organization for Industrial Research (OIR). It includes a whole series of analytical and retrieval programs. In addition to drawing retrieval, some of these can identify production-related information, such as unusual lot sizes or similar routings; others can analyze machine-tool requirements or process-related information.

No universal scheme

The problem is to choose a classification-and-coding scheme so that the needs of all users of the system are served adequately. There is no universal classification-and-coding scheme, although the Air Force ICAM (Integrated Computer Aided Manufacturing) program has a project to develop a generic Group Technology Characterization Code (GTCC). That scheme is being developed initially for a sheetmetal center now in the planning stage.

Most GT systems have been implemented with classification-and-coding schemes developed for the specific needs of the organization, or existing schemes have been adapted for the purpose. The John Deere GT system, which is based on the MICLASS system, is a good example. In fact, most commercially available schemes provide means for tailoring them to the specific needs and conditions of the user.

Different code structures

Classification-and-coding schemes differ in the classes of information established and the way symbols are assigned to the different classes. The structure of the code can influence the relative ease with which information can be processed by computer software and the level of distinct selections that can be achieved economically.

The coding systems themselves can be

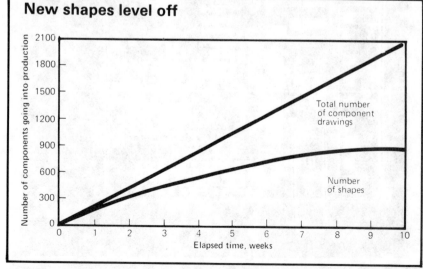

New shapes level off

Number of components going into production (y-axis): 0, 300, 600, 900, 1200, 1500, 1800, 2100

Total number of component drawings

Number of shapes

Elapsed time, weeks (x-axis): 0 1 2 3 4 5 6 7 8 9 10

constructed with only numerical symbols, only alphabetical symbols, or a combination of numbers and letters. Current codes are mostly numerical, although some alphanumerical systems do exist.

The actual construction of GT coding system typically falls into one of three types: monocodes, also referred to as hierarchical codes or tree structures; polycodes, also called attribute codes; and hybrids combining the two structures.

In a monocode, the meaning of every digit is dependent on the digit prior to it; each meaning is modified successively. In a polycode, each digit location defines a specific attribute assigned to that location and is independent of any other digit.

Monocodes can convey a lot of information in relatively few digits, but the interdependence of the digits makes them harder to use for conventional computer analysis. Polycodes facilitate computer analysis but tend to be long because a digit location must be reserved for every conceivable feature even though many of the features may not apply to a particular situation. For these reasons, most GT coding systems tend to use a hybrid construction to combine the best features of monocodes and polycodes.

Another key is CAPP

Closely related to group technology and another key factor in effecting computer-integrated manufacturing is computer-aided process planning (CAPP). Process planning—the systematic determination of the methods by which a product is to be manufactured economically and competitively—essentially involves selection, calculation, and documentation. Processes, machines, tools, operations, and sequences must be selected. Such factors as feeds, speeds, tolerances, dimensions, and costs must be calculated. Finally, documents in the form of setup instructions, work instructions, illustrated process sheets, and routings must be prepared.

A planner must manage and retrieve a great deal of data and many documents, including established standards, machinability data, machine specifications, tooling inventories, stock availability, and existing process plans. This is primarily an information-handling job, and the computer is an ideal companion.

There is another advantage to using computers to help with process planning. Because the task involves many interrelated activities, determining the optimum plan requires many iterations. Since computers can readily perform vast numbers of comparisons, many

A 'family-of-parts' CADCAM approach

In 1974, the cutter department at Ingersoll Milling Machine Co began to develop the procedures it now calls "CADCAM" and has had them in use since 1976. Basic cutter families developed apply to about 60% of the cutters produced by the department (this is about 85% of the cutters produced on NC machines).

When a new cutter is required, the appropriate cutter family is called up on the computer screen, and the designer enters the parameters that apply to the particular cutter. It is an APT-based program, and the designer does not use interactive graphics. Next, the mainframe computer develops the cutter geometry based on the product-design logic (this takes about 3-5 min of time on the CPU). The output can be to a graphics terminal in the CADAM system, so that the designer can revise the drawing if necessary, or (more likely) to any of four different types of plotters used in the company to produce drawings.

Meanwhile, the NC programmer taps the cutter geometry in the "online" source file of the CPU and proceeds to generate the necessary NC tapes, which may include lathe, keyway-cutting, and machining-center operations. Manufacturing logic is stored in the basic family-of-parts program along with the design logic.

The geometry originally developed is retained in the "source" files of the CPU and is considered the "original" drawing of the cutter. Any of the printed drawings are considered "copies."

When the cutterbodies are machined, the operators feed back suggestions for refining the programs. In one cutter for jet-engine parts that was needed in quantity, these operator suggestions eventually reduced the cycle time for machining from 45 min to 12 min.

Special cutters that don't fit any of the programs that have been developed for cutter families are designed directly on an interactive-graphics terminal using the CADAM system. (Edson Gaylord, chairman, says that Ingersoll was the first non-aerospace licensee of CADAM.) The NC programmer then develops the NC tapes for the special cutter, using the database created by the designer and possibly using the same CRT. Gaylord cites one recent case in which 17 hours was required for the designer and the programmer to design, plan the manu-

facturing of, and produce the tapes for a new special cutter. Then it took 14 hours in the shop to produce the cutter.

The designers and the programmers have desks in a single area divided by an invisible line (referred to locally as the Mason-Dixon line) but share the same CRTs in an adjoining room. "We crossed departmental boundary lines with reckless abandon to do this," says one of the managers involved.

Ingersoll is now in the process of extending this system, after seven years' use in the cutter department, to the machine division. Since almost all production there is one-of-a-kind special machines, Gaylord says, it would be impossible to use CAM effectively if the machines weren't first being designed by CAD. The present goal is to have a third of the work in the production-machinery department going through the computers by the end of this year.

In many cases, this will mean designing and preparing NC tapes on a CRT even when only one piece will be produced. Some workpieces recur several times, especially in multistation machines, but Gaylord says that the economy of CADAM has been proved for even a single piece.

For one thing, when the part geometry is in the computer, the programmer's work is greatly simplified. With designer and programmer working together, there is the opportunity to alter the design at an early stage if it will simplify machining. Later, because the programmer can run through the entire NC program and watch the cutter action on the CRT, it becomes easier to detect and correct the inevitable mistakes. "You don't have to try out the program by cutting the part in Styrofoam, and you don't have to have the programmer at the machine when the part is run," Gaylord says.

At present, Ingersoll has 38 programmers and is producing about 90,000 NC tapes a year. Just over a quarter of the machining operations in the machine division are being done on NC machines now. As additional lathes and machining centers become operational during the next three years and the program spreads through the company, the current target is for more than half of the cutting in the machine division to be done on NC machines.

THE SYSTEMS

more alternative plans can be explored than would be possible manually.

A third advantage in the use of computer-aided process planning is uniformity. It has been said that, if you ask ten different planners to develop a process plan for the same part, you would probably end up with ten different plans. Obviously, they can't all be the best plan. This also means that essentially the same job planned at different times will be made differently. Which plan will govern facilities planning? Which will be used for estimating future work? Which plan will be used for scheduling and shop loading?

Several specific benefits can be expected from the adoption of computer-aided process-planning techniques:

- Reduced clerical effort in preparation of instructions.
- Fewer calculation errors due to human error.
- Fewer oversights in logic or instructions because of the prompting capability available with interactive computer programs.
- Immediate access to up-to-date information from a central database.
- Consistent information, because every planner accesses the same database.
- Faster response to changes requested by engineering of other operating departments.
- Automatic use of the latest revision of a part drawing.
- More-detailed, more-uniform process-plan statements produced by word-processing techniques.
- More-effective use of inventories of tools, gages, and fixtures and a concomitant reduction in the variety of those items.
- Better communication with shop personnel because plans can be more specifically tailored to a particular task and presented in unambiguous, proven language.
- Better information for production-

planning, including cutter-life, forecasting, materials-requirements planning, scheduling, and inventory control.

Most important for CIM, computer-aided process planning produces machine-readable data instead of handwritten plans. Such data can readily be transferred to other systems within the CIM hierarchy for use in planning.

There are basically two approaches to computer-aided process planning: variant and generative.

In the variant approach, a set of standard process plans is established for all the parts families that have been identified through group technology. The standard plans are stored in computer memory and retrieved for new parts according to their family identification. Again, GT helps to place the new part in an appropriate family. The standard plan is then edited to suit the specific requirements of a particular job.

In the generative approach, an attempt is made to synthesize each individual plan using appropriate algorithms that define the various technological decisions that must be made in the course of manufacturing. In a truly generative process-planning system, the sequence of operations, as well as all the manufacturing-process parameters, would be automatically established without reference to prior plans. In its ultimate realization, such an approach would be universally applicable: present any plan to the system, and the computer produces the optimum process plan.

No such system exists, however. So-called generative process-planning systems—and probably for the foreseeable future—are still specialized systems developed for a specific operation or a particular type of manufacturing process. The logic is based on a combination of past practice and basic technology.

Among the first approaches to a generic computer-aided process-planning system is the CAPP system developed by

McDonnell-Douglas under the sponsorship of Computer Aided Manufacturing-International Inc (CAM-I). This variant system was developed primarily to demonstrate the feasibility of computer-aided process planning. Six versions have been released to date, some of which are being used and adapted by various companies as prototype systems.

Recently, computer-aided process planning has been combined with computer-graphics techniques. Using OIR's MIPLAN, process planners can work at graphics terminals and compose process plans made up of text and drawings. As implemented on Computervision computer-graphics systems, a drawing for an existing part or for one that has been recently designed can be called up on the screen, along with existing tooling.

The part can then be rotated to provide the proper machining orientation and can be graphically mated with the tooling to ensure a proper match and to check for interferences. Tooling paths can then be plotted to illustrate the machining sequences, and the setup can be viewed from various angles to check clearances. Text and drawing are then merged to generate a process plan with appropriate illustrations.

Must deal with conflicts

In the final analysis, the management of any manufacturing enterprise must constantly deal with a series of conflicting interests: the sales department would like to have the widest product range available in unlimited quantities at the hint of a customer's order; manufacturing would like a steady production and long runs; purchasing is interested in the lowest cost; while the comptroller fights every request for capital spending.

To deal with these conflicting interests rationally requires relevant information on a timely basis. Manufacturing-control and -planning systems are now available from most computer manufacturers and many software houses to address any or all of these information-handling tasks.

Most of these systems are modular, addressing such functions as materials-requirements planning (MRP), inventory control, capacity planning, scheduling, forecasting, and cost control. To be effective, these modules must be linked to an overall management-information system.

In the past, many of these "business" systems have been developed from the financial side of the business by systems people more familiar with software than with the real world of manufacturing. Now these information systems can be integrated with those stemming from the operating side of the business for truly computer-integrated manufacturing.

CAM-I's CAPP system

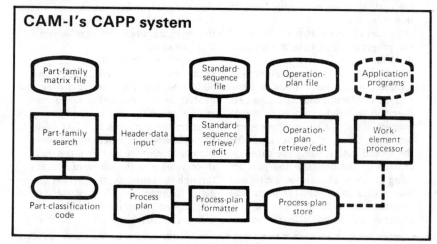

THE NETWORK

Data highways throughout the factory let computers talk to each other

AS THE ISLANDS of the computer-based systems proliferate throughout a plant, integrating them via the exchange of information becomes essential. The key to this exchange—and to the integration of all intelligent devices within a company—is the communications network.

Although there is no generally accepted definition, a communications network is basically a means by which computers and computer-like devices are connected so that information can pass rapidly and accurately between them. Most networks have two principle functions: data-flow control and data management. The network permits computers to signal each other to carry out functions in a coordinated manner. Also, through the network, the interconnected devices can share such resources as programs, databases, and memory space.

Network types

Networks can be arranged in many ways. One way networks can be broken down is into two fundamental types: a hierarchical, or supervisory-control, network and a peer-to-peer network.

In the hierarchical network, a central network controller (also called a master or host) controls the flow of data to and from the various devices connected to the network. No information can be exchanged without flowing first through the network controller. This central network controller requires considerable data-processing capability and is therefore usually a mainframe computer.

One drawback to the hierarchical system is that too many messages can accumulate and cause the system to slow down. Additionally, if the mainframe fails, the network fails also. The data, however, is not necessarily lost in the

system, because some systems have restart modes and failsafe devices to ensure against information loss.

By contrast, peer-to-peer systems use devices that communicate with each other directly without having to go through a network controller. Communication in this system is accomplished by building modules into an interface on the devices. Each interface-module contains a microprocessor and can individually control data flow on the network. Each device, therefore, can act as the network master at different times.

Of necessity, the interface-module is highly complex because it serves as a substitute for a central network controller. One drawback to this system, according to Mark Eckard, technical writer at Industrial Solid State Controls Inc, is that the inherent complexity of these devices makes them complicated to maintain.

These peer-to-peer systems, however, are suitable mainly for programmable controllers and are thus opening up new applications for PCs that can "talk to each other." Large-scale integrated circuitry in the form of microprocessors is changing these PCs from mere relay replacements to intelligent industrial controllers. These PCs can be set up in a peer-to-peer network and are particularly suitable for providing control, for example, in an application in which five or six robots perform the same task.

A network is a system intended to transfer data accurately and rapidly. Regardless of type or manufacturer, each network therefore requires a physical means of sending data from one end user (for example, a computer) to another end user (for example, a PC, CRT, or intelligent machine tool).

Data can be transmitted between

devices in either parallel or serial fashion. Parallel transmission requires the transmission of all the bits in a single word simultaneously over a suitable number of parallel lines. There must be as many lines as there are bits per word, in addition to lines for control signals. Speed is the main advantage of parallel transmission. The only limit to sending data in this manner is the maximum transmission rate of the sending device and the transmission capability of the transmission line.

At the current state of development, the components in most networks are connected by wire or cable. Twisted-pair wire is used when the transmission distance is relatively short and cost is an important factor. Typical data-transfer rate for twisted pair is 57,600 bits per sec (bps). But twisted-pair is susceptible to crosstalk and interference pickup.

In one local-area network offered by Industrial Solid State Controls Inc and called COPNET, the twisted-pair-wire alternative is offered, and it can hook up a maximum of 31 devices and can transmit data at no greater distance than 1000 ft. The company also offers the same system with coaxial cable, which, according to Eckard, is the "medium of choice."

Coaxial cable is relatively immune to electrical noise and can carry transmisons at rates of 500,000 bps or more to distances of about 5000 ft. Two forms of coaxial cable are available: baseband and broadband. Baseband is a single-channel cable that can transmit digital data only. By contrast, broadband is a multiple-channel cable that can transmit not only greater volumes of data over longer distances than baseband but can also support video and voice communications as well. According to Eckard, most factory-automation networks probably

43

Typical network scheme

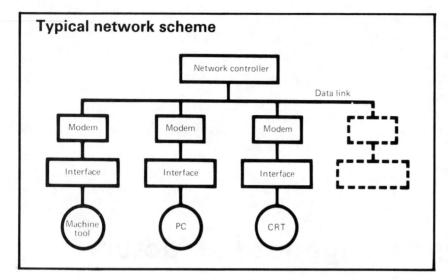

do not require the capacity of broadband cable—unless video and voice capabilities are desired—because the baseband can connect more than 200 machines.

At longer distances, transmission costs can be reduced through serial data transmission. In this method, the information content of every word is converted into serial form before the word enters the transmission line. In theory, only one transmission line is necessary for the entire data stream. The data-transmission rate, however, is slower than that of parallel transmission. Serial transmission can be asynchronous or synchronous.

When transmitted over short distances—via twisted-pair for example—data can be sent in digital form. But, in long-distance transmission through coaxial cable, digital data must be converted into analog (wavelike) signals. At the receiving end, the analog signals must then be retranslated into digital data usable by the end device. To accomplish this translation, the system requires a modulator/demodulator, known as a modem. Asynchronous modems (keyboard-entry terminal devices) transmit data in spurts, and synchronous modems (such as magnetic-tape equipment and computers) transmit data in steady streams.

Under development is an even more efficient transmission system: fiber optics. A fiber-optics cable is composed of thin hair-like glass fibers bound together. Light generated by lasers passes through the fibers and contains information in coded form. This cable is immune to electromagnetic interference, and communication-equipment manufacturers have begun to develop this technology. For networking systems already operative with coaxial cable, the changeover to fiber optics is possible.

In addition to the transmission cable and modems, every network requires interfaces. An interface is a device that translates data stored in an end device into a form acceptable by the modem, for transmission in analog form through the cable. Every different kind of end device requires an interface.

Also essential to the network is a communications discipline, or protocol, which defines the rules for controlling data communications between devices in computer systems or networks.

Local-area networks

In the past few years, a large number of local-area networks have been introduced for both office- and factory-automation networks. A local-area network is generally one that connects end devices within a single location or within several plants closely situated. Some local networks, however, are designed to be linked to remote domestic or overseas facilities via satellite or telephone lines. Although many different types of networks are available, most systems have a common goal, the eventual linking of all the intelligent machines in an automated factory into an integrated system, as General Electric expressed it in announcing its networking system GEnet.

The GEnet system, developed by GE's Intersil Systems Inc subsidiary, provides a family of communications hardware and firmware for local-area networks in both manufacturing and commercial applications. The system uses the GEnet bus interface unit (BIU), a multiple-microprocessor communications controller, which allows connected devices to gain access to broadband cable. The different user interfaces and protocols are supported by a family of microprocessor-driven I/O (input/output) modules, which minimize the burden on existing device software, according to the company. The BIU contains up to four I/O modules, each of which can connect up to four devices. With data-transfer rates of 5 megabits per sec, the cable provides 20 channels for up to 16 asynchronous or synchronous devices to access the network simultaneously. GEnet contrasts with many systems operating today using baseband or a single-channel cable.

The controller for GEnet is Intersil's Versatile Communications Controller (VCC). This programmable system allows different computers to talk to one another and provides fast translation of data between devices that use different protocols. The VCC provides a link that appears to the user, the computer, and the terminal to be a direct connection, according to the company.

To help install GEnet, the company is offering factory-automation-planning services. A GE team will analyze not only a company's manufacturing and engineering but also its operations-management system, data management, communications, and warehousing. Says Senior Vice President Donald K. Grierson, "The system will address productivity in its broadest definition, optimizing investment, reducing design and production cycles, enhancing product quality, and reducing overall cost."

Another communications network, introduced in January 1982, is called COP-NET and is manufactured by Industrial Solid State Controls Inc (ISSC). This system uses baseband cable and can support a wide range of devices, including competitive programmable-controller lines. Its multidrop bus configuration supports up to 254 addressed devices.

In addition, this system allows communications between programmable controllers from different manufacturers without special network-applications software. This comunication is accomplished through "personality modules" (firmware), which are based on ROM (read-only memory) and are resident in each network interface. These modules translate various data formats into one that is compatible with a standard HDLC (High Level Data Link Control) protocol. HDLC is a protocol specifying the method by which remote stations are addressed. In addition, COPNET is compatible with the DEC PDP-11 family of minicomputers for use as a network controller.

One of the local-area-network pioneers was Digital Equipment Corp, which, early in the 1970s, offered a set of software products called DECNET. These allow communication between various DEC operating systems so that they are able to function as communication networks.

DEC followed up in 1976 with its DEC-dataway, an industrial local-area network, which allows terminals and remote processors throughout a manufacturing facility to communicate over one cable. With this system, a host computer can communicate with as many as 31 remote devices at data-transfer rates of 56,000 bps. Communication is in block mode and is managed by a microprocessor-based controller, thus freeing the host

resources from the demands of network management.

The latest implementation of DECdataway, announced late last year and called VAX-11 DY32 DECdataway, enables VAX-11/750 and VAX-11/780 32-bit-word-length superminicomputers to be linked to a microcomputer-based distributed intelli-

gent subsystem (DIS) by synchronous multidrop shielded twisted-pair cable. The DECdataway DIS combination allows users to establish local-area networks in such applications as process monitoring and control, robotics, and data concentration from terminals.

Two industrial-control networks have

Whiting integrates CAD/CAM with MRP, inventory control

For years, Whiting Corp's in-house computers were strictly for processing accounting and financial data. The manufacturer of overhead cranes, metallurgical equipment and chemical-processing systems used outside computer services for its FORTRAN programming, NC-tape programming and finite-element-structural analysis. But, when these services began exceeding $6000 per month about two years ago, "it wasn't difficult convincing management that we needed an in-house computer just for engineering and manufacturing applications." says Charles R. Norman, manager, Engineering Services, Product Engineering.

Whiting, a subsidiary of Wheelabrator-Frye, chose the Prime 550, a mid-sized minicomputer having 500 kbytes of main memory, 96 Mbytes of hard-disk storage, and the ability to support up to 32 on-line terminals and other devices. The system was installed in January 1980, and, by September of that year, all three initial applications, including graphic numerical control (GNC), were up and running. The increase in productivity, according to Norman, has been "extraordinary."

"In FORTRAN alone, we've written more programs in the past two years than we had in the previous 17 years. By using GNC rather than APT or ADAPT for NC tapes, we have reduced tape-preparation cycles for our 22 NC machines from days to hours. And, since 90% of our stress analysis runs on SUPERSAP (purchased from Algor Interactive Systems), we have reduced the cost of outside finite-element-analysis services from more than $2000 to $100-$200 per month."

Once performing these initial tasks, Whiting added Prime's MEDUSA 3D CAD package to the system for electrical-circuit design. "Although we expected significant improvement in design productivity, we were totally unprepared for the 500% increase that we achieved in less than three months," Norman recalls. "What continues to amaze me is the simplicity of Prime/MEDUSA—it

even uses standard drafting terms.

The CAD stations comprise Prime data-entry and graphics display terminals, digitizing tablets, and a Tektronix plotter. Using the tablets, designers enter a string of symbols representing circuit elements, then the connecting lines and lettering, until the entire circuit is displayed. Once checked, the designer instructs the computer to output the circuit on the plotter. These drawings are then microfilmed. All the logic of the circuit is stored in the computer for future reference.

Whiting ordered a second MEDUSA for designing piping systems for chemical-processing equipment and various mechanical compoments. This entailed the addition of 512 kbytes of main memory and an 80-Mbyte disk-storage system. "The additional cost was well worth it," Norman says. "The people in our Chemical Engineering department claim an increase in productivity of eight to one for some piping schematics." And making customer changes—such schematics are designed before total system design has been fixed—is "a lot faster and easier than erasing and redrawing by hand since the drafter can simply recall the original schematic to the CRT, enter the changes on the tablet, and instruct the system to display and plot the new schematic."

Whiting plans to use the system to produce all piping and instrumentation schematics. "Some years, we have spent more than $100,000 for outside services for these drawings," Norman says, "but, over the next few years, we expect to move the work in-house."

Whiting was the first US company to integrate MEDUSA with GNC to form a CAD/CAM system. Integration of CAD and CAM began only recently, Norman notes, "but we have passed geometry created on the CAD system to the CAM GNC system. So we know we can do it. When up and running, we'll be able to do this regularly and also create NC tapes without ever making a drawing except for record purposes. Right now, Industrial Engineering has to recreate

geometry from our drawings to generate the tapes."

Last year, with the help of the company's Commercial Data Processing Group and Wheelabrator-Frye's Corporate Systems Group, Whiting added an integrated manufacturing-resource planning (MRP) and inventory-control system to the CAD/CAM operation. It runs on an IBM system using Product Engineering's Prime 550 at the front end for data collection, editing, and remote job entry.

Product Engineering and Industrial Engineering input data on Prime CRTs during the day. This data is stored in the 550 until the end of the day, when it's transmitted to the IBM for overnight integration into files. Each morning, the IBM sends back a printout of the previous day's entries.

All data entry is handled in a batch mode, but, once the data is filed, it can be accessed on-line from any of five Prime terminals within Whiting. In addition, by using the Prime system to check input data before transmitting it to the IBM, we're taking a big load off the IBM system, Norman says. In the inquiry mode, Whiting's Accounting, Purchasing, Product Engineering, and Industrial Engineering departments access the IBM data throughout the day from Prime CRTs and Prime's DPTX (distributed-processing-terminal-executive) system. The DPTX emulates IBM 3270 equipment. "It sounds complicated," Norman admits, "but setting up this hybrid system was quite easy, and it's saving us a lot of money."

An unexpected bonus was the Prime 550's built-in writing package called Runoff. When combined with the text-editor software, the program met many of the company's document and proposal-writing needs, at no extra cost.

The complete system entailed an investment of $350,000, and expansion of the present two-CAD- and two-CAM-station system is already underway. By year end, Norman says, there will be at least nine stations—five for CAD, four for CAM.

recently been announced by Texas Instruments: TIWAY I, which is an extension of the company's programmable-controller hierarchical network, and TIWAY II, which is a peer-to-peer network in which devices on the net can communicate directly between themselves.

The TIWAY I system is currently limited to certain of the company's own programmable controllers, and each PC must talk to the host computer in order to communicate with another PC on the network. By contrast, TIWAY II (not yet being sold) will allow communication directly between PCs. It is a broadband system designed to be compatible with other communications media, such as fiber optics and twisted-pair cables. The data-transfer rate on this network will be greater than 1-million bps, according to the company.

Allen-Bradley's data highway is designed as a communications link between PCs and such devices as compatible computers, printers, and graphics display terminals. This system transfers data over a maximum of 10,000 cable ft at a speed of 57,000 bps. Up to 64 devices can exchange data on the same highway and are connected through a special communications module. Through the data highway, control and monitoring equipment is tied into one data-communications system, and a central computer can monitor and print out information that will enable managers to keep track of factory operations.

In addition, through a so-called Floating Master, the data highway brings to the network an innovation that can help improve reliability. In most distributed-control systems, all messages are routed through a single master (usually a central computer). If the master breaks down, the whole system follows, resulting in downtime. In the data highway, the mastership passes constantly from one station to another as needed. If a device fails while acting as master, the mastership is automatically transferred to another operating station, permitting the system to continue operating.

Collecting production data

Collecting and communicating production data is central to the success of a computer-integrated system. The Factory Controller, manufactured by the Factory Automation Div of Gould Inc, is a monitoring system that can collect, process, and distribute timely production information. This system has been designed to gather and distribute information from intelligent devices, such as programmable controllers, robots, CNC, and other electronic monitoring or control devices on the factory floor.

Independent processing modules

called Cybloks—of which there are several types, each preprogrammed for specific functions—are the heart of the system. Several Cybloks are necessary in a basic system for first-level production monitoring. For example, the polling Cyblok is responsible for polling PCs and other devices and then transferring this information to other processors in the Factory Controller system.

This system can be combined into a larger system. For example, according to the company, the Factory Controller system is part of a concept called Autofactor, which provides the means to extend plant monitoring beyond the first level. The addition of a high-speed computer, for instance, enables statistical analysis, database management, and other functions to be merged with the monitoring system.

Some companies have developed their own network to meet the problem of linking a number of different vendors' computers in different locations. At Grumman Aerospace Corp, 73 IBM 3250 or equivalent interactive graphics terminals are in operation in five separate plant locations in the Bethpage complex. These terminals are all interconnected via a 10,000-ft cable-TV (CTV) multiplex network system, according to Steve Petrovits, program manager of GEMS (Grumman Engineering & Manufacturing System). The terminals are linked to four Grumman Data System Corp's host computers, an IBM 3033, and three IBM 4341 Group IIs, located in company headquarters.

To ensure adequate facilities for the expected growth of GEMS, two sets of cables were laid in the underground conduits. To support graphics terminals with hard-copy facilities for production applications, many plotters are needed. In one plant, two flat-bed plotters create production drawings and digitized tapes for NC-manufacturing requirements. In several other plants, 36-in.-wide Versatec electrostatic plotters installed in the main graphics-terminal rooms provide users with hard-copy plots of models stored in the computer within 10-15 minutes of request. An underground fiber-optic network transmits plotter data between headquarters and four outlying plants.

Another company that has created its own network is Boeing Commercial Airplane Co. Its CIIN (CAD/CAM Integrated Information Network) system was developed with the "objective of providing the environment that would support a heterogenous collection of CAD/CAM systems," according to W. Braithwaite, manager of engineering scientific systems at Boeing, which for years had had a variety of software systems that

required integration. The functions of the network include data management, physical and logical data communications, and data administration. It also provides the interfaces for connecting the many hardware and software types in use throughout the Seattle complex.

Sikorsky Aircraft, a division of United Technologies Corp, is undertaking a major effort during the 1980s to increase the integration of data for improved

Sikorsky Aircraft

In 1981, Sikorsky Aircraft's interactive computer graphics consisted of 13 terminals—mostly Adage 4100s, some IBM 2250s—shared by Design Engineering and Manufacturing Engineering. By '83, that number will swell to 54, and, by the end of the decade, computer graphics will be the dominant design method. The reason for this expansion is, of course, greater productivity.

"A designer is, on average, three times more productive at a terminal than on a drawing board," asserts Kenneth M. Rosen, manager of Air Vehicle Design & Development, "and, in some cases, as much as eight times more productive." From the planned expansion, Rosen projects a saving of 500,000 hours in the '81-'85 period alone.

The producer of both military and commercial helicopters relies on two CAD/CAM systems: CAIDS (Computer-Aided Interactive Design System), a 3D (wire-frame modeling) system for which the company has developed its own software; and Lockheed's 2D CAD-AM. Sikorsky developed CAIDS on its own because, at the time, the early '70s, commercial 3D systems were just emerging, and none satisfied the company's specific needs. The CADAM system was purchased just last year.

Through this decade, CADAM is expected to satisfy all anticipated 2D needs. For 3D requirements, Sikorsky will continue using and further developing CAIDS while also considering combining CADAM with available 3D systems, such as Dassault's CATIA and Northrop's NCAD.

CAIDS is tutorial. Users select from major menus displayed on the CRT the particular function to be performed—say, define a circle. They then choose from the methods of performing the function, which are displayed at the screen edge. Virtually every method of defining points, lines, planes, circles, arcs, conics, and airfoils is possible.

information flow between design engineering, manufacturing engineering, and production; enhanced communications between graphics systems; improved procedures for data management and protection; and electronic data transmission to downstream users, other UTC divisions, subcontractors, and vendors.

CAIDS (Computer-Aided Interactive Design System) is the company's distributed-processing system consisting of a network of user work stations linked via minicomputers and high-speed transmission lines to an IBM 3081 mainframe computer. Each work station is composed of a 20-in. CRT and a 36- x 48-in. datatablet worktable. One controller is used per work station. A minicomputer located near the graphics controller handles buffer-management display, menus and messages, verification of input data, and data-transmission formatting and queuing. Each minicomputer handles two work stations.

The communications link is designed to handle up to 16 work stations. Network hardware includes a direct-channel interface to the mainframe computer, a minicomputer that buffers and directs data blocks sent and received between the mainframe and each user work station, and communication boxes capable of transmitting data at the rate of 2.2

undertakes major computer-graphics expansion

Other system features permit transforming geometry to aid designers in preparing isometrics, generating 2D projections of 3D lines, and defining details by scaling geometry; determining cross-section properties; output to plotters and drafting machines; automatic dimensioning—inch, metric, or both; on-line sketching and nesting of parts; and overlaying standard parts, notes, and symbols on the display. Rotating, translating, or zooming the image and erasing, fixing, and restoring views at any time markedly facilitate operator use.

CAIDS interfaces with IFEMS, the company-developed Interactive Finite-Element-Analysis System, which is coupled to a mesh generator for structural analysis. IFEMS accepts CAIDS geometry, combines it with the structural analyst's defined model attributes, and prepares an input file of these attributes for the mesh generator, which generates and displays the final

mesh and bulk data, typically NASTRAN, on a CRT.

For a current development program involving the construction of two prototype helicopter airframes made entirely of advanced composites, virtually all of the design and structural analysis and much of the tool design have been or will be accomplished via CAIDS. Design Engineering established contour lines from which an aerodynamic finite-element model was developed and, ultimately, a wind-tunnel model constructed. The NASTRAN model for structural analysis comprised more than 8000 elements. The detail design of a major bulkhead for the composite airframe is shown below.

Two other systems, which operate on their own databases, facilitate manufacturing and process planning. SIMPLAN, a batch and interactive Manufacturing Engineering system, automatically generates and revises operation sheets, complete with time standards and tooling notations, for the manufacture of detail parts that are made from sheetmetal, extrusions, or composites.

EPATS—Electrical Planning and Tooling System—is a computer-automated engineering, manufacturing, and production-control system for wire-harness assemblies. For Design Engineering, it replaces manual methods of preparing data sheets used to define harnesses, termination reference numbers, and components lists. For Manufacturing Engineering, it supplants manual methods of preparing operation sheets for processing harness components and assembling, routing, and installing the harnesses. EPATS also supports Field Service by generating data sheets for maintenance handbooks.

Much of the automation that both CADAM and CAIDS can provide manufacturing is just around the corner. By 1983, the company aims to generate NC tapes directly from CADAM. This will require little development effort because this software package is fully capable of generating the tapes right now. To date, however, NC tapes have been produced by NC programmers using Sikorsky graphics software, which requires recreating part geometry. With CADAM, the geometry would be in the database.

CADAM-generated tapes will be used to run lathes, rout nested sheetmetal patterns, cut nested ply patterns for composites, and operate computer-aided coordinate measuring machines. CAIDS-generated tapes will be used to drive NC tube-bending machines and, possibly, the CMMs.

Over the long term, Sikorsky expects to acquire solids-modeling capability in support of NC programming, process planning, and tool design, as well as parts-classification coding in support of process planning, shop-load scheduling and projections, and retrieval of tool-design drawings.

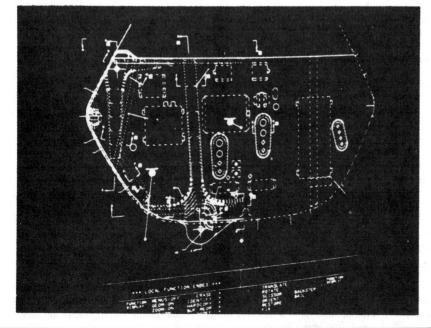

megabytes over coaxial cable as far as 1 mile from the computer room.

CAIDS software permits a variety of operations from the mainframe operator's console. The communications minicomputer software can be loaded, and the graphics controller can be started and its software loaded. The network can be stopped and then restarted, as can any single work station, which can also be put off-line. Messages can be sent to any work station or to all and also from the work stations to the mainframe operator. Memory of any of the minicomputers can be transferred to a mainframe printer. In addition, jobs can be submitted through a mainframe reader.

The mainframe or host computer handles all floating-point computations, houses the design database, and blocks or unblocks all data communication. It also formats and converts all data sent to and from the remote host and interfaces with all output devices for plotting and printing.

These companies described are in relatively advanced stages of networking. Although an increasing number of manufacturing companies are using computers for a large assortment of purposes on and off the factory floor, most have yet to electronically link these disparate computers and computer-like devices. For example, many companies have computer-aided-design systems in different plants, and they share data by physically transferring magnetic tapes from one system to the other.

At the Link Div, Singer Co, for example, divisions send magnetic tapes back and forth through the mail. Typically, an overloaded division sends the extra workload to another division that is capable of handling similar kinds of work. According to Robert K. Warner, section head, CADDS Dept, although the exchange is currently strictly by mail, there are plans under way to link the divisions electronically. Says he, "It's a matter of getting everybody to decide on the same type of communications device."

Standards for networking

Networking standards are in various stages of promulgation by several organizations and private companies, but few such standards have yet been fully developed or accepted.

Basically, the framework for standards is the International Organization for Standardization's (ISO) reference model for open-systems interconnection.

This reference model breaks down the problem of connecting systems into seven layers. For the most part, standards exist at the first three layers, the first of which is the physical link. For example, the Electronic Industry Assn's RS232C is a standard that governs the first layer, or physical link, and designates pin assignments, signal levels, and modem-control signals. It specifies variations in voltage, not current, to convey digital data.

In some instances, de facto standards have emerged. For example, the High Level Data Link Control (HDLC) is a protocol that specifies the method by which remote stations are addressed and thereby controls the information flow between them. It is a protocol for layer two, or the link layer, of ISO's overall reference model and is particularly applicable for telecommunications.

Also under way at the National Bureau of Standards is the IGES (Initial Graphics Exchange Specification) project, which aims at standardizing a data format to store geometric information and drawings typical of CAD/CAM programs. It has become time-consuming and costly to transfer geometric data between systems that use different graphics software for manufacturing-related tasks, such as NC-tape preparation and tooling design. To solve this problem, the IGES standard would permit designers and manufacturing engineers to transfer data between two incompatible CAD/CAM systems through a common IGES data listing. In practice, every developer of a separate system would supply appropriate codes to translate data between its system and the IGES listing. An initial version was recently issued by ANSI.

Since robots are playing an increasingly important role in the automated factory, General Motors, a large user of robots, has recently sent a letter to its robot suppliers calling for appropriate hardware and software within their robot-control systems that will provide a functionally common computer-to-robot link. These data links, in addition, should comply with the company's Manufacturing Automation Protocol (MAP) specification, a networking standard to be released upon completion sometime in 1983.

According to GM, robot-control systems should meet several guidelines. First of all, they should provide uploading/downloading of systems and application programs and data. With proper security, the request for data should be able to be initiated at either end of the communications link. In addition, the control system should "examine all external input/output lines and examine all internal status variables."

Security of data

The advent of computer technology has raised a number of security problems. The issue of security is a hierarchy in itself. Its multiple levels include such concerns as the security of data stored in the computer itself and the integrity of data transmission. In addition, as more and more transmission takes place over telephone lines, companies are beginning to think about ways to ensure the safety of sensitive data.

Most computer systems have some method of limiting access to and usage of data. The most common method is by entering a password to gain entry to the computer's files. To ensure tighter security, multiple passwords are commonly required (for department, location, function, etc).

A more sophisticated electronic system is to build security into software. According to Alex Beavers, manager of strategic planning and business development at General Electric, the company is developing a software package, called Data Management & Control System, that will act as an entry- and use-control system for databases to help reduce such risks.

Procedural methods can also ensure limited access to data. For example, at Kirk & Blum Mfg Co, the data-processing department is physically located in a separate structure, and only people with credentials are admitted to the room.

All these systems are designed as deterrents to both misappropriation and invasion of privacy within the computer. An even more important security concern is the integrity of data during transmission in networking systems. This problem has grown recently as networking systems have spread.

The objective, of course, is to ensure that data is received in the same form in which it was sent. Integrity is maintained in most transmissions, but, in a small percentage, data is transformed.

Several measures can be taken to protect data integrity. According to Gordon McAlpine, director of computer graphics at Time Engineering, one way is to retransmit the message to the sender.

To prevent unauthorized access to data during transmission, coding systems (encryption) can be used. The national defense community and the National Bureau of Standards have developed the technique of data encryption to sophisticated levels. In particular, a standard called DES (Data Encryption Scheme) is now being developed to protect data transmission.

In spite of these various security systems available, most experts agree that there is no such thing as a perfect security system. However, in many cases, elaborate security systems are unnecessary, and computer users should keep in mind that security should be applied only as the need arises or a threat is determined.

THE PEOPLE

Integration puts the manufacturing engineer in the center of things

WHERE does the manufacturing engineer fit in this high-tech world of hardware, software, and systems? Obviously, the role of the manufacturing engineer is changing with the advent of this powerful new manufacturing tool, the computer, and, in the long term, these changes will be profound.

Not only will the evolution of manufacturing into a computer-integrated system require increasingly sophisticated expertise, but, as the designer and operator of such a system, the manufacturing engineer will be the pivotal figure in the drive to control manufacturing costs.

This expertise will be much broader based than is traditionally associated with the function of the manufacturing engineer. Besides an understanding of the basic manufacturing processes, the job will require an ability to perceive as an integrated whole all of the factors associated with the manufacture of a product: the control structure, the management structure, production planning, the scheduling and tracking of a part through production, the scheduling of resources, the introduction of modifications, the proper use of automation, the economics of manufacturing.

"To get the most out of the system," says Charles F. Carter, technical director of Cincinnati Milacron, "we're going to need a class of manufacturing engineers who are skilled at combining complex multiple operations."

Michael P. Deisenroth, associate professor of mechanical and industrial engineering at Michigan Technological Univ, predicts the need for a new breed of manufacturing engineer: "It will be a new person or an old person who is interested in the systems approach."

The computer is both the driver and the enabler of these changing demands. On the one hand, the application of the computer in integrating manufacturing requires a very thorough, detailed analysis of the manufacturing process. The tools of this analysis—simulation, operations-research techniques, statistical techniques—have long existed but require a great deal of computation. The vast computational power of the computer, on the other hand, permits very large analysis programs to be run, providing better control over the data and, therefore, better data.

"We are able to do all of the things we've wanted to do but have never had the technology for," says Robert E. Young, director of the Industrial Automation Lab at Texas A&M Univ. "We have the ability to make good decisions with good data. We've always made decisions, and someone with 15 years' experience has probably seen enough to know what effect a decision will have, but those people are becoming fewer."

That experience will reside in the computer, but, as Arthur R. Thomson, professor and director of manufacturing engineering at Cleveland State Univ, puts it, "the computer is a moron in the midst of a lot of smart people." For manufacturing, those smart people will be the manufacturing engineers, who will be responsible for creating the logic of the manufacturing system.

For example, a demonstration project at Virginia Technological Institute & State Univ has developed a program that writes process plans for a Sundstrand Omnimil machining center. After designing a part on the computer-graphics terminal, the designer signals the computer, which checks the tolerances, inquires which are critical, and displays the processes required to produce the part, as well as the amount of time and the relative cost of the operations.

The application of this program, predicts Richard A. Wysk, associate professor in the Dept of Industrial Engineering & Operations Research, is five years out. Currently applicable to one machine with specified tolerances and tooling, he explains, the program needs to be expanded to the entire family of machines, tolerances, and tooling.

The "smart person" that develops the algorithms that the computer legislates and executes in that program will be the manufacturing engineer.

Glen Dunlap, supervisor of operational planning at Garrett Corp's Garrett Turbine Engine Co division, puts it this way: "We will now use what we pay for, and that's a lot of analytical talent."

The need to develop this analytical talent is focusing new attention on the education and training of the manufacturing engineer, an engineering specialty largely neglected in the past. "There really isn't any person trained specifically as a manufacturing engineer," Thomson declares, "Manufacturing engineering has really been the application of all kinds of engineering to manufacturing."

In fact, according to the Accrediting Board for Engineering Technology, only three higher-education institutions in the country currently offer degrees in manufacturing engineering.

There is evidence that this past neglect is being rectified. The increasing regard for manufacturing as an area in which costs can be held down, the continued concern over US productivity, and, particularly, the growing sophistication of manufacturing technology are awakening both industry and academia to the need for new approaches.

There is still, however, disagreement

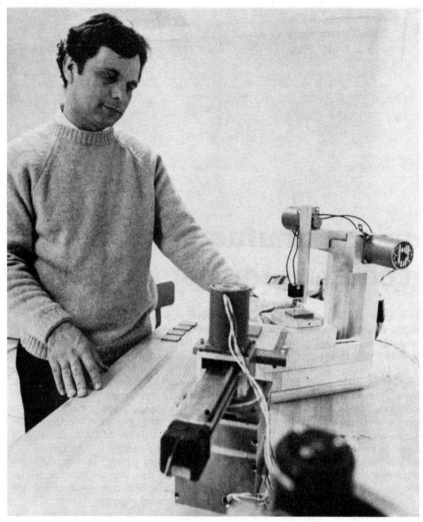

Prof Richard A. Wysk, associate professor at Virginia Tech, observes iconic models of CNC milling machine and CNC robot in table-top-size automated system

that allow weeks or months of a system's operation to be studied in, say, an hour. Such study might reveal, for example, that the system was down 60% of the time. In an hour's observation of the physical models, Prof Deisenroth explains, the models might never be down.

Texas A&M has engineering students apply the computer in solving problems in manufacturing analysis, production control, etc. "In the past," Prof Young says, "we would basically create a paper model of a system. Today we use advanced analytical tools to come up with a design, and computer graphics allows us to refine it. We can do perhaps five to ten times the analysis."

Here, too, the computer is both driver and enabler: while computer integration is forcing the systems approach to manufacturing, the computer's expanding capabilities provide the analytical power that makes such an approach possible. And the declining size and cost of computers are permitting what would be a prohibitively expensive education.

Industry is involved

Industry is being involved in much of this educational emphasis on manufacturing engineering, frequently in the form of internships. Cleveland State's Thomson likens this approach to physicians' training: "They have their high technology, too—anatomy, physiology, hematology, for instance—but they have the opportunity to marry these technologies together in real-life situations in internships. There is no counterpart in engineering. It's a rare engineering student who can come out with a solid idea of how it all goes together." Thomson was director of manufacturing engineering at TRW before assuming directorship of Cleveland State's new graduate program in manufacturing engineering.

This program, which currently has ten students in it, had been scheduled to begin in April of this year, but, Thomson explains, interest was so intense that it started early, in January. To be accepted, a student must have a bachelor's degree in any field of engineering, have 1½ years of experience in industry, and be currently employed in industry.

Courses are taught in the evening and are geared to teaching engineers how to run the manufacturing system. Continuing the medical analogy, Thomson says, "The factory is their patient. They should know how to decide whether it's healthy or not, what the symptoms are, where to get the data, how accurate the data is, and what to do with the data."

To provide the best instruction in a number of varied disciplines, Thomson explains, the program draws from other departments at the university and, espe-

about what this education should consist of and even, to some degree, whether there should be a discipline called manufacturing engineering.

At Texas A&M, for example, the Engineering School decided that manufacturing engineering really encompasses three degree programs and large sections of two others: mechanical engineering, industrial engineering, and engineering technology and segments of computer science and electrical engineering.

Joseph ElGomayel, director of the Manufacturing Systems Lab in Purdue Univ's School of Industrial Engineering, on the other hand, says that he would like to see a bachelor's degree given in manufacturing engineering. Then, he continues, the engineer should take a master's degree concentrating in computer-aided manufacturing.

Whatever the disagreement in how this discipline is categorized, there is recognition of the expanding dimensions of the manufacturing engineer's role in the manufacturing system. And attempts are being made to produce engineers with this systems orientation.

At least a dozen schools, for example, have developed the use of iconic models, miniature machine tools, to permit the laboratory study of an automated factory. At Virginia Tech, a functioning system occupies two table tops and comprises two CNC milling machined and two CNC robots, with an automatic storage-and-retrieval system under construction.

With external dimensions of 12 x 12 x 12 in. and a 45-oz-in. drive motor, each CNC mill can machine a part 4 x 4 x 4 in. In full scale, each machine would cost at least $100,000, and the system would probably require a 60,000-sq-ft building. For $30,000-$50,000 and a fraction of the space, Prof Wysk points out, the lab is able to integrate machining and handling into a system for study.

Besides iconic models, which operate more or less in real time, Michigan Tech is developing digital simulation models

cially, from local industry. A special short course in welding, for example is taught at Lincoln Electric Co's welding school. Some managerial courses are taught by executives from local firms.

Thomson considers the school ideally situated geographically: "There's wonderful talent right here in industry. I have more than 200 engineering companies right within an hour's drive."

During a six-month internship, the students take manufacturing problems at their respective companies to study and evaluate under the guidance of company mentors and faculty advisors. Generally, the special projects are at the students' own companies, but occasionally the university arranges for students to do work for other firms.

The emphasis is on the students' using all the new things they have learned, plus their own experience, to solve real problems. "We believe," says Thomson, "that, if it's done right, the students will do something of value for their companies as well as for themselves."

Impetus for the program came from industry, according to Thomson, who was on the Engineering School's Industrial Advisory Committee.

General Electric was the instigator of a new program at the Univ of Cincinnati College of Engineers. The company is underwriting development costs of a three-year graduate-level program called the Advanced Course in Manufacturing (ACM). Currently in its first year, the program has 30 students from GE in it.

The goal of the program, according to Dr Patricia J. Sommerkamp, administrator of the Manufacturing Training Program at GE's Aircraft Engine Group, is "to produce up-to-date problem solvers who can design a system to work as a unit, assess its short- and long-range cost ramifications, have credibility to sell it, know enough to specify what is needed, and be able to administer/coordinate its implementation."

The first year of the ACM consists of required courses in three disciplines: electrical computer, utilization, materials, and mechanical-industrial engineering. "In manufacturing," Sommerkamp explains, "the problems are multidisciplinary, involving identification as well as solution.."

In the second and third years, students will specialize in control of manufacturing operations, the materials aspects of manufacturing, or the production aspects of manufacturing. Here, too, however, a number of interdisciplinary courses are offered, Sommerkamp points out.

Homework from the shop floor

In all three years, Sommerkamp emphasizes, students will be required to

Landis Tool absorbed computers gradually

Computers were first applied at Litton Industries' Landis Tool Div in the early '60s to develop the master cams used in the grinders for internal-combustion-engine crankshafts. The procedure is to take lift figures supplied by the customer and insert them in a program that produces an NC tape, which operates a jig grinder to produce the master cams. No drawing of the precise outline of the cam is ever made.

The same technique produces the profile bars that guide the dressing tool when irregular surfaces are to be ground. The contours are generated in a computer program that generates the NC tapes to operate the jig grinder that produces the profile bars.

Then, "when we started using programmable controllers on production machines in 1970," says William Shank, vice president—engineering, "it became obvious that we needed some way to avoid having the electrician out on the floor program each unit by hand, and so we developed software that allowed a typist to set up and type a logic diagram. Then we developed a way to put this on a computer and put it on a tape that we could play into the PC on the assembly floor."

That development was really a rudimentary form of CAD, but it was a drafting problem that caused the move to true interactive graphics, an Applicon four-terminal system, installed about three years ago. The slightest change in a machine requires a new electrical diagram that typically takes 60-100 pages. "We have gone as high as 540 pages, each 24 x 36 in., for a single automotive-pin grinder with automatic transfer," says Stan Schoonover, manager of electronics. "It was very boring work. With graphics terminals and a drafting machine, we've reduced it by 45-48% and expect to reduce it even more."

A second four-terminal Applicon system was installed last year for mechanical detailing, but one of these terminals has been dedicated to printed-circuit-board design. The latest Landis microprocessor control system uses a single two-layer board about 19 x 17 in. that was developed on this terminal in about six months. Part of that time was learning-curve time, and Schoonover estimates that it could be done now in three months. The completed design was sent to a

firm with a photo plotter to produce the boards. Actually, this firm had to convert the program to its Calma system to present it to its plotter.

Conversion between a number of CAD systems in this way is possible. However, the normal NC programs at Landis Tool are generated by MDSI COMPACT II on IBM computers at the Litton computer center. There is, at present, no way to convert to this from the DEC computer that drives the Applicon terminals. The early cam-production program, which still produces NC tapes, is older and does not go through the computer center.

Shop-floor production control is currently operating on a batch-processing system updated daily by the computer center. The batch-processed data is available in 24-48 hr.

An IBM 8100 on-line system now being installed will have an input terminal within 25-40 ft of each worker. Each department will have one CRT terminal for two-way communication between the foreman and the data bank, but shop-floor data will be input via wands (four per terminal, each up to 180 ft from the terminal) hanging alongside building columns.

Workers will enter data by moving the wand across the magnetic strip on their badge and across the strip on the "traveler," the card that travels with each batch of parts; they will also input the operation code and number of pieces by using a magnetic coded series of numbers mounted on an instruction card on the column. A series of lights on the wand indicates proper receipt (or nonreceipt) and sequence of each message.

Foremen will be able to pre-assign a day's jobs to workers, who will not be able to enter the start of jobs that have not been assigned to them.

Landis Tool has what L.E. Jenneke, president, calls an 80%-complete MRP system and has begun installation of a group-technology system based on the OIR MICLASS coding method. Real integration of the systems that have been developing over two decades will depend, however, on the development of software that will permit IBM and DEC computers to communicate with each other. "Somebody will get exasperated and sit down and solve the problem," says Shank, "and then realize that the software can be sold to people like us."

apply the concepts to identifying and solving real-world manufacturing problems drawn from the shop floor.

Finding the pedagogical materials to teach the systems approach to manufacturing is difficult. For one thing, as Purdue's ElGomayel points out, there have been very few books written about computer-integrated manufacturing. "Everybody is writing a book on the subject, but the problem is that, by the time anything gets written and finally published, chances are it is going to be obsolete."

To try to keep up with this burgeoning technology, Purdue is sponsoring a project called ECAM (for Education in Computer-Aided Manufacturing) to develop educational modules. Funded by the National Science Foundation and evolving out of the Manufacturing Productivity Education Committee (MAPEC), the ECAM project is endeavoring to classify elements of CAM and determine how they fit together and should be taught.

In addition to the CAM-related modules from the MAPEC project, new subjects will be specified and experts in the field solicited to write them.

ElGomayel likens these modules to chapters in a book. Each is 40-50 pages long and covers a specific topic. Several are case histories, and others are accompanied by a computer program.

The goal is to provide self-paced instruction that can be used in a company training program or an academic course. The modules are made available to anyone who needs them.

Work today is changing, too

The changes for which this education is preparation will be gradual, of course, but computer-integrated manufacturing is affecting the day-to-day work of manufacturing engineers today. Primarily, this involves discovering the power of the computer and learning how to get the most out of this new tool.

One of the most important attributes of the computer is its speed, which contributes to improved communication between the manufacturing engineer and other departments in the plant.

One example of this improved communication can be seen in a marked reduction in the time required for Design and Manufacturing to interact. Some people speak of this as "breaking down the wall between Design and Manufacturing," though few predict that the two functions will ever become one.

Joe Tulkoff, director of manufacturing technology at Lockheed-Georgia, describes the computer as catching up with the speed of the mind. "One of the depressing things of the precomputer days was to have these very talented process planners and design engineers,

whose minds were very quick and whose knowledge was very fine, communicate their ideas with pencil and paper. The computer allows these highly skilled people to work more of the time on the more demanding aspects of their jobs."

It is perhaps this freedom from the mundane that produces the general enthusiasm that manufacturing engineers exhibit once they have mastered the tool. "The people who generally use the system," says Robert Warner, section head, CADDS Dept, Singer Co's Link Div, "you couldn't get back to paper and pencil. The system has so much computing power that, by writing programs that input the data correctly, they can get the system to do the tedious work.

"The system is addictive," he continues. "As a matter of fact, you have to pry these people away from the terminals at the end of their shift."

Ed Cappel, data-processing manager for Kirk & Blum Mfg Co, has found that even people who were initially reluctant to join the computer age eventually come around. "Once they begin to see what the computer can do," he says, "they begin asking for new programs."

Sometimes the computer's spectacular speed is still not fast enough. "As engineers become more proficient in using the computer," says Lockheed-Georgia's Tulkoff, "they become less tolerant of lapses in response time."

Cappel agrees: "Three seconds becomes an eternity when you're sitting at a CRT."

Most companies discover that computerization changes the work habits of the people using the system. For one thing, few companies can afford to supply a terminal for each engineer, and terminals may be shared by product designers, tool designers, process planners, NC programmers, etc.

Ensuring that the terminals are used to their fullest, therefore, requires that time at the terminals be scheduled very tightly. This, in turn, forces individual users to plan their work ahead of time.

"They must schedule the amount of time they want," says Tulkoff. "And they have to do the appropriate desk work so that, when they do sit down at the terminal, they are prepared with all the information they need to intelligently use the computer." The result is more-efficient use of the engineer's also valuable time as well.

Users become totally absorbed

The computer demands a lot of concentration, Tulkoff adds. "The user is paced by the computer's instant response," he points out. "We've found that users concentrate so intently that they become almost unmindful of the

break whistle or lunch hour or conversations going on around them. This is a phenomenon we hadn't predicted."

Surprisingly (if computerization evokes images of dehumanization), through the sharing of terminals, the computer has also contributed to increased personal contact between the people who work on the design and processing of a part, according to Tulkoff. "They are getting a chance to get together, when previously they may have never met. Designers and manufacturing people can discuss the problems of translating or modifying a design or creating one that can be easily manufactured."

Training for the computer

Most computer-aided manufacturing systems can be operated by people without computer backgrounds, and companies generally train manufacturing engineers in use of their systems. But some firms, like Singer Co's Link Div, look for people with some computer training. "Ideally," says Warner, "a person should have a technical degree with a minor in computer science. We write our own software for portions of our graphics system," he explains, "and we need people who have the ability to program."

Computer-system suppliers offer a wide range of services to assist companies in training system users. Some of the services are included in the cost of the system; others, usually for advanced training, are extra.

Both Applicon Inc and Computervision Corp, for example, include in the system price a basic system-operation course. Both courses comprise classroom and on-terminal work; Applicon's course lasts five days, and Computervision's takes two weeks. Typically, a company sends one or two employees to the supplier's training facility, and they train their fellow employees, although the course can also be set up at the buyer's plant.

Advanced courses help companies get the most out of their systems. Geared to specific applications, they generally are taken about six months after the system goes into operation. Typical applications include mechanical design, system management, system operation, graphics-system programming, macro commands, and NC postprocessors. Such courses generally last a week or two and cost about $800 a week.

Applicon also provides customized training. If, for example, a company is standardizing the system in use through its plant and wants a companywide training program, Applicon will develop the content and run such a program. It may last several weeks or even several months, and its cost depends on the extent, the length of the course, and the number of trainees involved.

Video- and audio-tape training packages are also available for specific applications and include workbooks and starter files. Costing about $3000-$4000, these packages are designed to be essentially self-teaching and can be used in conjunction with an in-plant course.

Field personnel are also available to help buyers train users, solve problems that might arise, and generally use the system to its fullest.

Overcoming resistance

Many companies experience initial resistance on the part of some prospective users. Some engineers are intimidated by the prospect of interacting with a computer, or they profess an inability to type. At Xerox Corp's North American Mfg Div, the instructor overcame this reluctance by giving trainees a piece of cake and a gold star when they did something right. Says George Cooke, manager of Tool Engineering & Services, "They loved it. They couldn't wait to get to class each day, and they got over this 'I-can't-type' syndrome."

Grumman Aerospace Corp provided its own comprehensive training program when it implemented the Grumman Engineering & Manufacturing System (GEMS). First, representatives from the various areas of the GEMS organization received two weeks of basic training in CADAM at Lockheed and then three weeks of advanced instruction and three weeks of on-the-job training given by Lockheed people at Grumman's Bethpage, NY, facility.

This nucleus of Grumman employees then served as instructors for other Grumman personnel, who took the course on their own time two hours a day two days a week for six weeks. To date, some 800 employees have taken this basic course, and 300 of these have taken the advanced course.

Newly hired engineers, whether they have had CAD/CAM instruction in school or not, generally take the basic course and possibly the advanced course, too. Stephen Petrovits, manager of the GEMS program, reports, "Most recent graduates are eager for the training, realizing that it's the way of the future."

Ron Pelletier, NC CAM supervisor for BIF, a subsidiary of General Signal Corp, sums up his company's experience with training: "It was really no problem. It was just a matter of getting used to the system and working on it for a few weeks or a month. Then we found that the system would do everything and more that we wanted it to."

The same can be said of computer-integrated manufacturing.

Operators, too, will be paid for what they know

A common image evoked by the concept of computer-integrated manufacturing is that of a peopleless factory. Though popular perhaps with managers dreaming of eliminating labor costs, the image is an unrealistic one. There will be people on the shop floor, even in the highly computerized, ideal factory of the future.

There may be fewer people, but there is not likely to be wholesale displacement of factory workers.

For one thing, as is frequently pointed out, productivity improvements like automation and computerization tend to create more jobs than they eliminate. There is, of course, a time lag, which may dislocate workers unable or unwilling to adjust to the new way of doing business.

But, on the other hand, the computerization of the shop floor can be seen, in some respects, as a response to a changing work force. For example, the World War II baby boom ended about 1955, and the birth rate since then has been fairly flat. This means that the bulge in the population is already well into the job market and the number of people entering the work force is diminishing, despite the evidence of the current high unemployment rate. And this will be true through the end of this century, when the babies born during the current mini boom finally reach the job market.

Moreover, fewer of the workers entering the work force today are going into manufacturing to replace those who are retiring. A Univ of Wisconsin study of the skilled-worker shortage in Milwaukee points out that, in 1975, when the end of the baby boom could be said to be reaching the job market, 14 out of every 20 people retiring were blue-collar workers; only nine of every 20 people entering, however, were seeking blue-collar work.

The workers of today are better educated than those in years past. Arthur R. Thomson, professor of manufacturing engineering at Cleveland State Univ, estimates that 80% of the people retiring today have less than a high-school education. More than half of the people entering the job market, he says, have more than a high-school education.

It could be said, therefore, that the technology for computerization and automation is developing at a time when there are fewer and fewer work-

ers willing to do tedious, back-breaking work in environments inhospitable to human beings. And the new high-tech image should help to attract workers to manufacturing.

In implementing computer-integrated manufacturing, however, a company's management can't ignore the people on the shop floor. Overcoming the common fear of the computer as Big Brother looking over workers' shoulders and the fear of job loss, for example, requires considerable management effort in involving workers in planning computer integration. All workers have a stake in the success of a system that they have had a hand in developing.

This makes sense not only from a labor/management perspective: after all, more than anybody in the plant, the workers producing the product know the manufacturing problems and whether a system will work.

There aren't likely to be many places for unskilled workers in the computer-integrated factory. Thomson, who used to be director of manufacturing engineering at TRW, describes how it was when "we first began to buy NC machines. People thought that they could run them with unskilled people because the machine would be smart. But they soon learned that, if you did that, the unskilled person was unable to cope when things went wrong."

And that's a mighty expensive piece of equipment for an unskilled worker to be responsible for.

Also, Thomson adds, "Once you program a machine, if you don't learn from it as you go along, you're never going to upgrade the program. A smart operator will keep making suggestions of how to change that program and make it better."

The operators of these "smart machines," then, will be far from unskilled, though perhaps they will be skilled in different ways from workers today. "Operators," Thomson opines, "are going to become more responsible for maintaining their equipment. They know more about them than anybody else. And the more they know about hydraulics, for instance, and electronics, the more they can see to it that their machines stay tuned up. People on the floor, as well as managers, are going to be paid for what they know, rather than for what they can do with their hands and their backs."

THE MANAGEMENT
Developing a fresh and organized approach to CIM is the challenge

THE PROPER APPLICATION of metalworking's new tool, the computer, poses a challenge for company management. Implementing computer-integrated manufacturing requires both commitment and flexibility, an organized approach as well as a willingness to diverge from traditional managerial strategies.

In an age when change is continuous and sometimes drastic, managers are seeking a fresh perspective, a way to find stability and improvement. Industry is being affected, more now than ever before, by international economic and political issues that influence such basic production concerns as availability of materials, labor demographics, manufacturing costs, and consumer preferences.

The nature of change is that it is unpredictable, causing people, businesses, and industries to concentrate on reacting rather than planning. Consequently, access to information on happenings while they occur, at a machine or in a market, is becoming more than an advantage over the competition; it is becoming a necessity. To provide this access, the computer is essential.

The computer, a fundamental managerial tool, can help minimize reaction time and allow decision makers to effectively plan, organize, and control their operations as well as improve their products.

Its use means that managers "will stop bringing the problem to the computer but instead will take the computer to the problem," states C.H. Link, former senior vice president and general manager of Computer Aided Manufacturing-International Inc (CAM-I).

In fact, today's manufacturing strategy is a new art, says Wickham Skinner, James E. Robison Professor of business administration at Harvard Business School.

Simply, the computer instantly provides organized data to serve as a basis for meaningful interpretation. This accurate and timely information, combined with human experience and judgment, results in faster, less costly, and more effective decision-making capability.

Significant computer applications succeed, however, only in an environment where the planners understand computer technology, at least from a user's point of view, and are comfortable with it. In the past, says Link, ownership of land and resources was important; now access to knowledge and data provides greater influence.

For this reason, managers need to carefully plan the application of computers to manufacturing. Even when systems are installed in piecemeal fashion, an overall plan is required to prevent the purchase of incompatible units.

A critical part of master-plan development is the justification of initial implementation costs and assessment of the advantages.

This all-encompassing project forces managers and planners to consider intangibles, such as an overall productivity improvement that may result from computerization of specific areas of the operation.

Justifying the intangibles

Too frequently, technology investments are made because their benefits include either a short-term cost saving or cost avoidance, and, often, minimal alterations are made once the new machine or system is in place. With CIM, however, there are other considerations, which often cannot be judged solely on measurable, purely objective benefits,

and occasionally, the true benefit may not become apparent until the system is in place.

Non-quantifiable considerations include improved product quality; flexibility in meeting market demand; and shorter, more predictable delivery cycles—important contributors to the goal of heightened competitiveness.

The concept of totally automated, paperless factories can be realized as long as the implementation is organized with the dedication of top management. Computer-integrated manufacturing cannot be attained by permitting "each little functional group to go its own way, hoping they will all meet somewhere," observes Northrop Corp's Don Stanbarger, manager of the Factory of the Future.

The next step is to design a flexible system so that the company can grow, change, and rearrange with existing equipment or with new, compatible equipment.

"We laid out a dream factory in 1975," Stanbarger says. In order to justify the investments involved, "we did a detailed cost analysis, looking at life-cycle costs and return on investment (ROI)."

With a commitment from the general manager of the aircraft division, the 200-employee project was initiated in the shop, producing graphite rudder skins for the FA-18A aircraft.

Some firms claim that they are unable to accurately determine the financial benefits of CIM because computers do not directly produce salable products; their use, however, can upgrade the product's quality and reduce the costs of manufacturing. In essence, each individual and piece of equipment can become more productive.

Gordon Schuster, president of machine-tool builder Timesavers Inc, justified the purchase of a CAD system in accordance with the company's normal method—a "formal but not rigid" modified payback procedure. Behind the justification, though, was the attitude that "we can't afford not to have it."

Where to expect improvement.

In design engineering, quality improvement arises from the capability for more-accurate part descriptions and data transfer, as well as better analytical performance. Cost savings are accrued by reducing drawing time and shortening the time it takes to make design iterations. Achieving all of this can decrease the permanent-staff requirements.

In manufacturing-engineering departments, quality improvement stems again from less human interpretation and more-accurate data transfer, in addition to direct simulation of fabrication techniques.

Consistency, or having the precise dimensions in the database at all times, is another time-saving factor that must be considered in the justification of expenditures.

"Primarily, we see that the design can be accomplished more accurately and with more innovation," states Alex Marchese, group engineer of Rohr Industries' Computer Graphics Systems. The firm uses four Computervision systems tied to an IBM mainframe.

"Instead of looking at only one way of designing and building a product, we'll be able to look at four or five," he notes.

Smoothing the transition

Dana Corp's Center for Technology recently purchased an $850,000 Computervision CAD system to demonstrate what computers can do for the company's numerous divisions. The decision to buy the system was made by a CAD/CAM task force that comprises 14 individuals representing ten divisions and including two people from the center. The group meets periodically to discuss strategy for developing a centralized computer system.

The divisions are autonomous and are, therefore, free to buy incompatible systems if they choose, says Gene Swartz, vice president of Technical Services for Dana. But this new system can help individual divisions generate their own databases for their manufacturing personnel and can serve as a "central information clearinghouse."

The task force hopes to advise its divisions on how to achieve greater efficiency; with a central database, perhaps "reinvention of the wheel can be avoid-

ed," says Swartz. At least, "it will let us show that CAD/CAM is an engineer's tool and not a career change," he asserts.

Regarding justification of this expenditure, Swartz says, "We've got too many unknowns to do a typical payback analysis, and I would question the accuracy" of such a figure.

If different departments or divisions install computers that cannot communicate with each other, confusion results, as well as huge expenses for translation equipment; access to a common database is the key.

A task force has been assembled at Xerox Corp's North American Manufacturing Div for this particular purpose. George Cooke, manager of Tool Engineering & Services, says the company wants to "see whether we can reach a

decision to go with one particular supplier of equipment to create a common database. Now we have a mixed set, and we have to eventually select which equipment to centralize with."

Grumman Aerospace Corp has been working toward CIM since 1975, when its level of automation was determined solely by 90 numerically controlled machines and support equipment. The developing challenge for Grumman was clear: engineering and manufacturing were dealing with a growing proliferation of data as designs became increasingly complex and greater use of the same data by many disciplines lengthened design- and manufacturing-cycle times.

Improved data-processing power alleviated some of the burden, but it was not a solution. It could not resolve the diffi-

Solving problems one by one

"If there are problems, computerize. If not, leave well enough alone," advises Frank G. Zagar, president of Zagar Inc, a manufacturer of multi-spindle drillheads and machines.

Believing that the best approach is to solve one problem, or one group of problems, at a time, he has learned a few valuable lessons about implementation in the 15 years that he has been "dedicated to computer procedures."

Via computerization, Zagar has attacked and resolved such problems as unrealistic price quoting, off-schedule delivery, and flawed inventory and factory control. Now the company's goals include improvement in sales programs and creation of product designs on a terminal.

The engineering terminal will be connected directly to an existing IBM 1034 system, which has more capacity than the business is currently using and can be expanded later if necessary. The engineering system will operate independently of all the accounting functions.

Inventory, one of the most important areas for improvement in terms of cost reduction, has been decreased by at least one-third at Zagar—with faster turnover, also.

Included in the larger category of inventory is work-in-process (WIP) inventory, which often represents a considerable investment in materials and in work already performed. Therefore, says Zagar, the only work-in-process existing in an organized manufacturing facility should be what is needed.

WIP describes a product in various

stages of completion, including both raw material that has been released for initial processing and completely processed material awaiting final inspection or shipment.

Until the products are on their way to the customer, WIP inventory severely blocks cash flow, and any reduction in the amount of inventory being carried can produce immediate and sizable savings.

To remedy inefficiencies in inventory control, machine loading, cash flow, and financial statements, Zagar "went through four or five programmers and three or four models of IBM machines, all of which was quite a fiasco until Frank Henry [son of Frank G. and presently district sales manager] took a ten-week course at IBM."

Through this experience, it became clear to Zagar that programming must be accomplished by individuals who are familiar with the user's needs and routines, as well as the computer system's capabilities.

This situation was encountered again at the accounting level and was similarly solved; Frank Henry earned a finance degree and returned to "straighten out the odds and ends of the computer routines."

According to Zagar, "programmers do what you tell them to do. It is the systems analyst who is responsible for the real improvements and who sets up the overall approach." To guarantee the analyst's effectiveness, however, the individual "must be trained out of the company's own resources, in-house," Zagar states.

culties in data communication between people and functions nor lessen the increasing time required for the growing number of complex jobs.

An ad-hoc committee, established in 1974 when these problems became evident, was responsible for Grumman's decision in 1975 to lease Lockheed's Computer Graphic Augmented Design and Manufacturing (CADAM) system. Selected to combine with existing in-house graphics programs, the system is oriented to design, drafting, NC, and manufacturing. (The company purchased the package one year later.)

To justify the investment, Grumman estimated that CADAM could, on specific jobs, reduce design-drawing hours by 66-75%, NC-programming hours by 50%, and tooling- and manufacturing-drawing hours by 50%. Applied to an entire aircraft program, use of CADAM for 100% drafting of machined parts and sheetmetal parts and for 80% of NC programming was projected to provide a cost saving of nearly $3-million. Subtracting terminal, computer, and high-speed-plotter costs produced a net saving calculated at almost $2.5-million.

By 1980, the Grumman Engineering & Manufacturing System (GEMS) was in effect. This CADAM-based system supports design, drafting, tooling, manufacturing, and quality-assurance functions. It provides "the picture": master dimensions, model data, tool geometry and dimensions, part geometry, and NC-machining and nesting data.

In that year, typical anticipated time savings were 65% in contours and drawings, 50-75% in engineering drafting, 30% in manufacturing-engineering methods, 40-50% in NC programming and tool design, 70-80% in manufacture of tools used to make tools (tooling tools), and 10-25% in production tools.

CIM can simplify the complex

One of the most significant cost savings resulting from the implementation of GEMS derives from the reduction or elimination of tooling tools, such as mock-up fixtures, models, jig masters, and flat-pattern templets for master tools and blocks. This is possible because math models of components can now be called up on the CRT display and cutting paths can be established for direct manufacture of the production tool.

For detail-part tools, GEMS is projected to eliminate 75% of the tooling tools (flat-pattern masters and record templets) previously required, effecting an 85% reduction in worker-hours and 5-10% of the production tools, for a 25% time saving.

AMF's Potter & Brumfield Div, which produces electromechanical and solid-state components, also conducted an in-depth study of CAD/CAM's advantages. However, justifying the purchase of its DEC-based Applicon system was not difficult because it was viewed as a pilot program within AMF and, as such, was encouraged by high-level management. Needless to say, the anticipated cost savings may have hastened approval for the project.

The division created a hypothetical design process for its product, a 5- x 10-in. printed-circuit board (PCB) for cost-justification purposes. The exemplary process involved a schematic, bill of materials, artwork, film of the circuit, and other stages; if manufactured, the PCB itself would contain 50 integrated circuits and 35 discrete components. The complex product would take 115 hr to complete manually, 30 hr with CAD/CAM.

Preparation of the manufacturing specifications (legend screens, component-insertion drawings, title blocks, and more) would take 100 hr manually, or 2-3 hr using CAD/CAM since most of the steps would already have been handled at the design stage. Preparation of NC drilling/routing tapes would be reduced from a 4-hr project to one that takes 0.1 hr; preparation of insertion tape, from 5 hr to 0.2 hr.

In all, it was estimated that 255 hr could be saved in putting one PCB into production; for approximately 25% of new PCBs manufactured by the company in one year, CAD/CAM might eliminate as many as 11,475 work hours.

Taking the present and future cost benefits of CIM strictly into account, as Grumman and Potter & Brumfield did, is an effective and organized approach. Not all plants, divisions, or companies are motivated by the same factors, however, or can benefit for similar reasons. And not all systems need to be company-wide.

New England Aircraft Products, for example, was unable to find skilled workers to replace some of its near-retirement employee population, and so it decided that computerization was required to fill the anticipated void. NEAP, one of Howmet Turbine Components Corp's 20 divisions, is not subject to any particular master plan regarding CAD/CAM but must justify equipment purchases on the basis of ROI, as most firms do.

The Computervision system that NEAP selected in 1980 is used about 90% of the time for manufacturing operations and 10% for precision drafting of shadowgraph charts, tool design, and plant layout.

The need, originally, was to strengthen the model-making department, according to Bob Siedzik, chief industrial engineer.

The division's system, which cost $250,000, was part of a $1-million plant upgrade; within 1½ years, NEAP recouped the entire investment.

Anticipating the future

The flexibility that CIM affords goes beyond the reduction in dependence on uncontrollable business concerns, such as NEAP's. One of the long-term considerations in investment justification is the ability to handle large increases in demand or sudden changes in product mix.

In some companies, justification works by necessity. As one engineer says, approval is sought when "the guy out there perceives a horrendous work load and has time constraints."

With increased reliance on databases, many such situations may be alleviated. Generally, new-product designing and testing does not necessitate designing from scratch with CAD/CAM. Applying a fixed monetary value to these advantages is a subjective effort, though it remains a necessary one. Purchases, of course, should make dollar-sense, and ROI must be proven, but the possible positive consequences, particularly in more-volatile markets, must be reflected in the dollar figures.

"What we do in industry today," observes Daniel J. Madden, manager of the User Application Center at GE's Computer Management Operation, "is to take a piece and work the hell out of it to get a cost justification for it.

"Then we envision it as it relates to other things. With technology moving so fast, I am not so sure that you can look at a piece in any way other than conceptually."

Similarly, Mike Kutcher, chairman of the Corporate Automation Council of IBM's Data Systems Div, says that "what we couldn't justify, we knew intellectually. The question is 'what's the real value of the system?'" The answer depends on the strategic views and innovative goals of individual companies—a master plan that can be adhered to only if it is determined by upper-level management and implemented at all levels.

In mid-1980, General Electric Co completed a survey to find out just how extensive computer integration had become within the company and what its effects were. The study was conducted by an in-house Computer Aided Engineering & Manufacturing Council.

At the time that the survey was completed, the company's estimated capital investment totaled $1.4-billion for the year, ¼ to ⅓ of which was tagged for CAD/CAM investments. According to Paul

Quantz, then council chairman, the survey findings showed that the use of computers in engineering and manufacturing was growing at an overall rate of about 20% per year.

For interactive-graphics applications (not hardware), the growth rate proved to be approximately 52% per year, totaling 300 applications by the end of 1980 with 1200 forecast by the end of 1981.

Computer use in text processing and display graphics had eliminated much of the paperwork involved in generating technical publications and drawings and

was growing at a rate of approximately 60% annually.

Other rates of growth: 25% in testing and inspection processes; 25% in position controls, such as robots, numerical control, DNC, and CNC; 12% in information storage and retrieval, including data banks and on-line shop-floor systems; and 12% in functional computing, an area that covers conventional use of computers for analytical programs, such as finite-element analysis.

CAD/CAM claims at least partial credit for roughly 40% of GE's cost of sales, and

the company's costs were rising. Computerization of nesting patterns for flame-cutting operations on steel sheet and plate had increased utilization of material from about 65% in many parts of the company to 85-90% in others. In addition, parts that had to be scrapped were reduced by 3:1.

Creating 'superplanners'

Strategy provides a method for implementing CAD/CAM, but it may not greatly influence the modifications that are caused by computerization. Certain jobs

Pooling resources for greater capacity

Three medium-sized companies in Cincinnati have devised an approach that provides each company access to computer capabilities that none of them could have afforded on its own: backed by an agreement under which two of the firms contracted to purchase computer time for eight years, the largest of the three bought an $800,000 Honeywell 66/05 system and provides computer access and complete programming services for all three operations.

The arrangement was a fairly logical step for the three firms, which have had formal and informal links for a number of years. Setco Industries Inc, for example, a manufacturer of machine-tool components, had at one time sold excess computer time for data processing to Cincinnati Gilbert Machine Co, a builder of horizontal boring, drilling, and milling machines. Ed Cappel, data-processing manager for Kirk & Blum Mfg Co, a sheetmetal fabricator, had previously worked in data processing at Setco. And Cappel, the treasurer of Setco, and the treasurer of Cincinnati Gilbert served together on the finance committee of a local church group.

It was through this last link that the mutual-benefit arrangement was conceived. "The idea was born on a street corner," says Cappel, who is generally considered the instigator of the plan. The three were casually lamenting the fact that all three companies had outgrown their existing computer systems when Cappel pointed out that, "if we put our money together, we could buy a system to do all the things we wanted to do and still do them in a timely fashion."

The two treasurers posed the idea to their respective presidents, and Cappel was commissioned to elicit preliminary proposals from vendors. The result,

says Cappel, was that "we bought nearly a million dollars worth of computer, which is a lot more than any of us individually could have purchased."

And, as Cincinnati Gilbert Treasurer Joe Deidesheimer points out, his firm and Setco have the benefit of the computer system without the massive investment in hardware, software, and programming staff. Moreover, he adds, "we have a much more personal relationship than you would normally have in a data-processing arrangement."

Under the plan, the mainframe computer is housed at Kirk & Blum and is linked to terminals at Setco and Cincinnati Gilbert by data lines. Computer time is managed and programming and systems analysis performed by Cappel and his staff at Kirk & Blum.

Priorities are managed much as if the system handled many departments in one company. Capable of handling both on-line and time-sharing processing, the system is programmed to give highest priority to on-line jobs and can run ten such jobs simultaneously. "We give those jobs highest priority," says Cappel, "because we feel that, when people are sitting in front of a terminal trying to interact with the computer, we can't let them get disgusted. We have to give them quick response."

According to Cappel, 45-50% of the system is used for accounting functions, and 35-40% is used for on-line work, including manufacturing.

Setco was the first to move onto the new system. Its three data lines are connected to eight CRTs located throughout the 150-employee facility. The system is used primarily for order tracking and inventory control, with all sales orders, purchase orders, and part-production folders processed through it. All accounting functions, too, are tied into the system. The engineering

department uses an in-house-developed program to design machine-tool spindles according to customer requirements, and manufacturing produces NC tapes via an APT postprocessor.

Kirk & Blum, with 520 employees, has ten terminals in five remotely located plants. Besides doing order tracking, inventory control, and accounting through the system, the company also models the air-pollution-control equipment produced by one of its two divisions, does shop scheduling, and produces NC tapes.

Cincinnati Gilbert, having long ago computerized its accounting functions, is in the process of moving manufacturing and design functions onto the system. Currently, bills of materials and shop routers are being adapted to the system, and, when its five CRTs are on stream, the company plans to write postprocessors for its line of machine tools.

Cappel reports that, in the fourth year of the eight-year contract, there has been no difficulty with the three companies sharing the computer. "You are dealing with unique people," he notes. "The presidents of the three companies pounded out the agreement among themselves so that it's equitable to all parties. The attorneys for Kirk & Blum were rather dumbfounded that the contract did not include some kind of kick-out clause, under which Kirk & Blum could drop Setco and Cincinnati Gilbert.

"The president of Kirk & Blum said, 'We agreed to do this for eight years, and that's the term. We don't want to get out after four years or whatever.' It's really kind of amazing.

"I report to the president of Kirk & Blum," Cappel adds, "but I also kind of report to the presidents of Setco and Cincinnati Gilbert."

may be upgraded or shuffled around, and, perhaps, a few will be eliminated.

Mostly, the difference seems to be that there will be a diminished need to hire new personnel at the same rate as before. Each professional will be able to take on more and varied responsibilities when much of the tedious or mundane work is eliminated.

"What we've seen happen is that engineer and tool designers have, for the first time in their careers, met each other personally and had a chance to talk about a design in a meaningful way," says Lockheed Georgia's Joe Tulkoff.

"Engineers are getting immediate feedback from the skills that are downstream from them." Inevitably, then, there is "going to be a transformation of knowledge among these people," he says.

Taking this theory a few steps further, Tulkoff predicts a "telescoping within the manufacturing-engineering function of several of these different disciplines, and they will gradually merge into 'superplanners'—a term that we've already used at Lockheed. The superplanner knows the total requirements of the thousands of parts and what they mean."

The literal translation of that term may seem a bit farfetched, but there is some validity to the observation that design and manufacturing engineers' responsibilities are beginning to change. With computer-aided design, more manufacturing information can be dealt with earlier, in the design stages of production.

At Westinghouse's Defense & Electronic Systems Div, little has officially changed regarding roles. According to Rivera, "we have a manufacturing engineer resident with the design group in our printed-circuit-designs area. He has been around for a while. This is one specific example in which we have a manufacturing engineer, who is familiar with the manufacturing process and with the printed circuits and reviews the design." However, he adds, none of this is new.

"It is a carryover from when we designed manually. When a drawing package is created for a product, it is reviewed by electrical engineering, manufacturing engineering, and mechanical engineering. Right now, they're reviewing drawings; in the future, they may sit around the computer terminals," Rivera adds.

Northrop's Stanbarger finds that engineers' functional responsibilities at the Factory of the Future are also basically the same, but people are doing their jobs differently from before.

"We're starting to knock down the walls" between design, manufacturing, and quality assurance so that "you almost can't tell one from another anymore," he says.

Each engineer has an area of expertise, but they are interacting and conversing more now and, consequently, learning about other aspects of producing their product. Instead of calling another engineer over only for problem solving, Stanbarger notes, his engineers sit around the CRT, evaluating various production methods on their own.

The immediate availability of information provided by the computer permits such interchange, simulation, and testing.

"The day is going to come quickly," Stanbarger predicts, "when all three [design, manufacturing, and quality-assurance personnel] report to a central functional head." Particularly in the "advanced-composite world," where a variety of materials offer many design capabilities, an integrated group of engineers is better equipped to devise viable part plans, he states.

Working faster and better

At Grumman, the advent of CAD/CAM has been more of a change for design-engineering than for manufacturing engineering so far, although both groups have retained their traditional functions. The organization—who reports to whom—has not been altered. As always, the two units work closely together, from the concept stage to production.

CAD/CAM has, nevertheless, markedly reduced the time in which design and manufacturing can interact, as well as the time required for each to perform its traditional tasks. Thus, everything that was required before can be done faster today or with fewer people.

Furthermore, this improved productivity can be used for product improvement. For instance, the length of time required to design an aircraft in the 1960s might now be used to design a different plane, but the two are not necessarily comparable products; the latter has far greater capabilities.

Since both design and manufacturing can contribute more quickly to new designs and proposals, Grumman estimates that what may have taken months before may now take days on a computer terminal.

In fact, Kenneth M. Rosen, manager of Air Vehicle Design & Development at Sikorsky Aircraft, suggests that a designer at a terminal is about three times more productive than on a drawing board. In some cases, an eight-fold improvement is supposed.

With such vast productivity increases, Sikorsky may be able to accomplish in-house some work that is now completed by outside vendors.

Despite these changes, each function will survive because specialists will always be needed. Improved communication makes it possible for design engineers to speak with some authority about manufacturing and vice versa, but nei-

Boeing experiments

The old organization chart is the single greatest inhibitor to CAD/CAM implementation, says Jack Ulmer, chief of Design Technology at Boeing Military Airplane Co (BMAC). Consequently, "finding a way to cross the functional lines of design and manufacturing, in order to integrate them, should provide the sort of revolution we've been expecting from CAD/CAM."

To test this theory, BMAC initiated an experimental program in which CAD, NC-programming, and tool-design personnel report to the chief engineer. (The charts show the contrast between the two systems.)

Within one year of the program's inception, the company's return on its investment totaled $2.8-million.

This experimental system permits such typical problems as budget and schedule controversies to be resolved at a lower organizational level, and more quickly. Other encouraging results include elimination of duplicated efforts, faster reaction to changes, and improved coordination and communication in drawing reviews; thus far, $1.5-million has been saved.

Better drawing quality has meant fewer engineering changes, saving about $500,000; and reduced scrap and rework, as well as improved control of NC tapes and setup documents, has saved $154,000.

Rather than routinely performing a narrow task, employees are able to diversify their abilities and exert influence in areas beyond their usual jobs. For example, an NC programmer and tool designer now discuss the product design with the engineer, and vice versa, to effect changes. Such idea exchanges are facilitated by sharing CAD equipment and systems.

Cross-utilization of personnel not only saved $180,000 but also represents stability to the employees; without the threat of labor fluctuations, they expend a steadier level of effort.

Perhaps, Ulmer notes, integrating functions will also help alleviate the persisting classical barrier between

ther could replace or eliminate the need for the other.

Garrett's Glen Dunlap believes that the benefits of CAD/CAM are not related as much to the meshing of roles as to more efficiency within them. In short, the computer permits people to work at the highest level of their skills.

"The design engineer has now been elevated to a level where we use what we pay for," he notes, "and that's a lot of analytical talent."

Any alteration of roles and the enhanced effectiveness that results can be included in the list of intangibles that are inevitable in considering computer-

integrated manufacturing. Recognizing and accepting such changes, even those as radical as altering traditional organizational structures, is critical to the successful management of computer-integrated manufacturing and to the possibility of reaping more than the expected cost and productivity benefits.

with integrated design and manufacturing

engineering and manufacturing, which is reinforced by the traditional hierarchical ranking system.

Often, he says, "large companies break down tasks functionally so that each becomes divorced from the others

and from the end product. This produces insular attitudes in the people assigned to each function."

Generally, Boeing has found that similar results can be obtained by either the integrated organization or the team concept. In a team arrangement, each group is assigned a section of a project. For instance, groups working on project design, planning, tool design, NC programming, and producibility report to a team leader. This method was applied at BMAC's sister company, Boeing Commercial Airplane Co (BCAC), in Seattle.

In a modified version of this concept, flat patterns (Mylar strips that transfer two-dimensional drawing features to a 3D master model of the actual product) are now created in BMAC's engineering department instead of during tool design, which occurs later in the cycle.

BMAC now produces master models four months sooner than on previous programs, with less flow time and on more-predictable schedules.

Informal management across functional lines requires an inordinate amount of time for communication and cooperation. But such dedication is necessary for monitoring individual functions and promoting innovations.

Some of BMAC's concerns include defining functional responsibility and evaluating the individuals doing those jobs. Resistance by employees reluctant to abandon old perceptions of work structure must be considered.

Using CAD/CAM to reduce recurring costs is a more tangible goal. At BCAC, for example, error-free drilling of floor substructures on the 747 airplane, via CAD-defined data sets and automated drilling equipment, permitted an annual saving of $900,000.

These strides have been made with an emphasis by management on the total product. Boeing has found that reorganization of the traditional manufacturing environment, where the narrow confines of a single job remain the primary concern, is the first step toward implementing CAD/CAM.

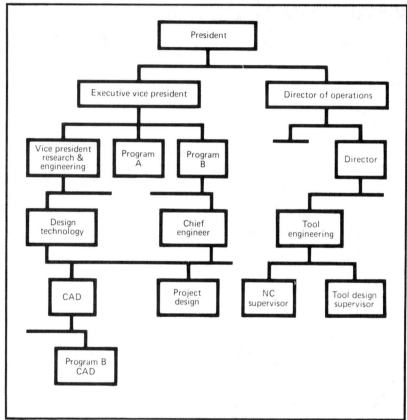

Traditional organizational structure

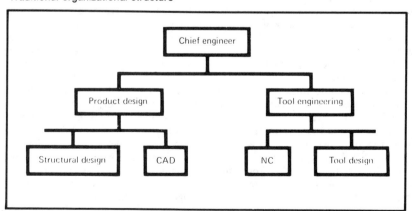

Integrated organizational structure

THE COALITIONS
Cooperative development and enabling technology will ultimately produce CIM

EXPERTS in industry, government, and academia have long agreed that computer-based technology offers the greatest potential for advances in manufacturing and that realization of this potential requires increased and improved cooperation among their respective institutions. In most industrial nations, manufacturing-technology efforts for private industry are carried out by loosely knit consortia of government, academia, private industry, trade associations, societies, and labor unions.

There are no comparable institutional arrangements in the US, but there are several coalition-type programs that address the development of systems and enabling technology for CIM.

The most prominent and, probably, most far-reaching of these is the Air Force ICAM (Integrated Computer Aided Manufacturing) program operated under the auspices of the Air Force Materials Laboratory's Manufacturing Technology Div out of Wright Patterson Air Force Base. The program is funded with approximately $100-million through fiscal 1984.

The ICAM program, which got its official start in 1977, is an outcome of an earlier Air Force study on computer-aided manufacture (AFCAM), which, in 1973, produced a conceptual master plan identifying and grouping some of the major functions of aerospace manufacture. Further studies concluded that, in general, although the savings from separate computer-assisted applications are substantial, the major benefits will be realized when individually developed CAM subsystems are integrated according to a plan that combines them into one manageable system.

The ICAM program is a long-term effort that includes the establishment of modular computer subsystems designed to assist and tie together various phases of design, fabrication, and distribution processes and their associated management hierarchy, according to a prioritized plan. To effect this, the program provides seed money for projects to advance the frontier of technology.

More specifically, the objectives of the ICAM program are to establish manufacturing technology that will accomplish the following:

■ Reduce defense-system costs by developing and applying computer-aided-manufacturing technology to the fabrication of defense material.

■ Establish a model for the integrated application of computer technology to all phases of production/manufacturing.

■ Improve the long-term competence, efficiency, and responsiveness of American aerospace and related industries to defense needs.

■ Provide a mechanism for integrated computer-aided-manufacturing technology transfer to and within US industry.

■ Validate and demonstrate the cost-saving benefits and flexibility of ICAM for representative elements of Air Force systems production.

The overall ICAM approach involves top-down planning through the establishment of an "architecture" of manufacturing and bottom-up implementation of individual subsystems, or modules, through specific demonstration projects. To narrow the scope to a practical demonstration level, projects have been limited to the sheetmetal "wedge," or group of subsystems, of manufacturing functions.

Much of the early ICAM work has dealt with planning and development of an architecture of manufacturing—a gener-

ally applicable model of batch manufacturing. Concurrently, it was essential to develop a common communication vehicle, or language, both for developing the architecture of manufacturing and for planning, developing, and implementing the subsystems to be worked on by the various subcontractors. The result has been IDEF, the ICAM DEFinition method for depicting the characteristics of manufacturing. IDEF comprises three modeling methodologies that graphically characterize manufacturing:

■ $IDEF_0$ is used to produce a function model, which is a structured representation of the functions of a manufacturing-system environment and of the information and objects that interrelate those functions.

■ $IDEF_1$ is used to produce an information model, which represents the structure of information needed to support the functions of a manufacturing system or environment.

■ $IDEF_2$ is used to produce a dynamics model, which represents the time-varying behavior of functions, information, and resources of a manufacturing system or environment.

The $IDEF_0$ modeling technique has become the standard means of planning and communicating ICAM project information; it is an extremely efficient, unambiguous method for recording the interrelationship of functions within a manufacturing system. $IDEF_0$ is based on the Structured Analysis & Design Technique (SADT) developed by SofTech. SADT, in turn, is based on cell-modeling techniques developed by Dr Shizuo Hori during his work on the APT Long Range Program at IITRI.

Cell modeling is essentially a means of communication in which each activity, or function, within an organization is characterized by four distinct features: an input, an output, a control, and a mechanism. The functions can be as varied as called for by an organization, including those in the areas of manufacturing, management, and service—anything that contributes to orderly operation.

For example, if NC machining is considered a *function*, the *input* is the raw material or blanks, and the *output* is a properly machined part. The *control* is the NC data that operates on the *mechanism*, the NC machine, to produce the *output*. The NC data, on the other hand, is also the *output* of the tape-preparation *function*, and here the programmer constitutes the *mechanism*. In this way, all the activities of an organization and their interrelationships can be represented with the same four features.

In cell-modeling-diagram convention, the function is represented as a box with the four characteristic features arranged as a series of arrows: inputs enter from the left, controls enter from above, mechanisms enter from below, and outputs leave from the right of the function box. A series of such "constraint diagrams" are linked to show the interrelationship of the various functions composing a subsystem or entire enterprise.

The emphasis changes

More recently, the ICAM-program emphasis has shifted from the planning stage into more application-oriented projects. The ICAM program has established a hierarchy of manufacturing stages of increasing responsibility, complexity, and susceptibility to computer enhancement. These are categorized, respectively, as process, station, cell, center, and factory stages, each having its own software needs and operating modes.

At the cell level, work is under way at Fairchild Republic and Avco Aerostructures to demonstrate stand-alone blanking and bending systems, respectively. Prime contractor for the work is Booz, Allen & Hamilton Inc.

Conceptual design of the blanking cell centers around a Trumpf BMZ CNC router with associated materials-handling systems, all under control of a minicomputer. The bending cell will be required to process one or two identical parts per order and to correctly produce parts on a first-bed trial; automated part handling at the press and robot handling between modules within the cell (straightening, brake, inspection) are envisioned.

Competition for a sheetmetal-center demonstration has begun with the award of preliminary contracts to Boeing Military Airplane Co, General Dynamics Corp and Lockheed-Georgia Co. Each contractor is to complete the following

tasks: establish the scope, planning, and scheduling for an ICAM sheetmetal center; define how the company currently does its sheetmetal manufacturing; and prepare a conceptual design for the new center. Goals for the integrated sheetmetal center are to increase machine utilization by 4%, reduce the number of machines by 44%, reduce floor space 39%, reduce the number of people by 44%, increase production by 25%, and have an ROI of 24%, once the program has settled down.

Although the ICAM program deals primarily with manufacturing, there is an awareness of the need to interface with computer-aided design, and, in fact, there is a program interface with the NASA IPAD (Integrated Program for Aerospace Vehicle Design) program.

A program for electronics

Another government program, somewhat similar to ICAM and just getting started, is ECAM (Electronics Computer Aided Manufacturing). This tri-service program, managed by the US Army Missile Command, is intended to improve productivity and reduce costs associated with the procurement of electronic equipment for military systems.

The program will focus on flexible automation of electronics manufacturing to provide rapid changeover from one product to another. The products covered include panels, covers, and chassis; cables and harnesses; printed wiring boards; integrated circuits; hybrid microelectronics; wire-wound magnetic components; and electronic assemblies.

The initial phase of the program, now under way, will develop a detailed program plan, using IDEF$_0$ methodologies. Later, implementation phases will include technology development, demonstrations, and transfer. Throughout the program, techniques and results developed in related programs—such as ICAM, IPAD, and Manufacturing Technology projects of all three services—will be applied.

Another Air Force program is specifi-

cally directed at developing an "advanced machining system"—a fully integrated flexible manufacturing system (FMS) for the production of batch-manufactured aerospace components. Contacts for Phase I have been awarded to Boeing Commercial Airplane Co ($4,730,000), General Dynamics Corp ($780,000), and Northrop Corp ($694,000). This phase will produce primarily paper: a plan, which will lay out the overall strategy, define the requirements for the system to manufacture an aerospace part family, determine what's within the current state of the art and forecast necessary developments, and provide a preliminary plan for the FMS and its modules.

Phase II will follow up with a two-year effort to build modules—machining cells—based on current technology to be integrated into the final system. Phase III will overlap with Phase II and will take care of those technologies needed but not readily available "off the shelf" now.

According to the Air Force, this project will provide the mechanism by which the state-of-the-art of manufacturing methods and systems technology will be integrated into a machined-parts system that is truly flexible, efficient, and integrated into the automated manufacturing environments of the 1990s. The FMS concept intended goes beyond the manufacturing cell or the semiflexible transfer line because it will use on-line methods of part sequencing for palletized parts, utilizing such schemes as buffers, loops, or networks under sequence control. It will also encompass central tool management to optimize the economical use of expendable tools in the system. The system envisioned will also include planning and control systems to build an automated information bridge between engineering and the FMS.

Although all of these government programs are aimed at defense-related manufacturing needs, industry in general is bound to benefit through technology transfer and through the participation of a large range of subcontractors in the fulfillment of the various contracts. NC was originally developed by MIT under an Air Force contract for defense-related purposes, and look at it now!

Another government program not aimed solely at the defense community is an Automated Manufacturing Research Facility (AMRF) being established at the National Bureau of Standards. It is designed to provide extreme flexibility and to be capable of emulating a wide variety of manufacturing cells typical of a small machine shop. In fact, the facility is being installed in the bureau's instrument shop and will operate side-by-side with a conventional job-shop-

Cell-modeling convention

Controls

Inputs — Function — Outputs

Mechanisms

THE COALITIONS

type-operation. The control architecture will be hierarchical and highly modular.

The facility will be used for research on interface standards and metrology in an automated environment and will use much computer-based technology. Many of the research projects will deal with new and improved sensors to monitor machine performance. Like other NBS facilities, the AMRF will be made available to university and industrial groups for non-proprietary manufacturing-engineering research further afield than the metrology and standards of NBS.

An international coalition

One of the most prominent and successful coalitions on the CIM scene is Computer Aided Manufacturing-International Inc, an international, member-supported, not-for-profit organization of industrial, governmental, and educational enterprises. Its purpose is to serve the public need in fostering collaborative problem-solving activities for using computers in manufacturing. CAM-I has six active project under way at present.

The CAM-I Framework Project represents a concerted effort to define the various modules of integrated, computer-aided manufacturing and their interaction, a quasi-master-plan model. The project is intended to develop a series of specific system architectures for given industries, rather than one major architecture, and it should develop tools and methodologies that will provide help for managers and technologists analyzing the application problems and to assist in implementation.

The other active CAM-I projects are attempting to develop major portions of the CIM framework. The Geometric Modeling Project, for example, will provide a means to computerize the access of geometric data from conceptual design to finished product. Recently, a request for proposal was issued for a geometric-modeling system with the capability of storing both dimensional and tolerance data as an integral part of the database.

The CAM-I Process Planning Project is developing a system to capture the logic required for the generation of process plans using such geometric data; a further development of the CAPP generic process-planning schemes already issued by CAM-I.

Advanced NC project

Projects for enhancing the use of computerized tools for controlling the production process include the Advanced NC and the Sculptured Surface Projects. The Advanced NC Project is intended to develop an NC system that will take full advantage of advances in geometric-modeling concepts and computer-aided process-planning and design.

The software envisioned for this project will access bounded-geometry data, machine technology, and planning information generated at the design stage. The functional specifications for the proposed processor include the requirement for a CLDATA interface to existing post-processors and for flexibility for both graphics and alphanumeric input and output.

When it comes to managing the actual production activities, CAM-I has a Factory Management Project to develop the necessary hierarchical information system. The system is to include advanced data-collection, -acquisition, and -measurement techniques; support of distinct management levels with appropriate information through a distributed database; predictive techniques for decision makers based on timely information; and responsive "closed loops" of communication and control among manufacturing activities and shop-service activities. It is also intended that such a system be capable of interfacing with established manufacturing-planning systems, such as MRP (materials-requirements planning), and process planning.

The significance of most of these programs does not lie with the possible development of new technology. In fact, most of the enabling technology for computer-integrated manufacturing exists; the problem is putting them to proper use. The coalition programs are attempting to tackle the job of building the systems to properly integrate the computer—the tool for today—into the overall manufacturing process.

ICAM programs and glossary

ARCH—Architecture of Manufacturing. A major study to determine the generic components and their interrelationships.

AUTOIDEF—A computerized version of the ICAM Definition (IDEF) method for depicting manufacturing functions.

CBIS—Computer-Based Information System. The information-support requirements, both for software and hardware, for the sheetmetal center.

Cell—Automated control of two or more stations, including materials handling.

Center—Automated control of two or more cells.

CM—Configuration Management. The ICAM Program Office configuration-management and documentation system.

ECAM—Electronics Computer-Aided Manufacturing. A Tri-Service (US Army-managed) program that uses ICAM methodologies for improving manufacturing capability in electronics.

GPP—Generative Process Planning.

GTCC—Group-Technology Classification Coding. A generic group-technology system that is configurable to a company's individual requirements.

GUS—General Utilities System. A generic graphics-interface support system for ICAM analytical software.

ICAD—Integrated Computer-Aided Design. Program of the Air Force Materials Laboratory, which is not yet funded.

ICAM—Integrated Computer-Aided Manufacturing program.

IDEF—ICAM Definition method for depicting the functions, information and dynamics of manufacturing.

IDSS—Integrated Decision-Support System. A system to provide the manufacturing-decision maker with the capability to use operations research tools for solving problems.

IGES—Initial Graphics-Exchange Specification.

IPAD—Integrated Program for Aerospace-Vehicle Design. A NASA program addressing the design process.

IPIMS—Integrated Program-Information-Management System, a management tool of the ICAM Program Office.

IPIPS—IPAD Integrated Planning System.

IPS—Integrated Planning System. The definition of a top-level planning system that will operate in an integrated manner with the MCMM system.

MCDG—Manufacturing-Cost Design Guide. A reference guide to provide manufacturing-cost information by specific operation to the design engineer.

MCDG-C—MCDG-Computerization. A computerized MCDG in which the company using it could insert its own cost data and update that data as new information became available.

MCMM—Manufacturing-Control/Material-Management. An on-line realtime planning and control system for shop-floor operations.

Roadmap—A program-management schematic diagram used by the ICAM office to show project schedules.

SEM—Systems-Engineering Methodologies. A project to identify and develop the tools and methodologies needed to design and build large, complex, integrated systems.

SMC—Sheetmetal Center. There are three major contractors working on the preliminary design of an Integrated Sheetmetal Center, which will be the demonstration of the ICAM systems.

SM FAB—Sheetmetal Fabrication. A project to investigate and develop new equipment for use in sheetmetal blanking and straight-line bending.

Station—Lowest level of automated control of manufacturing process.

TECH MOD—Technology Modernization. A multicontractor panel discussion on the Air Force's Technology-Modernization Program.

Thrust Area—A group of related projects that form a subdivision of the ICAM program; the ten thrust areas are designated by a four-digit number: 1000, ... 9000, 0000.

Wedge—An integrated set of subsystems of manufacturing functions, from broad systems definition to shop-floor implementation; current ICAM work is in the sheetmetal-fabrication wedge.

THE COMPUTER AND YOU
Manufacturing people who understand computers will end up running the plant

HOW MUCH of the computer's impact on manufacturing is real, and how much is media hype? If it is real, how much will it change your plant? How will it affect you?

The loop from design through manufacturing is definitely closing, in the opinion of Dr Patrick Hanratty, the man who laid the foundation for interactive graphics. "There are many systems that can go from design through manufacturing, if we mean by manufacturing the making of an NC tape," he says. "What hasn't happened yet is the full process in which we go from concept to complete factory automation with design engineers and manufacturing engineers taking advantage of a classification system to make use of designs that have already been produced, and with the integration of planning, scheduling, and programming for all manufacturing—including parts made by subcontractors, handling, and assembly."

Hanratty says, however, that he knows "a minimum of 50 companies that are working on total integration of design and manufacturing. It will burst on the scene after the first two or three make their trial runs, in the same way that microprocessors burst on the scene."

It has been the historic experience that doing anything cost more when computers were used. What you got for the extra money was the ability to do things you couldn't do before. Despite the rapid decline in the cost of computer equipment, that is probably still true. Richard E. Morley, director of Factory Automation at Gould Inc, says, "Computers are never cheaper. They generally just supply more functionality per dollar."

That extra functionality may be the source of gains elsewhere that more than offset the extra cost. At Gleason Machine Div, Edwin W. Newton, group vice president—engineering, says that the solids-modeling techniques the firm uses to analyze gear-tooth contact and minimize noise "have probably given Gleason Works more visibility in the customer's eyes than any other Gleason scientific program."

At Giddings & Lewis, Chairman George J. Becker says, the firm first began to apply computers in manufacturing 20 years ago. "Engineering is assured of having prototype parts on schedule, a relatively simple fact that accelerates development programs amazingly," Becker says. Structural modeling, which virtually ensures a satisfactory structure the first time, has greatly reduced modifications on new products.

In G&L's CADCAM system, designs are generated on a Gerber graphics system; then the programmers use the same system to generate the APT input for the IBM mainframe computer. "This interconnected combination of computers provides a good tradeoff between quick response for the design function and the computing power needed to produce numerical-control instructions at the lowest cost," Becker explains.

Many people seem to be finding that, though the major costs are in CAD, the major savings are in CAM. "Numerical control never became anywhere near as effective as it could have been," Hanratty points out, "because of the difficulties of generating NC tapes. Now, 25 years later, CAD provides a way of efficiently generating those tapes."

At Ingersoll Milling Machine, Chairman Edson Gaylord says, the costs of the CADCAM system amounted to $467,000 last year, but the savings generated totaled $1,481,000.

Many people complain about the incompatibility of software. Others find a way to make it portable. According to Hanratty, it is now possible to develop software programs so rapidly that, faced with a choice of three approaches to a problem, "rather than spending a year analyzing to select the best approach, we will go in and program all three of them and then throw away the two that are the least efficient." He concedes that, because most large companies are incapable of admitting mistakes, this is an approach that usually would not be tolerated.

Who'll be in charge?

Where integration of design and manufacturing is a reality, defining functional responsibility can be a major problem. Jack Ulmer, of Boeing Military Airplane Co, says that, with avid enthusiasts, informal coordination can work but managing across functional lines on an informal basis requires an inordinate amount of communication and coordination. Boeing has been using two formal structures, the integrated organization and the team approach.

Although IBM has tried some of the integrated-organization approaches, one executive says the company prefers to maintain the checks and balances provided by having separate organizations for design and for manufacturing.

At General Electric, integration of design engineering and manufacturing engineering seems to be viewed as mandatory. Last spring, the corporate consulting organization was restructured. The engineering group was enlarged to include advanced manufacturing engineering and process engineering and was renamed the Technical Management & Systems consulting group. Remaining operations in what is now called Production Management & Systems will be more concerned with the day-to-day operations of the plants. For its own plants, its suppliers, and the customers for its automation equipment, GE is proposing an organizational structure similar to that shown on page 140.

Conflict almost always seems to decline with experience in CAD/CAM. At Kingsbury Machine Tool, Richard Whipple, manager of product engineering, says, the use of interactive graphics "seems to be improving our relationship with manufacturing."

A greater problem than the conflict between design and manufacturing may arise from the gap between the engineers, who understand manufacturing problems, and the data-processing specialists, who understand the computers. Kingsbury became one of the first to go heavily into CAM but pulled back, according to President Charles J. Hanrahan, when "it became apparent that our goals were ahead of the software capabilities of our computer manufacturer."

The need to know

Computer programming is an arcane task that is little understood by most of the people using computers today. The ability to use a working software program does not require a knowledge of the computer architecture, the microcode in which the computer works, or the assembly language that translates between the microcode and the particular language (be it BASIC, PASCAL, FORTRAN, or whatever) used in writing the program. In fact, if the language and the program are user-friendly, the person at the terminal needs little knowledge that can't be acquired in a few hours.

To create that software, however, so that it will accomplish the desired ends does require much of that specialized knowledge. Too often, therefore, crucial management decisions are made by programmers who understand the computer system and its requirements but don't understand the real problems of the organization that will use the program. And managers who don't understand computer programming are going to be unaware that the decisions have been made until it is too late to do anything about it.

As the computer demonstrates its effectiveness as a manufacturing tool, the ability to understand just how to use it becomes as much a requirement for any manufacturing engineer or manager as the ability to read. The manufacturing manager who understands not only the real problems but also the capabilities of computers will be able to obtain the data-handling systems needed to remain (or to become) competitive.

This understanding of computers is not needed at some future time when the design and manufacturing operations are working on an integrated database. It is needed when systems must be found, developed, modified, and debugged to implement that integration. For the factory that intends to have a future, that time is now. ■

For more information

Associations that can help

American Production & Inventory
  Control Society (APICS)
500 W Annandale Rd
Falls Church, Va 22046-4274
Phone: 703/237-8344

Computer & Automated Systems Assn
  of Society of Mfg Engrs (CASA/SME)
One SME Drive, PO Box 930
Dearborn, Mich 48128
Phone: 313/271-1500

Computer Aided Manufacturing-
  International Inc (CAM-I)
611 Ryan Plaza Dr, Suite 1107
Arlington, Texas 76011
Phone: 817/265-5328

Electronic Industries Assn (EIA)
2001 Eye St, NW
Washington, DC 20006
Phone: 202/457-4900

Institute of Electrical & Electronic
  Engineers (IEEE)
345 E 47 St
New York, NY 10017
Phone: 212/644-7900

National Computer Graphics Assn
  (NCGA)
2033 M St, NW, Suite 330
Washington, DC 20036
Phone: 202/466-5895

Robot Institute of America (RIA)
One SME Drive, PO Box 930
Dearborn, Mich 48128
Phone: 313/271-1500

Robotics International (RI)
One SME Drive, PO Box 930
Dearborn, Mich 48128
Phone: 313/271-1500

World Computer Graphics Assn (WCGA)
2033 M Street, NW, Suite 250
Washington, DC 20036
Phone: 202/775-9556

Other sources

*A Survey of Commercial Turnkey CAD
CAM Systems*, 2nd Edition.
Published by Productivity International
PO Box 8100, 5622 Dyer St
Dallas, Tex 75205
Phone: 214/739-3056

Datapro Research Corp
1805 Underwood Blvd
Delran, NJ 08075
Phone: 609/764-0100
Datapro provides current reference services and information, such as reports and directories, on data processing, data communications, and other related areas.

*Guidebook for Planning Machine-tool
Investment.*
Published by AMERICAN MACHINIST
1221 Avenue of the Americas
New York, NY 10020
Phone: 212/997-3100

ICAM (Air Force Integrated Computer
  Aided Manufacturing) program office
Air Force Materials Laboratory
Wright-Patterson Air Force Base
Ohio 45433

New England Research Application
  Center (NERAC)
Mansfield Professional Park
Storrs, Conn 06268
Phone: 203/486-4533
NERAC is a technical-information center that helps solve technical problems by providing a computer printout of references pertaining to the subject. Companies can subscribe for a fee of $3400 per year.

Special Reports published by AMERICAN MACHINIST (see reprint list in this issue).
"CAM: an international comparison,"
  No. 740, Nov '81
"Computer graphics goes to work,"
  No. 724, Jul '80
"Computers in manufacturing,"
  No. 703, Apr '78
"Implementing CIM,"
  No. 736, Aug '81
"NC diagnostics,"
  No. 744, Apr '82

*Turnkey CAD/CAM Computer Graphics: A Survey and Buyers' Guide for
Manufacturers.*
Published by Daratech
PO Box 410
Cambridge, Mass 02238
Phone: 617/354-2339

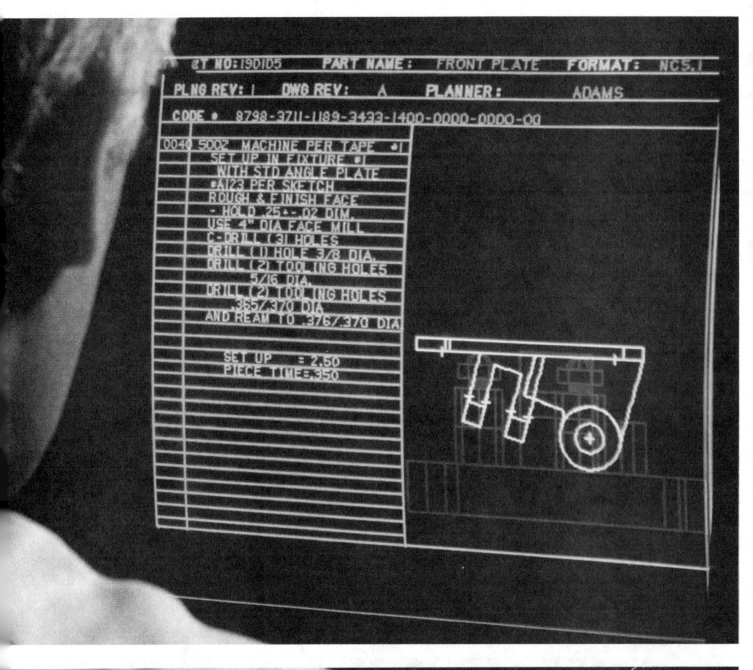

Implementing CIM

Computer-integrated manufacturing can make order out of the manufacturing chaos. Keys to unlocking its potential are group technology, computer-aided process planning, and manufacturing-resource planning

Implementing CIM

MANUFACTURING has been described as an activity resembling organized chaos, and there are those who would consider even that disparaging characterization as charitable. "Just plain chaotic would be closer to the mark," says one manufacturing engineer. Manufacturing management, to him, is simply a matter of solving one crisis after another, using the most expedient solution available at the time.

Such crisis management is hardly conducive to achieving an optimum manufacturing system. For some time now, the computer has been touted as the one tool that will bring order out of this chaos. But, to do so, computers cannot act in isolation, handling a particular machine-control function, such as numerical control, or aiding in the various aspects of resource management, planning, and scheduling.

Organizing discrete-parts manufacturing into an optimum production system requires the integration of many complex and interrelated functions, and the computer is undoubtedly the tool to effect that integration. Computer-integrated manufacturing (CIM), according to some of the best authorities, has already demonstrated greater potential for improving manufacturing capability than has been shown by all other known types of advanced manufacturing technology combined.

Unfortunately, computer-integrated manufacturing is not a shelf item readily available for application, nor can it be achieved through management fiat. It is an ongoing evolution in a changing manufacturing environment attempting to respond to the fickle demands of a changing socioeconomic climate. There are some identifiable features, however, some underlying technologies that are emerging as key elements of CIM: group technology, computer-automated process planning, and MRP (material-requirements planning or manufacturing-resource planning, depending on the level of sophistication).

Group technology attempts to take advantage of similarities in components and processes to bring some of the economies of mass production to today's batch-oriented manufacturing. Automated process planning attempts to select an optimum manufacturing process and prescribe the detailed steps involved, without relying on a planner's individual experience or preferences. MRP, in its most elaborate conceptualization, holds the promise of a closed-loop production- and inventory-control sys-

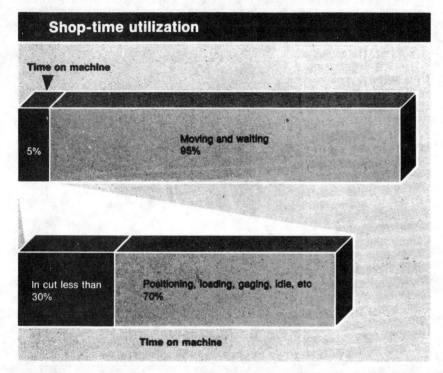

Shop-time utilization

Time on machine

5% / Moving and waiting 95%

In cut less than 30% / Positioning, loading, gaging, idle, etc 70%

Time on machine

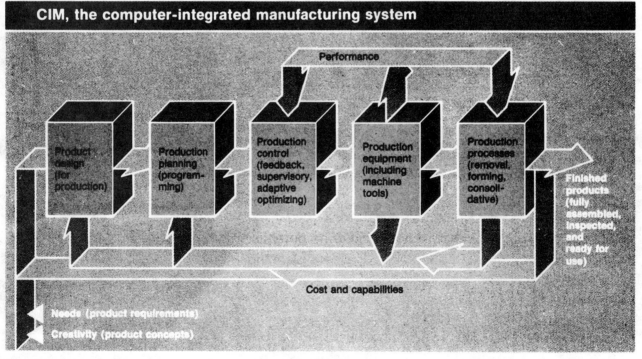

CIM, the computer-integrated manufacturing system

Performance

Product design (for production)

Production planning (programming)

Production control (feedback, supervisory, adaptive optimizing)

Production equipment (including machine tools)

Production processes (removal, forming, consolidative)

Finished products (fully assembled, inspected, and ready for use)

Cost and capabilities

Needs (product requirements)

Creativity (product concepts)

tem responsive to the constantly changing physical and financial resources of a company.

There is a subtle but significant interrelationship, a kind of synergism, between these computer-related technologies that will become evident in the course of this report. But, before we take a closer look at each technology, let's consider the emergence of CIM and the manufacturing problems it is expected to solve.

Nonproductive time is high

In view of the many on-going advances in machine-tool automation and metal-removal technology, we tend to think of modern mechanical manufacturing as a highly productive and efficient process. In fact, studies have indicated that, during the life of the average workpiece in the average batch-type production shop, it spends only 5% of its time on the machine tool. And, of that 5%, less than 30% is spent in actual metal removal. In other words, the part spends only about 1.5% of its time in the shop having useful work performed on it, and, even when it is actually on a machine, that machine is doing useful work on it only about 30% of the time.

No amount of further machine auto-

mation can substantially improve that situation. Some of the nonproductive time *is* built into the machine cycle for part loading and positioning and for tool-changing, but the greatest portion of nonproductive time stems from idle time resulting from an inability to deal with the complex moment-by-moment analysis, planning, and control required to turn production into a continuous process. And that inability stems from the very complex nature of mechanical manufacturing.

A typical manufactured product may consist of literally thousands of individual components—some in multiple quantities, some manufactured in-house, and others purchased—that must come together at many different locations and in very specific order to form the many subassemblies that eventually become the final product. Any hitch along the myriad paths in the production cycle can have disastrous effects.

Material delays, tooling selection, engineering changes, changing government regulations, rapidly changing market conditions, equipment failures, the uncertainties of the labor force—all affect the ability of the production process to produce economically. And, to make matters even worse, all these variables

interact, often rendering even the best-thought-out plans obsolete before they can be realized. It takes only a shortage of an otherwise insignificant component or the sudden breakdown of a relatively simple machine to bring the process to a halt. Hence the need for integrating the manufacturing functions.

CIM defined

M. Eugene Merchant, principal scientist at Cincinnati Milacron and a long-time proponent of the systems approach to manufacturing, has defined integrated manufacturing as a closed-loop feedback system whose prime inputs are product requirements and product concepts and whose prime outputs are finished products. It compromises a combination of software and hardware: product design, production planning, production control, production equipment, and production processes.

The primary objective of such a computer-integrated manufacturing system is to deal effectively with the real-time analysis, planning, and control of the manufacturing process. Group technology, automated process planning, and MRP are some of the fundamental tools for analysis, planning, and control in computer-aided manufacturing.

GT, an organizational principle

Group technology (GT) is a manufacturing philosophy, an organizational principle with far-reaching implications. The underlying concept is relatively simple and not particularly new: identify and bring together related or similar components and processes in order to take advantage of their similarities in design and/or manufacturing.

In other words, form families, or groups, of parts with similar characteristics, from a design and/or manufacturing point of view to reduce the number of unique tasks that must be dealt with. Historically, the principle has frequently been applied quite subjectively by the practiced designer or manufacturing engineer. Today, it is being achieved through the application of well-structured classification and coding schemes.

Frederick Taylor advocated the idea in 1920 to group parts requiring special operations. Also, in the early 1920s, the Jones & Lamson Machine Co built machine tools using principles of product standardization, departmentalization by product rather than by process, and minimal routing paths. Today the approach

would probably be referred to as group technology.

GT affects it all

The grouping principle can have a profound effect on virtually every aspect of the manufacturing cycle. This is particularly so in batch-manufacturing operations, which typically involve large numbers of nonstandard parts with seemingly endless variations. But are those variations truly unique?

Whenever a new part is required, the designer or manufacturing engineer is faced with the question of whether the same or a similar part has been designed or made in the past. Perhaps there is a usable or partially usable drawing already in the files. Most frequently, however, this question is unanswerable because there is no practical way to retrieve any or all designs belonging to a characteristic family.

The experienced designer probably has a batch of "standard" designs stashed away somewhere as a ready reference, but, in most instances, locating a similar design is impractical: there

be tens of thousands of drawings in the files. With inadequate descriptions, they can be difficult to sort out. Part numbers are usually quite arbitrary, and part names are frequently too general to be of any help. What good does it do, then, to know that you need a shaft when there may be thousands of "shafts" in the files?

It's easier to start from scratch?

The upshot of these difficulties is that it usually is easier, and thought to be less burdensome, to start from scratch, reinventing the wheel many times over rather than face the frustrating and time-consuming task of attempting to find a similar design, which is a little like trying to find a needle in a haystack.

As a result, designs proliferate, files grow larger, and the problems of retrieval are compounded. Large amounts of money are wasted because designers cannot make use of experience. Moreover, according to Alexander Houtzeel, president of Organization for Industrial Research (Waltham, Mass), one of the leading developers of group-technology

GT can help manufacturing engineering with process selection, tooling selection (and grouping), machine procurement, facilities planning, materials flow, and materials handling. It can also help to bring new technology to the attention of planners by automatically offering newly acquired equipment or capabilities as processing alternatives.

In production, GT can reduce lead-time, production delays, and setup times and can help with asset utilization, materials handling, communication, product quality, and production supervision.

Production control can use group technology for group scheduling, stock accountability, expediting, and reducing WIP inventory. Buy-or-make decisions, as well as establishment of economic order quantities, can also be handled with the application of GT. Ultimately, group technology can affect customer support by providing better handling of dealer inventory and shorter deliveries.

Such multifaceted benefits almost seem to be too good to be true, but experience seems to bear out the claims. In a report on group technology prepared by the Machinability Data Center (a DOD Information Analysis Center) operated by Metcut Research Associates Inc (Cincinnati), representative benefits are listed:

- 52% reduction in part design
- 10% reduction in the number of drawings through standardization
- 30% reduction in new shop drawings
- 60% reduction in industrial engineering time
- 20% reduction in production floor space required
- 40% reduction in raw-material stocks
- 69% reduction in setup time
- 70% reduction in production time
- 62% reduction in work-in-process inventory
- 82% reduction in overdue orders.

Quite an impressive array of benefits. And yet there is still another. Group technology can help to bridge the CAD/CAM functions and provide a key element in the computer-integrated manufacturing system.

It is important to recognize that the application of group technology is not restricted only to the physical. Abstractions, such as information, can also be characterized through GT. In fact, manufacturing deals primarily with information and its transformation into appropriate instructions: for example, part descriptions—such as shapes, size, and features—and instructions on their manufacture incorporated in a process plan.

The physical things to be dealt with are the part itself, the tools, and the

systems, new designs typically incur an additional $2000-$12,000 in manufacturing-preparation costs.

The scene is quite similar in manufacturing, which must deal with an almost random sequence of different parts. Efficient process planning under these circumstances is difficult. Machine tools have to be set up for every new batch, and tooling must be selected and delivered. Long and frequent setup times reduce machine utilization, and the overall effect is constant queues of work-in-process; parts that may require only a few minutes of actual machine time can spend weeks on the shop floor.

WIP is costly

Such work-in-process (WIP) inventory is costly. To begin with, it represents a significant investment in the cost of materials and work already performed

that cannot be recovered until the parts get to the shipping dock. Cash flow is a direct result of inventory turnover, and, therefore, the shorter the inventory cycle, the better the cash flow; and capital is really working to produce profits. The carrying costs for WIP inventory can be enormous, and any reduction in waiting time can lead to immediate and significant savings.

By helping to identify select similarities, GT, can have considerable influence on most of the functional areas in a manufacturing organization: product engineering, manufacturing engineering, production, production control, and procurement.

In product engineering, GT can help reduce part proliferation, encourage design standardization, provide manufacturing feedback, and help with cost estimating.

machines, but even these physical things are processed as information representative of the actual physical object.

The significance of this lies in the fact that group technology is concerned with the processing and transfer of information about parts and manufacturing processes and therefore is particularly compatible with CIM, which is driven by the transmission of relevant information. No wonder, then, that that GT is considered an organizational principle underlying the development of CIM.

What's the holdup?

If group technology can do all this, then why is it not more universally implemented? Two somewhat outdated and false premises have hindered its implementation. First, historically, group technology has been associated with a cellular concept of manufacturing in which machines used in the production of similar parts families are grouped together.

Although such cellular arrangement results in the most efficient material flow within the cell, the cost and disruption involved in the physical rearrangement of an existing facility is frequently difficult to justify. In some instances, such a rearrangement may be precluded by the physical limitations of the facility.

Also, a particular cellular arrangement is dictated by the product mix and quantities to be produced by a facility. Unless those factors remain constant, it is conceivable that a plant could be constantly subjected to rearrangements to satisfy rather transitory conditions. That is particularly true in today's job-shop-like manufacturing environment. No

serious manager could stand for such disruptions. In fact, it is difficult enough to convince management that any working production infrastructure should be changed. Production managers like to go with what they know is working.

No need for cells

But most practitioners now consider it a disservice to the concept of group technology to insist that physical rearrangement of equipment is an essential element. In fact, most of the benefits of GT can be realized through administrative means without such physical rearrangement. This has been amply demonstrated. For example, a trial implementation of cellular flow without actual rearrangement of machines at the Naval Avionics Center (Indianapolis) produced definite improvements in the percentage of schedules met, cost-effectiveness, status reporting, and communications (AM—Feb'79,p86).

The trial produced several results. The percent of schedules met rose from 37% to 54%. A related comparison showed that the average deviation between actual completion date and scheduled due date dropped from 6.5 to 1.1 days. The average number of machine-shop-cycle days dropped from 18.1 to 12.5 days. And the estimated cycles met increased from 32% to 54%, and the average deviation from estimated cycles decreased from 13.5 to 1.9 days. Cost-effectiveness (the ratio of estimated cost to actual cost) improved by 6.5%.

Too much up-front work?

The other barrier to the implementation of group technology is the amount of

"up-front" work needed to establish the families or groups. Conventional thought has it that, before any of the benefits of group technology can be realized, every single part in a company's inventory must be subjected to rigorous classification-and-coding routines for establishing appropriate families. If a company has, say, 200,000 drawings, that would probably take more time and effort than its management will allow in a reasonable period.

But the fact of the matter is that most companies do not manufacture a totally random array of unique parts. Every manufacturing organization, whether because of the product line it produces or because of the capabilities it possesses, deals with a surprisingly ordered group of parts. There really isn't that much variety, and an intelligent sampling approach can provide some significant data to help establish useful groupings. In fact, Houtzeel claims that, regardless of the number of parts in a company's drawing inventory, a random sampling of a maximum of 5000 parts is sufficient to establish the full range of variations that need to be considered for classification and coding of the entire population of parts.

The most common approach recommended, therefore, is to start classification and coding with only those parts

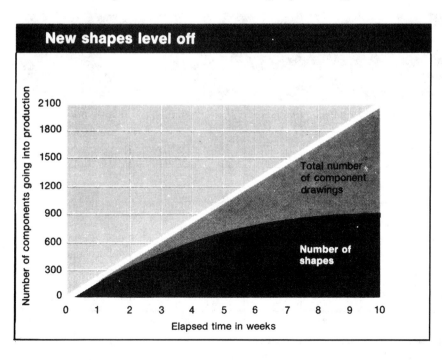

New shapes level off

Total number of component drawings

Number of shapes

Number of components going into production

Elapsed time in weeks

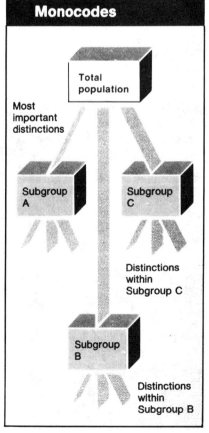

Monocodes

Total population

Most important distinctions

Subgroup A

Subgroup C

Distinctions within Subgroup C

Subgroup B

Distinctions within Subgroup B

currently being released to the shop. The nature of most manufacturing is such that the number of new component shapes released begins to level out within a short time after a classification and coding system is implemented, and, therefore, an increasingly high percentage of "new" part drawings can be retrieved easily from the existing files. The same leveling-off effect has been observed for process plans issued to the shop.

About classification and coding

A key element of any group-technology approach is the implementation of some kind of classification-and-coding scheme: parts must be classified according to appropriate characteristics, and then a meaningful code must be assigned to reflect those characteristics. It then becomes a relatively simple matter to use the code to retrieve or group parts according to similar characteristics. The problem is choosing an appropriate set of characteristics and a good scheme so that the needs of all the users of the system are served.

Classification schemes are nothing new, and they abound. Some of the earliest were devised by natural scientists, such as the taxonomy of botany. The country's mail-addressing scheme is perhaps the most common example of a classification-and-coding system and serves to illustrate the principle.

A specific geographic location is classified into progressive subdivisions: country, state, county, city, street, number. The ZIP code, in turn, represents a meaningful code that describes these classifi-

cations. Each digit of the ZIP code identifies a geographic region: digits further to the right indicate progressively smaller regions. A particular feature of the ZIP code is that codes close to one another numerically are also close to each other geographically. Sorting by ZIP code is therefore intended to make the handling and distribution of mail easier.

Classification-and-coding systems intended specifically for design and manufacturing are a relatively recent development. Much of the original work in group technology was started in the Soviet Union during World War II when machines were moved east to avoid capture by the Germans; they were grouped and coded. One of the first major works on group technology was published by a Russian, Mitrinov, in 1959. Early work on group technology was also carried out by E.G. Brisch in England, and work at the Technical Univ at Aachen under professor H. Opitz produced the so-called Opitz code.

The Brisch system is now available through Brisch, Birn & Partners Inc (Fort Lauderdale, Fla). An adaptation of the Brisch system, CODE, is marketed by Manufacturing Data Systems (Ann Arbor, Mich). By far the most popular and widely used commercially available coding system is MICLASS, originally developed by TNO (Holland) and now marketed as part of the group-technology services offered by Organization for Industrial Research (Waltham, Mass). Brigham Young Univ (Provo, Utah) has also developed a generic approach to classification and coding with its DCLASS system.

The Air Force ICAM (Integrated Computer Aided Manufacturing) program has been committed to the principles of group technology from its inception, and it has a project intended to establish a sound foundation for a generic group-technology characterization code (GTCC). The hope is that such a GTCC scheme may be the "glue" that binds all of design and manufacturing; GTCC is intended to cover the GT spectrum from part coding to design retrieval, to process-plan development, to forming part families. The present objective is to establish a working module of the scheme for aerospace sheetmetal parts and then to implement this module in a working environment.

There is no universal classification-and-coding system that can be directly applied to group technology; most GT approaches have been implemented with systems developed for the specific needs of the organization, or existing classification-and-coding systems have been adapted for the purpose. In fact, most commercially available schemes provide means for tailoring them to the specific needs and conditions of the user.

A particularly salient discussion by Prof Inyong Ham (Pennsylvania State Univ) puts this fact into perspective: "Classification and coding for group-technology applications is a very complex problem, and, although many systems have been developed throughout the world and countless efforts made to improve them, there is as yet no universally acclaimed system. Since each company has its own specific needs and considerations, it is necessary to search

Polycode structure

Digit	Class of feature	Possible values of digits							
		1	2	3	4	5	6	7	8
1	Ext shape	Shape₁	Shape₂	Shape₃	—	—	—	—	—
2	Int shape	None	Shape₁	—	—	—	—	—	—
3	≠ holes	0	1—2	3—5	5—8				
4	Type holes	axial	Cross	Axial and cross					
5	Flats	Ext	Int	Both					
6	Gear teeth	Spur	Helical						
7	Splines								

for a suitable system to meet the objectives and requirements of the company.

"Although there are many varieties of systems, basic types of classification-and-coding systems can be put into several categories, such as functional or descriptive, qualitative or quantitative criteria, design-oriented or production-oriented, hierarchic or chain-type (discrete) structure, monocodes vs polycodes, separate codes vs composite codes, long codes vs short codes, etc. However, in most cases, each system uses combinations of these features in one way or another, thus making it difficult to compare the system strictly from these points of view.

"Whether it is a so-called universal system or a tailor-made system, a system should be adapted and modified to meet the specific needs and requirements of the company. To select a suitable system, it is therefore necessary to make a comparative evaluation of the currently available system in view of the needs for specific applications in a company, especially from the standpoint of group technology.

"There are many useful applications of classification-and-coding systems, but basically they are used for two major purposes: (1) for design retrieval and rationalization and (2) for grouping of part families and group production. For successful group-technology applications, both aspects are equally important. A company, however, may emphasize one aspect more than another, and, in many cases, system selection is based on a biased view of particular emphasis on one aspect.

"It should also be noted that the currently available systems also vary in their strengths and weaknesses relative to the so-called 'design-oriented' system and the 'production-oriented' system, despite all claims that both aspects are well accommodated. Therefore, a user should look carefully into a system for its characterization and adaptability in view of the various company requirements."

Ham lists several factors that should be considered in selecting a suitable classification-and-coding system:

■ Objective. What is the major objective of the classification system? Why is a system needed? Is it primarily for design retrieval or part-family manufacturing or both?

■ Scope and application. What departments are involved in using the system? What are the specific needs and information to be coded? How wide is the range of products and how complex are the parts, shapes, process operations, tooling, etc?

■ Costs and time. How much expense will be involved in installation, training,

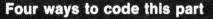

Four ways to code this part

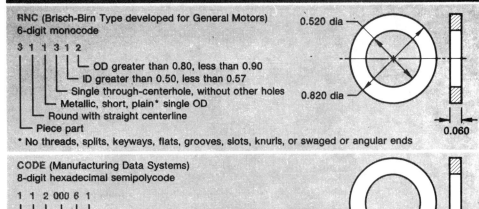

RNC (Brisch-Birn Type developed for General Motors)
6-digit monocode

3 1 1 3 1 2
— OD greater than 0.80, less than 0.90
— ID greater than 0.50, less than 0.57
— Single through-centerhole, without other holes
— Metallic, short, plain* single OD
— Round with straight centerline
— Piece part

0.520 dia
0.820 dia
0.060

* No threads, splits, keyways, flats, grooves, slots, knurls, or swaged or angular ends

CODE (Manufacturing Data Systems)
8-digit hexadecimal semipolycode

1 1 2 000 6 1
— Length greater than 0, less than 1.00
— OD greater than 0.72, less than 1.20
— No flats, slots, protrusions, grooves, or holes except centerhole
— Single-dia through centerhole without threads
— Single OD
— Round part concentric about straight centerline, no gear teeth or splines

MICLASS (TNO)
12-digit decimal semipolycode

1120 2211 21 33
— Material
— Tolerances
— Dimensions
— Main shape and shape elements

Round part with single OD and ID without faces, threads, slots, grooves, splines, or additional holes. OD and length are within certain size ranges

OPITZ (Dr H Opitz, Aachen, West Germany)
9-digit decimal semipolycode version

0 0 1 1 0 1 6 1 0
— Tolerance class
— Initial material form
— Material type and heat treat
— OD greater than 0.80, less than 2.00
— No auxiliary holes or gear teeth
— Planar machining of faces but no slots or grooves
— Single ID or stepped to one end without threads
— Single OD without threads
— Round part with L/D ratio less than ½ and with straight centerline

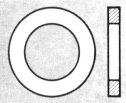

Information content	PNC	CODE	MICLASS	OPITZ
End shape	X		X	X
Outside shape	X	X	X	X
Inside shape	X	X	X	X
Protrusions		X	X	X
Additional holes	X	X	X	X
Threads	X	X		X
Grooves or slots	X	X	X	X
Flats	X	X	X	
Gear teeth or splines	X	X	X	X
Splits, keyways, knurls, or swages	X			
OD range	X	X	X	X
ID range	X			
Length range	X	X	X	X
Size ratios	X	X	X	X
Tolerance			X	X
Heat treat			X	X
Material form				X
Material type			X	X
Finish			X	

324 parts using 22 machine tools before GT

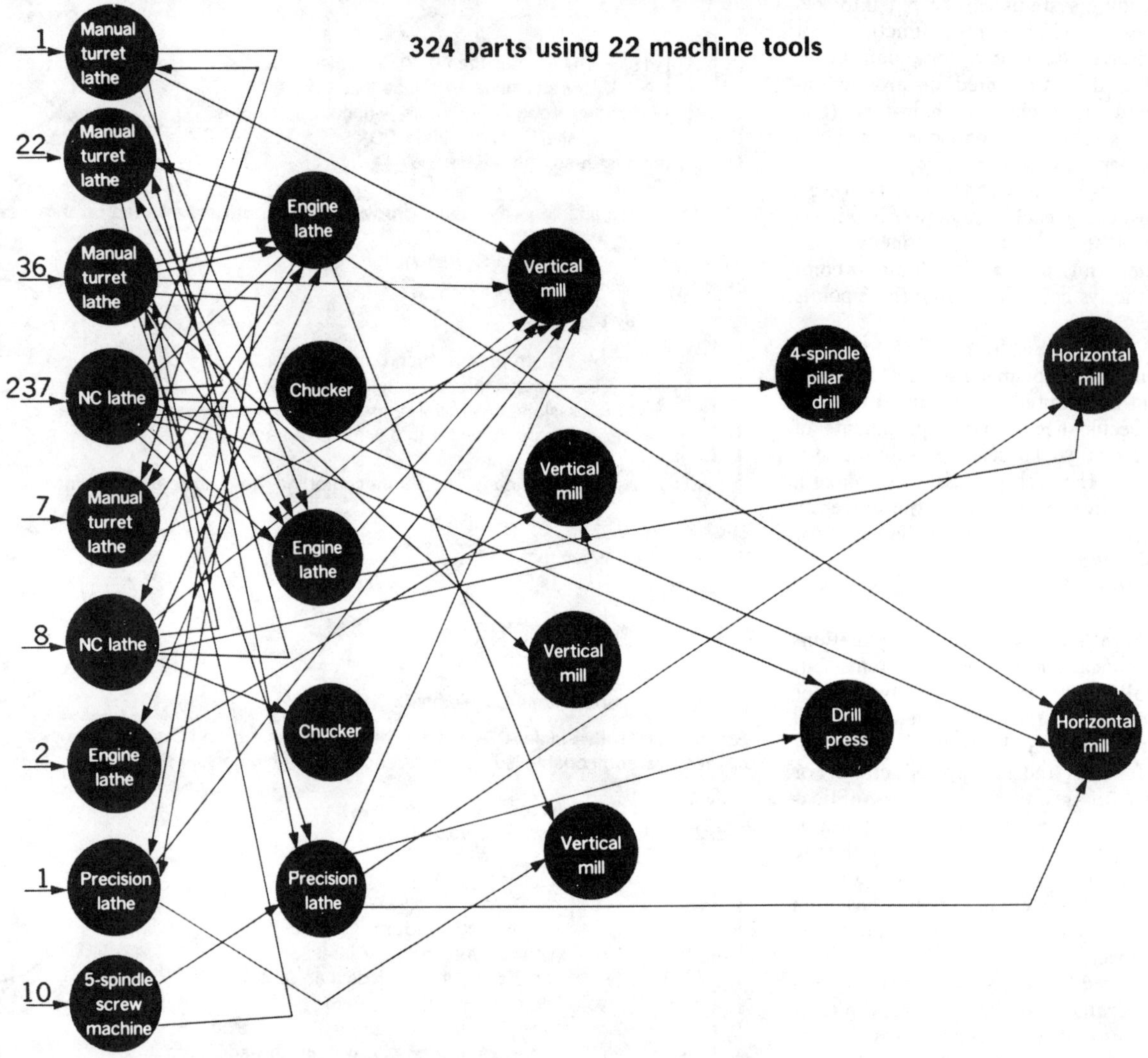

324 parts using 22 machine tools

1 — Manual turret lathe

22 — Manual turret lathe

36 — Manual turret lathe

237 — NC lathe

7 — Manual turret lathe

8 — NC lathe

2 — Engine lathe

1 — Precision lathe

10 — 5-spindle screw machine

Engine lathe · Chucker · Engine lathe · Chucker · Precision lathe

Vertical mill · Vertical mill · Vertical mill · Vertical mill

4-spindle pillar drill · Drill press

Horizontal mill · Horizontal mill

and system maintenance? What are the cost estimate for consultant fees, in-house design, training, etc? How long will it take to install and train the staff needed? How long will it take to realize the effects of the system in all areas of application, from design to production?

■ Adaptability to other systems. Is the system easily adaptable to the computer system and database being used in the company? Can the system be easily integrated with other systems, such as process planning, NC programming, management information systems, etc?

■ Management problems. Are all involved management personnel informed and supportive about installation of the system? Is there any union problem? Can good cooperation among the involved departments be obtained?

The various classification-and-coding systems differ primarily in the way symbols are assigned to the classes of information selected, and the structure of the code can determine how well a large database of information can be analyzed: how well the classification-and-coding system can be accessed and manipulated by computers, which, after all, is a primary virtue of an effective group-technology program.

Coding systems can be constructed with only numerical symbols, only alphabetical symbols, or a combination of numbers and letters. According to Houtzeel, numerical codes have certain advantages over alphabetical codes because of a lower risk of reading errors. On the other hand, alphabetical codes can have 26 different values per position

while the decimal system only has ten possible values. Current codes are mostly numerical, although some alphanumerical systems do exist.

Although the actual construction of a coding system can be quite arbitrary, there are basically three types of code construction used for GT applications: monocodes, also referred to as hierarchical codes or tree structures; polycodes, also referred to as attribute codes; and hybrids that combine monocode and polycode structures.

Monocode: interdependent digits

The monocode concept is probably the oldest classification scheme, having its origin with Swedish botanist Linnaeus, who used it for biological classification. A hierarchical code is set up as a tree

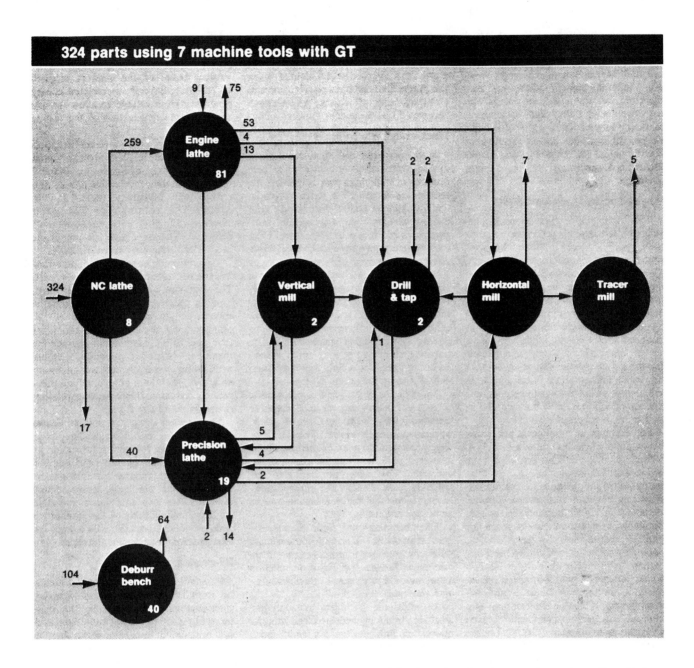

structure in which each element, or digit, amplifies the information given in the previous digit. Just as a family tree traces the lineage of an existing structure, a true monocode traces the order of a group of attributes.

The single most important feature of a monocode is that the meaning of every digit is dependent on the digits prior to it; the leaf refers to its twig, which refers to its branch, and eventually back to the trunk of the tree. A tree structure works well for describing an existing ordered structure but is more difficult to use in classifying things that have no apparent order.

A few related distinctions that can be used to divide the entire population of items into a number of subgroups must be established. For example, a work-

piece-classification tree might branch into rotationl or nonrotational designations. The rotational group could, in turn, branch into such distinctions as centric, eccentric, or gear-like; the nonrotational, into columnar, sheet form, box-like solid.

Although a hierarchical code is said to be difficult to construct, it can provide a very deep analysis of the items classified and can pack an enormous amount of information into a coding system. The resulting code is very compact and yet contains a wealth of information in a rather limited number of digits.

Once the hierarchical structure has been established, the actual coding of an item in a monocode is fairly simple: you start at the main trunk of the tree structure and, by answering questions about

that item, work your way from limb to branch and finally to a twig. As you make each choice, you record your decision, thus building up the code number.

However, determining the significance of any particular digit of a monocode is more difficult once it has been established for a particular item, because all preceding digits must be decoded before any meaning can be attached to the digit in question. It's a little like a telephone number: any individual digit is meaningless out of the context of the rest of the digits. This interdependence of digits makes it more difficult to use monocodes for conventional computer analysis and database manipulation.

Monocode systems have been in use in design departments for drawing retrieval for some time. A designer can readily

Implementing CIM

traverse the hierarchical tree and find the family of parts of interest. The groupings typically are primarily shape-oriented. Manufacturing engineers, however, have different requirements and, therefore, require a different hierarchical structure, one that deals with manufacturing requirements rather than with shape. Monocode coding structures equally useful for the design and manufacturing departments are very difficult to design.

Polycodes: independent digits

The other major type of code construction is based on a feature, or polycode, system. In such a system, the interpretation of each character in a given digit position is independent of any other digit: each digit in the code represents information in its own right and does not directly qualify the information provided by the other digits. Each feature is assigned a specific digit location, and a set of questions is asked about each feature to determine the value of that particular feature digit. If the questions are always asked in the same order and the associated feature value recorded in that order, a polycode results.

For example, in a polycode, the possible values of each digit may be 1, 2, 3, 4, 5, 6, 7, 8, 9, or 0. The first digit may define external shape, and a 1 in that location could designate cylindrical shape; a 2 could designate a conical shape; while a 3 might indicate a square. Similarly, designations can be given for internal shapes, holes, types of holes, flats, gear teeth, splines, etc. In the illustration on p70, a code number 324130 would indicate a part with an external shape 3, an internal shape 1, and 5-8 axial holes. It has both external and internal flats and no gear teeth. A part with the code number 124130, on the other hand, would differ only in the fact that the external shape is shape 1 rather than shape 3; all other attributes of the part are the same.

One advantage of a polycode over a monocode is that parts with a specific characteristic can be readily identified. This readily identifiable difference between two code numbers makes the polycode structure particularly attractive to the manufacturing engineer for comparing parts in terms of their processing needs. Because a polycode represents a class of items as a string of features, it is also particulary suitable for computer analysis.

The problem with polycodes is that they tend to be long. In order to describe every conceivable feature in the population in detail, all the associated digit locations must be reserved even though many of the features may not apply to

every part. As a result, polycodes can easily run into dozens of digits. Generally speaking, monocodes require fewer digits than polycodes. Of course when computers are used in the generation and manipulation of codes, the length becomes a less important factor.

Most codes are hybrids

Most industrial coding systems use a hybrid construction to combine the best features of moncodes and polycodes. To reduce the length of a strict polycode, the first digit of such a system may split the population into appropriate subgroups, as in a monocode structure. Then each subgroup can have its own polycode structure. This type of semipolycode, as it is sometimes referred to, is really a collection of shorter polycodes, and, within each one of these shorter polycodes the digits are independent of each other. Such an arrangement makes the coding system appropriate for design retrieval while also serving many manufacturing needs for which the ready location of similar attributes is important.

An example of a hybrid semipolycode is MICLASS, which uses up to 30 digits to deal with GT-related features of parts, equipment, and processes. The first four digits describe the main shape, the shape elements, and the position of the shape elements. The next four digits of the MICLASS code classify the main dimensions, the ratio of the dimensions, and an auxiliary dimension.

The ninth and tenth digits classify the part tolerances, including dimensional tolerance, surface roughness, and form tolerance. The last two digits of the main code indicate the part's machinability and materials.

An additional 18 digits are available as a supplmentary code to cover company-related information for each part, such as common lot size, piece time, major machining operations, or special information like vendor codes or existing in-house manufacturing data.

The first 12 digits are, in a way, a universal-type code applicable to most companies. According to OIR, it is identical for 99% of its customers. Digits 13 to 18 tend to apply universally to 50% of its customers while only 10% of its customers use the same arangement for digits 18 through 30; that's where the code is really customized.

Actual coding with the MICLASS system is accomplished by means of an interactive, "conversational" computer program, in which the computer interrogates the user with a series of questions in simple English. The number of questions asked varies according to the complexity of the part being coded. For a simple part, a minimum of seven ques-

tions are involved; 10-20 are required for the average complexity. The computer program automatically generates a code number based on the answers supplied by the user. Several interrelated coding programs are available to allow flexible and efficient organization of the coding task.

EG&G Sealol's Engineered Products Div (Providence, RI) has effectively used group-technology principles to simplify routing, improve production times, and reduce WIP inventory (AM—Jan'80, p130). The routing for 324 parts involved 22 different machine tools before GT. The same parts are now made in a GT cell with only seven machines.

Two computer runs are made to establish the MICLASS code for any given part. The first run establishes the universal, 12-digit element. The 12-digit code is entered on the part print used by the planner doing the coding and this print then goes to an independent planner for checking. Mistakes typically involve overlooking some element of geometry on a part, such as a groove, or misinterpreting directional information relating to the origin of a tool path.

The second computer run at Sealol establishes the remaining auxiliary-code digits by asking for such information as part name, annual quantity and number of lots per year, general operations to be performed on the part, machine-tool identification, and setup and run-time standards. A printout of the interactive code-generating session is then kept for final checking and future reference.

GT-related programs

But the MICLASS code is only a means for establishing various group-technology-related programs. In fact, OIR does not really market the MICLASS classification-and-coding program other than in connection with its group-technology-related analysis and retrieval programs:

- MICHECK, which checks the data files for unusual values and identifies abnormal circumstances, such as huge lot sizes or long setup times.
- MIDVL, which checks the data files for duplicate code numbers to identify different family structures.
- MIMIX, which shows the product mix by graphing the frequencies with which a specific part attribute or any specific machine-tool routing occurs in the data file. Additionally, it calculates the percentage of total population or loading.
- MICLUS, which analyzes production flow and simplifies routing by using a similarity-coefficient calculation. It can assign machine tools to various groups (cells) according to their frequency and sequence of use in part production.

■ MIROM retrieval routines, which develop matrixes of the code numbers of those parts produced by a specified machine-tool code.

■ MIFAMT, which identifies the additional machine-tool requirements and secondary operations needed to produce the parts assigned to a work cell.

■ MIMSP, which divides the analysis data file into one or more files containing all the parts having code numbers that fit the series of search matrixes and a residual file containing all the parts not selected by these matrixes.

■ MILOAD, which calculates for each machine-tool code the manufacturing loads as determined by the production requirements of the parts. This information is then compared with available machine-tool capacities.

■ MICELD, which produces a matrix of several MILOAD outputs showing the possible loading of the same machine tool in several work cells.

■ MIFLOW, which prints work-piece routing in readable form and is often used as a list program.

■ MICHAM, which is used to effect high-volume changes or deletions to machine-tool codes in the data file.

■ MICOST, which calculates manufacturing costs of workpieces.

■ MISEP, a conversational retrieval program that searches for drawings based on an entered code number, drawing number, or name.

■ MIAPP, a conversational program that searches for process plans based on an entered code number or drawing number.

■ MIGRAPHICS, which permits design- and manufacturing-information retrieval on a computer-graphics terminal.

■ MIPLAN, which combines search and retrieval with comprehensive editing and formatting routines for producing process plans interactively. Text and illustrations can be combined.

CAPP, at the crossroads of information

According to the *Tool & Manufacturing Engineers Handbook*, process planning is the systematic determination of the methods by which a product is to be manufactured, economically and competitively. It is an intermediate stage between designing and manufacturing the product. But how systematic is process planning really? And how well does it bridge design and manufacturing?

Most manufacturing engineers would agree that, if ten different planners were asked to develop a process plan for the same part, they would probably come up with ten different plans. Obviously, all these plans cannot reflect the most efficient manufacturing methods, and, in fact, there is no guarantee that any one of them will constitute the optimum method for manufacturing the part.

What may be even more disturbing is that a process plan developed for a part during a current manufacturing program may be quite different from the plan developed for the same or similar part during a previous manufacturing program and it may never be used again for the same or similar part. That represents a lot of wasted effort and produces a great many inconsistencies in routing, tooling, labor requirements, costing, and possibily even purchase requirements.

Plans must change

Of course, process plans should not necessarily remain static. As lot sizes change and new technology, equipment, and processes become available, the most effective way to manufacture a particular part also changes, and those changes should be reflected in current process plans released to the shop.

Unfortunately, however, the lack of uniformity of manually prepared process

Same part, different planners

| | Process planner | | | |
	One	Two	Three	Four
	Machine first face	Hole drilled in two steps: a. 20 mm dia b. 38 mm dia	Outside surface— 50 mm dia— turned	Hole drilled to finish in two steps: a. 30 mm dia b. 40 mm dia
	Hole finished in three steps: a. Drill 10 mm b. Drill 38 mm c. Bore 40 mm	Machine first face	Hole drilled to finish in one step with drill of 40 mm dia	Outside surface— 50 mm dia— turned
	Outside surface— 50 mm dia— turned	Cutoff	Machine first face	Machine first face
	Cutoff	Machine second face	Cutoff	Cutoff
	Machine second face	Outside surface— 50 mm dia— turned	Machine second face	Machine second face
		Hole finished to 40 mm dia by boring		

(Part drawing: 40φ ±0.05; 40φ ±0.1; 50φ ±0.05)

plans does not usually reflect the application of progressive manufacturing technology. On the contrary, process plans frequently reflect only stubborn commitment to the personal experience, preference, or even prejudice of the particular planner or, perhaps, a parochial view screened from alternative methods that may actually be readily available under the same roof. Computer-aided process planning (CAPP) attempts to rationalize the process.

Gideon Halevi, director of the CAM/CAD R&D Center, IMI (Tel Aviv, Israel), illustrates some of these factors in his provocative book *The Computer in Manufacturing Processes*: "Designing an economic process calls for thousands of computations. One has to examine all possible combinations of operations, machine tools, and so on. It is a huge job, almost impossible to perform without the aid of a computer. . . . It is highly dependent on individual skill, human memory, reference manuals, and, above all, experience."

Halevi describes a study supporting these contentions. Drawings of parts having different complexities were given to four process planners of different backgrounds, and they were asked to define the process. "It was amazing to note that the number of different processes defined per part coincided with the number of process planners participating," he says. In the case of the simplest part, four process planners recommended these four sets of operations to produce a 40-mm-dia hole:

■ Drill 10 mm, drill 38 mm, and bore to 40 mm
■ Drill 20 mm, drill 38 mm, and bore to 40 mm
■ Drill 40 mm
■ Drill 30 mm and drill to 40 mm.

Of course, this represents an oversimplification, and Halevi prejudices the results because no tolerances are stated. But, he points out, a simple glance at the results reveals the experience of each planner. The first was previously a foreman of a precision-parts-manufacturing department; the second was an instructor in a technical school; the third did machining of heavy-equipment parts; and the fourth worked in a job shop. The part drawing was given to the same process planners a few months later, and the specified process differed somewhat from the previous plan. "Mood should probably be added to the list of controlling parameters," says Halevi.

In another study, Halevi found that a company used 377 different process plans and 57 different types of machines to manufacture 425 relatively simple gears. Surely the application of group technology would result in the consolidation of routings and fewer, more-standard process plans in such an environment. Earlier in this report, we indicated how Sealol achieved an almost 40% reduction in the number of routings through group technology.

A key factor in CAD/CAM

Such inconsistencies in process plans and the unnecessary proliferation of different routings is not conducive to the implementation of CIM. As Joe Tulkoff, director of manufacturing technology at Lockheed-Georgia, puts it, the process-planning function is located at the crossroads of information between engineering design and the shop floor. "Process planning derives its input from the engineering side of the house as well as from lots of data about the factory itself," he says. "It is complemented by tool design and NC-programming functions."

Process planning, therefore, is a key factor in effecting the CAD/CAM link, and, according to Tulkoff, the wave of the future in process planning is the development and application of interactive computer-aided planning systems.

Generally speaking, process planning involves selection, calculation, and documentation. Processes, machines, tools, operations, and sequences must be selected. Calculations must be made in connection with such factors as costs, standards, feeds and speeds, stock removal, tolerances, and dimensions. Finally, documentation in the form of setup instructions, work instructions, illustrated process sheets, and routings must be prepared. Estimates suggest that planners typically spend 30% of their time writing plans (by hand), the rest explaining and proving them.

In the process, a planner must manage and retrieve reams of data and documents, such as old process plans, established standards, facilities data, specific machine specifications, tooling inventory, and stock availability. The computer is an ideal tool to help with all these tasks because it is particularly suited to rapid accurate calculation and to information management.

There is another advantage to using computers. All the activities of process planning are interrelated—one decision affects another—and optimum planning is an iterative function. The computer is an ideal traffic manager and has the capability to make the many kinds of comparisons necessary to achieving the optimum plan.

What are the benefits?

According to Tulkoff, the implementation of Lockheed's GENPLAN computer-aided process-planning system produced many benefits. Operations that took several hours to complete are typically performed now in 15-20 min; the number of steps required in routing the planning paperwork through the system has been reduced by 75%. And, reports Tulkoff, the capability to generate new and revised plans can support increased volumes of more than 300% over the former manual system.

Those are not isolated benefits. In a survey of 22 companies, the Illinois Institute of Technology Research Institute (IITRI) reports estimated cost savings of 58% in process planning, 10% in direct labor, 4% in material, 10% in scrap and rework, 12% in tooling, and 6% in WIP as a result of computer-aided process planning. The survey also indicated that CAPP benefited many other, less quantifiable areas, such as production lead-time, process-planning lead-time, machine utilization, cost-estimating procedures, make-or-buy decisions, production scheduling, capacity planning, plant layout, and quality.

No wonder that a recent Delphi study on manufacturing, conducted by the Society of Manufacturing Engineers

Estimated savings from CAPP

Cost area	Saving (%)
Process planning	58%
Direct labor	10%
Material	4%
Scrap and rework	10%
Tooling	12%
Work in process	6%

CAPP impact in less quantifiable areas

−2 : Significant adverse impact
−1 : Somewhat adverse impact
0 : No impact
+1 : Somewhat beneficial impact
+2 : Significant beneficial impact

Area	Impact
Production lead-time	1.47
Process-planning lead-time	1.89
Machine utilization	1.41
Product quality	0.79
Direct-labor utilization	1.00
Uniformity of process plans	1.89
Cost-estimating procedures	1.79
Make/buy decisions	1.33
Product standardization	1.33
Critical labor skills	0.78
Material standardization	0.89
Producibility of parts	1.11
Plant layout	0.84
Materials handling	1.06
Production scheduling	1.37
Capacity planning	1.37

Implementing CIM

(SME) and the Univ of Michigan predicts, that, in the US, the UK, and Japan, 50% of process plans used to make parts or assemblies will be computer-produced by 1990!

Several specific benefits can be expected in the planning department with implementation of computer-aided process planning:

- Reduced clerical effort in preparation of instructions.
- Fewer calculation errors due to human error.
- Fewer oversights in logic or instructions because of the prompting capability available with interactive computer programs.
- Immediate access to up-to-date information from a central database.
- Consistent information; every planner accesses the same database.
- Faster response to engineering changes (ECOs) or changes requested by production planning or the shop.
- Use of the latest revisions of part drawings.
- More-detailed, more-uniform process-plan statements produced by word-processing techniques.
- More-effective use of inventories of

tools, gages, fixtures and a concomitant reduction in the variety of those items.

On the shop floor, CAPP systems should facilitate the interpretation of work instructions by the production worker because they can be more specifically tailored to a particular task and presented in unambiguous proven language. Computer-graphics capability further enhances this aspect of CAPP.

From a production-planning point of view, CAPP systems can help with analysis to facilitate cutter-life forecasting, materials-requirement planning, scheduling, and inventory control.

For CIM, CAPP systems produce machine-readable data. Such data can readily be transferred to other systems within the hierarchy to deal with the various planning aspects of a manufacturing concern.

Variant vs generative approaches

There are basically two approaches to computer-aided process planning: variant and generative.

In the variant approach, a set of standard process plans is established for all the parts families that have been identified though the principles of group tech-

nology. The standard plans are filed in computer storage and retrieved when appropriate for a new or revised part. Again, GT helps in identifying an appropriate family for the new part. The standard plan is then edited to suit the specific requirements of a particular job.

A certain amount of "up-front" work is required to establish the standard plans, do some family-of-parts grouping, establish a classification-and-coding system, and, in general, apply the principles of GT. Then the computer, acting more or less as a word processor, helps to assemble and edit an appropriate process for the work at hand.

During the planning stage, various subroutines or canned programs can be invoked to help the planner with the many calculations and choices that must be made. All of this takes place in an interactive conversational mode at a CRT work station.

The generative approach uses the computer to synthesize each individual plan using appropriate algorithms that define the various technological decisions that must be made. It relies on the computer's memory logic and computational powers. The planner in such a system performs merely a monitoring function and arbitrates some elementary decision conflicts.

Several practical and successful versions of variant CAPP systems have been developed and are in operation. No truly generative system exists as yet, although some claim the designation. GENPLAN (which stands for GENerative process PLANning) perhaps comes closest, but even Tulkoff admits that it is really a semigenerative system, requiring a trained process planner in the loop.

A variant approach

Among the first approaches to a generic computer-aided process-planning system is the CAPP system developed under the sponsorship of Computer Aided Manufacturing-International Inc (CAM-I). CAM-I's CAPP is a variant system and was developed primarily to demonstrate the feasibility of computer-automated process planning. Its logic is based on group-technology methods of classifying and coding parts. The actual classification-and-coding scheme is immaterial to the system and must be established by the user.

A standard plan in the CAPP system is a sequential set of instructions that include general processing requirements, tools, machines, and detailed operation instructions (called work elements and work-element parameters) that would generally apply to a series of very similar parts, or a family.

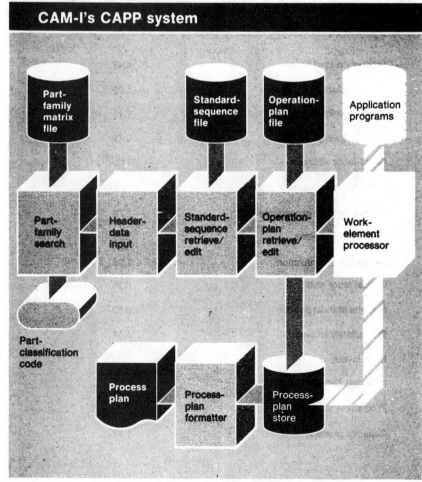

CAM-I's CAPP system

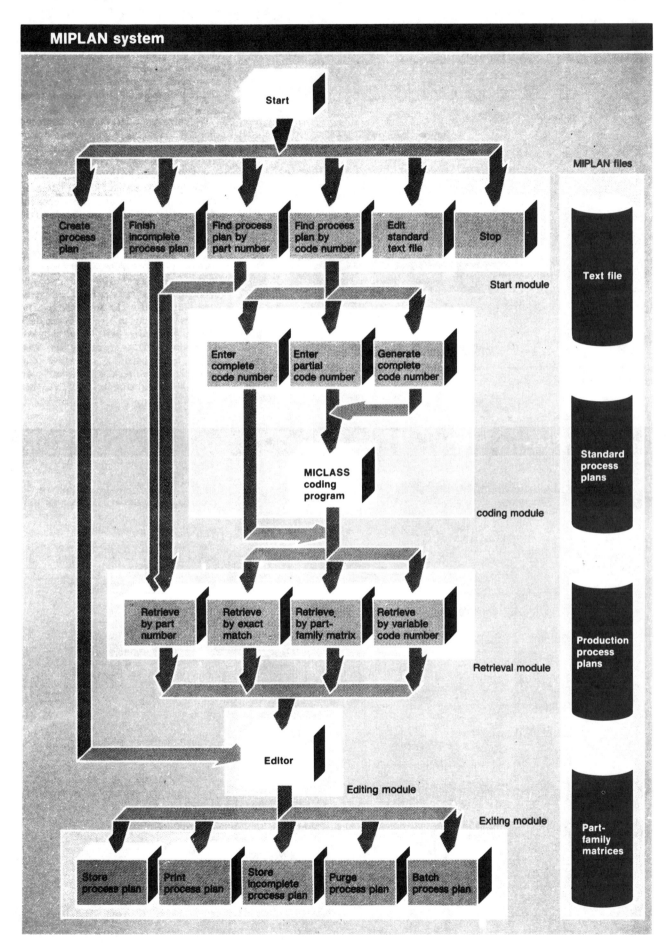

Start

Create process plan | Finish incomplete process plan | Find process plan by part number | Find process plan by code number | Edit standard text file | Stop

Start module

MIPLAN files

Text file

Enter complete code number | Enter partial code number | Generate complete code number

MICLASS coding program

coding module

Standard process plans

Retrieve by part number | Retrieve by exact match | Retrieve by part-family matrix | Retrieve by variable code number

Retrieval module

Production process plans

Editor

Editing module

Exiting module

Store process plan | Print process plan | Store incomplete process plan | Purge process plan | Batch process plan

Part-family matrices

Implementing CIM

One concept for generative CAPP

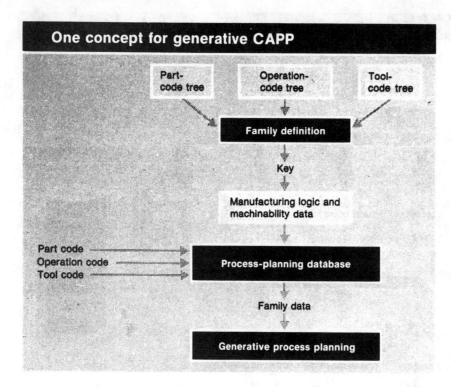

The data structure of CAPP requires six files: part-family matrix file, standard-sequence file, operation-code table, operation-plan file, part-family setup file, and process-plan store file. Again, these files must be established by the user.

In operation, a part-classification code is entered into a part-family search routine, which then interrogates the part-family matrix file. If a family match is found, that data is temporarily stored to allow for the creation of header data: the identification data and user-dependent description of the product to be planned.

After header data is completed, the system allows retrieval of a standard sequence of user-dependent operation codes (OPCODES). The sequence of OPCODES forms the user-defined standard sequence for the part family. The planner may then edit or modify the data for the particular part being planned. After the OPCODE sequence has been edited, each individual operation code can be retrieved from the standard-plan data file and edited to be specific for that

Decision tree

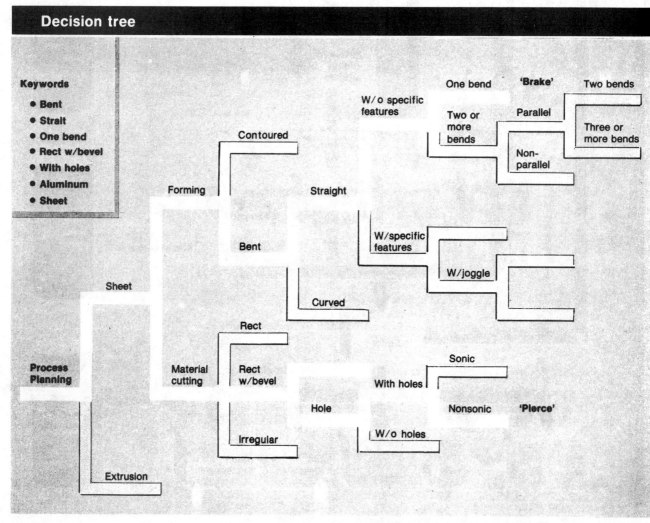

particular part. The completed information is then stored in the process-planning store file to be retrieved and printed out when needed.

Backing into GT via CAPP

The MIPLAN system from OIR uses a slightly different approach but is based on a similar variant principle. With MIPLAN, however, it is possible to start cold, without any of the up-front work of classification and coding and without establishment of standard plans. MIPLAN logic allows the user to back into group technology, establishing plans and codes as the process continues.

The MIPLAN system consists of a number of independent modules, interactive conversational software that runs on various computers, including the Digital Equipment PDP-11 family (including VAX), all IBM mainframes using OS or DOS, and GE time-share hookups. Each module serves a practical process-planning need.

The process planner has a choice of four different options for the creation of a process plan:

■ A plan can be created from scratch, from standard process-description texts that have been prepared and stored in the computer files. The text files are generated by the user, who is free to define how the file is arranged. For, example, some companies may want to access standard text via operation codes (somewhat like the OPCODES of CAM-I's CAPP) while others prefer to use machine-tool-identification numbers.

Regardless of the organization, a menu of standard text material is associated with a machine, a work station, or a process-identification code, and these menus can be constantly updated and edited as planners work with the system. These texts can then be assembled and edited for each step in the process.

■ An incomplete process plan can be retrieved from the computer and finished. This option is not only handy for necessary interruptions but is useful when some information turns out to be missing or unavailable after planning has been started. The incomplete plan need not be discarded; it can be retrieved and the information added when it becomes available or it is convenient.

■ A process plan can be retrieved by entering an existing part number. If the new part to be processed is different from the existing part, the retrieved process plan can be edited and a new one

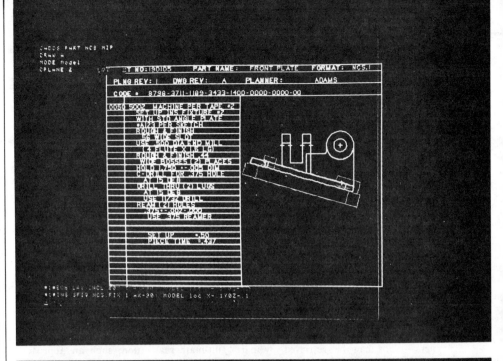

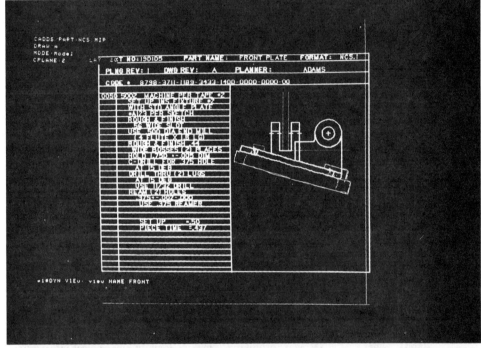

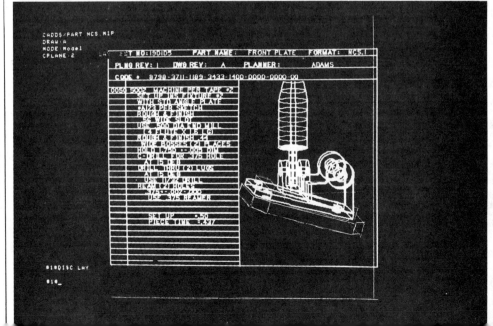

CV-MIPLAN enables planner to create pictorial process plan. Part and tooling are mated (top), tool paths are added (middle), and setup is checked for tooling interference

created without the original plan's being destroyed. In other words, existing plans can be modified to create new plans for similar parts, a step toward family-of-parts planning.

■ A process plan can be retrieved through the group-technology code number for the same or a similar part. To do this, the planner can enter a complete code number or a partial code number. If there is only a partial code number or no available code number for the part, the planner can generate one by invoking the MICLASS interactive classification-and-coding program, which is part of the MIPLAN system.

Once classification and coding has been established—and the task can be performed off-line by others than planners—plans can be retrieved by part family, thereby adding another dimension of group technology. After a process plan has been satisfactorily edited, the planner has several options:

■ Have the computer print the final process plan.

■ Store the plan in the company process-plan file.

■ Store an incomplete plan to be updated or completed later.

■ Purge any process plans that are not wanted.

One of the main advantages of any CAPP system is that the computer is also available for the many related calculations that must be made. In the MIPLAN system, the planner can switch from the planning mode at will by simply typing a question mark (?) in any field in the text section of the planning format. At that point, a user-defined module can be executed and its output entered in the field where the question mark (?) was originally issued.

At the Lamp Equipment Operation (LEO) of General Electric Co (Cleveland), where MIPLAN was originally implemented, various process-capability-study routines, originally run on a time-share basis, have been converted to such modules. This enables planners to generate standard times for use in developing process plans.

Recently, the MIPLAN system has been implemented on Computervision Corp (Bedford, Mass) computer-graphics systems to provide graphics capabilities. Now process planners can work at terminals and compose process plans made up of text and drawings.

A drawing for an existing part or for one that has been recently designed can be called up on the screen, as can existing tooling. The part can then be rotated to provide the proper machining orientation and can be pictorially mated with the tooling to ensure a proper match and to check out interferences. Tooling paths

can also be plotted to illustrate the entire machining sequence, and the setup can be viewed from various angles to check clearances.

Text and drawings can then be merged to generate a process plan with appropriate pictorial illustrations: sketches of tooling, setups, inspection points, layouts, and other intermediate process drawings. The idea of CV-MIPLAN is to reduce paperwork and provide clearer process instructions.

Generative approach is elusive

In a truly generative process-planning system, the sequence of operations, as well as all the manufacturing parameters, would be automatically established without reference to prior plans. In its ultimate realization, such an approach should be universally applicable: present any part to the system, and the computer spits out the optimum process plan. Processes are selected, machines designated, sequences established, and parameters assigned.

In actuality, however, decision logic may vary from industry to industry or company to company, and theoretical process parameters always need to be adjusted to the practical realities of a particular manufacturing environment with its specific capabilities.

So-called generative process-planning systems to date—and probably for the foreseeable future—are still specialized systems developed to suit a specific operation or for a particular type of manufacturing process, such as, say, multiple-spindle turning.

A typical way of achieving such a generative approach is to first establish the decision logic inherent in the process selection. Brigham Young Univ (Provo, Utah), for example, has developed a methodology for capturing decision-making logic in hierarchical information trees. These trees and associated tree-handling software developed at BYU—the DCLASS system—can be used to generate process plans.

A key element in DCLASS decision-making logic is the use of a comprehensive process taxonomy, or hierarchical tree, as a common denominator, so to speak, against which key words or codes from other process-parameter-related trees are evaluated. Process-related trees and key words include part-family codes, size, tolerance, precision, materials, production requirements, process capability, equipment loading, tooling availability, and criteria for production, such as minimum cost, minimum time, shop loading.

Of course, DCLASS is strictly a computer-compatible tree-handling methodology. Traversing various trees—part classification, materials classification, process

selection—permits selection of all the processes that can produce a particular shape from a particular material, for example. But, to use DCLASS, it is first necessary to hang all the leaves on the tree: to establish all the taxonomies pertinent to the particular operation.

GENPLAN gets close

Perhaps one of the most extensive attempts at achieving a generative-like computer-aided process-planning system is Lockheed Georgia's GENPLAN. According to Tulkoff, one of its principal architects, the system synthesizes plans based on "1000 worker-years of experience." A very exhaustive study and computer analysis of process plans created over the past 25 years forms the basis of a manufacturing-technology database accessed through a specially developed group-techology code.

The code takes into consideration part geometry, size, and manufacturing processes. The study of previous process plans also involved a detailed parts-flow analysis to determine just where and in what particular sequence specific machined parts were manufactured. Shop equipment and their capacities and capabilities were inventoried and stored in the computer database.

GENPLAN, according to Tulkoff, automatically determines the sequence of operations, selects proper machine tools, and calculates machining times based on manufacturing logic included in the database. The process planner assigns the special code based on part description. The GENPLAN software then quickly analyzes the data, evaluates alternatives, and makes the basic planning decisions. The process plan so generated requires only minor fill-ins by the planner.

The result: process plans that are consistent not only in methodology but also in sequence, format, and terminology and incorporate the latest technology. And it is all done without reliance on retrieval of standard plans. "The system captures both the art and science of manufacturing," says Tulkoff.

CAPP for the small user

On a less ambitious scale, various in-house CAPP systems have been developed to address the specific planning requirements of a particular manufacturing process, and now such systems designed for specific processes are beginning to appear commercially. One example is a computer-assisted system developed for work on multiple-spindle screw machines by Tipnis Associates Inc (Cincinnati). Called LETS-MB (for Layout, Estimation, Tooling & tooling design, and Setup for Multiple-spindle Bar automatics), the system is said to do just that.

LETS-MB software comprises a series of step-by-step procedures to be followed in a prompting mode run on a microcomputer, an Apple II. Data on material, tolerances, special operations, etc, and machine-characteristics data are kept on floppy disks.

As the planner enters part dimensions into the system, a blueprint outline is generated on an associated graphics screen to help visualize the process. Then, using machining-allowance and machine-data disks developed by the user or supplied by Tipnis, the system balances the necessary cuts and assigns the operations to each spindle.

A tool-design stage steps the planner through dovetail- and circular-form-tool design, including tolerancing, tool dimensions, and setup-gage locations. The setup instructions provide a complete list of the necessary collets, holders, fixtures, and tools at each spindle, along with the complete spindle and station layout of the part and tools printed out on a high-speed graphics printer. The system also has limited capability to store and retrieve plans already generated.

According to Vijay Tipnis, president of Tipnis Associates, process planning is really the starting point for planning the entire manufacturing system. Even though computer-aided process-planning systems are on the increase, he believes that the demand for CIM requires even further refinement of these systems in a very fundamental way, "much more than we have thought about.

"Now we must link not just the sequence of operations," Tipnis continues, "but all the sequences of activities—tooling, fixtures, machines, and people—and how they are to be brought together at the right place at the right time to execute their particular functions so that no one function holds up another. That is the principle of the integrated manufacturing system."

MRP, and attempts at factory control

Material-requirements planning, the original definition of MRP, is a relatively simple concept. It is a computerized method for managing inventories and issuing orders for parts and materials, probably one of the earliest applications of computers in manufacturing control. Software is available from various vendors, albeit it usually must be tailored to the specific needs of the user.

Major computer manufacturers—such as Burroughs, Hewlett-Packard, Honeywell, IBM, and Sperry-Univac—offer MRP modules as part of their manufacturing-planning-and-control software. GEISCO (General Electric Information Service Co) and Xerox Computer Services offer MRP as part of such systems available on a time-share basis.

In addition, numerous software houses such as ASK Computer Systems (Los Altos, Calif), Formation Inc (Mt Laurel, NJ), and MRP Software International (Andover, Mass), as well as consulting firms, such as Arthur Andersen & Co (Chicago), offer MRP software packages to run on various computers, both mainframe and mini.

MRP II another matter

The more recent elevation of MRP to stand for "manufacturing-resource planning" is another matter. MRP II, as this mutation is being called, is an attempt to tie material-requirements planning to the financial system of a company and thereby, according to its promoters, achieve a "company operating system" and "a total business plan."

MRP II promises that such a tie-up between MRP and the so-called financial system can provide an effective planning tool for a manufacturing company, including a computer model of the busi-

Implementing CIM

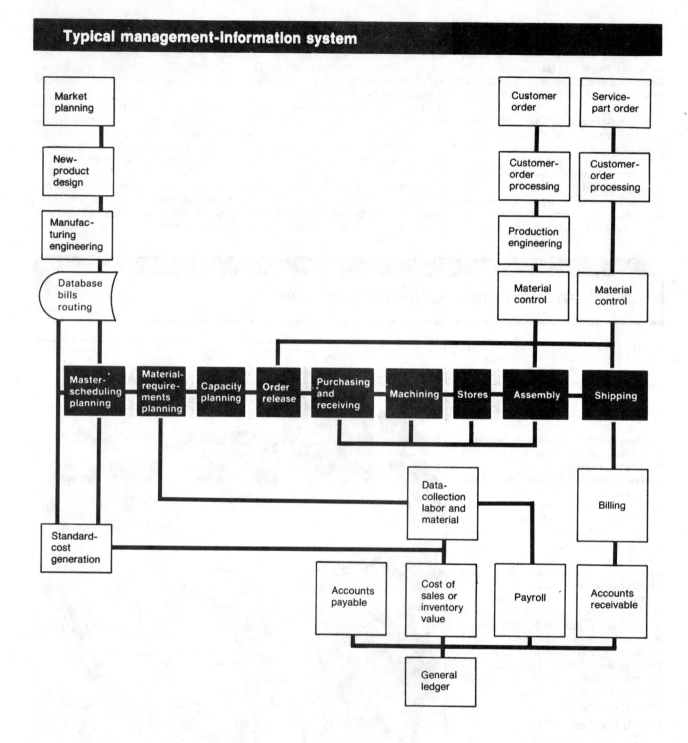

ness for simulation and what-if planning. Realization of MRP II is based on the assumption that an appropriate and complete computerized business system exists and that a proper simulation model can be created. Moreover, it assumes that all the information systems are compatible, permitting exchange and interaction of information.

In its own sphere, MRP II seems to suggest what CIM seeks: a closed-loop feedback system for effective real-time analysis, planning, and control of the manufacturing process. To gain a better perspective, lets first take a closer look at MRP, material-requirements planning.

MRP, a matter of priorities

Fundamentally, MRP uses the computer in the following way:

■ It compares a previously prepared master schedule with the bills of materials and determines which parts and materials are needed in what quantity to make the products planned.

■ It then checks the existing inventory to see whether the necessary parts and materials are on hand or will be available when needed.

■ If the parts and material are not on hand or on order, it establishes an appropriate due date and then initiates or generates the necessary purchase or shop orders.

■ If there is an open order for the parts or material, it re-evaluates the due date and, if necessary, calls for an adjustment.

In a nutshell, MRP helps to plan priorities, and that is what any reasonably good manual production- and inventory-control system should do. When computers became available, it seemed only logical to apply them to this relatively simple but tedious accounting-like procedure. But the results of such attempts were far from successful.

"A few failed disastrously, and the companies took many years to recover from their experiences with their first computer systems," says Oliver W. Wight, a long-time proponent of MRP and president of Oliver Wight Inc, a New Hampshire-based consulting firm in the field. "Most systems failed far less dramatically. They simply failed to generate anything near the results that management had been led to expect," he continues.

Manual systems never worked

The reasons, according to Wight, are deceptively simple: manual production- and inventory-control systems never really worked in the first place, and so formalizing such a system by translating it into software didn't have a chance. The point is that most companies have informal systems reflecting management's concept of how the company is operating but the actual day-to-day task of managing a manufacturing environment usually works by way of a much less structured, informal system. "Because manual systems were not able to cope with the complexity of the logistics problems in a typical manufacturing company, the real system was largely informal," says Wight.

The informal system amounts to order picking: expediting and by assembling ahead of time all the parts called for by the bill of materials, an expediter can readily determine any real shortages and then start pushing to get these parts made or purchased in time. Of course, the shortages are invariably determined too late, and the push for special handling and priority changes throws everything into a further muddle.

Properly implemented, MRP is a formal system that works according to plan to predict shortages. In contrast to the harassed expediter, it looks far enough ahead to allow something to be done to prevent the shortages. MRP has also been referred to as "time phasing" because it shows the requirements, scheduled receipts, projected available balances, and planned order releases in their proper relationships.

Benefits are impressive

The statistics touted for a well-managed MRP system are impressive: productivity up 5-30%, WIP inventories down 30-50%, late orders slashed 90%, labor

requirements reduced 10%. As an example, the Di-Acro Div of Houdaille Industries is said to have cut its overtime from an average of 4000 hr a month to an average of 800 hr a month with the implementation of MRP. Before this, 75-85% of its product was shipped in the last five days of the month. Now, only 35% is shipped in the last five days.

However, in order to work effectively, MRP systems must have accurate and timely information, something not always available before the implementation of computer systems. Many MRP systems have foundered or even failed, simply because the data—be it bill of materials or inventory records—was neither timely nor accurate. Specifically,

MRP systems require the following data:
■ A realistic master production schedule that specifies what manufacturing is to produce in a given period.
■ Accurate bills of material, or structured parts lists, that show exactly the way a product is actually put together. They must uniquely identify, by part number, each item requiring priority planning.
■ Accurate inventory-record files that include planning such factors as lot sizes, lead-times, safety stock, and scrap allowances.
■ A thorough and well-planned employee-education program to instill confidence in the formal system and eliminate the practice of hedging for safety

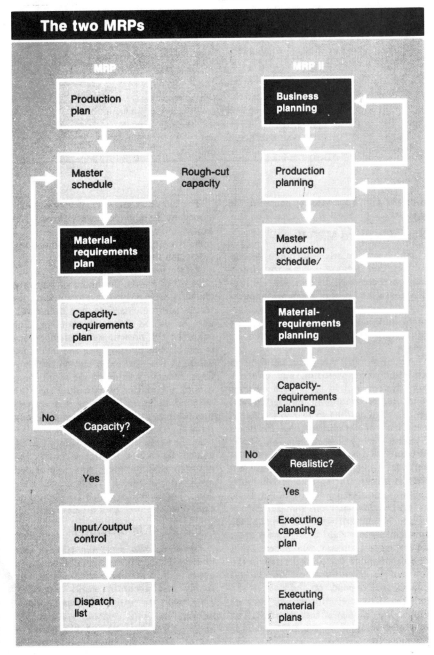

The two MRPs

The four classes of MRP users

Class of user	How company operates with MRP
A	Uses MRP as a model to run the business (closed-loop system) Uses MRP as a game plan for sales, finance, manufacturing, purchasing, and engineering Uses MRP schedules for foremen and purchasing people Needs no shortage list to override schedules
B	Uses MRP as a production-control system only Needs help from shortage list Has capacity planning and shop-floor-control systems in place Has more inventory than necessary
C	Uses MRP as an inventory-ordering system only Needs shortage list for scheduling Uses overloaded master schedule Has more inventory than necessary
D	Uses MRP in data processing only Relies entirely on shortage lists and expediting Has mismanaged master schedule, if any Has poor inventory records

over and above the safeties built into the system.

Stepping up to MRP II

MRP is particularly susceptible to computerization because it deals with information processing. In fact, MRP is usually considered part of a typical management-information system. And management information is the key to the kind of factory management envisioned by MRP II.

Achieving MRP II requires building on an established, well-run, and effective MRP system and involves such systems work as programming and additional software. According to Darryl Lanvater, president of Manufacturing Software Systems Inc (Milliston, Vt), an Oliver Wight company that specializes in MRP-software evalutions, the conversion from MRP to manufacturing-resource planning requires additional software in two basic categories: financial and simulation.

Developing software to create the financial logic should be relatively easy, according to Lanvater, who believes that one experienced person dedicated to the job can do it within a few months. Of course, that depends on the state of the existing financial-information systems and the complexity of the operation. The task of developing a simulation model is far more complicated.

The financial software of MRP as envisioned by Landvater, covers three basic areas:
- Inventory valuation and projections
- Cash-flow allocations
- Overhead allocations.

In other words, the financial software converts time-phased inventory and material-requirements data into dollar values for use in financial planning. For example, the present value of inventory is established by summing the inventory values in the stockroom and on the shop floor. Inventory value of the stock room is simply a matter of extending the MRP on-hand balance, including any inspection inventory, by the costs and summing these for all items.

In the same way, WIP inventory can be valued by adding material costs, the reported cost of labor, and a prorated overhead cost for all orders on the shop floor. The same logic can be applied to cash-flow and overhead allocations.

A matter of information

Obviously, the implementation of MRP II depends largely on an effective management-information system, including timely and accurate status reporting. The need for effective management-information and -control systems has long been recognized and has been the subject of intense investigation by the

Air Force ICAM (Integrated Computer Aided Manufacturing) project and Computer Aided-Manufacturing-International (CAM-I). The IBM COPICS (Communications-Oriented Production-Information and -Control System) concept was among the first attempts to address integrated computer solutions to business-information processing and communications problems created by the dynamic nature of manufacturing.

Managing batch-manufacturing operations, which constitute about 75% of total US industrial output, is a complex matter. For this reason, CAM-I initated a so-called Job-shop Control Interest Group in late 1976 to investigate the state-of-the-art and possibilities for improvement.

A survey of machine operators and their management from a variety of industries revealed that most factory-control problems are common to all industries. But existing systems were found to depend heavily on people to obtain information from the shop floor and to lack adequate responsiveness to meet production schedules and maintain balanced loads. The need for feedback from the shop floor to process planners, for example, is highlighted by the survey discovery that approximately 50% of work instructions are modified on the shop floor.

The system requirements identified by this survey of shop personnel were compared with features currently available in commercial software packages. "Although a large number of manufacturing-control systems are currently on the market, the greatest emphasis is on bill-of-material processing and material-requirements planning (MRP), with little emphasis on shop-floor control," states B. Neil Snodgrass, CAM-I senior project manager for the CAM-I Factory Management Project initiated by the original interest group in January 1979. "We found no distributed system oriented for separate levels of factory management and implementing closed-loop communication and control, including the coordination of all shop service functions, as well as material-flow control."

The CAM-I Factory Management Project was established to develop and evaluate the concepts required to implement an advanced factory-management system. The intent of the proposed system is to aid the allocation and control of the various factory resources used directly and indirectly to produce discrete parts as well as to monitor and control the events that take place within a factory.

CAM-I wants to include several concepts in a hierarchically distributed real-time information system using the latest computer hardware capabilities. Such a system would be able to accomplish the following:

■ Solve fundamental problems not currently solved in most systems: measurement of the rate of material transformation, support of distinct management levels with distributed database aid to managers in predicting the results of decisions, and closed-loop communication and control.

■ Interface with manufacturing planning and support systems, such as MRP, process planning, purchasing, etc.

■ Be modular in concept and allow for evolutionary implementation.

■ Be economically attractive for even partial implementation.

■ Be applicable to a large number of shops and industries.

Such a hierarchical information system would facilitate efficient management of the production activities and help bring the job shop a step closer to computer-integrated manufacturing.

The real key to implementing CIM is learning to deal with and process the information required to transform ideas into product: information about parts, processes, and material. Group technology, process planning, and MRP are some of the tools to help deal with that information and to make computer-integrated manufacturing a reality.

Glossary

The following definitions have been culled from several sources and contain some that were developed during the preparation of this report. Most of them have been adapted from the APICS Dictionary, issued by the American Production and Inventory Control Society Inc (Washington, DC). For related glossaries, see "Computers in manufacturing" (AM Special Report 703, April 1978) and "Computer graphics goes to work" (AM Special Report 724, July 1980).

ABC classification. Classification of the items in an inventory in decreasing order of annual dollar volume. This array is then split into three classes, called A, B, and C. Class A contains the items with the highest annual dollar volume and receives the most attention. The medium Class B receives less attention, and Class C, which contains the low-dollar-volume items, is controlled routinely. The ABC principle is that effort saved through relaxed controls on low-value items will be applied to reduce inventories of high-value items.

Allocation. (1) In an MRP system, an item for which a picking order has been released to the stock room but not yet sent out of the stock room. It is an "uncashed" stock-room requisition. (2) A process used to distribute material in short supply.

Backward scheduling. A scheduling technique in which the schedule is computed by starting with the due date for the order and working backward to determine required start date. This can generate negative times, identifying where time must be made up.

Balanced loading. Loading a starting department with a product mix that should not overload or underload subsequent departments.

Bill of material. A listing of all the subassemblies, parts, and raw materials that go into a parent assembly, showing the quantity of each required to make an assembly.

Bill-of-material processor. The computer applications supplied by many manufacturers for maintaining, updating, and retrieving bill-of-material information on direct-access files.

Block scheduling. A detailed scheduling technique in which each operation is allowed a fairly long period, or 'block,' of time, such as a week.

Bottleneck. A facility function, department, etc, that impedes production—for example, a machine or work center at which jobs arrive at a faster rate than they leave.

Bucketed system. An MRP system under which all time-phased data is displayed in accumulated time periods, or 'buckets.' If the period of accumulation would be one week, then the system would be said to have weekly buckets.

Capacity-requirements planning (CRP). The function of establishing, measuring, and adjusting capacity limits or levels that are consistent with a production plan. The term *capacity requirements planning* in this context is the process of determining the labor and machine resources required to accomplish the tasks of production. Open shop orders, and planned orders in the MRP system, are CRP input that 'translates' these orders into hours of work by work center and by time period.

Classification and coding. The grouping of items (parts, processes, machines) on the basis of similar attributes and the assigning of a related identifier to each unique member of the groups.

Closed-loop MRP. A system built around MRP and including the additional planning functions of production planning, master production scheduling, and capacity-requirements planning. Further, once the planning phase is complete and the plans have been accepted as realistic and attainable, the execution functions come into play. These include the shop-floor control functions of input-output measurement, detailed scheduling and dispatching, plus anticipated-delay reports from both the shops and vendors, purchasing follow-up and control, etc. The term *closed-loop* implies not only that each of these elements is included in the overall system but also that there is feedback from the execution functions so that the planning can be kept valid at all times.

Computer-integrated manufacturing (CIM). The logical organization of individual engineering, production, and marketing/support system. Functional areas—such as design, inventory control, physical distribution, cost accounting, planning, purchasing, etc—are integrated with direct materials management and shop-floor-data acquisition and control. Thus the loop is closed between the shop floor and its controlling activities. Shop-floor machines serve as data-acquisition devices for the control system and often its direct *command*. Strategic plans smoothly give way to tactical operations—at known cost.

Common-parts bill (of material). A type of planning bill that groups all common components for a product or family of products into one bill of material.

Cost factors. The units of input that represent costs to the manufacturing system; for example: labor hours, purchased material.

Cumulative lead-time. The longest length of time involved to accomplish the activity in question. For any item planned through MRP, it is found by reviewing each bill-of-material path below the item; whichever path adds up to the greatest number defines cumulative material lead-time. Also called 'aggregate lead-time,' 'stacked lead time,' 'composite lead-time,' 'critical-path lead-time.'

Cycle counting. A physical inventory-taking technique in which inventory is counted on a periodic schedule rather than once a year. For example, a cycle inventory count may be taken when an item reaches its reorder point, when new stock is received, or on a regular basis, usually more frequently for high-value fast-moving items and less frequently for low-value or slow-moving items. Most effective cycle-counting systems require the counting of a certain number of items every work day.

Dampeners. User input parameters to suppress the reporting of insignificant or unimportant action messages from computer processing of MRP.

Decision table. (1) A tally of all contingencies to be considered in the description of a problem, with the actions taken. (2) A presentation in either matrix or tabular form of a set of conditions and their corresponding actions.

Decision tree. A graphic version of a decision table, in which the conditions and corresponding actions are represented as a set of paths along the branches of a tree-like diagram.

Dependent demand. Demand that is directly related to or derived from the demand for other items or end products. Such demands are therefore calculated and need not and should not be forecast. A given inventory item may have both dependent and independent demand at any given time.

Detailed scheduling. The actual assignment of target starting and/or completion dates to operations or groups of operations to show when these must be performed if the manufacturing order is to be completed on time. These dates are used in the dispatching operation. Also, 'operations scheduling.'

Direct-deduct inventory-transaction processing. A bookkeeping method that decreases the book (computer) inventory of an item as material is issued from stock and increases the book inventory as material is received into stock. The key concept here is that the book record is updated coincident with the movement of material out of or into stock. As a result, the book record is a representation of what is physically in stock.

Economic order quantity (EOQ). A type of fixed order quantity that determines the amount of product to be purchased or manufactured at one time in order to minimize the total cost involved, including the ordering costs (of machine setup, order writing, receipt checking, etc.) and carrying costs (cost of capital invested, insurance, taxes, space, obsolescence, and spoilage). The economic order quantity may be calculated from the equation Q = 2AS ÷ rv, where Q is the quantity to be ordered, S is the annual sales, A is the ordering cost, r is the carrying cost, and v is the unit cost.

Equivalent days. The standard hour requirements to a job converted to calendar days for scheduling purposes.

Explosion. An extension of a bill of material into the total of each of the components required to manufacture a given quantity of upper-level assembly or subassembly.

Families. Convenient groupings of related orders or similar parts.

FIFO. First-in-first-out method of inventory evaluation. The assumption is that oldest inventory (first in) is the first to be used (first out).

Finite loading. Conceptually, putting no more work into a factory than the factory can be expected to execute. The specific term usually refers to a computer technique that involves automatic shop-priority revision to level load operation by operation.

First-come-first-served rule. A dispatching rule under which the jobs are sequenced by their arrival times.

Fixed-interval reorder system. A periodic reordering system in which the time interval between orders is fixed—such as weekly, monthly, or quarterly—but the size of the order is not fixed and orders vary according to use since the last review. Used where examining inventory stocks on a fixed cycle is convenient: in warehouse control systems, in systems in which orders are placed mechanically, or for handling inventories involving a very large variety of items under some form of clerical control. Also, 'fixed-reorder-cycle system.'

Fixed order quantity. An MRP lot-sizing technique that

87

Implementing CIM

always causes planned orders to be generated for a predetermined fixed quantity (or multiples thereof if net requirements for the period exceed the fixed order quantity).

Fixed-order system. An inventory control in which the size of the order is fixed but the time interval between orders depends on actual demand. The practice of ordering a fixed quantity when needed assumes that individual inventories are under constant watch. This system consists of placing an order of a fixed quantity (the reorder quantity) whenever the amount on hand plus the amount on order falls to or below a specified level (the order point or reorder point).

Floating order point. An order point responsive to changes in demand and or to changes in lead-time.

Forward scheduling. A scheduling technique in which the scheduler proceeds from a known start date and computes the completion date for an order, usually proceeding from the first operation to the last.

Generative automated process planning. Computer synthesis of a process plan using decision logic and appropriate technology algorithms.

Group technology (GT). An engineering and manufacturing philosophy that recognizes the similarities in the design and manufacture of discrete parts. It provides for rapid retrieval of existing practice and seeks to achieve some of the economies of mass production in a batch-production environment.

Header record. A record containing common, constant, or identifying information for a group of records that follow.

Hedge. (1) In master production scheduling, a quantity of stock used to protect against uncertainty in demand. The hedge is similar to safety stock, except that a hedge has the dimension of timing as well as amount. (2) In purchasing, any purchase or sale transaction having as its purpose the elimination of the negative aspects of price fluctuations.

Infinite loading. Showing the work behind work centers in the time periods required regardless of the capacity available to perform this work.

Inventory turnover. The number of times that an inventory 'turns over,' or cycles, during the year. One way to compute inventory turnover is to divide the average inventory level into the annual cost of sales. For example, if average inventory were $3-million and cost of sales were $21-million, the inventory would be considered to 'turn' seven times per year.

Inventory valuation. The value of the inventory at either its cost or its market value. Because inventory value can change with time, some recognition must be taken of the age distribution of inventory. Therefore, the cost value of inventory, under accounting practice, is usually computed on a first-in-first-out (FIFO), last-in-first-out (LIFO) basis, or a standard cost system to establish the cost of goods sold.

Job-shop simulation. Simulation of work flow through a manufacturing facility, usually using a computer program.

Kit. An assembly's components that have been pulled from stock and readied for movement to the assembly area.

LIFO. Last-in-first-out method of inventory evaluation. The assumption is that the most recently received (last in) is the first to be used or sold (first out).

Line balancing. Assignment of elemental tasks to assembly-line work stations to minimize the number of work stations and the total amount of unassigned time at all stations. *Line balancing* can also mean a technique for determining the product mix that can be run down an assembly line to provide a fairly consistent flow of work through that assembly line at the planned line rate. For example, if an automotive assembly line happened to be scheduled one day with nothing but convertibles, some workers would be standing idle while others would not be able to keep pace with the line.

Load leveling. Spreading orders out in time or rescheduling operation so that the amount of work to be done in the time periods tends to be distributed evenly.

Low-level code. Identification of the lowest level in any bill of material at which a particular component may appear. Net requirements for a given component are not calculated until all the gross requirements have been calculated down to that level. Low-level codes are normally calculated and maintained automatically by the computer software.

Management-information system. A manual or computerized system that anticipates the wide use of data for management planning and control. Accordingly, the

data is organized in a database and is readily available to a variety of management functions.

Manufacturing-resource planning (MRP II). A method for the effective planning of all the resources of a manufacturing company. Ideally, it addresses operational planning in units and financial planning in dollars and has a simulation capability to answer 'what-if' questions. It is made up of a variety of functions, each linked together: business planning, production planning, master production scheduling, material-requirements planning, capacity-requirements planning, and the execution systems for capacity and priority. Outputs from these systems would be integrated with financial reports, such as the business plan, purchase-commitment report, shipping budget, inventory projections in dollars, etc. Manufacturing-resource planning is a direct outgrowth and extension of MRP. Often referred to as MRP II.

Master production schedule (MPS). For selected items, a statement of what the company expects to manufacture. It is the anticipated build schedule for those selected items assigned to the master scheduler. The master scheduler maintains this schedule, and, in turn, it becomes a set of planning numbers that 'drives' MRP. It represents what the company plans to produce expressed in specific configurations, quantities, and dates. The MPS should not be confused with a sales forecast, which represents a statement of demand. The master production schedule must take forecast plus other important considerations (backlog, availability of material, availability of capacity, management policy and goals, etc) into account prior to determining the best manufacturing strategy. Also 'master schedule.'

Material-requirements planning (MRP). A system that uses bill-of-material, inventory, and open-order data and master-production-schedule information to calculate requirements for material. It makes recommendations to release replenishment orders for material. Further, since it is time-phased, it makes recommendations to reschedule open orders when due dates and need dates are not in phase. Originally seen as merely a better way to order inventory, today it is thought of primarily as a scheduling technique, a method for establishing and maintaining valid due dates on orders.

Methods-time measurement (MTM). A system of predetermined motion-time standards, a procedure that analyzes any operation into certain human motions and assigns to each motion a predetermined time standard determined by the nature of the motion and the conditions under which it was made.

Monocode. A code based on a tree structure that divides a population into a number of subgroups. The digits in a monocode have variable significance.

Net-change MRP. An approach in which the material-requirements plan is continually retained in the computer. Whenever there is a change in requirements, open order or inventory status, or engineering use, a partial explosion is made only for those parts affected by the change. Net-changes systems may be continuous and totally transaction-oriented or done in a periodic (often daily) batch.

Polycode. A code based on a set of multiple-choice questions dealing with a class of features. The digits in a polycode have a fixed significance.

Process planning. Determining what steps are required to manufacture a part and what facilities are necessary.

Regeneration MRP. An approach in which the master production schedule is totally re-exploded down through all bills of material at least once per week to maintain valid priorities. New requirements and planned orders are completely 'regenerated' at that time.

Resource-requirements planning. The process of converting the production plan and/or the master production schedule into the effect on key resources, such as worker hours, machine hours, storage, standard-cost dollars, shipping dollars, inventory levels, etc. Product-load profiles or bills of resources could be used to accomplish this. The purpose of this is to evaluate the plan prior to attempting to implement it. Sometimes referred to as a rough-cut check on capacity. Capacity-requirements planning is a detailed review of capacity requirements. Also, 'rough-cut capacity planning,' 'rough-cut resource planning.'

Route sheet. A document that specifies the operations on a part and the sequence of these operations, with alternate operations and routings whenever feasible; prepared by process engineers at the time the part is first put into production. Other processing specifications that can be included on a route sheet are the

material requirements (kind and quantity); machining tolerances; the tools, jigs, and fixtures required; and the time allowance for each operation. Also, 'operation list,' 'operation sheet or chart,' 'process chart,' 'manufacturing-data sheet.'

Shop-floor control. A system for utilizing data from the shop floor as well as from data-processing files to maintain and communicate status information on shop orders and work centers. The major subfunctions of shop-floor control: (1) assigning priority to each shop order, (2) maintaining WIP quantity information for MRP; (3) conveying shop-order-status information to the office; (4) providing actual output data for capacity control.

Variant automated process planning. Computer-aided generation of a process plan through selection of an appropriate master plan (usually with the application of group technology) and editing of the master plan to suit the particular needs of the part on hand.

What-if analysis. The process of evaluating alternate strategies, answering the consequences of changes to forecasts, manufacturing plans, inventory levels, etc. Some companies have the capability of submitting various plans as a "trial fit" in order to find the best one. Also, 'simulation.'

Work-in-process (WIP). Product in various stages of completion throughout the plant, including raw material that has been released for initial processing and completely processed material awaiting final inspection and acceptance as finished product or shipment to a customer. Many accounting systems also include semifinished stock and components in this category. ■

Bibliography

Group Technology, An Overview and Bibliography, Machinability Data Center, Metcut Research Associates, Cincinnati, Ohio

Introduction to Group Technology in Manufacturing and Engineering, Institute of Science & Technology, Univ of Mich, Ann Arbor, Mich

Managing Work-in-Process Inventory, Kenneth Kivenko, Marcel Dekker Inc, New York

Material Requirements Planning, Joseph Orlicky, McGraw-Hill, New York

Production and Inventory Management in the Computer Age, Oliver W. Wight, CBI Publishing Co Inc, Boston

The Role of Computers in Manufacturing Processes, Gideon Halevi, John Wiley & Sons, New York

Acknowledgements

The following associations have been extremely helpful in the preparation of this report: American Production and Inventory Control Society (APICS), Computer Aided Manufacturing-International Inc (CAM-I), Numerical Control Society (NCS), Society of Manufacturing Engineers (SME).

CHAPTER II

Computer-Aided Design and Graphics

Computer graphics goes to work

Human-oriented computer systems are beginning to bridge the gap between design and manufacturing in today's communications-oriented factory

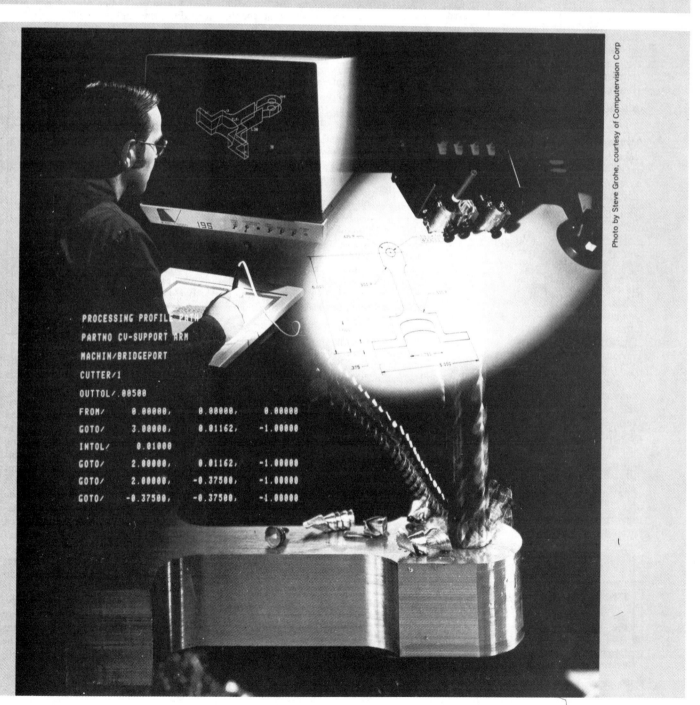

Photo by Steve Grohe, courtesy of Computervision Corp

```
PROCESSING PROFIL  ARM
PARTNO CU-SUPPORT ARM
MACHIN/BRIDGEPORT
CUTTER/1
OUTTOL/.00500
FROM/     0.00000,     0.00000,     0.00000
GOTO/     3.00000,     0.01162,    -1.00000
IMTOL/    0.01000
GOTO/     2.00000,     0.01162,    -1.00000
GOTO/     2.00000,    -0.37500,    -1.00000
GOTO/    -0.37500,    -0.37500,    -1.00000
```

Computer graphics goes to work

THE INTRODUCTION of computers into manufacturing has been perhaps the most significant change in manufacturing since the beginning of the Industrial Revolution. It has led to a new vision of the manufacturing process, one that abandons the traditional, fragmented picture with its disjointed functional departments, each competing for dominance in the management hierarchy.

That new vision is one of a series of interdependent and overlapping functions bound into a smooth manufacturing flow by an up-to-date stream of pertinent information that has been generated, processed, transformed, stored, and retrieved with the aid of the ubiquitous computer. The problem has been one of communicating with that simple-minded, bit-structured machine. The solution rests with the increasing introduction of computer graphics into the computer-aided design/manufacturing (CAD/CAM) environment.

A human-oriented system

Computer graphics can be defined as a human-oriented system that uses the capabilities of a computer to create, transform, and display pictorial and symbolic data. As such, it helps organize and transform masses of often unintelligible raw data into meaningful information, the kind essential for manufacturing managers.

The effective application of computers has forced detailed analysis of all the processes needed to bring a product from its conception to the marketplace. And, when you analyze the architecture of manufacturing, you soon realize that it runs mostly on information and its transformation into appropriate forms for the various functions to be performed.

Traditionally, a concept is transformed into design information that is communicated to others by drawings and related documents. That information, in turn, is transformed into a plethora of drawings and documents embodying the instructions required by the various operating departments constituting the manufacturing organization: purchasing, stores, tool design, production, assembly—all the way to distribution and customer service.

All of this information must be communicated accurately, efficiently, and in a timely fashion if it is to serve manufacturing properly in a fast-changing market. Conventional drawings and documents are no longer the best or most efficient means for conditioning and communicating the flood of information needed to run today's computer-oriented manufacturing facility.

Conventional drawings and documents are cumbersome and expensive to generate, involving a great deal of time-consuming labor. And, perhaps more important, they are passive: there is no fast or convenient way to interact with the information in response to the chaotic demands put on manufacturing by the present socioeconomic climate.

The only thing a manufacturing manager can plan on these days is change. We live in an era of uncertainty in which change dominates all facets of human endeavor: changing social and economic values, changing lifestyles, changing markets and products.

In manufacturing, that change is perhaps most readily perceived as a switch from mass production to high-volume production: a switch from manufacturing a continuous stream of identical parts for stock to manufacturing a large output with great variety produced in varying quantities to satisfy the kaleidoscope of consumer demand. Only some form of computer-aided manufacturing can provide that kind of flexibility. And the key to success is a common stream of information readily accessible to all who need it.

From a common database

In fact, the wellspring for almost all manufacturing-related information in the near future will surely be the common database generated with the aid of a computer during the design and engineering phase of a manufacturing program and archived in associated storage. Computer graphics represents a rational and convenient port to that database—a means for instantaneous exchange of information between people—be they engineers, designers, draftsmen, scientists, or planners—and the otherwise enigmatic computer.

"In our 20th-century world of print and paper, we tend to think of information in terms of documents," said Lewis M. Branscomb at a recent industry symposium. He is a former director of the National Bureau of Standards and is now vice president and chief scientist at IBM. "In the future, our information machines will permit us to enjoy more-immediate access to all kinds of information-gathering capabilities. Documents will become only occasional by-products of information access, not the primary embodiment." A paperless factory?

When it comes to flexible manufacturing response to market demands, Branscomb talks of the "promise of personal manufacturing and service" that he sees as a great step forward from the Industrial Revolution, when economy of production depended on the sameness of each item produced. "With the computer, manufacturers may for the first time make articles on a mass basis, yet have

Geometric modeling applications*

Purpose	Number of applications reported
NC programming	66
Preparing drawings	65
Calculations	55
Organizing parts lists	32
Assembly studies	32
Work planning	30
Tolerance calculations	27
Cost calculations	22

*Based on analysis of 90 CAD systems

Source: Battelle (Columbus) Laboratories, from Spur, G., et al, "A Survey about Geometric Modeling Systems," *CIRP Annals*, 28(2), 519-530 (1979)

each fit the specific requirements of the intended end user," he suggests.

Branscomb was addressing the question of what will happen in information technology in the next 100 years. But, to some degree, his vision is already coming into focus as CAD/CAM applications continue to proliferate. The spectrum of computer-graphics functions within that environment varies all the way from the relatively simple representation of alphanumeric data to the most complex manipulations and constructions of three-dimensional models.

At one end of the spectrum, computer graphics is itself used as a passive medium to merely display data and provide management information. Increasingly, management-information systems are providing computer-generated graphs and charts to complement or replace the relatively uninspiring stacks of dull,

Programming confidence

Programming type	Probability NC programming will run correctly	
	Machining	Metalforming
Manual	10%	25%
Computer w/o plotter	55%	70%
Computer with plotter	75%	95%

Source: Structural Dynamics Research Corp

often unintelligible computer printouts. A bar chart, possibly in living color, displayed at a manager's terminal can be much more effective than reams of paper.

It's happening at Lockheed-Georgia Co, where executives are beginning to locate the critically important data they need in seconds and by simply touching a few buttons. "No phone calls, no reports, no briefings, and no computer print-outs," says Robert B. Ormsby, president of the company. He claims that the Management Information and Decision Support (MIDS) system that Lockheed-Georgia is developing provides current, correct, and important management information instantly.

The system comprises special desktop computers, a central host computer, and terminals that allow executives to rapidly call up any preprogrammed chart or graph from a large host computer and to display it on a color cathode-ray-tube (CRT) display. The system is not interactive, and editing, as well as updating of the underlying data, is performed off-line with a microcomputer-based floppy-disk setup.

Charts and graphs to be displayed on an executive's 13-in. color CRT are selected from a menu (a listing of files, chart codes, and general information in the MIDS), and, when necessary, a black-and-white hard copy of the data on the screen can be prepared on the spot.

But according to Bob Pittman, manager of management information and control services at Lockheed-Georgia, the use of color is very important. "It is easier to read, and the information is more readily retained," he points out. For that reason, L-G will soon be interfacing a color copier with the MIDS to provide color hard copies and transparencies for special presentations.

Plotting raises confidence

Computer-generated plots of numerical data have long been used to help with tape verification of NC programs. Plots of CL (cutter-location) or postprocessed data—the path of the cutter—are normally overlaid on a print of the final shape of the part, and the programmer is able to detect gross errors faster than by studying the CL-file printout. Such plotting techniques catch many programming errors and increase the probability that an NC part-program will run correctly the first time it is put on the machine.

Leonard A. Weibel, product manager for NC-programming services at Structural Dynamics Research Corp (Milford, Ohio), reports that, for machining, the probability that a manually prepared NC program is correct is typically about

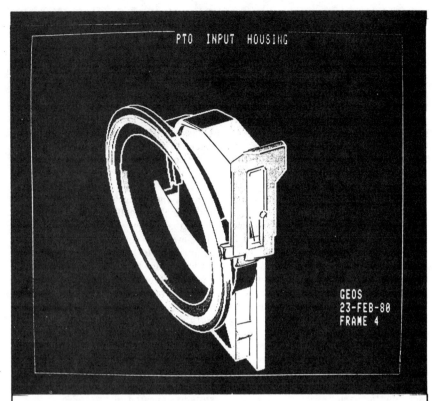

PTO INPUT HOUSING

GEOS
23-FEB-80
FRAME 4

Color will continue to grow in importance, and most computer-graphics output will be in color by the end of the decade, according to Carl Manchover, a long-time expert and consultant in the field. To date, most color for industrial applications has been limited to line work. But full-color surface depictions are also possible. At GE Ordnance Systems (Pittsfield, Mass), experimental work under way uses the SynthaVision modeling system developed by Mathematical Applications Group Inc (Elmsford, NY) to create full 3-D color views of such components as the casting shown above. The hope is that identification of different surfaces with separate colors will help in process planning by providing operators with color identifications for surfaces requiring machining. Other applications may be to check for physical interferences in complex assemblies or tooling

10%. When computer-assisted programming is used, the probability moves up to 55%; when plotting is added, it goes to 75%. For metalforming jobs, Weibel claims, the probability that a program is correct is about 25% for manual programming and moves to 95% for computer-assisted programming with plotting.

Plotting, however, is generally effective for three-axis parts of relatively low complexity, and accurate verification of five-axis plots is virtually impossible with current plotting techniques. Interactive-computer-graphics techniques may hold the answer for such tasks.

There also is an increasing use of graphics displays associated with stand-alone computer controls, such as CNC (computer numerical control), many of which feature a CRT for displaying program data and diagnostic information. A few can also display the cutter path as stored in the CNC memory.

By far the most significant developments in the industrial application of

computer graphics is the proliferating use of *interactive* computer-graphics (ICG) systems, which increasingly are providing the means for truly integrating the CAD/CAM functions. In fact, some practitioners consider interactive computer graphics synonymous with CAD/CAM.

Interactive graphics

The remainder of this report deals primarily with interactive computer graphics—basically software that provides the ability to interactively perform geometric constructions and manipulations using a computer and appropriate graphics terminals. For a long time, the technique was relegated strictly to automated drafting or, at best, to related engineering and design functions.

But manufacturing is also concerned with parts and assemblies that can be described by their geometry, and this descriptive information is needed for all stages of the manufacturing process. Interactive computer graphics is beginning to bridge the gap between design and manufacturing information. Its application can be very pervasive.

For example, ICG can be used to construct a mathematical model of a part in the early design stages for engineering analysis. Finite-modeling techniques can then be used for stress and loading analysis, and the design can be graphically manipulated to evaluate the effect of, say, material strength and thickness. As the design progresses, manufacturing engineers can be called into the process to view the model and evaluate it in terms of cost, tooling requirements, and process capabilities.

Once an acceptable design is reached, the database so created can be used to automatically generate detailed engineering drawings, if they are needed. At the same time, a bill of materials for production planning can be automatically generated. The same database can then be used to plan the manufacturing process and to actually generate toolpath information for NC machining. By the same token, the graphic part model can be used to design and fabricate the fixtures and tooling required for manufacturing the part.

Some of these techniques are already in full use in the aerospace and automobile industries. In fact, it is probably no exaggeration to suggest that General Motors' mid-sized cars could not have been developed and put into production in such timely fashion without the aid of interactive computer graphics. GM President E.M. "Pete" Estes himself acknowledges that, without CAD/CAM the company's X-body 1979 models would not have been available for another year.

The shift of graphics applications from the design function into the manufacturing arena is amply demonstrated by a survey of geometric-modeling applications made by Prof G. Spur (Technical University of Berlin). *Geometric modeling* refers to techniques for providing computer-compatible descriptions of the geometry of a part, and various schemes for the most efficient computer utilization are under development. Spur looked at some 90 so-called CAD systems and found that the largest number of applications were in connection with NC programming. Next came the preparation of drawings and third in line was calculations, presumably engineering analysis.

When interactive computer-graphics systems first emerged in industry, they were typically implemented with in-house-developed software on large mainframe computers. Then, with the development of graphics software to run on minicomputers, a whole new market for stand-alone turnkey interactive graphics systems appeared.

Now these systems, originally developed primarily for automated drafting, are beginning to be used as nodes in distributed hierarchical CAD/CAM systems, performing a wide range of manufacturing tasks.

The development of interactive graphics systems has been enhanced by a fortunate coupling of circumstances: the increasing availability of appropriate technology in a rapidly growing market. "In 1979, CAD/CAM was a $300-million industry," says Fontaine Richardson, vice president of Applicon Inc (Burlington, Mass). "For 1980, we expect it to top $400-million. And, by 1985, we anticipate the industry to be well over $1.5-billion." The industry's current annual growth rate is around 50%.

A good part of that market represents computer-graphics systems. According to Gerber Systems Technology Inc (South Windsor, Conn), by 1986, the overall market for interactive graphics systems is expected to be $750-million. Of course, that includes 2-D systems, such as are used for printed-circuit-board and integrated-circuit design. But Gerber officials believe that the fastest-growing portion of that market will be in connection with the more complex 3-D CAD/CAM applications.

Such predictions do not arise out of idle fascination with new technology. They reflect confidence that interactive computer graphics can help reach three main business objectives:

■ Reducing the lead time required to bring a product to market.

■ Reducing cost by improving productivity.

■ Improving quality.

Those are the promises of interactive computer graphics. Let's now take a closer look at the technology behind those promises.

Basics of interactive computer graphics

A typical turnkey interactive-computer-graphics system is a hardware/software combination comprising a series of modules operating on a distributed-processing principle. It commonly includes a computer subsystem that can communicate with a host computer, one or more workstations (the display terminals), and peripheral devices, such as plotters, drafting systems, and line printers.

The computer subsystem handles the major computational and control functions and acts as traffic manager in a multiterminal system. For example, the IDS-80 system offered by Gerber Technology Inc controls many simultaneous activities of graphics-workstation operation, program development (for special user-oriented programs) communications (with a host, among terminals and peripherals, and with other IDS systems), data management, and background-program development.

The workstation is where the action is. It accepts digital signals from the central processor and converts them into commands for function generators that produce the lines, circles, curves, and symbols used to create the pictorial display on an associated CRT. These display instructions are typically handled by a built-in minicomputer that also handles such picture transformations as scaling, zooming, clipping, and translating.

In addition to the CRT, workstations also include a variety of input devices to help the operator communicate with the system. These include alphanumeric keyboards, function keys, cursor manipulators, light pens, and so-called tablets or sketch pads. More about those later.

Most important, workstations are interactive devices that provide almost immediate response to the user's inquiries or commands. Multiple-workstation systems operate in a time-share mode: each terminal "thinks" it has its own exclusive central processor. The only time significant delays may be experienced is when the CPU is overloaded with too many requests, but that is usually only a matter of seconds.

The cathode ray tube is the standard display device of all present ICG systems. It is essentially the same device that produces the picture on your home TV set. Although there is a constant search for devices that can retain images more readily or can be accommodated in smaller spaces, the CRT is presently the only economical and practical device for interactive-graphics applications.

The CRT uses electric fields to generate a finely focused, high-speed beam of electrons and to deflect the beam to various parts of a phosphor-coated screen surface. When the phosphor coating is excited by the impinging electron beam, it glows to produce a visible trace

Cathode ray tube

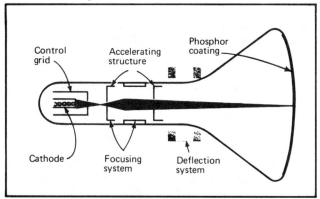

Direct-view storage tube

Tektronix Inc

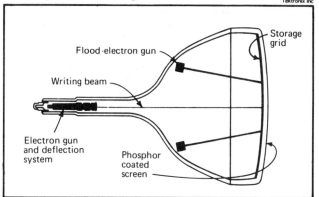

of the beam position. The basic elements of a CRT are these:

- A cathode, which, when heated, emits electrons.
- A control grid to control direction and rate of electron emission.
- An accelerating structure that produces a high-velocity beam of electrons.
- A focusing system that creates a fine spot when the beam hits the screen.
- A deflection system for moving the beam around on the screen.
- A phosphor coating that glows when the beam strikes it.

These components are enclosed in the familiar cone-shaped glass bottle.

Several deflection schemes are available to generate a pictorial display from digital data. The electron beam can be positioned in a point-to-point fashion along the desired path, and the beam can be intensified at each point to produce a visible spot. With enough spots, a smooth continuous line can be displayed.

In a refinement of this technique, the beam is moved simultaneously in X and Y directions under the control of an appropriate function generator that produces the desired path between end points. For example, vector generators will produce straight lines connecting designated end points, thereby reducing the amount of data that must be handled to draw a single line. Circles, curves, and splines can be generated in a similar manner. Such random-position techniques allow faster display response than the point-to-point approach permits.

Another approach gaining increasing popularity is a deflection scheme similar to that used in the common TV set: the image is generated by modulating the beam intensity as the beam is moved through a regular pattern or raster. Hence the term *raster-scan video display*.

A fundamental characteristic of the basic CRT is that, under normal circumstances, the visible glow produced by the electron beam dies away soon after the beam has moved away from a spot. Typ-

ically, over half the brightness has disappeared in 1/5 second. On the one hand, this presents a problem for preserving an image on the screen for any duration; on the other hand, it also provides the opportunity to generate fast-moving dynamic displays and to rapidly edit an existing display.

Various display techniques combining different deflection schemes and methods for preserving or rewriting the image have developed over the years. Three basic schemes are generally used for interactive-computer-graphics applications: vector refresh, direct-view storage, and raster scan.

The vector-refresh approach

Historically the oldest and probably the most widely used display technique

Beam-deflection schemes

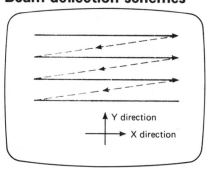

Raster scan

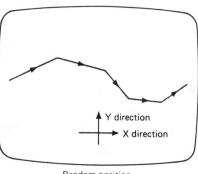

Random position

until recently is the vector-refresh process. It is sometimes referred to as stroke writing or random scan. The image is continuously regenerated, or "refreshed," to overcome the fading characteristics of the phosphor screen.

The rate at which this refreshing takes place determines whether the image will appear to flicker. A high rate will refresh the phosphor before it begins to fade below a visible level, with no flicker occuring. The refresh must occur at a minimum rate of 30 times per second, or faster than the flicker-fusion rate of the eye, for the image to appear steady.

The need to refresh the image presents a problem as well as an advantage. The problem occurs in complex images (in excess of 4000 vector inches) in which the refresh cycle or the point-to-point image refresh may take longer than the phosphor can stay lighted. Therefore, a large image may flicker. Another disadvantage is that the vector-refresh approach requires additional hardware and/or memory for the refresh cycle, increasing system complexity and cost.

The main advantage of this type of display is that a high degree of dynamics—movement of the display, editing—is possible. High resolution, good image brightness, and a high speed of interaction are other advantages. Also, because the image is generated in a fixed time sequence, it is possible to interface interactive pointing devices, such as light pens with the display.

The direct-storage approach

For the past ten years or so, direct-view storage tubes (DSVT)—an adaptation of the CRT, pioneered by Tektronix Inc, to provide a stored image—have been the most popular graphics display devices. The tube behaves like a CRT with an extremely long-persistent phosphor screen (one that stays lighted a long time). An image on it remains visible almost indefinitely. Here's how it's done:

Instead of "writing" directly on the

phosphor-coated face of the tube, the controlled electron beam is directed at a very fine-mesh wire grid coated with dielectric and mounted just behind the face of the tube. This produces an image pattern of positive charges on the grid which is then "copied" onto the phosphor viewing surface by a continuous flood of electrons issuing from a separate cathode. The flood of electrons maintains the image first generated by the writing beam and prevents it from fading. The result is a flicker-free image, one that does not blink on and off regardless of the amount of data to be handled.

Unlimited amount of data

That's what makes the storage tube so attractive: the amount of data that can be handled is essentially unlimited. Also, lower costs are possible because no separate refresh memory is needed. The resolution of the storage tube is dependent on the density of the storage grid's wire mesh and the capability of the associated software to control the direction of the electron beam.

The main disadvantage of the DVST is that it is a relatively static device. Dynamic representation, or the ability to move an object on the screen to represent motion, is not possible because, once an image is stored and displayed, it must be completely "repainted" for any change. In other words, the entire screen must first be erased and the image redrawn from scratch. No selective erasing is possible.

In complex graphic representations, the need to do a full repaint for a partial image change can become rather tedious and time consuming. Some DVST systems can be operated in a nonstorage write-through mode for limited dynamic and editing features.

One other problem with the storage tube is that it has a relatively low brightness and contrast level and therefore requires dimmed ambient lighting for most effective use. This can lead to additional expenses in the way of special room lighting or shielding.

The raster-scan approach

The size of memory has been a major factor in limiting the development of raster-scan video techniques for interactive-graphics-display purposes. The dramatic decline in the cost of semiconductor memory is changing that picture. Like vector-refresh systems, raster-scan systems use an electron beam directed at the phosphor-coated viewing screen of a CRT and require refreshing. Here, however, the similarity ends.

Instead of going point to point, the beam scans along closely spaced hori-

Prompting messages on Gerber workstation appear on LED display panel above keyboard which is flanked by function buttons. Operator's left hand operates cursor-control

Operator uses light pen and function keys to interact directly with image on screen of IBM CADAM-system terminal. Pen can be used to point, place symbols, or 'draw'

zontal lines composed of a fixed number of dots called pixels (picture elements). Each pixel has an associated memory location specifying its on or off condition. The beam scans across each horizontal line in sequence, starting at the top of the screen, and energizes pixels in accordance with the on/off pattern stored in memory. In effect, the picture is refreshed constantly at the fixed scanning rate and is not dependent on the complexity of the image the way a vector-refresh system does.

Because resolution is determined by the number of pixels and each pixel requires a separate memory element, the resolution of raster-scan video is a direct function of the size of the memory available. For example, a resolution of 500 X 500 pixels requires 250,000 memory elements; doubling the resolution would require 1,000,000 elements, four times as many for twice the resolution! As memory costs continue to plummet, increasing memory size may no longer offer a hindrance to improved resolution.

Other features of raster-scan displays are good brightness, accuracy, and the opportunity for unlimited color.

Inputs are human-oriented

What makes computer graphics such an effective CAD/CAM tool is that it is a "friendly" interface with the computer. Not only does it communicate with pictures, but it also allows the user to interact with those pictures in a very comfortable way, through familiar eye/hand coordination.

Of course, there are the familiar alphanumeric keyboards common to all computer terminals. They are used to issue instructions and enter data. Points can be established by entering coordinate locations, and commands can be issued on how to connect those points.

In addition, most systems have function keyboards, which can be set up so that each key initiates a particular preprogrammed routine. The routines are readily changed by merely loading an appropriate operating program into the system, and overlay shields identify the key functions accordingly. In this way, a system is quickly converted from, say, performing a straight drafting function to preparing an NC program.

But interactive graphics deals, for the most part, with tasks involving geometric constructions that are not unlike drawings. Such tasks are best performed with direct eye/hand coordinated motions, the kind used with pencil and paper. For example, it may be desirable to issue an instruction by simply pointing to a feature on the display screen: erasing a symbol or line or moving an entire feature. Or it may be desirable to add lines

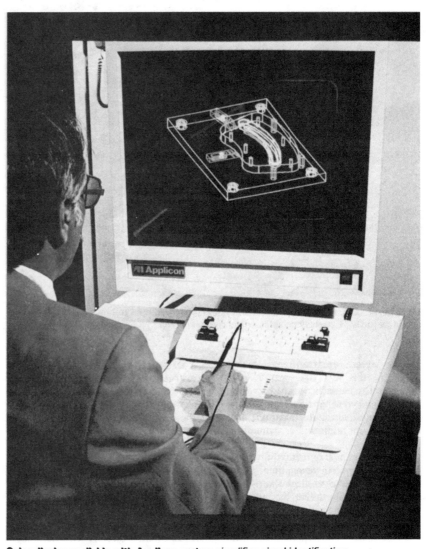

Color display available with Applicon system simplifies visual identification of information. Tablet character-recognition system allows use of free-hand symbols

or symbols or even construct a part by "drawing" it on the screen, much like sketching on paper, and letting the system clean up the sketch and add dimensions.

A variety of input devices are available to handle such pointing and positioning tasks. Those used for CAD/CAM applications include cursors, tablets, stylus pens, and light pens. Cursor devices rely on visual feedback from a symbol that can be moved about the screen with a hand-operated mechanical device, such as a joy stick. For example, a standard input method with Gerber systems is a handy desktop control arm that controls the position of a "+" cursor on the screen. Other systems use a joy stick to control a set of cross hairs.

Tablets use touch or stylus

A variety of tablets and sketch pads are used for interacting with graphics systems. These flat surfaces, usually sep-

arate from the display and easily moved, are used to generate commands or to "draw" pictures and symbols.

In the simplest form, tablets are arranged with a matrix of touch-sensitive squares that can be tied to specific user-defined symbols or functions. The user can select symbols or patterns associated with each square and, by means of a cursor, indicate a location on the screen, and, when the square is touched, that symbol automatically appears on the screen. Overlays that illustrate the symbols can be generated by the graphics system and produced on some type of associated hard-copy device.

Other tablets provide digitizing so that any pattern drawn on its surface with an electronically coupled stylus is automatically converted into graphics data and is also displayed on the CRT. Symbolic data entry is often included on such a sketch pad: an area at the top is reserved for symbol squares, which, when touched

Part of tablet used with Computervision system is reserved for symbolic and menu entries. Large DVST displays graphics only; refresh CRT with keyboard is for prompting

with the stylus, are transferred to the screen. In this way, the operator can draw, point to a specific location on that drawing while viewing the screen (a cursor is displayed for stylus location), and then select an appropriate symbol or instruction.

Applicon goes a step further in the use of the tablet: symbol recognition. Using the electronic stylus to draw short-hand like symbols on the tablet, the operator can issue system commands without looking away from the display. The system automatically interprets these free-hand-drawn symbols, executes the commands, and displays the results on the CRT screen.

The free-hand symbols used with the Applicon tablet-recognition system are user-definable: they are "taught" to the system. A standard set of symbols that can be readily modified comes with the system.

Most tablets also are used to set up a menu of commands to make the opera-tor's task easier. Instead of a long string of instructions that have to be typed at the keyboard, these can be arranged as single commands initiated with the touch of the stylus on an appropriate square. Tablet menus typically include standard geometric construction and editing commands but can also include special commands created by the user for a particular application.

Light pens work on the screen

Light pens are photo-optical devices that can interact directly with the image on the CRT screen. When pointed at an item on the screen, they generate information from which the item can be identified by a tracking program.

With refresh systems, the refresh cycle provides the tracking. The pen responds only to very bright light and therefore sees a spot on the screen only at the instant it is being refreshed. When the pen is triggered, the system immediately searches the refresh buffer and locates the data being refreshed at the instant the pen was triggered.

The CADAM system offered by IBM uses such a pen-like device to pinpoint the location of lines, points, or characters and communicates the information to the computer. (CADAM stands for Computer-graphics Augmented Design and Manufacturing, an interactive CAD/CAM system developed by Lockheed Corp.) Under application-program control, the IBM light pen can also be used as a tracing or sketching instrument that permits the direct "drawing" of lines and points on the CRT screen.

Pointing at buttons

Another common way of interacting with graphics systems is to display a menu of commands on the CRT screen and select functions from it by pointing at an individual symbol or line of text with a light pen or a stylus-and-pad arrangement. These so-called "light buttons" can be called up to the screen when needed or, in some systems, can be available in a reserved location on the screen at all times.

The buttons can actually be complete text statements describing the function to help the operator select the correct one. Also, most ICG systems provide prompting messages, either on the screen or on an associated LED (light-emitting diode) display.

In some instances, dual-screen setups are used: a fast-responding refresh CRT provides prompting messages for interacting with the system and a direct-view storage tube provides flicker-free graphics output regardless of the amount of graphic data displayed. For example, IBM's new Softcopy system for CADAM uses such a setup to allow a user to view and visually manipulate, but not modify, drawings in the CADAM database. Softcopy provides graphic inquiry to the design database for users in manufacturing, planning, quality control, or management—without the chance that the database will be altered.

Tasks for interactive computer graphics

Nesting groups of parts for automatic cutting and the preparation of NC programs are ideally suited for computer-graphics handling. In each case, a given geometric configuration, the part, must be transformed into machining instructions, and data transformation is something these systems do most efficiently. Let's take a look at some typical nesting examples.

In aircraft work, there is frequent need to rout many diversely shaped parts from sheetmetal. The shapes are odd, and common practice has been to use templets to manually rout stacks of identical parts. That requires preparing blanks, with attendant material waste, and then mounting stacks of blanks and their templets to a backing plate before they go to the router. Usually, a chang-ing group of different parts is required by the production schedule, further complicating a highly labor-intensive job.

ICG builds a nest

Recently, several aircraft companies have switched to automatic routing schemes, in which a group of closely nested parts is routed from a stack of aluminum sheets. Nesting of the parts, as well as the preparation of an NC program for the router, is accomplished with computer graphics. McDonnell Douglas Corp (St Louis) was among the first companies to follow this course, with the installation of a Trumpf Trumatic Model 3000 BFZ CNC drilling and milling center (AM—Dec'79, p101).

NC-program development at McDonnell Douglas starts with the automatic arrangement of an appropriate nest of parts. This nesting is achieved by first loading the digitized data for individual parts into a database working in conjunction with a mainframe computer. Production planners then access this nesting database through an IBM 2250 graphics terminal that displays a computer-generated nest intended to achieve maximum material utilization of the basic 4- x 6-ft sheets of aluminum used for the stacks.

Using the graphics nesting software, a planner can obtain a reading of the actual material utilization—the system figures out how much scrap there will be—and, if it falls below a certain minimum, can rearrange the nest.

Individual part shapes displayed on the graphics terminal can be moved and rotated as desired with a light pen and function keys. The nesting routine will also automatically establish a preferred sequence of machining—the drilling and routing of all the parts in the nest as well as a riveting pattern for holding the sheets to a backing plate.

Once the planner is satisfied with the nest and the prescribed sequence of operations, a postprocessor run is invoked to convert the nesting data into an NC part-program for the entire nest. The program is then stored in an object file at the host computer until required for manufacturing, when it is transmitted to a DNC computer that performs the final data transformations (interpolation and conversions) for the individual machines hooked up to the DNC system.

You might think that only a large aircraft company with its vast computer networks and ample programming capabilities can set up such a scheme. Not so. Several turnkey nesting systems are available for routing and flame cutting operations. For example, Camsco (Richardson, Tex) offers the Command system, which it has recently hooked up with the same Trumpf machine. It has also been applied to cutting with lasers, flame cutters, and waterjet machines.

The Command system is a complete stand-alone affair for the design and nesting of flat templet parts and for the preparation of output to drive NC cutting equipment. In addition to its own part-

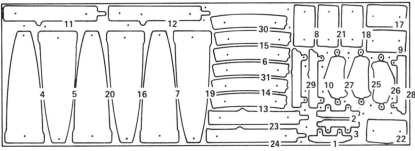

Nesting arrangement (above) for sheet-aluminum parts produced by computer graphics at McDonnell Douglas. The nesting routine establishes a preferred sequence of machining for Trumpf Trumatic BFZ 3000 drilling and milling machine (below) as well as a riveting pattern for holding the stack of sheets to a backing plate during machining

design capability, the system accepts digitized part data, as well as input from in-house design and part-programming systems already in use.

Flamecutting applications

Automated parts nesting through computer graphics is becoming increasingly popular for flamecutting operations. At Minster Machine Co (Minster, Ohio), for example, an Applicon computer-graphics system was installed a couple of years ago primarily to help generate parts nests and NC programs for a Union Carbide computer-controlled burning table (AM—Jan'79,p105).

The first task was to establish a database for the plates to be burned, and this was accomplished by entering them into the system as drawings. Each drawing was handled as a "cell" so that the associated data could be accessed and moved as a unit. These cells were stored under a drawing number of the weldment into which they eventually are assembled.

Once the drawing database was established, it was available for creating nesting patterns and to generate NC programs for the flame cutter. Six separate but integrated graphics routines are used for these tasks. One routine initially sets up the graphics terminal and displays a part menu. By specifying the name of the panel or the raw-plate size to be used, the software divides the screen into two areas, displaying the panel on the top half of the screen.

When a menu command is given, the program selects drawings from the library of parts suitable for the material thickness selected and from those required to meet the manufacturing schedule. These part drawings then appear on the lower half of the screen in preparation for the nesting procedure.

Once the screen is set up, another program is used to move and rotate part drawings so that specific line and arc segments are parallel and separated by a given kerf width. The planner selects the lines and segments simply by indicating them with a screen cursor operated by a data tablet and stylus.

Here is where Applicon's symbol-recognition feature comes in handy. Certain symbols, such as a check mark, executed with the stylus are interpreted as specific instructions regarding the disposition of the drawing, so that, with literally the same motion, a feature can be identified and an instruction given. In this way, parts are arranged as desired until the entire panel is filled to the operator's satisfaction.

Next the planner uses another program to generate the flame path in the desired sequence. Then APT-like statements are used to generate the required tool path. The resulting cutter-location (CL) file is then run through a custom-tailored postprocessor residing in the graphics system, and a part-program for the Linde machine is automatically generated.

The appeal of computer graphics to NC part-programming is simple: What you see on the screen is what you get in the shop. At least that's the promise, and there is no question that the ability to visualize a part, its tooling, and the tool path invariably raises the probability that a part-program will do what it is supposed to when it gets to the shop. At the most, it may require only minor revisions. Certainly the chance of a catastrophic crash becomes minimal.

Relief from tedious work

NC programming with interactive graphics frees the programmer from a lot of the tedious work involved in more-conventional computer-assisted programming—provided that the geometric database has been established during the design phase. Once that database is available, it is a relatively simple matter to call up the part to the CRT, and APT labels (describing elements of geometry, such as lines and points) can be added automatically.

Next the programmer can graphically generate tool paths interactively, while viewing the part as if sighting down the machine spindle. In the CADDS 3 system from Computervision (Bedford, Mass), this is accomplished by the following steps:

- Select tool.
- Define type of entry and exit such as ramp or plunge, for example.
- Select relationship between tool motion and part surfaces such as "tangent to," for example.
- Select drive and check surfaces.
- Define number of rough cuts and sequence numbers.
- Define parameters that do not directly affect tool-path generation, such as feedrate, spindle speed, coolant on/off, etc.

Once the tool paths are selected, they can be verified visually on the CRT, which displays various views of the part with its associated tool paths. An isometric view will show a fairly good 3D representation of how the part will be machined, further enhancing the credibility of the final program. Of course, interactive editing of the tool path can be performed at any point during this verification process.

Once the tool path has been generated, the data is readily converted to a variety of different NC-tape sources for final postprocessing. For CAPPS 3, this includes APT, COMPACT II, IBM 360, CL FILE. Computervision, like other ICG vendors, also offers a library of postprocessors that can reside in the graphics system for on-line postprocessing. Custom postprocessors can also be developed for most graphics systems to provide on-line tape-preparation facility.

Tooling as you go

Interactive computer graphics really pays off when it is applied from start to finish in the manufacture of a product, because the opportunity exists to better integrate and overlap such related tasks as tool design. Once the part can be displayed for NC-tape preparation, why not also design the tooling—at the same terminal and concurrent with the programming activity? And, once the tooling has been designed, applying NC machining via graphics programming for tooling construction becomes feasible. Under normal circumstances, that might be hard to justify.

The approach has particular advantage in aircraft-type work, for which tooling construction is a complex time-consuming process with many intermediate steps. A combination of computer graphics and NC can eliminate some of the master tools (the tooling tools) needed to produce production tooling. Here are some of the advantages of interactive graphics in connection with tooling as noted by Robert Sanderson, of Grumman Aerospace Corp (Bethpage, NY), where a number of graphics systems are in use:

- Lower overall tooling costs. As the requirements for certain tools are eliminated or reduced and the time associated with the remaining tools is reduced, overall tooling-fabrication costs are also reduced.
- Earlier tool delivery. When tooling tools, such as mockups, fixtures, models, masters, templets, etc, are no longer required for coordination of production tools, the delivery of those production tools is vastly improved.
- No accumulative tool errors. It is possible to accumulate and transmit errors through each successive tooling-tool step—especially in a complicated family-tree scheme—to the point where tolerance of the production tool is compromised. These cumulative errors are eliminated when the production tool is generated directly on an NC machine.
- Faster tool repair/rework. Engineering revisions will be incorporated directly into the production tools rather than into the tooling tools first, as is current practice.
- Reduced storage requirements. Warehouse costs, including space and
[Continued]

From concept to prototype with graphics

The time needed to bring a product to market can often spell success or disaster for the product. Most often, the design and manufacture of tooling is a critical factor, and the ongoing shortage of skilled labor is no help. Effective utilization of computer graphics in the fabrication of tooling and models can substantially reduce the lead-time.

The CompuTool CAD/CAM system developed by the CAD/CAM (CDM) Div of National Computer Systems Inc (Minneapolis) is specifically intended for tool-making and prototype work. The concept is based on integrating interactive graphics functions with NC software that controls the machine tool for producing the part.

"We are quite opinionated about the need to have the graphics and the machine tool controls integrated," says Larry Martin, vice president, product development at CDM. 'That's how, we think, you get really meaningful performance, the kind you need for the complex surfaces, close tolerances, and good finish associated with tool-and-die work.'

Three hardware elements are involved: CompuScanner, a 3-D coordinate measuring machine to capture data from models, molds, drawings, prototypes, or the like; CompuScope, an interactive-graphics design center for creating complex 2-D and 3-D designs; and CompuMill, a four-axis milling machine specifically designed to convert the magnetic-tape output from the CompuScope into machining operations.

The technique used in the manufacture of this prototype for an automobile wheel is typical of the CompuTool approach.

It starts with the creation of a 2-D design on the CompuScope. First the rim and hub diameters were established, and five intersecting lines were created dividing the circle into five equal parts.

Next the outer circular limit for the decorative wheel design was established, and offset lines were drawn for each spoke interval. Stud-hole locations were defined, and extraneous construction lines were deleted. This produced a basic design envelope.

Then one of the spoke lines was converted to a three-point control curve for a B-spline and a pleasing curve was generated to replace one of the straight radial spoke lines. This curve was then automatically copied, mirrored, and rotated to replace all other radial spoke lines. Now a clear image of the designer's intent was available on the CompuScope screen.

Further interactive-graphics manipulations were then used to generate a foreground and background pattern to be used for the final 3-D finished wheel design. The foreground pattern was set at one depth and the background pattern deeper and a general spherical concave shape was choosen.

The final design data was then automatically converted into a control program for a CompuMill, and a foam prototype was produced.

Time for the entire process: 6 hours.

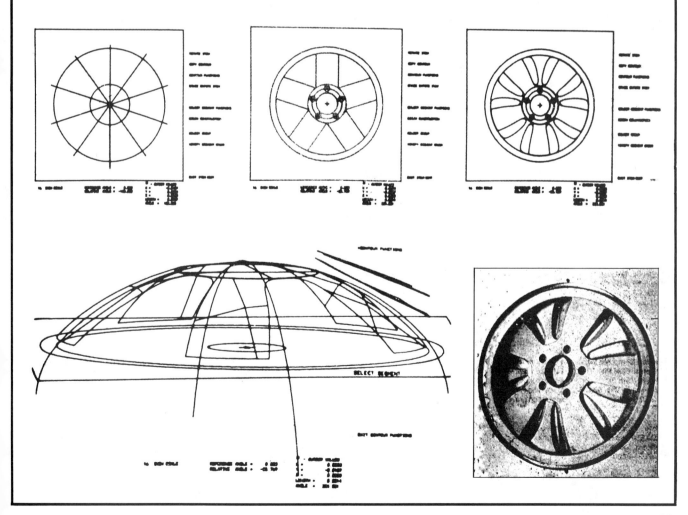

Turnkey computer-graphics systems

Company	Maximum and recommended number of terminals per system	Typical instruction-execution speed	Does the system support on-line communication with host processors? Which ones?	Speed of link to host	What display technology is used?	Is color available? How many
Applicon Inc 32 Second Ave Burlington, Mass 01803 617/272-7070	Recommended: 4	Flat access: 150 ns Typical access: 350-500 ns Worst case: 650 ns	Yes; IBM, Honeywell, CDC, Univac, DEC	Up to 9600 bps	Storage and raster scan	Yes, 8
Auto-trol Technology Corp 5650 Pecos St Denver, Colo 80221 303/458-5900	Maximum: 12 Recommended: 4-9	400 ns	IBM	Up to 60k baud	Combined storage and refresh vector	No
Calma 527 Lakeside Dr Sunnyvale, Calif 94086 408/245-7522	Maximum: 6 Recommended: 4	1 sec	Yes	1.4 Mbits/sec	Raster scan and storage	Yes, 7 primary with 4096 variations
Computervision Corp 201 Burlington Rd Bedford, Mass 01730 617/275-1800	Maximum: 10 Recommended: 8	900 ns	IBM 360/370, CDC 6000, Univac 1108, Sigma 7, Cyber 174, Honeywell 6000	Sync: 4800/9600/up to 40.8k baud Async: 1200 baud	Storage and raster	No
Digital Equipment Corp 200 Forest St. Marlboro, Mass 01752 617/897-5111	Variable	Floating point 'AddF' with FPA (reg to reg) = 0.8 μsec	VAX is a host. Communication to other mainframes available	Options available to link to other hosts	Support of all types	Color available via VS11, TEK 4022, Ramtek
Evans & Sutherland 580 Arapeen Dr Salt Lake City, Utah 84108 801/582-5847	Maximum: 4 Recommended: 1-4	System is interfaced to DEC PDP-11 or VAX 11/780 CPUs	DEC CPUs	$1.8 Mbytes/sec	Vector refresh	Yes, 449
Gerber Systems Technology Inc 40 Gerber Rd East South Windsor, Conn 06074 203/644-2581	4 per CPU, networking to 16 terminals; more available through networking	175 ns	Gerber Communications Controller (GCSS) permits bidirectional communication between host with RS-232C modems	Up to 9600 baud, depending on user's modem capacity	Storage standard, partial refresh in IDS, full refresh in IDS-80	No, Gerber is studying this option to incorporate in 1980s
IBM Corp (CADAM) 1133 Westchester Ave White Plains, NY 10604 914/696-1900	Depends on CPU used	Depends on CPU used	Yes, some CPUs	User choice	IBM 3250	No
McDonnell Douglas Automation Co (MCAUTO) PO Box 516 St. Louis, Mo 63166 314/232-8021	S/230:6 S/250:8 11/70:8	Depends on CPU	Yes	Depends on CPU	Standard storage, Tektronix 4014	No
National Computer Inc Systems, CDM Div 4444 W 76th St Minneapolis, Minn 55435 612/830-8564	11/34:2 maximum 11/70:6 maximum, simultaneously processing full application program	See DEC manual	Yes, DEC and any other offered by DEC	Reference Adage for given host	Vector refresh, DEC RSX 11M	Yes, same as number of stations supported
Nicolet Zeta Corp 2300 Stanwell Dr Concord, Calif 94520 415/671-0600	Maximum: 2 Recommended: 1	NA	Yes, all major FORTRAN mainframes	110-9600 baud	Storage DVST	No

Do prompting messages share the display with the graphic image?	What are standard and optional input devices?	What are the standard output devices?	Does the system use wire-frame, geometric description of objects, or just picture description?	Are objects described in 2, 2½, or 3D?	Are attributes—for example, non-graphic information—attached to a geometric entity supported?	Is interactive generation of NC tool paths supported?	Is direct generation of NC tape from drawing available? Is it in APT format?
Optional; information display may be turned off	Electronic pen/tablet for character recognition and tablet menu. Function keyboard and alphanumeric keyboard	Line plotter, photoplotter, mag tape, line printer, electrostatic printer, paper/Mylar tape	Wire frame and surface	True 3D	Yes	Yes	Yes; yes
No	Programmable function keys, thumb wheels, joy stick, digitizer, electronic pen/tablet	Flat-bed plotter, hard-copy unit, typewriter console	Both wire frame and geometric	2D and 3D	Fully supported	Fully supported	Fully supported; yes
No, separate side-by-side screens graphic/alpha-numeric	Programmable function keys and electronic pen/tablets	Plotters, printers, tape, pattern generators, paper tape	All three	2D and 3D	Fully supported	Yes, fully supported	Yes; fully supported
Yes, raster; no, storage	Standard: telewriter, alphanumeric display, menu, electronic pen/tablet. Options: programmable function keys	Line printer, tape drive, pen plotter, electrostatic plotter, paper-tape reader/punch, card reader	All three	Yes. All three modes (full 2D and 3D) from same database, depending on application	Yes	Yes	Yes
Either way	Variable	All these	Geometric description of objects	3D	Fully supported	Fully supported	Fully supported; APT format
Option	Data tablet and other I/O devices. DECwriter	Printer/plotter	Wire frame	2,3,4D with perspective and depth cueing	User programmable	User programmable	Plugs available
No	Keyboard with function buttons and cursor control arm, paper-tape reader, mag tape, digitizers; tablet optional	Pen-and-ink plotter, printer, paper tape, mag tape, photo plotter, hard-copy unit; electrostatic available	Wire frame	2, 2½, or 3D	Fully supported	Fully supported	Fully supported in APT source, and APT cutter location is postprocessed for final NC application
Yes	Alphanumeric keyboard, function keyboard, light pen	Plotter	Both	All three	Fully supported	Fully supported	Fully supported; APT
No, separate refreshed message monitor used for prompting messages	Standard: programmable function keyboard with thumbwheel; Optional: joystick, data tablet/pen, digitizer	Mag tape, line printers, paper tape for NC	Wire frame and geometric	Any of the above	Yes, in schematics module	Yes, for all types of machine tools; separate module for lathe work	Yes; APT C/L format
Yes	Light pen, digitizing table, 3D scanner	Plotter printer, machine-tool cassettes, tape	Wire frame	3D	NA	Fully supported	Fully supported; can be APT format
Yes	Optional 36- x 48-in. digitizer, standard 36-in. 4-color drum plotter	Plotter	Picture description	2D	NA	Fully supported	Not supported

Note: This table was excerpted and adapted from *A Survey of Commercial Turnkey CAD/CAM Systems*, published by Productivity International Inc. The 164-page survey lists 112 attributes for 20 turnkey CAD/CAM systems, as well as information about hardware and software. It is available from Productivity International Inc, PO Box 8100, 5622 Dyer St, Dallas, Texas 75205. Price is $95

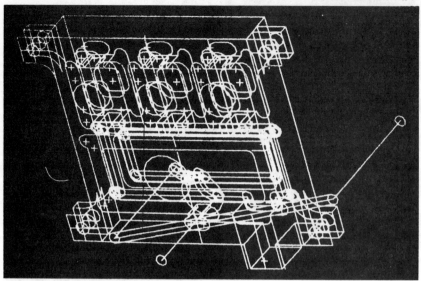

Gerber Systems Technology Inc

The ability to visualize a part and the toolpath to make it raises the probability that an NC program will do what it is supposed to do when it gets to the shop

handling, are reduced because fewer tooling tools are required for a manufacturing program.

■ Decreased dependence on manual skills. The move to production tools made with NC machines will decrease the requirement for such specialized crafts as model makers and plastermen, skills that are fast disappearing.

■ Decreased production problems. When all aircraft components are made with machine tools that obtain their instructions from a single engineering database, they will mate with greater precision. Parts and subassembly coordination will improve to the point where assembly will progress more efficiently, and there will be a reduction in

scrapped or reworked parts with an increase in overall quality.

While Sanderson's last claim for the advantages of computer graphics may yet be more promise than reality, it certainly is a promise that can be held out to any manufacturing environment, not just aerospace.

One of the inherent advantages of interactive-computer-graphics systems is that they offer the possibility of instant call-up of any part in the database. With appropriate data management and some coding and classification, group-technology (GT) techniques can be applied. In this way, redundant work—"reinventing the wheel"—can be eliminated. Family-of-parts programs can provide a look at all similar parts, and an appropriate "model" part can then be altered or used as-is. The same is true for part-programs.

Computervision provides such group-technology features in CV-MIGRAPHICS, a GT software package originally developed by Organization for Industrial Research (Waltham, Mass). With it, the advantages of a computerized drawing file and the benefits of a logical code number combine to create a fast, efficient retrieval system for both design and manufacturing. CV-MIGRAPHICS provides the coding and classification routines that make family-of-parts design and programming possible.

Systems evaluation

Whatever you do, don't for a moment think that you can choose an interactive-computer-graphics system by simply consulting a list of specifications or reviewing a table of characteristics, such as the one presented in this report. Such material is intended only to lead you to formulate the right questions and to point you in an appropriate direction.

Evaluating a computer-graphics system is a most difficult and frustrating task: the technology is complex, and the field is still in a constant state of flux. One of the best guides around is *The Guide for the Evaluation and Implementation of CAD/CAM Systems*, by S.H. Chasen and J.W. Dow. Here is what they suggest as some rules to help both the investigative process and the continuing involvement in CAD/CAM. It applies to computer graphics:

"When possible, use a qualified consultant and/or references at all levels of investigation, because their cost is minimal in comparison to the costs of misdirection, false starts, and the acquisition and operation of the 'wrong' system. It is

worthwhile to take care and time to locate qualified consultants. Study of their track record in the field is essential to ensure competent support.

"Seek advice from vendors and attend their seminars. Remember to discount many of their promises—especially as they relate to future vendor products and projects. It is hard for them to be completely objective.

"Talk to as many users as possible, preferably referred by other than vendors. Remember that users may do well describing the pros and cons of their systems; but without considerable specific experience, they may be very poor at making systems comparisons.

"Attend conferences, seminars, and short courses. However, it is most important that the offerings be studied carefully to see if they contribute to corporate objectives which change and mature with time. Read the brochures very carefully. Do not assume that, because a conference or course has the right title, it truly relates to your needs. Remember that such presentations must be responsive to

a broad audience, many of whom have different objectives from yours. Use your attendance to communicate with others in the field with similar goals.

"Subscribe to periodicals and journals that tell what's going on in the field, what documents are useful, what people are doing, what equipment is being purchased, what new hardware and software are available, and what related events are coming."

Grumman Aerospace has gone through a thorough evaluation procedure prior to implementation of its GEMS (Grumman Engineering/Manufacturing System), which relies heavily on computer-graphics activities at all levels of the design/manufacturing cycle. Company management is convinced that this type of CAD/CAM will become a way of life. But there are some concerns, which were expressed at the 17th Annual Meeting & Conference of the Numerical Control Society by Paul Wiedenhaefer, director of the GEMS program:

■ You have to go all the way; a partial effort is wasted.

■ You must provide ample time for acquiring the necessary equipment, facilities, and people. You cannot suddenly rent equipment and hire trained people or go to a vendor.

■ Once the math-model database system is established as the base for all departments, no department can lapse back into the "old way."

■ The implementation of such systems tends to hasten the demise and disappearance of certain skills that are already scarce.

■ You must pay the costs of two systems—the old and the new—during a lengthy period.

■ You become very capital intense and locked into equipment, systems, and a small crew of highly trained, uniquely skilled people.

Of course, not all of these factors need be major concerns, particularly when installing a stand-alone turnkey computer-graphics systems. All of them do their jobs more efficiently than previous manual methods.

Typically, interactive-graphics systems tend to increase productivity by anywhere from 3:1 to 5:1 depending on whether you talk to vendor or user. As to bringing your product to market in a timely fashion, the automobile industry has reported decreases in new-model lead-times of up to three years, thanks partly to computer graphics. No matter what your concerns, there is no question that, backed up by proper investigation and planning, computer graphics can fulfill the promise it holds out: reduce the lead-time required to bring a product to market, increase productivity, and improve quality. ■

Glossary

The following glossary of terms used in computer graphics has been culled from several sources and contains some descriptions developed during the preparation of this report. The bulk of them have been adapted from a *Glossary of Computer Aided Manufacturing Terms* issued by Computer Aided Manufacturing—International Inc (Arlington, Tex) and the *Data Processing Glossary* available from IBM through its branch offices

Aiming circle. A circle or other pattern of light projected by a light pen onto the surface of the display to guide the accurate positioning of the pen and/or to describe the light pen's field of view.

Algorithm. A prescribed set of well defined rules or processes for the solution of a problem in a finite number of steps; for example, a full statement of an arithmetic procedure for evaluating sin x to a stated precision.

Alphanumeric character set. A set that contains both letters, digits., and other characters.

Alphanumeric display device. A device capable of displaying only letters, digits, and special characters, such as the ASCII characters, from a fixed repertoire of such characters in one or more character fonts.

Application programs. Computer program(s) devised for a specific task.

ASCII. American Standard Code for Information Interchange.

Assembly language. An operation language composed of brief expressions which is translated by an assembler into a machine language. The language result (object code) from the assembler is a character-for-character translated version of the original.

Baud. A unit of signaling speed equal to the number of discrete conditions of signal events per second.

Blinking control. A programming technique or hardware option on a display element that is repeatedly displayed and erased to attract the attention of the user.

Bounded geometry. A definition of the extent of a solid object in space.

Buffer storage. Any type of storage that holds data from an input device for the active or processing storage.

CAD. Computer-Aided Design.

CAM. Computer-Aided Manufacturing.

Canned cycle. A fixed function in hardware or software in which several operations are performed in a predetermined sequence and ends with return to the beginning cycle.

CAPP. CAM-I Automated Process Planning.

Cathode ray tube (CRT). A device that presents data in visual form by means of controlled electron beams.

CL. Cutter location.

Clipping. Removing parts of display elements that lie outside a window. Also referred to as 'scissoring.'

Computer graphics. A human-oriented system that uses the capabilities of a computer to create, transform, and display pictorial and symbolic data.

Conversational mode. Communication between a terminal and the computer in which each entry from the terminal elicits a response from the computer and vice versa.

CRT. Cathode ray tube.

Cursor. Visual, movable pointer used on a CRT.

Database. A collection of data fundamental to an enterprise, comprising comprehensive files of information having predetermined structure and organization and suitable for communication, interpretation, or processing by humans or automatic means.

Data link. The communication lines, modems, and communication controls of all stations connected to the line, used in the transmission of information between two or more stations.

Data set. (1) An organized collection of information. (2) The major unit of data storage and retrieval in the operating system, consisting of a collection of data in one of several prescribed arrangements and described by control information to which the system has access.

Data structures. The organization of datum, data, or data sets into classification categories with identifiers and referencing relationships.

Descriptor. In information retrieval, a word used to categorize or index information.

Direct-view storage tube (DVST). A CRT that generates a long-lasting image. This is accomplished by first using a writing beam of electrons to create a transient image on a storage grid and copying this image on the viewing screen using a continuous flood of electrons.

Distributed processing. A method of performing a data-processing task by performing the needed simultaneous operations in several interconnected processors of a distributed computer network, thereby improving the efficiency of the data processing task.

Edit. To modify the form or format of data: for example, to insert or delete characters.

Emulate. To imitate one system with another so that the imitating system accepts the same data, executes the same programs, and achieves the same results as the imitated system.

Emulator. A device or program that emulates.

Flicker. An undesirable pulsation of a display image on a CRT, occurring when the refresh rate is so low that regeneration becomes noticeable.

Font. A family or assortment of characters of a given size and style.

Function keyboard. An input device for an interactive display terminal consisting of a number of function keys.

Geometric modeling. A system that represents three-dimensional shape in a computer and renders it transportable.

Hard copy. A printed copy of machine output in a visually readable form: for instance, printed reports, listings, documents, and summaries.

Host computer. The primary or controlling computer in a multiple computer operation.

Interactive graphics. The use of a display terminal in a conversational or interactive mode.

Interactive mode. A method that allows on-line worker-machine communication. Commonly used to enter data and to direct the course of a program.

Light button. A display element, usually text, that may be selected with a light pen in order to issue commands.

Light pen. A photosensitive stylus used to identify display elements or to detect the light generated within an aiming symbol.

Light-pen detect. The sensing by a light pen of light generated on a CRT. It can provide an interrupt that may be interpreted by a display-control program to determine either positional or display-element identifying information.

Light-pen tracking. The process of tracking the movement of a light pen across the screen of a CRT display device.

Macro. A language instruction from which many instructions can be generated.

Management-information systems. (MIS). Management performed with the aid of automatic data processing.

Mapping. A transformation from one coordinate system into another.

Matrix. (1) In mathematics, a two-dimensional rectangular array of quantities. Matrices are manipulated in accordance with the rules of matrix algebra. (2) In computers, a logic network in the form of an array of input leads and output leads with logic elements connected at some of their intersections. (3) By extension, an array of any number of dimensions.

Menu. A display of options on a terminal device for user selection.

MIS. Management Information System.

Operating system. Software that controls the execution of computer programs and that may provide scheduling, debugging, input/output control, accounting, compilation, storage assignment, data management, and related services.

Outline representation. A wire-frame representation of an object but with hidden lines removed.

Passive mode. A method of operation of a display device that does not allow any online interaction or alteration.

Password. A unique string of characters that a program, computer operator, or user must supply to meet security requirements before gaining access to data.

Pixel. Pictue element, a term used to describe the information contained in one unit of display surface.

Postprocessor. A computer program that converts all the cutter-path coordinate data (obtained from the general-purpose processor and all other programming instructions and specifications for the particular machine and control) into a form that the machine can interpret correctly.

Protocol. The rules for controlling data communication between devices in computer systems or computer networks.

Raster-scan display. A CRT display that generates an image by modulating the beam intensity as the beam is moved through a regular pattern, or raster. Also referred to as 'digital TV.'

Refresh. To repeatedly produce the same display image on a CRT so that the image remains visible. Without refresh, the image would decay rapidly.

Scissoring. Removing parts of display elements that lie outside defined bounds.

Scroll. The controlled vertical or horizontal movement of the display image on a cathode ray tube with automatic scissoring: for example, new data appears on the display surface at one edge as

other data disappears at the opposite edge.

Software portability. Software easily installed in a variety of makes of computers and computer hardware configurations.

Spline. In part-programming, a special cubic interpolation routine for fairing of curves. The slopes of the curve are adjusted by an iterative procedure until curvature is continuous over the length of the curve.

Stylus. A hand-held pointer that provides coordinate data of a display surface, or tablet: for example, a light pen, sonic pen, tablet stylus. The coordinate data may be used to generate a display element, move an element, or issue a system command.

Tablet. An input device that has a writing surface with a direct correspondence betwen positions on the tablet and addressable points on the display surface of a display device.

Transform. To change a display image by, for instance, scaling, rotating, or translating.

Unbounded geometry. An object as defined by the intersection of a series of infinite surfaces. APT descriptions use unbounded geometry.

Vector-refresh display. A CRT that generates an image as a series of vectors drawn from point to point in a random fashion; the image is regenerated or refreshed to avoid fading.

Window. A bounded area, within a display image, that contains a scissored subset of the displayable data.

Wire-frame representation. A perspective projection of a three-dimensional object as viewed from an arbitrary position. Hidden lines are not removed.

Zoom. To continuously scale all the display elements of a display image to more clearly perceive and manipulate details not readily perceived in the previous view.

Master models are essentially accurate full-scale three-dimensional models of various sections of an aircraft airframe. They are used to construct master gages for making production tooling

Tooling built with computer graphics

Working from a common database, designers and NC programmers use the same computer graphics system to design masters, then prepare NC tapes for their manufacture

"Conservatively speaking, for selected applications, use of our computer graphics systems typically results in a 2:1 improvement over previous methods," says Roger Marvel, a tool-engineering project manager at Boeing Wichita Co. One of those selected applications is in connection with the design and manufacture of master models used for making airframe-assembly tooling.

Working from a common database that originates with engineering, both tool designers and part-programmers use the same terminals of a Gerber IDS interactive graphics system first to generate the design and then to develop the necessary NC part-programs for the manufacture of the master models. "What really makes the computer-graphics approach so productive is the fact that it is an interactive system that responds to the operator's interrogations on a real-time

basis," notes Marvel. "You can get a picture of what you are doing almost immediately, and, if you don't like it, you can change it until you have what you want."

Master models are essentially accurate full-scale three-dimensional models of the various sections of an aircraft airframe. They are used as masters for making production tooling for construction and assembly of the aircraft. In some instances, the models are used to construct other master gages or master tools, as they are sometimes called.

Skeleton defines shape

The construction of a master model involves, first, erecting a skeleton of contoured ribs and stringers (some call them headers and spars) on an appropriate base and then aligning them so that their outer envelope accurately

defines the shape of the particular aircraft section involved. In order to render a full-bodied model, the surface area between the skeleton members is filled with plaster that is "swept," or faired, to produce the finished surface contour of the model.

Drafting practice prevailed

Before introduction of computer graphics, the design procedure involved manual drafting-board practice. The designer would first obtain a printout of data—the mathematical definition—for the master curve of the particular airframe section for which the tool was to be designed. This data, generated by the mainframe computer, was used to draw the master curve to which the tooling must fit.

An appropriate base was determined, and then the indidivual skeleton mem-

Contoured ribs await installation on base for construction of 747 side-panel master model. The ribs were cut on NC router with control tape prepared on computer graphics

bers, including necessary mounting hardware, was designed, with conventional design/drafting techniques.

Once the design is complete, the NC programmer builds an APT-program manuscript for computer generation of the NC tapes required to cut the various elements of the master skeleton. The programmer includes commands for the computer to furnish the same master-curve data used by the designer. The APT statements are entered in the mainframe computer via a keypunch or other terminal, and the data is processed in a batch mode.

In order to view the cutter path and verify that it is what is needed, the programmer must call for a plot on a flat-bed plotter. Usually it takes a number of tries before the programmer is satisfied and the program can be post-processed for the specific NC machine to be used.

With the graphic system, both the designer and the NC programmer have visual access to the master curves and can observe the various plotting tries directly on a CRT terminal. Also, it is possible to "overlay" related information so that various design and programming functions can be integrated. For example, the construction holes for all the ribs of a master can be related to a grid pattern of threaded holes on a subplate used on the milling machine. Each time the designer starts on a new rib, the grid pattern can be overlayed and appropriate locations chosen.

By the same token, a programmer can overlay a picture of the selected holddown clamps to ensure that they do not interfere with the cutter path. In both instances, designer and programmer have the information at their fingertips instantly though the CRT terminal.

A hardware/software combination

The Gerber interactive graphics system is a combination of hardware and software, consisting of a central processing unit (CPU) and one or more work stations. The CPU is a Hewlett-Packard 2113 minicomputer equipped with mass storage and input/output (I/O) peripherals. It updates the working database and handles the system's calculations, communications, and management routines.

Each IDS work station contains its own H-P minicomputer devoted to directing the design, drafting, digitizing, or programming operation. A number of different work stations are available to suit specific needs: design/edit, drafting, drafting/digitizing, or digitizing.

At Boeing Wichita Co, the Tool Engineering Unit has three separate IDS systems, each with four work stations. Each work station has a CRT terminal

Erection of skeleton for master model involves great care in aligning the various elements. Here workers use optical alignment tooling to make sure ribs sit true

The surface area between the skeleton members is filled with plaster that is "swept," or faired, to produce the finished surface contour of the full-bodied model

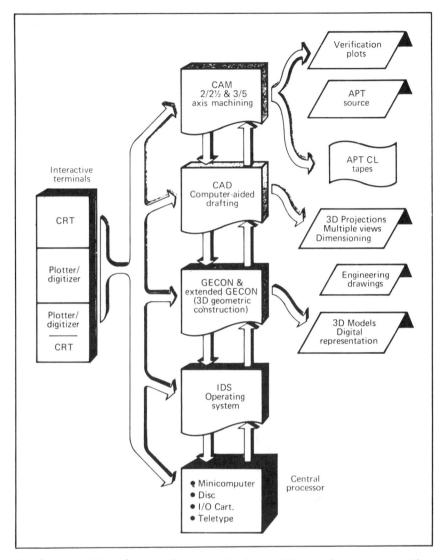

The Gerber graphics software package is designed around three major areas: geometric definition functions (Gecon), computer-aided drafting, and computer-aided machining

Production tool is checked against master gage to ensure proper fit. The master gage (lower member) represents a section of a master model from which it was copied

with function keys and alphanumeric keyboard for design/edit and programming work; one station of each system also has a plotter/digitizer.

In the actual design process with the Gerber system, the designer uses various functions to create and display the points, lines, arcs, cones, splines, and surfaces of the geometry of the part under consideration. During this design process, a database that completely describes the part is created in the computer, and a drawing is generated.

Once the database is created, it can be used to generate NC part-programs. The process is conceptually similar to using a high-level language, such as APT or COMPACT, but it allows more interaction with the operator and directly provides tool-path editing and verification.

Geometry is already available

The first part of an APT program describes the geometry of the part in terms of basic geometric entities, such as points, lines, and arcs. In the interactive graphics system, this information is already stored in the database describing the part.

The second part of an APT program consists of the motion statements that describe the motion of the cutting tool with respect to the geometry of the part already defined. For more complex parts, drive, part, and check surfaces are defined to control the motion of the tool. In the Gerber interactive graphics systems, essentially the same procedure is used to define tool paths.

The operator selects the appropriate functions for such operations as point-to-point moves, pocketing, or profiling, using the function buttons on the workstation keyboard. Appropriate lines or surfaces on the part are selected with a cursor display operated with a desktop control arm. The approximate location of the cursor, as viewed on the CRT screen, indicates the surface to the computer, which then computes the tool path and displays it on the graphics screen. Verification and editing are performed immediately.

In an APT program, once the geometry and motion statements are set and post-processing commands are added, the statements are entered into a computer and compiled by the APT compiler into a cutter-location (CL) data file. This CL data is then postprocessed to produce the NC tape for the machine used.

Basically, the same procedures can be followed with the Gerber system. Once the tool paths are defined by the operator, the part geometry and tool motion can be converted to APT source statements and used as input to an APT compiler. Alternately, the tool motion

Tooling built with computer graphics

can be described in CL-file format and transmitted to a mainframe computer for postprocessing.

Finally, postprocessors can be installed on the interactive graphics system, and the CL-file data can be processed locally, with direct output of an NC tape. The number of attempts required to produce a good tape is usually reduced because of the direct tool-path verification available with the graphics approach.

All approaches are used

At Boeing, all three approaches for producing NC tapes are used. Postprocessors for some NC machines, such as a Wiedematic punch press and an NC router, are resident in the Gerber computer-graphics system, allowing for direct NC-tape generation. For other machines, CL data is transmitted to the mainframe computer, where postprocessing and final tape cutting are performed. In some instances, such as full 3-D work from nondimensioned drawings, the Gerber system is used to digitize the data and convert it to APT source statements that are used as input to the APT program running on the mainframe computer.

A systems operator takes care of all the peripheral and support tasks of the graphics system not directly related to NC programming or tool designing. For example, daily backup tapes of work in progress preserve data in case of a system failure. Also, the systems operator provides plots for the designers or programmers. In this way, they get the most efficient use of the system without having to know all the operating details.

Computer graphics is a rapidly growing field, and the software capabilities of such systems is growing with it. "Initially, we reviewed the software and then picked applications that it could do comfortably," says Marvel. "We didn't necessarily choose the jobs we would prefer to do." That was in 1976, when Marvel's group became the first manufacturing group to use computer graphics at Boeing. "You wouldn't recognize the original software by looking at the present system," he says now.

A communication network

The applications for computer graphics in tool engineering are continuously growing as the IDS software is updated. Now Marvel is expecting delivery of a Gerber DMS data-management setup that will tie the three IDS systems into a communications network to provide even greater flexibility. The DMS will provide data transfer among the IDS systems and will perform the peripheral work without tying up valuable terminal time that can be used for productive work. ∎

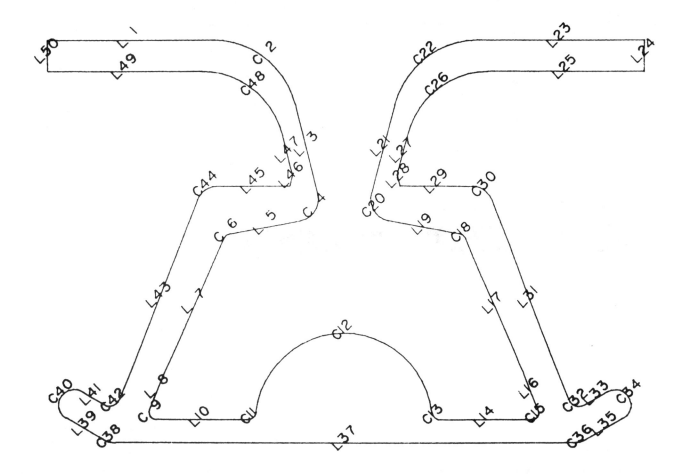

CAD/CAM is good for small shop

Introduction of a computer-graphics system into a relatively small shop has done more than just improve productivity

AMONG SOME manufacturing engineers and managers, there is a notion that only large companies making relatively complex products can truly benefit from CAD/CAM, computer-aided design/computer-aided manufacture. Not so. In fact, many managers of medium-size and small companies are rapidly coming to the conclusion that it's CAD/CAM or die.

"I honestly believe that manufacturing companies in the $30- to $50-million range that are not involved with computer systems have only two choices: get on board or get out of business," says William F. McAnirlin Jr, CAD/CAM-systems manager at Kingston-Warren Corp (Newfields, NH). The 450-employee company specializes in the engineering and manufacture of precision, custom

roll-formed metal shapes as well as its own line of King-Way modular materials-storage systems, and it recently decided to "get on board" with the installation of a Computervision (Bedford, Mass) computer-graphics system to help with design and manufacturing tasks.

Productivity is not all

Although its potential for improving overall productivity was an important reason for installing the CV system, there were other, equally important considerations. "We did, of course, work out an estimated return on investment," notes Dr Victor Azzi, vice president and director of engineering at K-W. "But there are many intangibles when it comes to justifying a CAD/CAM system, and I would say that my arguments to the president and, in turn, to the board of directors were based not so much on economics

and a favorable ROI as on our ability to enhance our position in the marketplace and do work we otherwise could not. The primary thrust of my presentation was our ability to do our work better, not necessarily to save a lot of money in doing that work."

Another important consideration, according to Azzi, was that the system would allow the company to continue growing at a relatively fast rate. In the custom business, such growth is more dependent on the ability to achieve fast response to a customer's request for quotations and fast turnaround from design to manufacture than on increased productivity in individual design or manufacturing tasks.

Productivity up 4:1

As expected, there have been considerable improvements in productivity. On King-Way jobs, the system is used pri-

	X	Y	RAD OR ANG	LENGTH
P0	0.000000	0.000000		
L 1	-0.447923	0.642343	0.000000E-01	0.277444
C 2	-0.220479	0.499343	0.143060	0.187186
C 3	-0.2....	0.451343	0.140000	0.183...
L 4	-0.236675	0.591343	0.000000E-01	0.259848
L 50	-0.447923	0.591343	90.000000	5.099998E-02
TOTAL LENGTH =	5.460...			

Computer-generated image of die-block aperture (far right) is labeled to identify its geometric elements—in this case, a series of lines and circles. The program available on the computer-graphics system then generates the data table (left) for NC EDM work by subcontractor

marily as an automated drafting tool to help designers select and assemble storage systems from standard components that have been committed to computer memory, and output is running about 4:1 over manual methods. "On an average, it used to take 2½-3 days to prepare a typical King-Way quotation; now we are shooting for 4 hr," says McAnirlin. In addition to the faster turnaround, the computer-generated drawings are better looking than their manually produced equivalents, which makes them an effective marketing tool.

System good for die work

"But the computer-graphics system is really dynamite when it comes to die work," notes McAnirlin with unbridled enthusiasm. The roll-forming operation requires the use of cutoff dies, and the die blocks are frequently best made on NC-operated wire-EDM machines by a local subcontractor. "It used to take four days to a week to get one of those die blocks because the subcontractor had to convert our drawings into appropriate NC programs to run the EDM machine," he recalls. "It now takes about an hour to enter a design into the CV system and another 10-15 min to get the information out again in a form compatible with our subcontractor's NC machines. We mail

them that data, and, a couple of days later, we get the block back ready to be installed into the dieset."

K-W's roll-forming equipment typically handles metal coil stock from 0.008 to 0.120 in. thick and from ⅛ to 6½ in. wide. The coil stock is fed through successive pairs of rolls that progressively cold-form the stock into shapes of uniform cross-section. At the end of the line, the finished stock enters a mating die-block aperture in a flying-shear-type cutoff die, which cuts the stock to appropriate lengths.

Such cutoff dies are ideal applications for the CAD/CAM approach because the diesets fall into related families determined primarily by the stock width, and the cross-section of the die-block aperture closely resembles the cross-section shape of the finished product. Once the product shape has been entered into the system, it is necessary only to add appropriate clearances and then to use the computer-graphics software to create the particular geometric statements required by the EDM machine.

To take full advantage of the computer-graphics system, the entire die-design process has been automated. "It takes just as long to create a line on a CAD system as it does to draw it on a drafting board," points out McAnirlin. "It's the

power of the system that boosts productivity."

A library of standard diesets

Using that power, K-W engineers have built up a library of standard diesets and components, which is stored in the computer-graphics-system memory. Actually, there are families of diesets suitable for a variety of typical jobs, and the designer chooses accordingly. Once the basic dieset has been selected and brought up on the CV screen, the designer adds the inserts, blocks, and other components that are unique to a particular part. Whenever possible, the designer tries to modify an existing dieset rather than starting from scratch.

In order to develop the die block, the designer works with the cross-section shape of the product as previously developed by a product engineer on the same CV system; product engineers and die designers work at the same computer-graphics work stations. At present, the design department has three work stations hooked up to the graphics-system central processor, which is located in a separate computer room. About 16 designers, out of a total of 50 people in the department, including managers, use the system.

The die designers at K-W actually

Designer uses tablet and keyboard to select and arrange standard components for dieset from system's memory

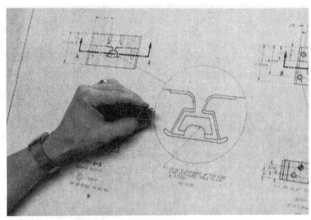
Computer-generated die-block drawing includes blow-up of aperture shape. Designer holds piece removed by the process

The dieset is made up of standard components. The die block (center) has aperture to match cross-section of finished product

Cut-off dieset gets final adjustment from designer, who spends much of his time on the shop floor helping to set up and debug

function more as manufacturing engineers because they really determine the manufacturing process, and they spend much of their time on the shop floor helping to set up a new roll-forming line and taking care of process-related problems. "A designer may be on the terminal one or two days a week and the rest of the time out in the shop helping to debug the line," McAnirlin points out.

A typical recent roll-forming job involved manufacture of the metal mounting track for a popular brand-name do-it-yourself ceiling-tile system. The cutoff die block has an aperture that matches the cross-section shape of the track, and it was produced by a subcontractor on an NC EDM machine from data generated on the CV system.

Contour is labeled

In the design process, the cross-section shape of the track is first brought up on the screen of the CV system, and all extraneous elements, such as dimensions and notes, are removed. Then the remaining contour is labeled with a series of tags to designate its geometric elements—in this case, a series of lines

and circles (see lead illustration). The software program then automatically develops an associated data table listing the coordinate location and angles for the line elements and the center coordinates and radii for the circle elements that make up the die-aperture shape. This is the data form preferred by K-W's subcontractor for its EDM machine. Of course, it would also be possible to develop an APT-processed NC program for in-house applications or other NC equipment.

The program simultaneously calculates the length of each geometric element and then sums up the total die-aperture perimeter. The availability of that data means that the price of the die block is just a phone call away: subcontractors are prepared to give an estimate based on the required length of the EDM cut because the blocks are relatively standard and K-W's overall requirements are familiar to subcontractors.

It attracts employees

One unexpected benefit resulting from the installation of the computer-graphics system is that its presence attracts new

employees, and, with a scarcity of qualified designers, that gives K-W a competitive edge in the job market. "People are attracted to us because they want to work in a modern, technologically sophisticated environment," says Azzi. "And, by the same token, we are able to keep bright young people because they would be inclined to go elsewhere to work with such a tool if we didn't have it."

Azzi has future plans for the CV system: help with the overall design of a roll-forming line, including the rather tricky and experience-laden task of developing the so-called "flower," a superimposition of the progressive stock shapes at each rolling stage. "Ultimately, I predict, we will be able to enter the finished section shape into the system, and then a series of analytical programs will first develop the flower and then design the rolls necessary to produce each of the stations within that flower." At that stage, Azzi expects to complete the CAD/CAM cycle by purchasing a CNC lathe and using the CV system to generate the NC program to produce the rolls it helped to design. ∎

Bridge of Linde CM 150-26 flame cutting machine has two plasma-arc burning stations for dual cutting

Computer-graphics flame cutting

Burning parts to shape may appear very unsophisticated, but plasma-arc cutting, CNC, and now computer graphics have raised the technique to aerospace-like CAD/CAM

To the uninitiated, flame cutting evokes images of unsophisticated boiler-shop burning operations or, at best, the preparation of platework used in shipbuilding. In fact, most flame cutting today is used to cut relatively complex contoured profiles for a variety of welded constructions ranging from farm equipment to machine tools and, therefore, usually involves some level of automation and control.

For a long time, optical tracer systems have been the mainstay for such flame-cutting control. More recently, numerical control (NC) and computer numerical control (CNC) systems have been replacing tracer controls because they are more reliable and provide added flexibility and programming options.

Early in 1977, Minster Machine Co

(Minster, Ohio) elevated flame-cutting technology to a new level of sophistication by linking a state-of-the-art CNC flame cutting machine with an up-to-date interactive computer-graphics design system. This mini-CAD/CAM system rivals the kind of high-technology computer-aided manufacturing expected of the aerospace industry.

The results: replacement of an existing machine with the new setup has increased flame-cutting production by 30%; overall weld-shop productivity has improved 15-17%; engineering is on schedule, despite a dramatic increase in workload; and company officials agree that, if they had to do it all over again, they would choose the same approach.

What makes a builder of metalforming presses install such sophisticated equipment in the first place? After all, mechanical presses, like flame cutters, hardly conjure up visions of computer-

aided manufacturing. But that, too, is true only for the uninitiated.

Early start with computers

Minster got its feet wet with computers in 1964 with the installation of an IBM 1440, then used primarily for business-related EDP work. Today, the company's mainframe computer runs a comprehensive scheduling system for coordinating all phases of its manufacturing. Software currently being implemented will permit interactive preparation of quotations by sales personnel and word processing of the actual customized document.

The early and continuing use of computers is in line with a well-established Minster management principle to take advantage of new technology whenever it is available and applicable to a problem at hand. It is a principle that has helped to transform a local farm-belt

Most large presses are constructed, to a large degree, of weldments using a great variety of flame-cut parts like these, some with relatively complex profiles

Massive weldments like this are not uncommon. Plate here is 7 in. thick

machine shop specializing in sharpening plowshares into a major world-renowned machine-tool builder.

It was the commitment to that principle that led Minster to computerized flame cutting to overcome a production bottleneck in its weld shop. Two semiautomatic burning machines, each equipped with optical tracer systems, were unable to keep up with the constant increase of customers requiring larger and more powerful presses over the last five years. "The two existing flame cutters were pressed into round-the-clock service," recalls Terry Wissman, manager of product engineering and a prime mover in implementing the new system. "But the need for flame-cut parts exceeded even this capacity, and we had to subcontract some cutting of selected components to outside vendors."

Burning: must for large presses

Most large presses are constructed, to a large degree, of weldments using a great variety of flame-cut parts, some with relatively complex profiles. Castings for major components of large presses would be too difficult to handle and would not provide the flexibility available with weldments. In fact, flexibility to satisfy individual customer needs is a major advantage of welded press construction.

A customer ordering a 400-ton press, such as the company's E–400 Hevi-Stamper, invariably has special requirements that call for variations in construction: die cushions vary, some customers want wider flanges, special knockouts for scrap removal are common, and ribbing often has to be altered to accommodate special requirements.

"If you told me to stock a set of parts for E2-400 presses, other than counterbalance cylinders and the like, I would say there are probably a dozen candidates," says Wissman.

It all adds up to large-volume, small-batch cutting—a manufacturing headache, by any standard. In 1976, Minster processed 2011 tons of plate in its weldshop; this year, it expects to produce a record 3200 tons of weldments. But the number of duplicate parts and identical combinations of parts needed at any time are relatively small.

The constraints of such job-shop-like operations had a great influence on the choice of equipment selected to solve the weld-shop problem. A high-speed NC flame cutting machine seemed to be the obvious answer: plasma-arc cutting could provide maximum cutting speed; numerical control would supply the kind of flexibility needed to produce custom machines.

Requiring less operator intervention than optical tracer systems need, NC also held out the promise of greater overall efficiency. Parts to be flame-cut from the same material (type and thickness) are commonly nested for minimum material waste, regardless of whether the parts belong to one weldment. With optical tracers, some of the nesting is left to the discretion of the operator on the shop floor, who physically arranges the line-drawing patterns on the tracing table. NC would impose better control over the process.

Also, with an optical-tracer system, the operator must manually start each burn-in for each separate part within the nest and manually move the torch for each new start. Under NC, the entire

complement of parts, including all moves between parts (with the torch turned off), and all burn-ins can be programmed, and an entire plate can be cut into its individual parts in one uninterrupted run. Finally, the high speeds attainable with plasma-arc burning almost demand the kind of automatic and accurate control available only through NC.

"Once the decision was made to acquire a numerically controlled flame cutting machine with a plasma-arc-torch, the next decision that had to be made was how this equipment was to be programmed," says Wissman. Considering the special production requirement of low-volume custom-designed parts, company planners thought that the variety of parts and the one-time use of completed nests would be a continual NC programmer's headache. Not that Minster was a novice when it comes to NC programming: the company boasts a large number of NC machines in its machine shop and has an experienced and accomplished programming department.

"But there's a basic difference between the NC programming required for the machine shop and that needed to run a flame cutter," Wissman points out. "In a machine shop, you run individual parts one at a time, and you may run hundreds or thousands of those identical parts to satisfy one order. When you need to program a new part, you can select a tape of a similar part, edit it, and run as many parts as required."

But, when you nest a constantly changing array of parts, such as in flame cutting, you are dealing with totally new geometry for each NC tape. The pattern of nested parts hardly ever repeats or is

Computer-graphics flame cutting

similar enough to allow tape editing of an existing program. If you stored a nested program, it probably would be 100 years, if ever, before that combination of parts was again required at the same time. That sort of programming requirement complicates the NC programmer's job tremendously.

Minster's solution to these complex problems is the marriage of NC plasma-arc flame cutting and computer graphics. A Linde (division of Union Carbide) CM 150-26 combination plasma-arc/oxy-fuel cutting machine equipped with Union Carbide's UCNC-3 computer numerical control was installed in January 1977 to replace the oldest of the two existing burning machines. Shortly thereafter, Minster took delivery of an Applicon (Burlington, Mass) computer-graphics CAD system comprising two central processing units (CPUs), a Model 835 and a Model 875, linked in a master/satellite arrangement; a 12-million-word disk memory; a Decwriter (Digital Equipment Corp) line printer, and three CRT graphics terminals. The system was also interfaced to an existing CalComp drum plotter to produce hard-copy drawings. Since then, an additional terminal and digitizing table have been added.

A host of other tasks

Although a main purpose of the computer-aided-design system was to provide nesting and NC-programming capability for the weld shop, the Applicon graphics system is also used for a host of other tasks. For example, it is used to produce all the wiring diagrams for Minster's electrical control systems; with some of the recent safety requirements dictated by OSHA, these get rather sophisticated and complex.

The 875 system is also used to produce full-size electrical-panel layouts for custom control panels. Such a layout shows the exact position of all components, the location of mounting holes, and the size of these holes. These layouts are used as an aid in assembly work and, according to Wissman, have reduced panel-assembly time by as much as 70% in some cases.

Another interesting application of the computer-graphics system is the production of masters used to make foreign legend plates and warning signs. These labels with their symbols and diagrams are typically one-of-a-kind and are made in plastic using an Ozalid printing process similar to blueprint-making. The paper masters are generated directly on the graphics terminal and produced by the associated plotter.

The system is also used to prepare preliminary die-spacing layout drawings,

which are sent to customers, who then supply information concerning tooling needs, sketching in their requirements. These changes are then readily incorporated into the database of the Applicon system, and a revised drawing is then automatically generated for use in production.

Graphics from the start

The computer-graphics system has been used as the only means for NC programming of the new flame cutting machine. The first task was to establish a database representing the plate work to be burned. For this purpose, all plates to be burned were initially entered into the system as drawings. Each plate was generated as a "cell," associated data that can be accessed and moved together within the computer system, and was stored under a drawing number of the weldment into which it will eventually be assembled.

Although the flame cutting operation itself does not require drawings with detailed dimensions, such detailed information is entered with each drawing to permit generating detailed drawings for secondary operations, such as beveling and forming.

Initially, two members of the engineering department worked full time for six months to establish the database. Once that was accomplished, it was found that 75% of the drawings can be generated by editing existing data, and now one person is able to handle all the drawings required to support the weld

shop. During editing, a reference drawing of a part already in the database is marked up with the desired changes. The reference drawing is then called up on the graphics system, and the changes are made with a few strokes of the terminal's electronic stylus and some keyboard entries. The new drawing can then be stored without destroying the original reference drawing, which is also placed in storage for future use.

After the drawing database has been established, it can be accessed to create nesting patterns and to generate NC programs that run the Linde flame cutting machine. Six software packages, referred to as IOs and residing in the Applicon computer, are used to manipulate the data and accomplish nesting and tape preparation.

They have several functions:

- IO 98 — part-menu creation
- IO 99 — nesting
- IO 2 — NC programming
- IO 12 — postprocessing
- IO 97 — tool-path verification
- IO 23 — file transfer via modem.

IO 98 is used to initially set up the screen of the graphics terminal and to display a part "menu." By specifying the name of the panel or the raw plate size to be used, the software divides the screen into two areas, displaying the panel on the top half of the screen. When a menu command is given, the software selects drawings from the library of parts suitable for the material thickness selected and from those required to meet present scheduling dates. [Continued]

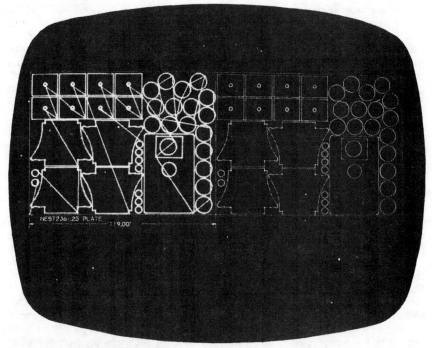

Nesting and part-program are verified visually on screen of computer-graphics terminal. Dotted lines indicate sequence, and torch separation is shown

Applicon system is used for host of other computer-aided design tasks. Here designer uses drawing tablet, keyboard, and screen to develop wiring diagram

These part drawings then appear on the lower half of the screen in preparation for the nesting procedure, in which they are moved onto the panel display. If the menu contains more part drawings than can fit onto the screen, the software remembers this, and the remaining parts are called up as screen space becomes available until the library is completely exhausted.

Once the screen is set up, IO 99 is used to move and rotate part drawings so that specified line and arc segments are parallel and separated by a given kerf width. The lines and arc segments are selected by simply touching them with a screen cursor that is operated by moving the electronic stylus across a data tablet that duplicates the screen area.

Certain symbols, such as a check mark, executed with the stylus are interpreted by the software as specific instructions regarding the disposition of the drawing, and the data tablet is also divided into command fields that can be actuated with the stylus. With these manipulations, parts can be placed so that desired sides are parallel to each other. This process is continued until the entire panel is filled to the operator's satisfaction.

Next the planner uses IO 2 to generate the flame path in the desired sequence. First the vertex of the part at which the burn is to start is selected, and a canned program adds an appropriate burn-in path. Then APT-like statements are used to generate the required tool path. The operator continues to select vertices and

to issue burn-in commands in the desired sequence until the tool paths for the entire panel are generated. Sequence is important to ensure that sufficient support material is always available to prevent burned portions of the panel from dropping off the burning table.

After the entire sequence is established, proper auxiliary functions are added by the operator. For example, the operator specifies kerf left or right to determine on which side of the cutting path the part lies and also when the torch is to be turned on and off.

The resulting cutter-location file is then run through a custom-tailored postprocessor residing in the Applicon system, and a part-program for the Linde UCNC-3 is generated. The program is stored on disk until it is required by the weld shop. Before going to disk storage however, IO 97 is used to produce a visual verification of the cutter path. On the plot produced by this software, dashed lines indicate rapid-traverse movements between burn-ins, and solid lines indicate torch movement with the flame on.

In this way, the planner can see that the desired sequence has been produced. A hard-copy plot goes to the weld shop to assist the operator with setup. Where two torches are to be used in a master/slave arrangement to cut two sets of identical parts, the plot shows the parts to be cut by the master torch in heavy lines and the parts to be cut by the slave torch in fine lines. In addition, the computer calculates the appropriate

torch spacing to be set up on the machine, and this dimension appears on the plot sent to the shop.

Programs are transmitted to the weld shop via a dedicated shielded-cable transmission line between the Applicon system, located in the main engineering building, and the weld shop. Usually, a whole day's programs are transmitted to the Linde machine, where the program file is transferred to a floppy-disk unit. It typically takes about five minutes to transmit a complete day's burn. A voice intercom provides communication between the operator and personnel at the Applicon system to coordinate data transmission. When a new file is transmitted, the old programs are wiped off the floppy, but it is also possible to save floppy disks for future work.

Bridge-type flame cutter

The flame cutting machine itself is a bridge-type machine with 30-ft travel on railroad-type rails and 26-ft cutting-width capability. The operator's console is mounted on one end of the bridge and travels with it so that it is always near the area of cutting. Four separate Anderson SC-200 self-cleaning water tables have been constructed in line under the bridge to provide efficient material handling. While one water table is used for burning parts, plate for the next job can be mounted to another table, and parts that have been burned are removed from the previously used tables. To help protect the operator, the water in these tables is colored with a green dye to reduce reflection from the cutting arc.

The bridge has two plasma-arc stations and provisions for up to eight oxyfuel stations. A beveling attachment and plate-marking head are also provided. In plasma-arc cutting, an inert gas (nitrogen) is partially ionized by an initial pilot arc. Once established, the arc generates heat, which in turn increases the ionization process. The ionized gas, or plasma, becomes a high-energy arc directed toward the work plate, which itself is part of the electrical circuit.

Constriction of the arc at the torch nozzle forms a "plasma jet," greatly increasing the energy and, therefore, the temperature. The result is very fast cutting rates. For example, on 1-in.-thick plate, cutting speeds have increased from 14 ipm with oxyfuel to 120 ipm.

To date, with a stacked high-current power-supply arrangement, Minster has successfully used the plasma-arc heads to cut plate as thick as 1 in. The maximum plate thickness cut on the new machine, as currently set up, is about 7 in. Thicker plates—up to 23½ in.—are cut on the remaining manual flame cutting machine. ∎

Stepping up to CAM

A commitment to computer-aided manufacturing and experience with a successful DNC system provide the basis for a full CAM system now being implemented at GE

The Evendale Mfg Operation of the General Electric Co Aircraft Engine Group is no neophyte when it comes to modern manufacturing methods. Aircraft engines are sophisticated, complex products that constantly demand the application of the latest manufacturing technologies. No wonder, then, that the Rotating Parts Operation at Evendale is well on its way toward an effective computer-aided manufacturing (CAM) system.

It didn't happen overnight. Evendale got started with numerical control (NC) in the early Fifties. By 1976, more than 200 NC machines were on line. NC provides better, faster, more accurate control over machining functions than any previous, manual method. But, as the number of NC machines grew, so did a variety of problems associated with this new technology.

Tape preparation gets complex

Among the most troublesome were tape-reader breakdowns and part-programming difficulties and delays. Also, repeated program-verification processes became more involved as part complexity advanced. In time, GE Evendale was generating more than 2000 part-programs a year, and some complex parts require nearly four miles of tape. Generating those tapes was a complex, error-prone procedure. Although NC proved efficient and effective compared with manual machine operation, GE managers soon started to look for a better way to support and control their NC activities. It was quite evident that improved productivity and better quality would require expanded NC techniques, including some aspects of computer-aided manufacturing. In fact, it was quite clear that computer technology held the key to meeting the continuing

An updated version of the AMEN part-programming system has been implemented on the master computer and is operated from eight Hewlett-Packard 2640 CRT terminals

LeBlond NC lathe with old GE 100 Series control is one of 100 machines now linked to DNC system. Operator station includes CRT and keyboard (top left) for communication

demands for more-complex machining operations.

Using experience gained with the application of NC, Evendale manufacturing engineers spent nearly four years studying and evaluating new computer techniques that would reduce the time and cost of support for the growing number of NC machine tools in their shops. In 1971, Evendale started to implement an in-house-developed interactive minicomputer-based programming system called AMEN (APT menu) (AM—Mar'76,p113). It is specifically structured to streamline program construction and editing; to eliminate statement format, spelling, and punctuation errors (the causes of many programming difficulties in writing source programs with APT); and to eliminate punched cards required for a standard APT processing procedure.

APT menus are stored

With AMEN, part-programs are constructed with preprogrammed APT statements, or menus, stored on disk memory associated with a minicomputer and displayed on a CRT terminal. Menu statements are called up at the terminal by number only. Once they are called up, the programmer merely adds the appropriate variable information, such as names and dimensions, and the mini automatically does all the formatting, spelling, and punctuation. Also, the programmer can edit any of the stored menu statements to suit a particular programming need.

The AMEN software also incorporates a series of macro programs—computer subroutines that group APT statements into a predetermined arrangement—to reduce the task of menu selection. And programmers can establish their own macros to help with repetitive programming routines. For example, one macro covers startup routines, handling information like part number, postprocessor identification, tolerance considerations, and other standard data relating to program origin or centerline/baseline/baseplane location. Other macros cover such operations as roughing and finishing.

Programmers build and edit

Using a combination of menu selections and macros, programmers build and edit a source program until they are satisfied that a decent program has been achieved. All this is done at the local minicomputer adjacent to the shop area. This source-language program, together with some necessary control statements for operating the APT program, is transmitted to the corporate business computer, a Honeywell HISI 6080, which acts as

CAM system for Rotating Parts Operation

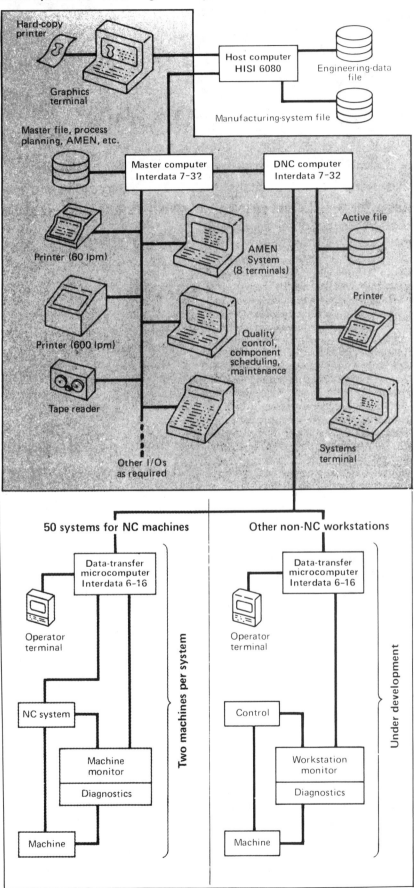

Stepping up to CAM

DNC system also operates this GE Mark Century 550 NC on Gray VTL. CRT displays information normally transmitted with operations sheets. Graphics will follow

Two Interdata 7-32 minicomputers are at the heart of the budding CAM system. Master computer (at left) can run machines in the event DNC computer (right) breaks down

host for all the manufacturing-related computer applications. The host then does the number crunching, including the necessary postprocessing, to create an appropriate NC program for a particular machine tool.

Although most of the processing by the host is performed during off hours (after 4:30 pm), the output from any level of the APT processing run can be brought back to the programmer's terminal or other peripheral equipment for checking purposes. Once a good program has been established, the source-language program goes into file storage at the AMEN computer to be available for future retrieval and also to provide a model for similar programming jobs. New source programs can then be easily

generated by altering an existing proved-out program. Tape-image data (postprocessed data) are actually generated only on command as needed and are stored on disk files of the host computer.

Implementation of the AMEN system permitted fewer programmers to produce more tapes for an increasing number of NC machines. In fact, the number of active part-programmers was reduced from 27 to 8 because the system's library of source-language programs can be readily massaged to generate new programs for about 80% of the jobs that are run.

A commitment to CAM

Development and implementation of the AMEN part-programming system,

however, is only one element of an ongoing commitment to computer-aided manufacturing at Evendale. Parallel with the commissioning of AMEN was the installation of a 15-machine minicomputer-based DNC system in the Casings Operation. The cost of that system was offset by a 15% improvement in machine utilization that obviated purchase of an additional machine tool needed for increased manufacturing capacity.

This DNC system, which utilizes a GE CommanDir System, also uses the company's business computer, the Honeywell HISI 6080, as a host for the number crunching and supervisory tasks while the CommanDir's GEPAC minicomputer handles the storage and transfer of active tape-image data for the behind-the-tape-reader DNC system. The CAM hierarchy was building: the HISI 6080 at the top and, linked to it, a series of minicomputer-based satellites serving the operational need of the various manufacturing facilities at Evendale.

Another DNC leads to CAM

Success with the DNC system in the Casings Operation led GE manufacturing engineers to look around for an opportunity to use their experience in building a full-blown CAM system. The Rotating Parts Operation (RPO) seemed like the nearly perfect laboratory for further CAM developments: of about 300 workstations, 100 are NC machines. Such a concentration of NC suggested another go at DNC. Based on the experience with the Casings Operation, Evendale decided to design and implement its own home-grown DNC as a first step of an overall CAM system that will eventually control, coordinate, and monitor all of the work stations in the RPO shop.

Two Interdata 7-32 minicomputers are at the heart of the satellite system that is, again, tied to the company's HISI 6080. One 7-32, dubbed master computer, will eventually handle all of the management and data-handling functions for the Rotating Parts Operation, including part-programming, process planning, production control, quality control, and maintenance diagnostics and control.

Already implemented on the master computer and operated from eight Hewlett-Packard 2640 alphanumeric CRT terminals is an updated version of the AMEN part-programming system. With the new AMEN version, programmers can access APT-like descriptions of part geometry prepared by the engineering department during the design stage and kept in the database at the host computer. Programmers no longer need redefine the part, and full computer-aided manufacturing is another step closer: all engineering data required by manufacturing are retained at the host and available on a distributive basis.

Now under development by Metcut Research Associates (Cincinnati) is an automated computer-aided process-planning system for the Rotating Parts Operation. When implemented, the system will work in conjunction with the AMEN system and will require the addition of terminals with full graphic capability. It is also possible that the master computer may have to be expanded or replaced to handle the process planning. The system is being developed for one family of parts at a time for a total of seven families.

The second Interdata 7-32 minicomput-er, referred to as the DNC computer, is an exact duplicate (except for reduced memory capacity) of the master computer. This computer presently operates approximately 100 NC systems (mostly GE systems ranging in vintage from early 100 Series to the latest 1050s) in a DNC hookup. Eventually it will distribute instructions to and gather data from all 300 work stations in the RPO.

Data transfer between the DNC computer, where the active part-programs are kept on file, and the individual machine tools is via a network of Interdata 6-16 microcomputers. Fifty such microcomputers are located on the shop floor, each serving two machines. Machines are grouped in pairs with the microcomputers, and each pair is operated by one operator. Each 6-16 can buffer up to around 7½ ft of tape-equivalent data and calls for new data from the DNC computer as its buffer empties. Specially designed interface boards, built at GE's NC Products Div in Waynesboro, Va, and installed in each NC system provide the behind-the-tape-reader link with the micros.

Ralph Jansen, manager CAM systems engineering, holds duplicate interface board mounted in each NC system to provide behind-the-tape-reader link with the DNC system

Instruction via graphics terminals

Each operator station includes a Tektronix 4004 graphics video terminal (see cover) as a communications link between the operator/machine and the DNC system. The intent is to ultimately make the shop as nearly paperless as possible: all detailed operating instructions normally transmitted on a set of operations sheets—including tooling descriptions, cuts to be made, gaging to be performed, and checks and records to be kept—are displayed for the operator. Eventually all the sketches associated with the operations sheets also will be displayed on the graphics terminals.

The same graphic-communications approach will be used at all final inspection stations, and eventually all management-data collection for the RPO will feed up-stream through the DNC computer. And, in the event the DNC computer should go down, the master computer can operate as a backup to keep the manufacturing operation on schedule.

No doubt about it, Evendale is committed to CAM and is doing something about it. Evendale managers recognize that it makes people and machines more productive; improves product quality; reduces inventory and cycle time; reduces error, redundancy, and waste; and provides timely information for sound management decisions. They also agree emphatically with a GE corporate study claiming that CAD/CAM "is probably the most attractive single technical opportunity for improving productivity throughout the company." ∎

Interdata 6-16 microcomputers mounted near the machines perform data-transfer function. Each 6-16 handles two machines and can buffer 7½ ft of tape-equivalent data

119

From CAD to CAM via expanded factory

The addition of computer-aided manufacturing functions to this dual-computer system helps management control the present, plan the future, and correct problems faster

First computer systems in metalworking plants are usually justified for one basic application, such as computer-aided design (CAD) or computer-aided NC part-programming. But why limit a general-purpose computer to one task in the manufacturing environment?

Second, third, and fourth applications of the computer can be developed with relative ease if the need for further automation exists. The declining cost of electronic hardware, increased availability of standard software packages, and the pressing need for higher productivity combine to make continuously expandable factory-computer systems practical in shops that aren't already highly computerized.

One of the most promising directions for computer expansion is factory-data collection. Systems for collecting factory data arrived in the late 1950s, when the aerospace industry geared up to put a man on the moon. Today factory-data collection is a mature technology in the aerospace industry and is beginning to find application in less sophisticated manufacturing environments. Around the world, industry has already invested nearly $1-billion in factory-data-collection terminals and related computer equipment.

Industrial Fabricating Co (Tulsa, Okla) recently completed expansion of its computer system to help with the manufacture of custom heat exchangers, and the multipurpose system now includes factory-data collection among other tasks. Originally we had one mainframe computer to assist in the thermal and mechanical design of heat exchangers. That was in the early 1960s. Now we have two minicomputers, both manufactured by General Automation (Anaheim, Calif).

System performs many tasks

These computers collect time-and-attendance and factory labor data from seven General Automation (GA) termi-

By Larry Rist
Manager, Data Processing
Industrial Fabricating Co, Tulsa, Okla

nals located in our 144,000-sq-ft shop area, where 250 hourly employees operate machining, welding, rolling, cutting, and assembly equipment. These workers also prepare management reports for cost estimating, work-force scheduling, forecasting of work-force requirements, payroll, and related employee activities.

As a further task, the dual-computer system prepares NC tapes and automatically distributes part-program data to five new Carlton horizontal drilling machines equipped with GA Adapt-A-Path CNC systems. Mechanical and thermal design—the initial justification for the computer—is still the most important single application and serves as a foundation for tape preparation and distributed NC.

Adding new functions

The accompanying schematic shows the system as it existed before 1977, as well as the new hardware and software added as part of the communications link between the existing GA-18/30 batch-processing computer and the newer GA-SPC-16/65 real-time computer. The real-time computer has the speed (960 nanoseconds) needed for interactive processing and provides the basis for the computer-aided-manufacturing functions added after 1977.

The batch-processing-type computer handles design functions and can also run a plotter or prepare NC part-program data and NC tapes. However, it cannot do more than two tasks at once. The real-time computer, in contrast, supervises several devices on the shop floor while exchanging information with the batch-type computer.

The main reason for adding the real-time computer was to upgrade the system of collecting factory data. In fact, the GA-18/30 batch-processing computer was used for NC-tape preparation before the second computer was purchased, and we were satisfied with this and other applications. However, the data used in preparing management reports lacked the timeliness and reliability needed to improve cost control and production scheduling.

Interactive factory-data collection and

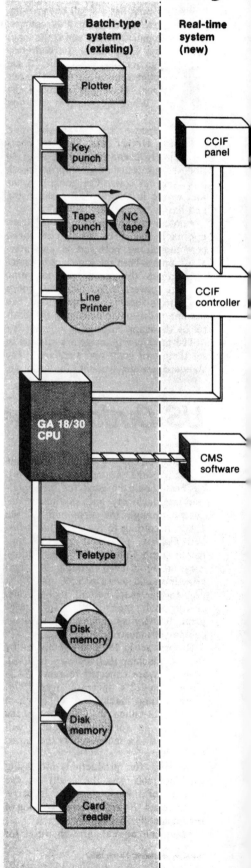

applications of computers

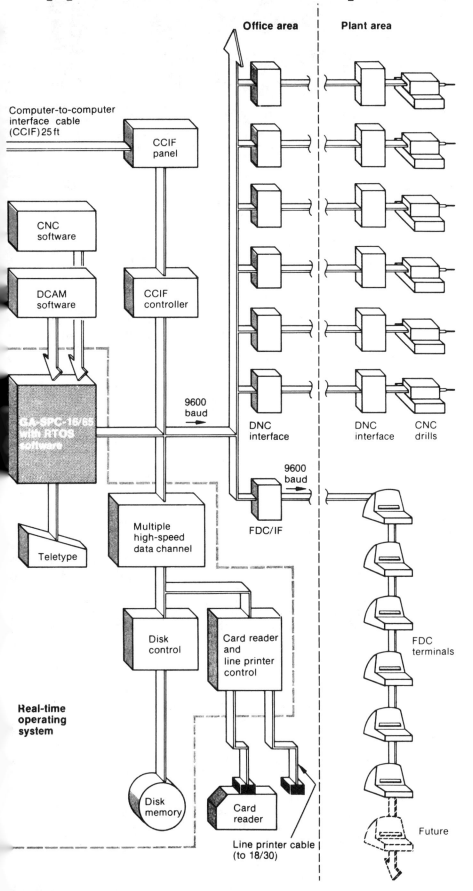

Office area

Plant area

Computer-to-computer interface cable (CCIF) 25 ft

CCIF panel

CNC software

DCAM software

CCIF controller

GA-SPC-16/65 with RTOS software

9600 baud

DNC interface

DNC interface

CNC drills

Teletype

9600 baud

FDC/IF

Multiple high-speed data channel

Real-time operating system

Disk control

Card reader and line printer control

FDC terminals

Disk memory

Card reader

Future

Line printer cable (to 18/30)

computer NC (CNC) were becoming practical state-of-the-art products by 1975. CNC, in turn, has been very instrumental in developing direct NC (DNC) techniques. Industrial Fabricating implemented these new technologies when relocating, in 1975, to its present headquarters and manufacturing facility. The decision to use these technologies was also related directly to the fact that a single supplier, General Automation, offered all of the products needed to implement them. Essentially, DNC was a logical way to offset the cost of the real-time computer; it was also a logical extension of using the computer to automatically prepare part-programs for engineering-design data.

Terminals are in series loop

A single-shielded cable connects the GA-SPC-16/65 supervisory computer to seven GA-2801 factory-data-collection (FDC) terminals. These terminals are linked in series, and new terminals may be added to the loop as required. The transmission of data to and from these terminals is slow compared with rates required for supplying the CNC drills with machining data, and so a series control loop is sufficient. A spare terminal is kept in the data-processing room as a replacement when a terminal in the shop needs repair.

For DNC, the supervisory computer stores part-programs prepared by the GA-18/30 and transmits data to each of five Carlton CNC drilling machines at the request of the drill operators. To guarantee smooth transmission of data, each CNC drill has a separate, shielded-cable connection to the supervisory computer. A sixth, older NC drill is still operated from NC tape.

The real-time operating system includes disk storage, a card reader, and a teletypewriter. This and all other computer systems, except the CNC units, are in the data-processing room.

The seven FDC terminals are located throughout the plant: three in the machining area, two in the welding area, and one each in the rolling and cutting area and the assembly area. These terminals and the CNC units are about 2000 ft from the data-processing room.

Collecting shop data

At the start of a new work shift, each hourly employee enters his or her badge number on one of the seven terminals. This is accomplished by inserting a

From CAD to CAM

Two minis (SPC-16/65, GA-18/20) act in concert for CAD, data collection, DNC, and related management functions

Time-and-attendance and factory labor data are collected at seven GA factory-data-collection terminals throughout shop

special plastic badge into a slot in the terminal housing or using the terminal keyboard to enter a four-digit employee number. Either way, an LED display indicates the number entered and the time. Employees also enter their badge numbers when they leave for the day, thereby completing entries required for payroll, scheduling, and other functions.

During the day, an average employee clocks in and out on three different jobs. Some employees work on as many as 20 different jobs a day; others work on only one. Supervisors make daily assignments for workers not already assigned.

Industrial Fabricating specializes in custom-design shell-and-tube heat exchangers for oil and gas processing and other applications. These heat exchangers are made from a wide variety of metals, ranging from brass and carbon steel to titanium and stainless steel. Annual production includes 350-400 exchangers, each having 50-100 different parts. In addition to standard manufacturing work, an hourly employee may be required to handle special cladding of the vessels or component repairs.

An extremely valuable feature of the FDC system is that the supervisory computer automatically checks each of several entries that workers make during the day. If an invalid number is entered, the computer indicates on the interactive display that the entry is not valid.

Employees enter the following data each time they begin work on a new job:

- The employee badge number.
- An eight-character alphanumeric code for the work order.
- A two-digit operation code, ranging from 01 to 66, depending on the basic type of manufacturing to be performed: rolling and cutting, welding, machining, or assembly. Drilling, for example has the code number 13.
- The type of work being done: standard (S), cladding (C), or repair (R).

Both DNC and all conventional work,

then, is coordinated through the same computer system. Employees like the data-collection system because it's simpler, faster, and more convenient than the previous system of filling out job cards. Management, in its turn, receives data needed to manage day-to-day work schedules and to keep cost estimates realistic.

In the past, the job cards filled out by employees were processed every two weeks. The data on the cards was often inaccurate and difficult to read. If someone transposed a work-order number or entered, say, 73 for 13, no one could tell what the correct number should be.

Employees can read entries

Today employees can read the numbers they enter right on the interactive display. A typical response to an entry: "OK JOB IN 10:45." Error possibilities in the interactive system are very slight compared with the previous system, in which errors in badge numbers, work-order numbers, operation codes, and types of work being done were common.

One of the important advantages of the new system is that data is available instantly, not just every two weeks. Management can locate delays on work orders and determine the causes while all the facts are still fresh in the minds of supervisors and operators. The responsible managers can see right away whether a given job is progressing according to schedule. Therefore, it is easy to determine from day to day and week to week whether production goals are being achieved or whether some corrective action is necessary.

System computes work remaining

We have developed mathematical curves to describe the number of worker-hours and types of operations needed to produce various types of heat exchangers. For a given design category, the computer lists the hours of work per week required to complete the job.

During production, the system automatically computes the number of hours to be completed on each job, according to the information collected from the shop terminals.

Makes for realistic scheduling

Immediate availability of this production data allows us to set realistic delivery schedules and make accurate estimates of production costs for jobs being bid. And, once work is in progress, such availability allows adjustment of worker-hours allocated to specific operations and work classifications to ensure that those schedules and cost estimates are met.

Further, the computer compares total worker-hours required for all jobs in progress and for new orders expected. This allows a projection of future hours, indicating whether employees should be added, overtime allotted, or the work force allowed to decline.

Another cost-cutting purpose of the computer system is to analyze the cost of heat-exchanger parts and related materials, including all items that go into producing a heat exchanger, such as plate, forgings, tubes, fasteners, and welding materials. In the past, an accountant manually tabulated the individual part costs. The tabulation has been handled automatically by computer since 1972.

In the future, we expect to improve control of inventory through the use of computers. Each part number will be reported to the existing batch-processing computer as soon as the part number is released by engineering. The reporting method will then track the cost and movement of each part number through every stage of ordering, manufacturing, and shipment of the heat exchanger.

From CAD to CAM

Computer-aided design will remain the basic and most cost-effective use of computers at Industrial Fabricating. Engineers here must develop thermal designs for each new heat exchanger to be bid. The thermal analysis develops the most economical mechanical design to meet the customer's specifications, and only a digital computer can optimize all of the design calculations in a reasonable length of time.

The data to prepare part-programs for NC and DNC drilling is programmed into the batch-processing computer when thermal and mechanical details of the heat exchanger have been defined. This data includes precise hole locations in tube sheets and baffles, types of materials, component thicknesses, diameters, and other details.

Software resident in the GA-18/30 computer automatically generates part-programs for all drilling work on the basis of these design details. This saves a great amount of time, since we currently produce close to 400 part-programs each year for machining circular tube sheets and baffles. A typical tube sheet, measuring 100 in. dia x 15 in. thick, contains several thousand holes.

Each part-program is used to drill holes in at least two groups of parts for each heat exchanger. That is, each heat exchanger is a symmetrical design consisting of at least one tube sheet and baffle at each end to support the long cylindrical tubes mounted between them. The large number of holes to be made justifies numerical control. Other manufacturing operations, however, are manually controlled.

The advantages of NC over conventional machining are widely recognized. The advantages of CNC over NC are also clear enough to represent a major trend in metalworking. But one of the main advantages of CNC—tape editing—doesn't apply at Industrial Fabricating. Drill operators, setup people, and supervisors never change a part-program except to alter feeds and speeds when necessary. The part-programs are edited only in the computer room, with the GA-18/30.

CNC provides flexibility

However, there are several advantages to having a softwired computer-based controller on the shop floor rather than a conventional hardwired controller equipped with a DNC interface. The most important is the flexibility of communicating with the supervisory computer via the CNC operator console. As new part-programs are called into CNC memory, the drill operator can see on the control's CRT that the correct program was transmitted. If required, setup instructions can also be stored in CNC memory with the part-program data instantly available to the operator via the CNC CRT screen.

Operators find that it is quicker and easier to drill hole patterns when they aren't limited by the problems inherent in using tape. For example, the part-program may inadvertently omit a hole, or a hole may not be drilled completely through the workpiece. In these cases, the operator can quickly call the correct block of data into play using the CRT screen, and then manually drill the omitted hole or request that the partially drilled hole be re-drilled by the CNC unit.

Tape breakage isn't usually a serious problem on the NC-tape machine, but tapes can break when they're used over and over. In the NC mode, three paper tapes are prepared for each part or group of parts to provide some backup for tape failures. CNC avoids the need to use the tape except to read the part-program into CNC memory. DNC makes a tape unnecessary at all, except to serve as a backup if the supervisory computer isn't available for an extended period.

The ease and simplicity of operating a large drill in the DNC mode has allowed a single operator to run three drills. In the past, one operator was required for each drill.

Single source offers benefits

Having a single supplier for hardware and software provides advantages in maintaining the system and in planning future expansions. In addition to the computers, data-collection devices, and CNC systems, General Automation manufactured all the computer-to-computer interface devices and the interfaces between the computers and other system components. The company also supplied and installed related peripherals, such as teletypewriters and card readers. Industrial Fabricating supplied the cables connecting the computer system to the devices out on the factory floor.

Several software packages were supplied with the system:
- Software for the communications monitoring system that links the GA-18/30 to the GA-SPC-16/65.
- Real-time operating software for the SPC-16/65.
- Software to permit access to the real-time computer by CNC operators and users of the factory-data-collection terminals. This standard software package is called Data Communications Access Method (DCAM) by General Automation.
- Software to control the CNC units directly from the real-time computer.

Industrial Fabricating modified portions of these standard software packages during the time the real-time computer system and related devices were being installed. In-house software is used for part-programming and for preparing management reports.

Although thermal analysis and mechanical design of heat exchangers are still the primary tasks for our computer system, we no longer limit the system to such CAD functions. With the expanded CAM functions, management is able to control the present more easily, plan the future more intelligently, and correct problems more rapidly than before. ■

Carlton horizontal drilling machines equipped with General Automation CNC operate in DNC mode for machining tube sheets and baffles with thousands of holes

CHAPTER III

Manufacturing Planning with Computers

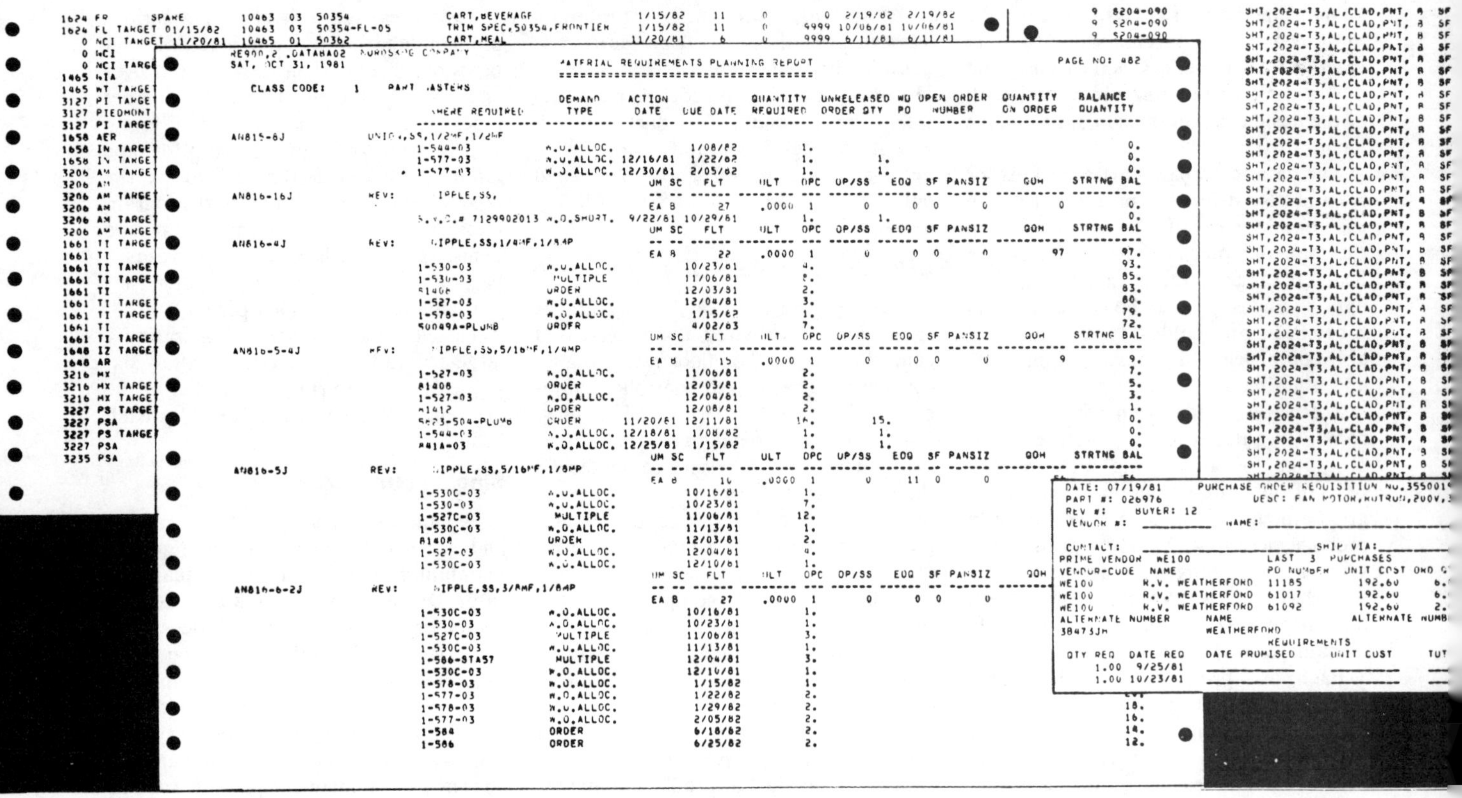

Computer slashes inventory

Excess inventory does not prevent daily materials shortages.
An in-house computer and proper software have reduced both

A SMALL ON-LINE COMPUTER and some specialized manufacturing software have helped Nordskog Industries Inc slash inventory by $500,000 and reduce daily materials shortages by 60%. In addition, the computer system has cut overall data-processing costs by $125,000 a year and saved an additional $20,000-30,000 by eliminating the need for physical inventory storage.

Nordskog (Van Nuys, Calif) designs and produces airline in-flight and ground-support equipment, electric golf carts, and in-plant vehicles. Three major operating divisions—Nordskog Co, Nordco Products, and Marketeer—build these products from an inventory of some 24,000 stockable parts.

By Chuck Nelson,
Assistant vice president
Material & Computer Services
Nordskog Industries, Van Nuys, Calif

Airline-related products alone include galleys, coffee makers, refrigerators, ovens, beverage and meal carriers, aisle-service carts, lavatories, passenger-service vehicles, baggage and cargo equipment, and highlift and maintenance vehicles. Keeping track of the raw materials needed to manufacture such a variety of products is a difficult task, and, several years ago, division managers realized that they had poor control over this process. Inventories were far in excess of what was actually required, and yet there were constant shortages on many parts.

Nordco Products alone, which manufactures ground-support equipment, had a stores inventory of $1,342,000. At least $500,000 of it was not needed, but we just didn't know how to make the necessary cuts. And the other divisions were in the same situation.

We had been getting computer support from a local service bureau, but that system offered little control except in the area of perpetual inventory. That's why we searched for a manufacturing system that would better serve our needs. We wanted a system that would not only allow us to have the right amount of inventory in-house but would ensure that we were paying competitive prices for these materials and that they were being properly accounted for. And, of course, we were looking for a system that was reliable, interactive, modifiable, and also relatively inexpensive.

An in-depth study led us to ASK Computer Systems Inc (Los Altos), a software house that had developed a manufacturing-management system called MANMAN to run on Hewlett-Packard 3000 computers. After an initial demonstration, we did a comprehensive benchmark study to make sure that the system could respond as required under normal, day-to-day conditions. Both the HP 3000 and the MANMAN software passed with flying

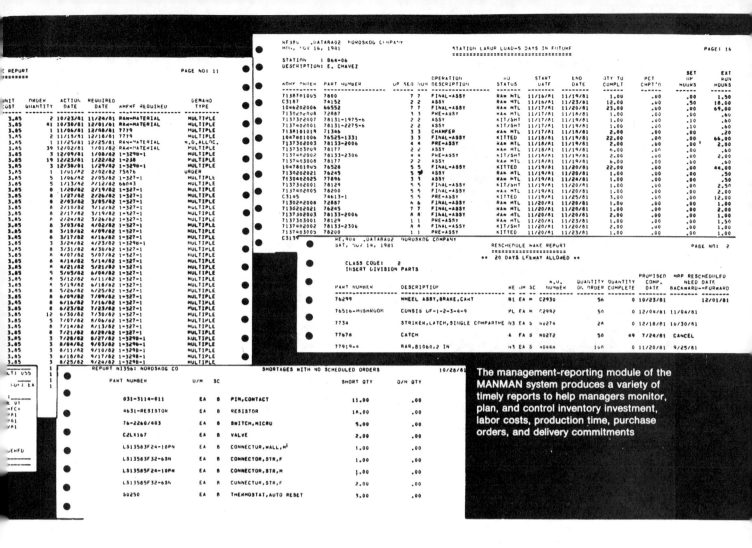

The management-reporting module of the MANMAN system produces a variety of timely reports to help managers monitor, plan, and control inventory investment, labor costs, production time, purchase orders, and delivery commitments

colors, and the system was installed. Then the divisions were gradually converted from the existing service to the in-house on-line approach. We did it gradually because we wanted the system to prove itself at every step of the way.

The MANMAN (MANufacturing MANagement) system consists of a family of proven, integrated, ready-to-use software programs that supply information about manufacturing, materials, engineering, marketing, finance, and accounting functions. Modules for several specific applications are available:

- Inventory control
- Bill-of-materials/engineering-design
- Work-in-progress/shop-floor control
- Purchasing
- Materials-requirements planning
- Capacity-requirements planning
- Cost accounting.

The MANMAN system allows information to be entered and retrieved by response to simple menu-oriented commands in a question-and-answer format. More important, numerous users throughout the facility, including remote locations, can simultaneously access information via on-line, interactive terminals connected to the system.

The present MANMAN system runs on an HP 3000 Series III computer located at

company headquarters in Van Nuys. The 2-Mbyte system includes three 120-Mbyte disk drives, a 600-line/min printer, and a tape drive. Access to the system is through a battery of 40 terminals: 30 HP 2621 terminals and ten 2635 terminals located at the various divisions, including Marketeer, which is 75 miles away in Redlands. Transmission is over leased lines.

Each department in the manufacturing divisions is responsible for entering its own data and ensuring its integrity. When customer orders are received, they are keyed into the HP 3000 via menu-oriented commands appearing on the CRT display and are processed by the MRP (materials-requirements-planning) module. This software examines the master production schedule for all actual and forecast requirements and determines what can be filled from on-hand inventory, work-in-process, and open purchase orders.

Demands that cannot be met from existing stock, purchase orders, and work orders are exploded into their component subassemblies and parts. Part requirements are then calculated, along with the appropriate due dates. Using these due dates, the system then calculates when work orders and purchase orders should be released to meet the schedule.

In support of MRP, the inventory-

control module keeps track of and updates quantities on hand, in process, and on order, as well as use for all finished goods, assemblies, components, etc. The bill-of-materials/engineering-design module of the MANMAN system records and updates product and subassembly structures and keeps track of effective dates, quantities, and other information relating to the components of these structures.

The work-in-process module maintains routing and work-center information as well as the current status on all open orders. Open orders and vendor histories are tracked by the purchasing module, which allows purchase orders to be rescheduled in line with the most recent MRP schedule.

To provide managers with the reports necessary for monitoring, planning, and controlling inventory investment, labor costs, manufacturing production time, and delivery commitments, the system uses the management-reporting module, along with a costing program developed in-house. This program estimates manufacturing costs and compares these estimates with the actual costs, thus enabling us to continuously refine estimating techniques.

This demonstrates one of the most attractive features of the HP/MANMAN combination: it permits customized ver-

Computer slashes inventory

Drawing releases and change orders are interpreted and entered into the system so that the stored bills of materials reflect the latest engineering requirements

sions of the various modules to be maintained and supported. And the HP IMAGE/3000 database-management system integrates the various manufacturing-management software modules through a common database. This integration not only eliminates redundancy but also reduces the amount of disk-storage space needed and allows efficient cross-checking, updating, and editing of data.

The first division up and running on the new manufacturing-management system was Marketeer, which manufactures the electric-vehicle line. The conversion was completed in two months. The Nordco Products conversion followed and took four months; the Nordskog Co conversion took about seven months.

The results were quite impressive. Nordco, for instance, initially reduced its operating inventory to $850,000; it then-leveled off at about $950,000. At the same time, daily shortage levels dropped 60% while shipping remained at the same level. In fact, the system provided such good control over raw materials that our auditing firm informed us that we would no longer have to do a yearly physical stores inventory.

The switch from timesharing to an in-house computer system has saved an annual data-processing cost of approximately $125,000 while the in-house operation can be supported by a relatively small staff. The system cost approximately $400,000, including about $50,000 for facilities.

We currently have one full-time programmer/analyst and a part-time operator using one terminal and the system console. On-going work not only includes developing new programs but also modifying the manufacturing-management software to meet changing needs.

One of the tools that has helped keep our staff so small is QUERY/3000, HP's ad-hoc database-inquiry program. Instead of having to write special test programs to validate the test results of new programs and modifications, we can simply use QUERY to look into the appropriate database to ensure that the program is generating the correct data. We also use QUERY extensively for software debugging.

Over the next year or two, we will be developing a number of new computer applications. Current plans call for the implementation of purchase-order printing, general ledger, accounts receivable, and job costing in the financial department. ∎

'Live' warehouse tracks inventory

High-rise automated storage-and-retrieval system offers savings, flexibility, and greater efficiency

THANKS TO AUTOMATION, a 40,000-sq-ft "warehouse" can provide 185,000 sq ft of storage space and still be classified as machinery, not as a building addition, for a faster depreciation rate.

Xerox Corp has achieved this, plus a 50% reduction in its materials-handling work force, with a high-rise automated storage-and-retrieval system. The AS/RS has been operational since May 1981 at the company's Joseph C. Wilson Center for Technology (Webster, NY).

Other advantages of the system are "live" inventory control and tracking and decreased inventory requirements, claims Xerox's John Clapp. Clapp, material-handling manager, was involved in all aspects of the project from justification and planning to installation.

Before the $7.3-million system was constructed, material had to be brought to the assembly plant by truck from a conventional warehouse located in the city of Rochester, 20 miles away. Transporting material this way required workers to load, unload, and drive the trucks—jobs that are time-consuming and essentially unproductive.

The AS/RS, which is actually built onto one of Xerox's manufacturing plants, requires 60% of the hourly workers and 40% of the salaried employees that were previously needed. In addition, almost all paperwork is eliminated because information is passed between computers instead of between people via printed tickets.

Human labor is required only to perform receiving and picking functions, tasks that are simplified by the tremendous reduction in paperwork.

Material is stored either on pallets or in bins, depending on part size, and is physically placed in storage and retrieved by stacker cranes that move in the aisles between racks of pallets. The computer-controlled cranes operate at 400 fpm and can reach as high as 73 ft.

In operation, a crane pulls a pallet off the rack and brings it to the front of the aisle to meet one of the system's eight Robocarrier wire-guided vehicles. Trav-

elling at 4.5 mph, the vehicle picks up the pallet and either places it on an outbound conveyor (to be transported to the plant floor) or takes it to a pick station.

Throughout this process, the AS/RS's computer keeps real-time track of all vehicles and pallets in the system. Therefore, the Robocarrier "knows" which pick stations are free and heads directly there.

If less than a pallet load is required, the computer tells the pick-station operator which parts to choose. The operator then attaches a ticket to the material—introducing the written word to a heretofore computerized system—and sends the material to the plant floor.

Computer-controlled stacker cranes reach as high as 73 ft to place pallets in storage and retrieve the material when needed

'Live' warehouse tracks inventory

The AS/RS, constructed in eight months by Eaton-Kenway Inc (Salt Lake City), consists of two bay areas. Its rack-supported high-bay area stores large parts, stands 73 ft high, and includes 12,064 pallet locations.

Small parts are stored in 1520 bins in the low-bay area, where operators receive and disperse materials from inbound and outbound conveyors and pick stations. Here, too, the untended Robocarriers, manufactured by Digitron (Switzerland), transport material to and from storage.

A Model PDP11/70 minicomputer, made by Digital Electronics Corp (Maynard, Mass), controls the entire warehouse operation and interfaces with two distinctly different kinds of systems.

One, a Data General 600 used as a "floor-planning tool," is told which models of office copiers will be assembled in the plant six weeks in advance. From this information and a knowledge of the materials in storage, the computer determines what must be ordered.

In addition, the DEC unit communicates with an IBM 360, which is more of a materials-requirements-planning (MRP) system, according to Clapp. It consolidates lead-time demands with the requests generated by the Data General computer, produces purchase orders, and keeps track of expected orders.

This unit is also responsible for recording quality-control decisions; for instance, the computer checks that every third order from a particular vendor is inspected and then retains the inspection results.

Immediacy is the key

The DEC, Data General, and IBM systems use the same protocol to ensure the availability of all recorded information at all times. When material is removed from a rack, a signal is sent back to one of the computers, and inventory is automatically and immediately updated.

By contrast, in a conventional warehouse, the time that elapses after the operator removes the material and before that information is brought back to some central point is lost. "In the case of an automated storage-and-retrieval system, as soon as that material hits the system, it's 'live.' You know it is available, and you can pull it out right away," Clapp notes.

Before the AS/RS installation, "we had to put material aside into a holding area for inspection. Now the time that it takes to get the material from the dock to the point where it's available for use is cut down. As a result, we can use the inventory faster and don't need to keep as much 'safety stock' around."

Without people working in most of the

Wire-guided vehicles, called Robocarriers, take the material from a stacker crane and bring it to either a pick station or an outbound conveyor

The AS/RS requires half the number of employees needed for conventional warehousing; workers now serve only receiving and picking functions

storage system, there is no need for lighting or heating the premises well; thus, energy savings are accumulated also.

If the computers or stacker cranes malfunction, three separate redundant systems are available.

The cranes can be run from the front of the aisle via a manual control; a panel on the back of the crane enables remote control; or an individual can actually ride the crane, directing it to a particular station by a control panel in front of the stacker.

Such flexibility is an inherent advantage of automation. In fact, Clapp maintains, "once you see an AS/RS in operation, you realize how many other things can be done. This may just be a stepping stone" to better, even more-efficient materials-handling systems. ∎

Computerized MRP pays off

Materials-requirement planning reduces in-process inventory, speeds production, and facilitates problem solving. Computerized data management is the key

With a diverse and complex product line—many products requiring 600 or more parts and subassemblies—Remex Div of Ex-Cell-O Corp (Irvine, Calif) began a concerted effort to solve some critical manufacturing problems. That was nearly three years ago. Today, thanks to the installation of a computer-based manufacturing-control system, we can boast some dramatic improvements, including a 30% reduction in the value of parts inventory, a 50% reduction in work-in-process inventory, and an average reduction of 25% in production time for typical work orders. The new system is being powered by a System/370 Model 115 computer, smallest in IBM's 370 line.

Remex has manufactured punched-tape readers and perforators for computer peripherals for more than 15 years. Our products are widely used in minicomputers and microcomputers as well as in numerical-control, phototypesetting, and communications applications. More recently, we have started to manufacture flexible-disk systems, and we now produce a variety of flexible-diskette drives, subsystems, and software-compatible systems for OEM and end-user applications. Remex presently employs about 200 people at its 52,000-sq-ft manufacturing, engineering, and office facility in Irvine.

Many parts are purchased

Many of the parts and subassemblies for our products are purchased. With our previous inventory system, we had no effective means of coordinating the flow of parts and subassemblies to the floor in phase with scheduled production. Our order-point system alerted us to replenish materials or parts when inventories reached a certain level, but it did not tell us when the items were needed according to the master schedule. As a result, many partially completed assemblies would sit on the floor for days or even weeks awaiting the arrival of one or two parts needed to finish them.

By William R. Sala, general manager
Remex Div, Ex-Cell-O Corp,
Irvine, Calif

Parts pull lists are generated by MRP program running on IBM 370 Model 115 computer. Lists detail all parts and subassemblies needed to complete a top assembly

MRP system helps solve critical manufacturing problems for Remex's diverse and complex product line. Here workers assemble power supplies for punched-tape units

129

Computerized MRP pays off

At the same time, since we had no way of identifying obsolescence in our inventory, we had a great deal of money tied up in parts and assemblies that had little or no movement. Also, our buying system did not provide a means for appraising historical vendor lead-times, which made it nearly impossible to properly time our procurements to ensure that purchased items would be on the floor when they were needed.

Data management is essential

The first step we took to solve these critical manufacturing problems was the installation of a computer hardware/software system oriented to the concept of data management, which is an essential prerequisite to the development of a full materials-requirement planning (MRP) system and for upgrading and improving existing manufacturing-control systems.

The IBM System/370 Model 115 comprises a central processor with 384,000 bytes of main memory, two Model 3340 disk-storage units, and associated tape and input/output peripherals. It is used to run Remex's manufacturing, order-entry, accounting, management-information, and other data-processing systems.

The computer operates under Disk Operating System/Virtual Storage (DOS/VS) and uses Data Language-1 (DL/1), a powerful data-base management system designed for smaller System/370 installations. Online inquiry applications run under Customer Information Control System (CICS) and are carried out through a network of CRT display terminals located in purchasing, material control, the spares-order section, receiving, the stockroom, and the computer-programming area.

The job took two years

Over a two-year period, our programmers, working closely with materials-control, purchasing, and key operating personnel in manufacturing, approached one problem at a time and built steadily toward an integrated set of programs.

The first thing done by Gary Galusha, our product-research manager and coordinator of the materials-control function of the MRP developmental project, was development of an accurate usage history on every inventory item so that we could identify obsolete stock and reduce our inventory costs. Next we tackled the problem of time-phasing our material requirements every week.

Once this was accomplished, we built a program that analyzed every work order for subassemblies and top assemblies that had gone through the plant during the previous 12 months; the program obtained summary reports of actual material and labor costs for each job. This gave us a basis for establishing accurate standards.

Throughout this period, we constantly monitored our bill of materials, inventory, and work-order systems so that we could establish more-effective controls. That is one area where our on-line inquiry system was a tremendous help, since we could use the CRTs to gain immediate access to the various files to track work orders, watch the flow of materials to the floor, and obtain historical summaries without having to wait for printed reports.

In early fall 1977, we reached a point where a full MRP system was in operation with inventory-control, purchasing, and work-order programs all tied to the master schedule and taking into consideration historical purchasing data and sales-forecast factors as well as actual orders.

Item data base is the key

The central feature of MRP at Remex is the item data base, which integrates the essential files involved in purchasing, inventory control, and manufacturing. The item-data-base segments include complete item-identification and inventory data for approximately 6000 parts and subassemblies, as well as purchasing and assembly lead-times, gross requirements, standard material and labor costs, product structures, where-used data, and a six-month usage history on each item. The same data base also identifies all open orders in effect for each item as well as monthly usage forecasts for a full year.

As new customer orders come in, they are entered into the computer through the order entry system. This information is then used for a monthly regeneration of material requirements to meet the needs of the revised master schedule. The regeneration takes into consideration independent and dependent demand as well as open orders, planned orders, firm planned orders, and sales-forecast data.

Order reports are generated

Planned-order reports for both manufactured and purchased items are generated by the system and reviewed by material control. Buying requirements then go to purchasing, and requirements for manufactured subassemblies are coded for entry into the computer to feed the work-order system. Concurrent with the printing of work orders, the computer produces pull lists for the stockroom, detailing the parts and lower assemblies required for each work order.

The system also generates exception reports to alert the material-control and purchasing departments to various conditions that may affect buying and manufacturing decisions. These include flags on items that are needed before normal lead-times, orders that have not arrived on schedule, and items or materials that have increased in price since they were last purchased.

Daily update is major advantage

A major advantage of the inventory-control system is that the parts information is now updated daily instead of weekly, enabling us to implement daily shortage reporting, daily inventory-status reporting, and daily cycle counting. With daily reports about our inventory, we can spot problems immediately and take actions before losses or shortages are compounded.

As a result of better inventory management, we were able to reduce the value of our total inventory by one-third in about 14 months. During the same period, because of better scheduling of parts to the floor, our production cycle was speeded resulting in a 50% reduction of work-in-process inventory.

And, since we can better predict our long-range requirements, we can take advantage of the savings available through volume purchases. For example, during the first six months our MRP system was in use, we realized a saving of about $200,000 through issuing more long-term, blanket purchase orders.

Problem solving is easier

Improved requirements planning also gives our management the ability to react more quickly and effectively to problems that could be costly from the standpoint of delayed production. For example, we recently had a problem with one of our suppliers involving a small aluminum casting that is widely used in many of our paper-tape units. We discovered that a defect in a hardening process caused the units to develop small fractures that could fail when put into operation.

Our MRP system quickly determined the number of units in house and on order, identified the vendor and the particular batch that failed, and looked at our production schedule and shipping commitments. With these facts in hand, we were able to change our product mix and redirect our production effort to meet our dollar goals for shipments that month.

The ability to develop an effective system to manage information is especially critical to a growing business. We're a growing business—and we are confident that our data-processing capabilities will help us meet future needs. ∎

Shop reporting and incentive pay

**This automated shop-floor reporting system covers 1000
machine operators in a 1.5-million-sq-ft plant—with
benefits to workers, to supervisors, and to management**

Effective production management requires measurement plus control. Major advances have been made in developing scientific work-measurement techniques to provide more-accurate standards and in developing more-advanced procedures for materials planning and cost and financial control. All too often, however, these advances have not been accompanied by equally advanced piece-count and time-reporting systems required for the accurate and timely information essential to effective shop management—whether for measured day work, incentive pay systems, or other management control.

In many situations, we find very sophisticated higher-level control systems that are not supported by accurate and timely shop-floor information. Information is frequently provided by operators and, generally, is only perfunctorily checked by supervisors. Figures are often based on the best guess of either operators or supervisors and are then massaged to the fourth decimal place by highly qualified management people, who make decisions using the "accurate" results computed from inaccurate data.

In the days of straight piecework, all that really mattered was the number of pieces reported by the operator for payment, and these could be checked relatively easily by counting or weighing. However, the development of modern cost-control systems (standard cost, variance analysis, etc) brought the need for more-detailed, more-accurate information for productivity control and, when applicable, incentive pay. It has become necessary to differentiate between production time and operator or machine downtime—and to provide reasons. And,

By George G. Fenton
Manager, Industrial Services
Warner Gear Div, Borg-Warner Corp
Muncie, Ind

1. **Approximately 800 work-station terminals** are currently on line in Warner Gear's 1.5-million-sq-ft plant, with the total ultimately to reach 1500

2. **Input/output terminal in central control room** incorporates CRT and keyboard. Three individual systems are interconnected to reduce staffing needs on late shifts

Shop reporting and incentive pay

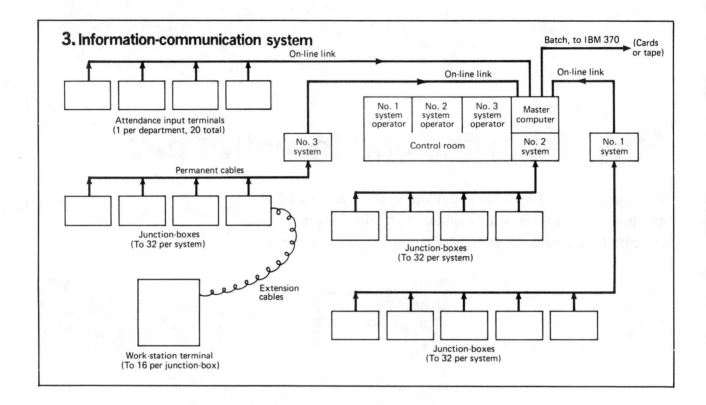

3. Information-communication system

On-line link

Batch, to IBM 370 (Cards or tape)

Attendance input terminals
(1 per department, 20 total)

On-line link

On-line link

No. 1 system operator · No. 2 system operator · No. 3 system operator · Master computer

Control room

No. 2 system

No. 1 system

No. 3 system

Permanent cables

Junction-boxes
(To 32 per system)

Junction-boxes
(To 32 per system)

Extension cables

Work-station terminal
(To 16 per junction-box)

Junction-boxes
(To 32 per system)

for maximum productivity, this data is essential on a minute-to-minute basis for dynamic control of shop operations, rather than after-the-fact analysis.

In reviewing "performance on standard" (comparing the amount of production with the standard time allowed), if performance falls within the expected bounds, it is easy to assume that the standards are correct and accurate. But this calculation depends on reports of the time spent producing the pieces to which the standards apply, and, if this "actual" run-time has been misreported, there is a chance that incorrect standards are being compensated by erroneous reporting of information.

Accurate reporting of run time, downtime, and piece counts is especially important in incentive installations, where operator pay depends on these factors and there may be a tendency to distort reporting. Incorrect reporting of downtime, running production while claiming downtime, and receiving credit for parts produced during setup, for example, can result in an operator's being credited twice for work performed. Such misreporting always results in fast deterioration and early demise of an incentive plan.

Such temptations to misreport also exist at the supervisory level when supervision is rated on the basis of labor performance and utilization.

At one end of the shop-reporting spectrum are handwritten daily or weekly piece and time reports compiled by oper-

ators and signed by a supervisor—often summarily. Similarly, operator-prepared job or work tickets—even if start and stop times are recorded by some time-recording device—are often very arbitrarily approved and controlled by supervisory pesonnel.

Yet it is not always reasonable to hold a supervisor fully responsible for approving or disapproving the correctness of time or job tickets. In many cases, he or she was not on the spot to authorize job starts, changeovers, or downtime when they occurred and must accept the operator's claims in order to maintain harmony in their mutual work environment.

Even more-sophisticated computer-input devices used in systems that are not foolproof may provide data of questionable accuracy.

Such systems do not solve the basic problems: How do we make sure that the foreman is present to authorize downtime? How do we ensure accurate piece counts? How do we eliminate errors in selection of static job information, such as part numbers, operation numbers, standards, etc?

Some systems require a large number of floor checkers or considerable supervisory time for verification of data, or data cannot be verified because it is checked after the fact and thus provides only historical records of events rather than timely information that would allow effective action to correct productivity-reducing situations.

In 1975, Warner Gear started to

develop a new incentive plan based on three principles:

1. Fair and equitable standards based on modern industrial-engineering techniques, including methods-time measurement (MTM).

2. One-for-one incentive motivation.

3. Effective and accurate control of piece counts, unmeasured work, setup, and downtime.

From the very beginning, we were convinced that only the installation of a very sophisticated time- and piece-count reporting system would give the degree of control necessary to ensure a healthy and strong incentive pay plan. We therefore made the installation of the new pay plan, agreed to during 1977 labor negotiations, conditional on the installation of the time- and piece-count reporting system described here.

The Warner Gear system

Warner Gear is a division of the Transmission Products Group of Borg-Warner Corp. We have some 1000 production operators engaged in the manufacture of automotive, industrial, and marine transmissions. Our activities consist mainly of metal-removing operations followed by assembly. We have UAW affiliation.

The system we have installed is a computerized communications network that automatically collects, analyzes, and disseminates accurate production information in real time with minimum effort. The system is called our "Information Communication System" (ICS), stressing "communication" rather than "control," and consists of five basic pieces of equipment.

A work-station terminal (Fig 1 and 4), is located at each controlling machine in each work station. This terminal, made by Information Automation (White Plains, NY), contains a green and a red signal light, an assistance-request selector, an assistance-request button, a key-activated downtime switch, and a multi-channel telephone intercom.

The selector switch is used by the operators for different types of assistance requests according to reason codes lettered in black around the switch. The switch positions also select the downtime condition codes, lettered in red, when the downtime key switch is actuated. Signals from a piece-count sensor, mounted on the machine, are transmitted into the work-station terminal and are recorded on the built-in piece-counter and by the computer.

Wired to a control room

The terminal is connected by cable to the control unit in a central control room, which contains the following: the control-console display and input unit (Fig 2), which is basically a cathode-ray-tube (CRT) unit with a typewriter keyboard; a minicomputer (Digital Equipment Corp PDP-11), which performs data collection, control functions, and processing functions; a report printer, which prints production summaries at shift ends and also prints out messages throughout the course of the shift; a keypunch unit, which is wired to the computer and keypunches information automatically into standard IBM cards, which are transmitted to the central IBM computer for batch preparation of productivity and payroll reports. This last unit is being supplanted by a magnetic-tape system.

Multichannel two-way voice communication is provided from each work-station terminal to the control room via a plug-in telephone, carried by the foreman, and a microphone and speaker in the control room. One two-way voice phone channel is connected directly from each work-station terminal to the maintenance dispatcher's desk. Foremen are paged by the control room to the work-stations requiring assistance by a Motorola one-way paging system, integrated with our Bell System 2000 telephone network. The foreman can be readily paged by the control room and directed to any particular station.

The system thus provides the machine operator with instant communication with the foreman, with plant maintenance, or with any other service department, without the operator's having to leave the work-station. Current moment-to-moment data is recorded from information available at the production machine and is displayed on the CRTs in the control room. Additional CRT monitors are installed in various foremen's offices.

Because of the plant's size, some 1.5-million sq ft, we have divided it into three control areas, each consisting of a completely independent system with its own computer, console, printer, and paging system. Because the system requires the continuous presence of control-room personnel at the consoles on all three shifts, two of the computers are interconnected to the third "master computer." All the consoles, printers, and communication equipment are installed in this central control room. This way, we do not have to staff the control room as fully during the afternoon and midnight shifts as we do on the day shift. Fig 3 shows the configuration of the system.

Warner Gear generally operates in machining flow lines, each consisting of a series of machine "cycles." A cycle is a number of individual machine tools attended by one operator, and cycles are arranged in lines, with storage banks between them. A typical line, for instance, takes a rough forging, completes all turning, boring, and drilling operations, and performs gear-cutting and -finishing operations, producing a complete gear ready for heat-treatment and subsequent grinding.

We have two basic cycle configurations. First, there is what we call the

4. Operator presses button on terminal to call for foreman's assistance

"series configuration," in which a part is processed through each of the machines in sequence. This can best be described as a human transfer machine. The operator unloads a part from machine A, reloads a new part and starts the machine; then takes the previously completed part from machine A, walks to machine B, unloads machine B, loads the part just taken from machine A into machine B, and starts the automatic cycle on machine B; then carries the part from machine B to machine C, continuing this way until the part has passed through all the machines in the cycle. The operator then deposits the part in a temporary storage bank.

The second typical configuration is a "parallel" cycle, in which a number of machines perform identical operations. In this case, the operator loads the first part from the storage bank into machine A, the next part into machine B, the third into machine C, etc, and then removes completed parts from each machine into the storage bank.

In a series cycle, we monitor only one machine. Generally we select the controlling machine, the one with the longest machining time. In a parallel cycle, we monitor each machine in the cycle, because it is possible to run this type of cycle even if one of the machines is down. In that instance, we record separately the downtime of that machine and pay the operator the appropriate amount of downtime to compensate for production lost by that machine.

Computer can say 'no'

Constant information (such as part numbers, operation numbers, standards, etc) is permanently entered, via the CRT keyboard, into the master-computer file from the operational route sheets. This information is stored in memory and automatically accessed by the computer when a particular job is assigned to a machine cycle. This minimizes the possibility of error, because any attempt to enter mismatches of cycle numbers relative to part or operation numbers is rejected automatically.

Before each shift, the foreman submits an assignment sheet to the control room, showing the assignment of each operator by clock number to a specific machine cycle, together with the part number and operation number to be run. Operators are assigned to the cycle by the control-room operator through the console. Once an operator has been assigned to a cycle, the computer will not accept a second assignment for the same operator, nor will it accept an assignment to a cycle if an operator has been previously assigned to it.

To transfer an operator from one cycle

Shop reporting and incentive pay

to another, the foreman calls the control room on the portable telephone and specifies the operation and cycle that the operator is being sent to. The instant the transaction is completed by the control room, the machine the operator is leaving is turned into the OFF mode, thus stopping all time recording and piece counts; at the same instant, it turns the new machine into the ON mode and starts to record pieces produced.

The piece-count information, combined with machine-status information, constitutes all the pertinent dynamic data concerning a work cycle. This data—combined with the static job information, such as part and operation number, and with operator data, such as clock number and shift—provides the basis for production control and payroll.

The work-station terminal (Fig 1 and 4) operates in the following manner:

When a job is running normally, the selector switch remains in the RUN position, and the green signal light stays on continuously. An operator requiring assistance moves the assistance switch selector to one of the HELP positions and pushes the ASSIST button, which causes the red and green signal lights to flash, a buzzer to sound in the control room, and the assistance request condition code to be displayed on the CRT.

The example (Fig 4) shows the operator requesting FOREMAN HELP. The assistance request is immediately displayed on the CRT in the control room, and the appropriate help (foreman, trucker, inspector, chip hauler) is paged and dispatched directly to the machine or cycle requiring assistance. The computer enters into memory the exact time at which the request originated.

If no problem exists, the foreman returns the switch to the RUN position, and the entry is disregarded by the computer. If, however, the machine is to be placed on downtime, the foreman inserts a key into the machine downtime-authorization lock and places the machine in the appropriate DOWN condition. Only supervisors are issued the special downtime keys.

After correction of the downtime condition, the operator pushes the reset button, putting the machine back on RUN time; the foreman's presence is not required. The elapsed downtime and the reason code are printed out by the computer.

The most essential features

While the cycle is on downtime or setup, pieces produced are recorded separately for production control. They are not reported for pay purposes because down-

time or setup has already been paid for on an elapsed-time basis. This and the necessity of the foreman's presence every time a cycle is placed on downtime are the important features of this system. They are essential for proper control of the incentive plan and to stimulate prompt action by supervision.

Throughout the shift, all transactions are continuously recorded, and the computer performs an automatic "end-of-shift" report. At this time, any information net yet recorded is printed and keypunched to produce a complete set of punched cards for the shift. These are then fed to the IBM 370 computer for the preparation of daily and weekly labor-performance reports.

The daily labor analysis by clock number (Fig 5) summarizes all work done by each operator during a shift. This report, which is posted in the department by 11:00 am the next day, shows the date, shift, department number, the cycles to which the operator has been assigned during the shift, operator clock number, the part and operation numbers worked on, and the standard in standard hours per piece. It shows any additional off-standard payments authorized by the standards department (OSPAs) for exceptional situations (such as hard stock), the quantity produced,

DATE+ SHIFT	DEPT NO.	CYCLE NO.	CLOCK NO.	PART NO.	OPN NO.	OSPA NO.	STD.	QTY PROD	MACH HRS.	C F	ACTL HRS.	ERND HRS.	AVAL HRS.	PCT EFF	PCT UTIL	CD	MACH HRS.	ACTL HRS.	ERND HRS.	ER CD	SEQ NO.
0920 2	F09	25524	103	1332-171-004	060		.0316	105	1.99	1	1.99	3.318									366
0920 2	F09	25524	103	1332-171-004	060		1.0000			1						XX	.24	.24	.240		370
0920 2	F09	25501	103	1301-171-001	026		.0144	248	1.97	1	1.97	3.571									459
0920 2	F09	25501	103	1301-171-001	026		1.0000	7		1						XX	.24	.24	.740		466
0920 2	F09	25501	103	1301-171-001	026		1.0000			1						10	.08	.08	.080		467
0920 2	F09	25506	103	1338-171-005	067		.0084	298	2.32	1	2.32	2.167									522
0920 2	F09	25506	103	1338-171-005	067		.0084	59	.41	1	.41	.496									543
0920 2	F09	25506	103	1338-171-005	067		1.0000			1						XX	.09	.09	.090		545
0920 2	F09	25506	103	1338-171-008	067		1.0000			1						XX	.01	.01	.010	L	546
0920 2	F09	25506	103	1338-171-008	067	SETUP	.3110			1						SU		.311			547
0920 2	F09	25506	103	1338-171-008	067		.0084			1						PS	.01	.01		L	548
0920 2	F09	25506	103	1338-171-008	067		.0084	34	.84	1	.64	.286								L	563
************		103T							7.33			9.838	134	91.6			.67		.971		
											7.33		8.00					.67			
0920 2	F09	25530	148	1332-171-004	075		.0162		.14	1	.14										289
0920 2	F09	25530	148	1332-171-004	075		.0162		.04	1	.04										296
0920 2	F09	25530	148	1332-171-004	075		1.0000	5		1						XX	.22	.22	.720		310
0920 2	F09	25530	148	1332-171-004	075		1.0000	33		1						MM	.45	.45	.450		329
0920 2	F09	25530	148	1332-171-004	075		.0162	365	3.00	1	3.00	5.913									447
0920 2	F09	25530	148	1332-171-004	075		1.0000			1						XX	.05	.05	.050		449
0920 2	F09	25495	148	1301-171-001	023		.0131	78	1.69	1	1.69	1.022									478
0920 2	F09	25495	148	1301-171-001	023		.0131	6	.05	1	.05	.074									484
0920 2	F09	25495	148	1301-171-001	023		1.0000			1						XX	.10	.10	.100		486
0920 2	F09	25495	148	1301-171-003	080		1.0000			1						XX	.01	.01	.010		487
0920 2	F09	25495	148	1301-171-003	080	SETUP	.6370			1						SU		.637			497
0920 2	F09	25495	148	1301-171-003	080		.0131	4		1						PS	.26	.26	.052		498
0920 2	F09	25495	148	1301-171-003	080		.0131		.44	1	.44										507
0920 2	F09	25495	148	1301-171-003	080		.0131	14	.35	1	.35	.249									517
************		148T							5.71			7.263	127	84.0			1.09		1.519		
											5.71		6.80					1.09			
25T									42.80			57.068	133	84.4			7.89		8.745		
											42.80		50.69					7.89			
											PS	1.13					1.13		.447		
											SU	.00					.00		1.538		
											MM	.49					.49		.490		
											SO	1.72					1.72		1.770		
											TC	1.83					1.83		1.830		
											10	.46					.46		.460		
											XX	2.26					2.26		2.260		

5. Daily labor analysis by clock number summarizes work done by each operator during shift, is posted next morning

```
TIME: 13.82          CYCLE REPORT - NK625001        SHIFT: 2   8/26/77

PART NUMBER:   1338-000-023    MULT:   1    PERFORMANCE:            113 %
DESCRIPTION:   T50 TRANSMISSION FACTOR: 1    UTILIZATION:            53 %
OPERATION:     001 - ASSEM LOW PAD              PRODUCTIVITY:        60 %
STANDARD:          0.0028      PRODUCTION COUNT (SHIFT):           175
SET-UP STANDARD:   0.0000      PRODUCTION COUNT (RUN):           2459
DELTA OSPA:             0.0000 BALANCE TO GO:                    2541
BANKS       A       B       TOTAL ORIGINAL ORDERED QUANTITY:     5000
  UPPER     0       0       0     DECREMENT:                        0
  LOWER     1751    0       1751  ETC:                              7.1
EMPLOYEE(S):   535
             RUN   DT    DOWN  S/U   ---- SHIFT ----
MACH STATUS  TIME  INCI  TIME  TIME  PC   PC/DT PC/SU CD
-- TOTAL --  0.38        0.34  0.00  154  21    0
   A  RUN    0.38  0.00  0.34  0.00  154  21    0     0
```

6. Cycle report on CRT shows real-time status of plant equipment, production, run time, downtime, setup time, and other data, plus calculated information

the machine and actual worker-hours spent producing that quantity, the earned hours (the product of the standard multiplied by the quantity produced), and the total available worker-hours.

The right-hand side of the report shows all time diverted to nonproduction, itemizing the machine-hours elapsed, the operator-hours elapsed for each incident, and the earned hours for such time. In some situations (such as instruction time), we pay at 1.25 standard hours per actual hour elapsed.

All incidents of nonproduction work or downtime are coded by reason for control and costing. For example, XX stands for foreman response time to answer assistance calls; ID stands for idle machine due to lack of stock; SU stands for setup.

In Fig 5, operator clock No. 103 has produced 9.838 standard hours during an actual production time of 7.33 hours. Total available hours were eight hours for the shift, and the difference between available hours and actual production hours is shown as 0.67 actual hours of nonproduction time, for which the operator earned 0.971 hours because one of the setups was performed on standard. The operator's efficiency on standard was 134%, and the utilization of his time on production was 91.6%.

The report also shows a summary for the whole group because our pay system is a group system, in which one production line generally forms one pay group. In this example, the average efficiency on standard for the whole group was 133%, and its utilization was 84.4%. That is, 84.4% of the available time was spent on production. The balance of the time was spent on nonproduction work as detailed in the lower right-hand corner. The daily labor analysis by clock number is summarized in a weekly report by clock number, which becomes the basis for the incentive-pay calculation.

A weekly labor analysis by cycle number resummarizes all information by cycle number and shows all the work done on each cycle during the previous week. This report shows total weekly efficiency generated by all workers assigned to the cycle, the utilization of available cycle time, and all time diverted to nonproduction, together with the reasons for the diversions. All weekly reports are available on the Wednesday morning following the end of the week, midnight Sunday.

The system has the capability for real-time displays on the CRTs, with hard copy if required, of various types of information. A normal control-center status report shows, at all times, cycles requiring assistance, cycles on downtime, and the time elapsed since that condition originated.

A line-status report indicates the status of each cycle in a production line, providing relevant information, such as balance of order to be completed, efficiency, utilization, and productivity of each cycle in the line and the estimated time to complete the order. This last provides leadtime for tooling preparation for the next setup.

On demand, the system provides a detailed report (Fig 6) that shows in real time the status of each cycle, the part number, operation numbers, quantity produced, downtime, run time, setup time, and pieces produced under each condition; it also provides a continuous calculation of on-standard performance, cycle utilization, and productivity.

The system also provides various exception reports on demand. For example, a performance-exception report shows all cycles with performances outside the preset limits, which can be readily altered through the CRT keyboard. A combined exception report shows all cycles whose performance,

utilization, or productivity are outside preset limits. These exception reports are very helpful in maintaining productivity, accuracy of standards, and reporting.

Another report is the production summary, which shows quantities of all parts and operations produced during the shift, run time, downtime, setup, performance, utilization, and productivity of each cycle in the department. This report is available at any time during the shift and at shift end. It is useful for production scheduling and overall departmental control.

What else is possible

There are virtually no limits to what else the system can provide, other than those imposed by our lack of imagination. We can use the system to signal the control room when tools require changing—especially when expensive tools such as hobs, shaper cutters, or gearshaving cutters are used. We can signal the control room if some of the equipment is running off speed, producing poor quality and ruining too many tools or not allowing the operator to make standard. We have direct communication from each cycle, via the portable phone, to the maintenance office, so that spare parts can be quickly requested and even diagnostic dialogue can take place between the maintenance people at the cycle and the craft foreman in the maintenance office.

Based on experience to date—the first terminal went on line late in 1976, and there are currently about 800 of an eventual 1500 on line—the benefits of the system are wide-ranging. Implementation of the system, along with establishment of new standards and new incentive-pay arrangements, has been on a department-by-department basis. Productivity has improved by a minimum of 10-15% in some departments and by as much as 35% in others, primarily as a result of reduced downtime and sharper production control.

Machine operators, benefiting from instant communication and accurate logging of information, have realized increases in pay and have gained in their job satisfaction. Shop supervision, with instant access to all production information, is better able to control downtime and other factors in a fair and equitable manner—and do it without handwritten reports. And management is better able to provide effective control in improving equipment utilization and productivity.

The system benefits the entire organization by permitting a strong incentive pay plan, providing the means to implement and maintain it, and thus ensuring high productivity with commensurate earnings. ∎

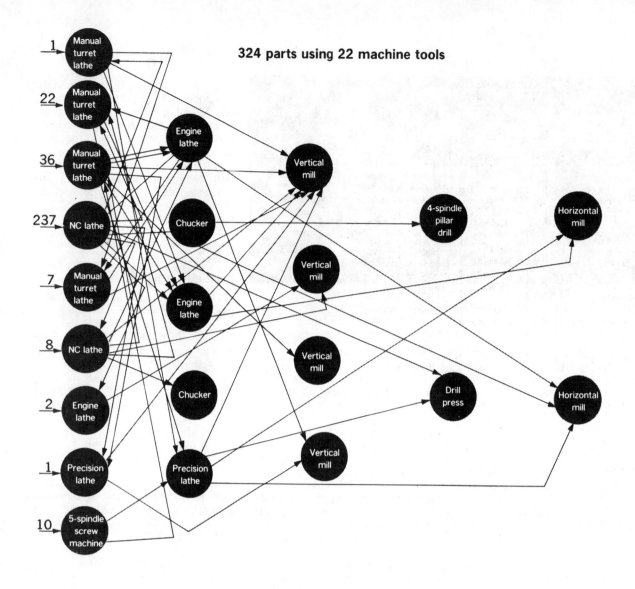

324 parts using 22 machine tools

GT expands capacity

The implementation of a manufacturing cell based on the MICLASS group-technology system has improved production times and reduced work-in-process inventory at this plant

If you were to analyze any individual manufacturing operation at EG&G Sealol, Engineered Products Div (Providence, RI), you would find hardly any increase in efficiency over the past few years. Yet the company is pushing more products out the door than ever, using basically the same facility, and work-in-process (WIP) inventory, as measured in part days, has been reduced a whopping 30% with a new manufacturing cell.

The paradox results from good man-

agement: a combination of group technology, a lot of good manufacturing engineering, and effective production control. The key element of Sealol's improved manufacturing posture has been the establishment of a manufacturing cell based on the implementation of the MICLASS system of group technology available from Organization for Industrial Research (formerly TNO), Waltham, Mass.

The use of group technology was instituted by the Engineered Products Div to help cope with its chief problem: increasing capacity limitations. In 1977, the

company recorded roughly $11.5-million in sales. In 1978, it had planned to ship something over $12-million, but business was so good that the company actually ended up shipping out more than $15-million worth of products. The original plan for 1979 was to ship $17.1-million, but it appears that the figure will be very close to $21-million.

With such consistent annual growth, the facility was constantly operating near the limit of its manufacturing capacity. Problems attendant with such a strained operation had a snowballing effect: every time one manufacturing

324 parts using 7 machine tools

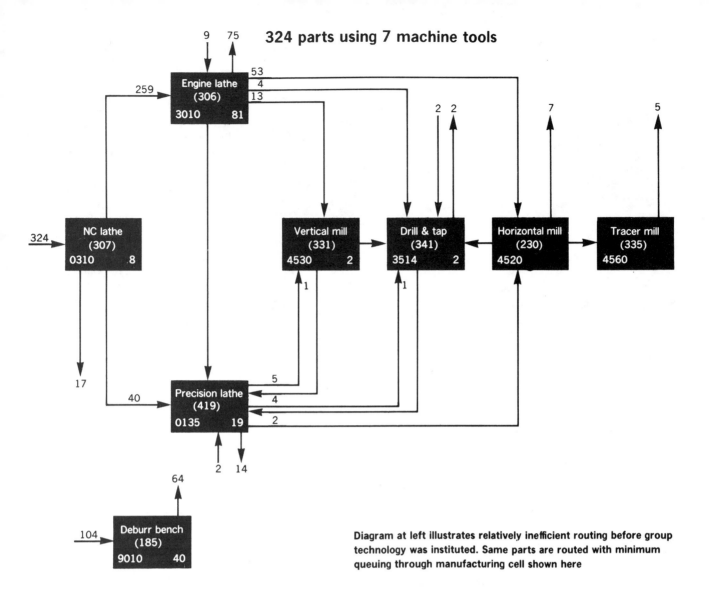

Diagram at left illustrates relatively inefficient routing before group technology was instituted. Same parts are routed with minimum queuing through manufacturing cell shown here

operation got into any kind of trouble, it complicated other aspects of the operation: planning, inventory, and machine-tool capacity were all mutually affected.

"We were already tight on capacity in 1977," says Jim Nolen, manufacturing-engineering manager. "So we had to start doing some smart things as well as buying some new equipment. We've just been getting to the point, in the last year or so, where, without group technology and a proper materials-requirements planning (MRP) system, there is no way we'd be able to keep up with demand."

GT principle is simple

The underlying principle of group technology (GT) is relatively simple: group similar parts with appropriately similar manufacturing processes for a smooth manufacturing flow that can achieve some of the advantages of mass production in a batch-oriented job-shop-like environment.

Putting GT into practice, however, is not so simple. The difficulties arise in identifying and bringing together appro-priate families of parts. The MICLASS system addresses these problems with a coding and classification scheme developed through an interactive computer-based approach, together with a series of related GT software packages.

The result is a rationalization of the manufacturing operation and increased management control. And that, rather than increased efficiency, is pushing more products out the door at Sealol. "The real improvements have come because we are able to plan our manufacturing schedules and then run them all the way through according to plan: no constant changing of tactics and disruption of the entire applecart," says Nolen.

Sealol makes a large variety of high-quality and special-purpose mechanical seals; constant growth has made it the second-largest manufacturer of such products in the world. Its divisions, the Industrial Div and the Engineered Products Div, serve a variety of original-equipment manufacturers and users in the automotive, aircraft, petrochemical, energy, electronic, nuclear, and marine industries. The Engineered Product Div has developed many original devices and is, for example, the sole supplier of mainshaft seals for the US Navy's nuclear submarines and a major supplier of seals to all jet-engine manufacturers.

The division also designed and provided 26 different bellows devices—it makes a large variety if bellows-type seals—that assisted in safely landing the first human on the moon. Many of its products are custom engineered, and most are intended for operation in adverse environments. "There's no cold-rolled steel in the shop," says Nolen. In fact, Sealol is one of the largest users of Monel forgings in the country.

Lot sizes are small

With that kind of product mix and the very specialized nature of many of the products, it stands to reason that lot sizes at Sealol are relatively small. A big run of parts is about 200 at one time; the highest volume for a single product is about 5000 per year. "We have many

GT expands capacity

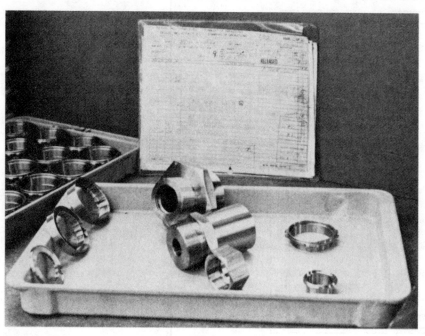

Parts for the initial manufacturing cell include those that had, historically, created machine-capacity and customer-service problems. 324 parts were selected

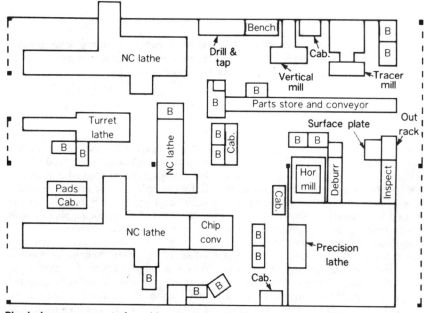

Physical rearrangement of machines and work stations into a manufacturing cell is an essential element of group technology, according to Sealol's Jim Nolen

runs of 50 parts and many that are much smaller," Nolen says. Such a small-batch job-shop manufacturing environment makes for difficult scheduling and routing problems, and the division had a reputation for running a long-lead-time business.

Part of that long-time has been due to relatively complex routings and the associated queuing times. In fact, before the institution of the manufacturing-cell arrangement, it was quite difficult to track the progress of a product through the manufacturing cycle. With the regular process-oriented shop, Nolen always figured that any part requiring four or five different operations would take 10-15 weeks to get through the shop. Sometimes it took longer, and sometimes the parts would seem to get lost. The

machine-loading scheme apparently followed the FIST system: First In and Still There!

"By contrast the manufacturing cell is set up so that once, a part starts through, we know we're going to get it out in anywhere from a few days to, usually, no more than two weeks, provided there are no outside vendor operations," notes Nolen. The difference in production time comes from the simplificaton of routings and the attendant elimination of long and unpredictable queuing times.

Excessive queuing time is by no means peculiar to Sealol's operation. It is a well established fact that, in any manufacturing operation, most of production time is devoted to waiting. In fact, in most batch manufacturing, waiting time usually accounts for 95% of production time, and only 5% is devoted to setup and run time.

One of the primary causes of excessive waiting time is the inefficient routing of parts as they go through the shop. The seemingly random variations in routing in any functionally departmentalized shop have always been difficult to control, and it is not uncommon to find some machines idle because of lack of work while others have long queues of work waiting to be processed.

More efficient routing

One of the major accomplishments resulting from the implementation of the MICLASS system at Sealol was the establishment of more-efficient routing to reduce waiting time. For example, the initial group of parts selected for the manufacturing cell consisted of 324 bar-type parts that had, historically, created machine-capacity and customer-service problems. In the traditional shop arrangement, these parts required operations on 22 machine tools and involved 115 routes. With the cell arrangement, these same parts go to only seven machines, and there are only 70 routes all together—an almost 40% reduction.

The MICLASS system makes it possible to group parts into families requiring similar machining operations and also to identify the specific machine tools through which these families should be routed. Although this does not necessarily mean that the machine tools must be moved and reorganized into a physical manufacturing cell, such an arrangement usually leads to even greater economies, and so Sealol rearranged its machines. Nolen believes that the physical cell arrangement is essential to the success of group technology.

The heart of any group-technology system is the coding program used to establish classification-code numbers identifying each workpiece. The MICLASS coding program classifies a part in relation to its characteristics—shape, dimensions, tolerances, and machinability—rather than by its function. The classification number forms the key for entering the database of the system, which, once it is established, contains the following information for each part:

- Classification number
- Drawing number
- Part nomenclature
- Manufacturing operations
- Machine-tool use
- Production time
- Setup time
- Other company information.

Data can be retrieved from the database through various codes: the classification number, the drawing number, or any in-house coding system that can be incorporated into the MICLASS code. Once the database has been established, a series of retrieval, sorting, and analysis programs can be used to automate various operational, manufacturing, and management activities:

- Retrieval of engineering drawings.
- Automatic generation of manufacturing route sheets and process plans.
- Standardization of drawings.
- Analysis of raw-material needs, production-group capacities, machine-tool requirements, and process lines.

The MICLASS classification number consists of two major parts. The first is a 12-digit universal code applicable to all parts regardless of the company or plant using the system. This makes it particularly useful in multidivisional or multinational organizations. The 12 digits classify the engineering and manufacturing characteristics of a part according part form, dimensions, tolerances, and materials.

In addition to the universal code, as many as 18 extra digits can be added for dealing with information specific to individual plants, companies, or industries. Such information may relate to lot sizes, piece times, costs, machining operations, vendor codes, or other appropriate manufacturing-related information. Coding is effected by means of an interactive, "conversational" computer program in which the computer interrogates the programmer with a series of questions in simple English.

At Sealol, two computer runs are made to estabish a complete classification number. The first run establishes the universal, 12-digit element of the classification number. Those 12 digits are then entered on the part print used by the planner performing the coding. Next, this print goes to an independent planner for checking. Typically, mistakes involve overlooking some element of geometry on a part, such as a groove, or

misinterpretation of directional information relating to the origin of a tool path.

The second computer run establishes the remaining digits by asking for such information as part name, annual quantity and number of lots per year, general operations to be performed on the part, machine-tool identification, and setup and run-time standards. A printout of the entire MICLASS interactive session is also kept for checking and possible future reference.

Implementation of group technology at Sealol was a team effort, with all parties, including union officials, kept informed of management intention. The actual GT team included the shop supervisor, who now runs the cell, and three people from manufacturing engineering. All went through coding and analysis training, including graphic illustrations of family similarities.

It all paid off, says Sealol, which has made an extensive study of the pilot GT

A roller conveyor was incorporated into the manufacturing cell to provide a convenient central storage location for parts awaiting work at any of the work station

Planner checks first 12 digits of code developed by computer and adds information for second run: part name, quantities and lots, operations, standard times, machines

139

GT expands capacity

Coding is effected by means of an interactive, 'conversational' computer program that interrogates the programmer with a series of questions in simple English

Two J&L Combi NC lathes were available when the cell was established. A manual lathe with special tooling is used to help carry the load

Hardinge manual lathe was collecting dust before the cell was introduced, because nearly everything was programmed for NC. Now it is used for secondary operations

cell, measuring results against previous analogous performance. Comparing a sample of in-house manufactured parts made prior to MICLASS implementation with an identical sample made in the cell revealed that the number of parts produced jumped from 2.26 to 5.7 per day and that the average production time in days per lot was cut almost in half. The time it would probably take to complete all lots was also projected, and here there was a significant difference: 30 working days for the cell, compared with 80 days for the standard shop.

In addition to comparing a sample of similar parts, the study also compared actual production for two months, one before and one after cell implementation. ("Production" includes both parts made in-house and those subcontracted.) The number of lots in the two months was almost the same—53 vs 54—and the average lot sizes were also roughly the same—99.9 vs 92. The number of parts produced during these months was also comparable—5300 before the cell and 5000 with it.

More work done in-house

There was, however, an important difference. Before implementing the cell, Sealol contracted out considerable work. In fact, the cell produced 5000 parts whereas the conventional shop had only produced 2019 parts—the rest had been subcontracted. So the average output per day jumped from 2.2 to 3.85 with the installation of the cell.

Finally, work-in-process inventory, measured in part days, was reduced 20%. Considering that EG&G's overall operation has a pretax return of about 35% on its investment, a reduction in WIP inventory can be figured as being worth 35% of the investment in those parts. Since the cell does roughly 25% of all machine-shop work and Sealol's average WIP inventory, although dropping, was about $1-million, EG&G can presumably earn $18,000 a year by not tying up that money at its Sealol Div.

Sealol managers are pleased because the facility is no longer straining at capacity, they are able to respond faster to special marketing needs, and the cell arrangement has meant a 400-sq-ft saving in floor space. An added benefit has been the company's ability to provide fast and accurate response to a request for a proposal for a venture into the manufacture of valve sets for the nuclear industry. MICLASS helped simulate the entire manufacturing process and arrive at a timely proposal that put Sealol into the final contender's ring. No wonder work is already in progress to add two more manufacturing cells later this year. ∎

NC PROGRAMMING

NC machines live on a diet of part-programs, and their nutritional value depends on the people, the hardware, and the software that generate these machining instructions

More than 60,000 numerically controlled machine tools are currently in US metalworking facilities, and the number is going up at the fastest rate in the 25-year history of NC. Probably a tenth of the lathes installed in the past decade, a quarter of the boring machines, and more than a quarter of the combined milling/machining-center category are NC machines. To justify the installation of this expensive equipment, users typically show that the NC machine will outproduce or replace a number of "traditional" machines—with a ratio of 3:1 to 5:1 being conservative and much higher not uncommon. NC *is* significantly affecting the nation's metalworking productivity, particularly in the area of general-purpose machine tools.

Yet a numerically controlled machine tool will operate only as productively as its part-program allows it.

A part-program is the detailed process plan for the machining steps to be performed on the particular NC machine involved. The program defines the final shape of the part being machined—whether by turning, milling, drilling, punching or by any other numerically controlled operation.

It sets the sequence of individual operations or individual cuts. It determines the cutting tool that is to be used—whether that tool is changed automatically by a toolchanger or indexing turret or manually by the operator. It carries the feeds and speeds and depths at which each cut will be made. In many cases—the manual toolchange, for example—it even provides instructions or reminders for the machine operator.

All of this information—and frequently much more—is contained in the part-program in the form of coded instructions, which are read by the NC system and translated into the commands to actuate the machine tool.

Certainly the part-program is not the only element contributing to the efficiency and effectiveness of the overall NC machining system—which includes the machine itself, the control, the cutting tools and fixturing, the operator, and still other factors—but it is just as true that the part-program can limit the profitable usefulness of the entire machining system.

As NC enters the decade of the '80s, the vast majority of part-programs are entered into the machine-control system in the form of 1-in. punched paper or various types of coated or laminated tape meeting Electronic Industries Assn (EIA) standard RS-227A. And, since most current-model NC and CNC (computerized numerical-control) systems are equipped for input in this form, the number of NC machines using punched tape is still increasing.

There is, however, increasing competition for punched tape as the primary part-program medium from other forms of data-storage devices, such as flexible magnetic disks (floppy disks, or floppies), digital magnetic-tape cassettes, and even direct storage in semiconductor memory or bubble memories. Various combinations of these are also offered; one is the currently common use of punched tape to load a control's semiconductor memory, from which the part-program is executed by the machine tool without further use of the tape. Some of the reasons for these newer approaches will be discussed subsequently.

Nevertheless, the tradition of a quarter century of NC practice still leaves the habit of equating "numerical control," or "NC," with "tape control" and "part-programming" with "tape-preparation." It should be kept in mind, therefore, that a simple swapping of peripheral devices will convert most "tape-preparation" systems to other program-storage media. Restated, "tape-preparation" is really only one step in the programming effort and can often be omitted, yet the term is frequently used as a synonym for "part-programming."

There are a variety of approaches to the overall function of part-programming. Each has its own individual twists, and no one is the single best way to get the job done in all cases.

Broadly, the techniques can be broken down into two categories: manual part-programming and computer-assisted part-programming. Selection of the proper approach in any specific case requires individual consideration of many variables:

■ The workpieces themselves. Are they geometrically simple, or are they so complex as to demand the power of a computer to calculate the machine moves necessary for their production? Are parts machined in small lots or long production runs? Are there many variations of basically similar parts? Are leadtimes typically relaxed, or is "fire-fighting" commonly required?

■ The NC machines. Is the NC installation a "turning" shop or a "milling" house? Or does it include a variety of different machine types? Are most of the machines the products of only one or two builders, with the same or similar controls? How many NC machines must be programmed?

■ The company itself. Do this shop and its people have long experience and familiarity with NC? Is it a big plant with a highly structured organization chart or a small, informal setup? Does a corporate data-processing facility already exist? Could other data-processing applications—such as payroll, inventory control, billing, and others—also be implemented on a minicomputer acquired primarily for part-programming?

Let's investigate these questions.

MANUAL PART-PROGRAMMING

Most shops starting out with their first numerically controlled machine tool prepare the necessary part-programs manually, at least initially. Overall, this process typically entails selection and justification of parts to be machined by NC, general process planning, tool and fixture design, step-by-step planning of each machining cut, preparation of a hand-written list of specific instructions to the machine control (the program manuscript), conversion of the manuscript into a punched tape (or other data-storage medium), verification of the recorded part-program, and—very likely—subsequent modification of the program to improve the machining process.

In smaller installations, one person may perform all of these functions—and then go on to operate the machine. In larger, more structured organizations, the manufacturing-engineering department may produce the general process plan in the form of operation sheets, a tool-design department may do its thing, and so forth.

It's done in machine code

The core of manual programming, however, is preparation of the manuscript, its conversion into a verified tape (or whatever), and subsequent editing, all of which must be done in the specific codes of the particular machine tool to be used.

Programmers need skills and considerable knowledge of machining and tooling practice. Beyond that, they need familiarity with the particular NC machine, its capabilities, and the specific codes it requires for activation of each function. But they need very little in the way of tape-preparation equipment. In fact, for manual-data-input (MDI) machines, they need none at all.

The geometry of most workpieces is certainly simple enough that it is not beyond the capability of human beings to prepare the instructions needed by a numerical control to direct the machine tool's motions without the aid of a separate computer—to program manually, in other words. The part may be complex in that it has many features to be machined, but those individual features are typically generated by only straight-line or circular-arc movements, and these are easily programmed into modern control systems that provide both linear and circular interpolation. Parts that are complex in this sense may be tedious and time-consuming to program manually, but they are certainly possible. And many parts are even simpler in that they have only a few or none of these line-and-arc features.

All numerical-control systems incorporate features to facilitate manual part-programming. This has always been true, but today's NC systems incorporating built-in mini- or micro-computers and, perhaps more significant, built-in memories for part-program storage have added some remarkable aids for the manual programmer.

Because manual-data-input (MDI) controls may involve no additional "tape-preparation" equipment, let us consider them and their programming first. Whether or not you classify MDI systems as true numerical controls is a semantic question that is irrelevant as far as programming is concerned. It's just as valid to call them "tapeless NC." The key distinction is that MDI controls do not incorporate built-in means for reading punched tape, although many at least optionally provide some means of automatic part-program input, and they are intended primarily for programming by the machine operator.

Labels are in English

One aid for operator-programmers that is provided by some manufacturers of MDI controls—especially those that prefer to distinguish between MDI and NC—is the use of "shop language" on the panel's pushbuttons and keyboards in place of the more esoteric alphanumeric codes typical of NC. The idea is that a button reading TABLE LEFT is less forbidding to the operator-programmer than one labeled +X and, more important, reduces the time needed for familiarization and training.

If that's catering to the unsophisticated, however, there's nothing unsophisticated about some of the other programming capabilities offered on MDI controls. For example, about half of the MDI controls listed in AM's Special Report 711, "Machining by the numbers"

(AM—May'79,p131), provide both linear and circular interpolation, and a few add parabolic or helical interpolation. (Helical interpolation is essentially a combination of two-axis circular interpolation with simultaneous linear control of a third axis—a useful capability, for example, in thread milling.)

Most MDI controls offer at least an optional capability to extract part-programs from memory for longer-term archival storage—the equivalent of a tape library in more-common NC parlance. This is generally in the form of a magnetic-tape cassette and read/write capability so that an edited program can be transferred from the MDI control's memory for library deposit and subsequent reuse whenever that workpiece is to go back into production simply by reinserting that cassette and reading its contents into active memory.

At this point, the MDI control is barely distinguishable from the "classic" NC system; the only difference is that one uses magnetic tape, the other uses punched tape. Inasmuch as CNC systems offer MDI capability and since many current control product lines offer archival storage on media other than punched tape—such as floppy disks—there's little point in differentiating the two.

Electronics replaces iron

From a programming point of view, however, manually entering the part-program at the machine tool offers the least departure from traditional machine-shop practice. Using a blueprint and, perhaps, a set of operation sheets from the manufacturing-engineering department, the machinist, or the setup man, figures out how to set up the machine and keys in the data. Electronically memorized codes and values replace stop dogs, jigs, cams, templets, and other such "iron memory" devices.

The principal advantages of MDI programming are minimal investment in tape-preparation equipment, organizational simplicity, and the psychological benefit of considerable operator involvement. These advantages seem to have a major attraction for small job shops, but one major aerospace manufacturer on the West Coast has a "Blue Streak Department," in which a number of MDI machines are operator-programmed to fill emergency needs for short runs of urgently required parts.

The biggest disadvantage to MDI programming is that the machine is not cutting metal while it's being programmed and is thus being used as rather high-priced tape-preparation equipment. One development aimed at eliminating this shortcoming is the capability of NC systems on wire-cut EDM machines

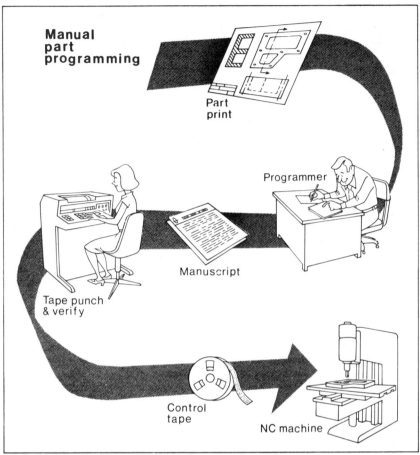

Manual part programming

Part print

Programmer

Manuscript

Tape punch & verify

Control tape

NC machine

Many variations of basic manual part-programming are possible. These include operator input of part-print data into the machine control and range up to systems using floppy-disk program-storage and data transmission to control's memory

to operate in a foreground/background mode, which allows one workpiece to be machined from data in memory while a new program is being entered. This is especially suitable for EDM operation because the requirement for operator attention is minimal.

In most NC installations, the programming function is removed from the shop floor and from the machine operator. The minimum additional equipment typically required for this is a tape-punching keyboard unit that also produces a hard-copy printout of the codes on the tape, such as a Flexowriter, a Teletype, or various other units. A hand calculator is another accessory frequently used by the manual programmer.

The part-programmer manually writes out the program manuscript block by block, usually on a specially designed programming form, and this is keyboarded into the tape-punching unit (by the programmer in some installations, by a typist in others). The hard-copy listing of codes for the NC machine is then scrupulously compared with the original hand-written program manuscript for verification, and the tape itself may also

be subjected to various forms of checking before it goes to the shop floor.

The added cost of the tape-punching unit is relatively modest in this minimal installation, but it frees the NC machine from programming duties and increases its utilization for the production of workpieces. A disadvantage is that new steps have been added to increase the opportunities for introducing errors.

Essentially, manual programming is a tedious process that once required the programmer to enter a block of coded data for every individual motion of the machine tool. One of the major advantages of computer-assisted programming, which will be discussed subsequently, is the compression of programming efforts with routines that generate many blocks of tape data—or tape-image data—from single statements.

The ability to do this has long been built into NC systems in the form of "canned cycles." Also called "fixed cycles," these are preset sequences of events triggered by a single command, such as a G83 for deep-hole drilling, which will cause a machine spindle, after positioning, to advance at rapid traverse to a clearance distance, switch to feedrate and advance to a series of increasing depths with intermediate retractions at rapid-traverse rate, and finally rapid-traverse out of the hole.

Such routines for commonly used cycles can be implemented either in hard-wired logic or in the basic software of a computerized NC system, and it is in this area that CNC begins to show some of its advantages over hard-wired controls. The ever increasing computer power and memory capacity of such systems increase the ability of the control system itself to multiply the block-generation of single commands, reducing programmer effort, cutting the number of opportunities for error and shortening the final machining tape if one is used.

There *is* a computer in there

It could, in fact, be said that manual programming of a CNC system is computer-assisted; it's just that the computer is built into the control.

Threading routines of lathe controls indicate some of the possibilities. Take General Electric's Mark Century 1050HL as an example. This control, which does not incorporate a built-in tape reader but does accept a variety of inputs to its part-program memory, provides four different threading cycles: G84 for multipass plunge-cut longitudinal threading of uniform diameters or tapers up to 45°; G85 for multipass plunge-cut face threading at angles from 0° to 45°; G86, analogous to G84 but with infeed at a compound angle (such as 29.5° for a standard 60° thread); and G87 for face threading at compound infeed. Infeeds are internally calculated to provide constant chip volume for each pass, and as many as nine passes can be called for at final depth to compensate for tool or workpiece deflection. These cycles are all programmed with a single block of input data, admittedly a lengthy one. And, if threading isn't a frequently required operation in any particular shop, it's only a small step backward in complexity to

automatic multipass roughing routines that might generate as many as 20 blocks of data from a single statement with a G81 command.

Today's controls offer still other automatic routines from single-block programmer inputs: rectangular hole patterns, bolt-hole circles, pocket- and peripheral-milling, etc. Parametric subroutines, offered by various control builders, even offer the possibility of creating specialized canned cycles tailored to the user's particular needs. Even "family" part-programs can be written, requiring only the insertion of new dimensions (parameters) for the machining of similar parts in different sizes.

Extending further aid for direct manual programming at the control are those CNC systems featuring CRTs—especially CRTs with graphic as well as alphanumeric capability (General Numeric and Tera Industrial Controls). With this type of CRT, it's possible to construct a part outline on the scope and then have the scope display all the passes of a multicut roughing routine as well as the alphanumeric messages presented by the scope of the former type.

Yet another programming advantage of storing machining data in a memory device rather than feeding it to the control via a tape is that memory permits random access while tape is serial or sequential. This allows entire multiblock segments of a part-program to be repeated, essentially by instructing the control to skip backward or forward to a particular block number and repeating a number of machining steps.

Many other programmer-oriented features are available in today's numerical controls, but only two others will be briefly mentioned here: diagnostics and editing.

Diagnostics is generally thought of as an automatic method for pinpointing malfunctions of the control system itself or the machine tool to which it's connected. It does make this valuable contribution to NC maintenance, but beyond that are diagnostic routines designed to aid in

machine setup, operation, and programming. Cincinnati Milacron's latest Acramatic CNCs, for example, boast more than 100 diagnostics in all, a number of which are designed for locating certain types of errors in programs. A case in point: an erroneously coded feedrate will bring a 15-character message up on the control's CRT, not only indicating that something's wrong with the F-word but also giving the block number in which it occurs.

Although this doesn't aid in the initial programming effort, it certainly speeds the debugging phase. And, with the control's built-in editing capability for making corrections without going back for a new tape—whether the first one was generated manually or with a computer—time is saved both in getting a good program for the machine to start producing and in getting the programmer on to the next job.

Controls are getting smarter

One development, even though it was aimed primarily at large NC installations using computer-aided programming for complex parts, emphasizes the potential for computer-assist that might be built into control systems of the future. This is the capability of some CNC systems to postprocess APT CL-data internally—first offered by Vega Servo-Control and now also available on other controls—which may be a precursor of a future CNC ability to process part-programs on a much larger scale than is possible today.

It is certainly true that the programming capabilities of today's controls allow many users at least to put off the day they must consider computer-aided programming external to the CNC system. In cases where part geometry does not rule out manual programming, where demands for new tapes are modest because of long production runs or frequent repeats, and where the variety of NC machines is limited to no more than a few, manual part-programming techniques are entirely suitable.

ADDING COMPUTER POWER

Despite the viability of manual part-programming for many applications, most NC machines today are probably programmed with the aid of a computer at least some of the time. Because new cost elements are added—whether the computer system is purchased, leased, or provided remotely by a time-sharing service—it's valid to ask why this is so.

Simplistically stated, it's because the computer is a tool that allows the programmer to produce more and better part-programs in less time.

First, of course, are those cases in which the complexity of either the workpieces or the machine tool makes manual programming impractical. Close-tolerance contouring to some mathematically

defined curve other than a circular arc is one example, requiring calculation of just too many coordinates to make manual programming practical. And the five-axis profilers widely used in the aerospace industry are examples of machines that typically demand computer-assisted programming.

As noted before, however, most part

prints are drawn with straightedge and compass, and thus the workpieces they depict could be manually programmed for an NC machine with linear- and circular-interpolation capability. For such parts, the computer enhances the programmer's capability in a number of ways:

■ It provides calculation capability beyond that of the machine's NC system and avoids burdening the programmer with manual calculation of coordinate data. The box on the next page cites an example involving angled lines, circle tangency, and pattern rotation. Others include line, grid, and circular pattern generation; translation of patterns or sequences as well as rotation; fairing of nonmathematically-defined surfaces; and, of course, provision for older hard-wired NC systems of all of the multipass capabilities cited for today's top CNC models.

■ Program reliability is enhanced. Using a computer, the programmer has fewer opportunities to make errors. Beyond that the computer provides many diagnostics and error messages to assist the programmer in producing a good tape or tape image. And computer-assisted NC programming systems are increasingly offering graphics capability—either with plotters or CRTs—that extend program-verification to part geometry.

■ The programmer's need for intimate knowledge of the idiosyncrasies of each NC machine and its specific coding requirements is greatly reduced because the computer's input is, in most cases, a higher-level "language" consisting of English-like words or symbols. Use of a single such language greatly facilitates the programmer's ability to handle the diverse array of machines and controls—often the products of different manufacturers—that are typical of most NC-equipped plants.

■ The computer is not restricted to generating only NC codes; it's also capable of producing such other data as total machining time for a program and other management information.

How about the timing?

Assuming that part complexity has not already forced the issue, it's valid to ask at what point in the growth and development of an NC department should a transition to computer-assisted programming be made. The most succinct answer—and it's not as flippant as it first appears—is this: as soon as it becomes necessary to hire a second programmer.

The point is simply that as long as one person can manually provide all the part-programs needed to keep the NC machin-

Computer-aided systems also vary widely, frequently involving direct programmer input via CRT/keyboard terminal to remote computer or time-sharing service. Several computers may be linked in DNC system, and a tape may never be punched

ery operating without program-induced delays, there's little point in spending additional funds for a computer or time-sharing service. As increased demands are placed on that lone programmer's time, the assistance of a computer should be considered.

The first step into computer-assisted programming is often via the use of a time-sharing service over telephone lines. This requires very little in the way of fixed cost—it may even be possible to use previously acquired tape-punching equipment as the remote terminal, although a faster terminal unit may cut costs by reducing the time it must remain connected to the time-sharing service while punching tapes.

Pricing of time-sharing services is complex in that it involves several cost elements, typically including these: terminal-connect time; actual computing time of the central processing unit (CPU); data- or software-storage; volume of data input and output; and development or maintenance of software.

Not all of the time-sharing services charge for all of these elements, and each element may be priced at several

different levels. For example, connect-time rates and input/output charges may be higher for high-speed data transmission (but the reduction of connect time makes this less costly). Then there's a difference between on-line storage and off-line storage—and the latter may be on disks or on magnetic tape. Rates may also vary according to the time of the day or the day of the week, or they may vary according to requested response time, which ranges from immediate and interactive to different categories of delay in batch-processing mode: one, two, four, or eight hours, overnight, or weekend.

Although the charges are complicated—obviously it's necessary to bill customers with the aid of a computer—and almost impossible to compare without actually running benchmark tests, the point should not be lost that opportunities for significant cost savings are inherent in these pricing schemes. At the same time, the user must keep in mind that delayed batch-processing means delays in receiving the computer's error messages, in other program-verification procedures, and in reprocessing for

This computer-assist really helped

The star-shaped punch set up on the table of a Moore continuous-path jig grinder—and its mating die just visible beyond the spindle—are hardly everyday workpieces. Nevertheless, they illustrate a number of fairly common characteristics that demonstrate some of the advantages of computer-assisted NC programming.

Part geometry is not so complex as to preclude manual programming, nor even of grinding the parts on a manual machine. The job was done by the contract manufacturing facility of Moore Special Tool Co (Bridgeport, Conn), and, to provide a direct comparison, the parts were machined first by manual jig grinding and then by NC.

Outlines consist entirely of straight lines and circular arcs—simple enough. It's the tapers that complicate matters, together with the requirement that lines and arcs blend perfectly. This demands calculation of the exact points of tangency, which do not fall exactly 180° apart on either root or tip circles. Layout and calculation to define coordinate and geometric data for machining on a manual Moore G-18 jig grinder took five hours. Contour grinding for 0.005 in. of stock removal, including setup and inspection, took 48 hours.

By contrast, programming the job for a Moore G-18 CP jig grinder with a General Electric 550 NC system took only one hour on a Digital Equipment PDP-11/70 minicomputer with UCC APT. Inherent in the APT software is a variety of ways to define lines and circles, permitting the computer to calculate exact line orientation and points of tangency. The programmer's input was further simplified by defining just one leg, then simply calling for 45° rotations to generate the other seven.

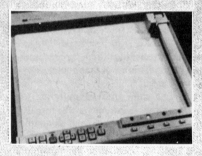

Before the tape was punched, the program was verified with a Hewlett-Packard Model 7221A plotter.

Demonstrating another advantage of NC machining, the same tape was then used to grind the mating die. To do this, the machine's head (C-axis) was turned 180° and reset at zero; the dovetail slide was backed to reestablish contact with the new part surface; and the C-axis was mirror-imaged along with X or Y as required.

Including setup and inspection as before, NC machining took 13.5 hours.

necessary corrections. Tapes for complex jobs often require several trips through the computer. Therefore, to gain the savings potential of reduced rates, it's necessary to work well in advance of the time a debugged program must go into production use.

Another benefit of time-sharing that is particularly attractive for firms just starting out in computer-assisted NC programming is that it is relatively painless to switch systems—if it's done early enough in the game. This might apply to software, for example, if this is found to be unsuitable for the type of work being done, or it might apply to the vendor's service itself. Indeed, several of the time-sharing services offer an assortment of different languages or special enhancements to tailor individual languages for specific types of machine tools, such as punch presses or lathes.

Training programs are also offered by these service companies. For example, Manufacturing Data Systems Inc (Ann Arbor, Mich), which is the largest in terms of NC customers, reports that approximately 2000 customer personnel attended its basic or advanced training programs during the firm's last fiscal year. And programmer support doesn't stop there; assistance is often rendered to customers on a "hotline" basis, putting one of the time-sharing company's NC specialists on the telephone to the customer while both have the program in question called up on their individual computer terminals.

How big are the NC installations typically using time-sharing services for their programming? It's difficult to generalize, but Manufacturing Software & Services (Cincinnati), a LeBlond subsidiary, says that its clients generally range from one to about eight NC machines, with an average of 3.23. MDSI claims 3100 customers with 14,300 NC machines, for an average of 4.6. General Electric Information Services Co (Rockville, Md) puts its average customer at about 5 NC machines.

Going all the way

In the usual growth pattern of NC installations, computer usage increases—and the monthly time-sharing bill goes up. For many, this is the time to consider the use of an in-house computer for NC programming. Experts in the time-sharing field, many of whom also offer stand-alone minicomputer systems for NC programming, suggest that, when monthly bills reach levels of perhaps $1000 to $10,000, that time may have arrived. Individual considerations for each installation vary widely.

Hardware costs for some of the more basic minicomputer systems start at as little as $20,000 or even less. As sophistication, multi-user capability, speed, peripherals, and other features are added, the investment (or monthly leasing costs) can rise considerably. Also space must be provided, maintenance must be considered (which is typically provided by the computer manufacturer), and additional personnel may be required.

For many smaller shops, however, there may be added benefits that are not related to NC programming. After all, what's being installed is a general-purpose computer with peripherals and software tailored to NC applications; this does not preclude the use of the new computer for the more conventional business, shop-management, or even engineering applications. And, in fact, many suppliers of NC-programming packages do offer additional software for these purposes.

Many larger firms use corporate data-processing facilities for NC part-programming. It's true that there have been priority clashes between data-processing and manufacturing departments in the past—for example, when an urgently needed part-program cannot go on the corporate computer because the payroll is being run—but this access problem seems to be diminishing today. There has been considerable technological progress in the field of large computers as well as minis and micros, and modern corporate systems increasingly have larger memory and processing capability with time-shared remote terminals located in NC-programming departments. The result may be a trend toward increasing use of a central computer for NC programming.

The languages of NC

Several allusions have been made above to "higher-level languages" used in computer-assisted NC programming. An NC language is a computer program (software) consisting of a specially structured set of symbols, rules, and conventions by means of which a human communicates the desired part-program information to the computer system. The language typically—but not always—involves a set vocabulary of mnemonic words similar to English, which the computer first translates into its own computer-code for the necessary calculations and data manipulations.

Finally the computer performs another translation to convert the program into the specific machine-command codes required for operation of the particular combination of machine tool and control system for which the part-program is intended.

In most cases, the language consists of two different computer programs: a

A 'conversational' mode for programming

Unique in the field of part-programming is the Voice Numerical Control (VNC) system developed by Threshold Technology Inc (Delran, NJ), which carries the concept of "conversational" interaction with a computer to the ultimate end of spoken commands by the human programmer and visual-display responses by the computer.

Hardware consists of six units: (1) a cabinet containing a 32k minicomputer (which is expandable to 128k); a 10-megabyte hard-disk drive, a high-speed perforated-tape reader/punch, and the speech processor that converts the analog voice signals into digital information; (2) a lightweight microphone headset; (3) a digital readout that immediately indicates the system's acceptance or rejection of each command and also "cues" the operator; (4) a CRT/keyboard that displays the NC commands and serves for alternate input; (5) a printer that outputs a hard copy of the NC program; and (6) a plotter for program verification.

The language consists of 89 words and phrases in typical shop terminology. Before using a VNC system for tape preparation, the programmer must "train" the equipment to recognize and accept his or her voice. This is done by repeating each command word into the microphone several times, after which each programmer need only identify himself to the system and then start the programming sequence. There is no limit to how many individual programmers can be accommodated.

The following example quotes a conversation in which four holes

would be positioned equidistantly along an arc of 3.2-in. radius with the first hole at 60° from the X-axis and the fourth at 135°:

Programmer	Display
'Arc'	ARC ANGLE 1 =
'Six zero'	ARC ANGLE 1 = 60
'Okay'	ARC ANGLE 2 =
'One three five'	ARC ANGLE 2 = 135
'Okay'	ARC RADIUS =
'Three point two'	ARC RADIUS = 3.2
'Okay'	NO. OF HOLES =
'Four'	NO. OF HOLES = 4
'Okay'	ARC 60 135 3.2 4

And the teleprinter would clack out: "ARC 60 135 3.2 4."

Threshold claims a number of advantages for its system:

It's easy to learn and to use—most often by a programmer who came out of the shop. No computer experience or typing skills are necessary. The language is simple, spelling doesn't matter, and there's constant cuing and confirmation.

There are fewer opportunities to make mistakes. No calculations are required, no data manipulations, no keypunch errors, no proofreading. And the system incorporates a series of safeguards to debug the program as it is entered.

Potential economies are offered in both time and money.

Finally, Threshold calls its VNC "the foundation of a complete manufacturing control system" with programs available or in development to generate such management information as cost estimates, status and inventory reports, sales accounts, payroll, and productivity.

Taking data from top to bottom

Mold and die work often presents the problem of artistically generated contours that defy line-and-arc definition. Developed specifically for such work—but applicable to other types of work—is the CompuTool CAD/CAM system offered by National Computer Systems Inc (Minneapolis).

Magnetic-tape cartridges, capable of storing the equivalent of three miles of punched tape, link the three hardware elements of the system:

1. The CompuScanner (above) is a 3-D coordinate-measuring machine to initially capture data from molds, drawings, models, or prototypes, and which can subsequently be used for verification or inspection.

2. The CompuScope (left below) is a computer-refreshed CRT display that allows dynamic manipulation and modification of images. Scaling, rotation, mirror images, and reversals for mating parts are all within its capabilities, as is the ability to view the image from various angles.

3. CompuMills or CompuGravers are precision NC milling machines with "work cubes" of 7 x 17 x 33 in., 13 x 13 x 23 in., and 6 x 6 x 6 in.

Alternately, output can be APT-postprocessed to run other machines.

processor, which converts the input information into a generalized set of data on cutter locations and machine motions (CL-data, CL-file, or CL-tape); and a postprocessor (or link), which converts the generalized data into the specific control codes of the machine tool. For any given version of an NC language—although standardization falls considerably short of 100%—the processor is uniform. Each different combination of machine tool and control system, however, requires a specially prepared postprocessor.

Some programming systems are structured to perform all processing steps in one computer run, in which case the output is a CL-file or CL-tape, with a subsequent computer run for postprocessing. Other systems alternate between processing and postprocessing, taking input statements one at a time and converting them to machine commands immediately.

Selecting a language

Literally dozens of such languages are currently available. One of the grand-daddies is APT (Automatically Programmed Tools) which has sired a line of related languages, subsets, supersets, and variants, which—in total—probably represent the dominant language family for NC part-programming. The single most widely used programming language is claimed to be MDSI's COMPACT II, an offshoot of Sundstrand's SPLIT; MDSI claims to have 3100 customers using its language for a total of 14,300 NC machine tools.

Beyond these are a variety of other languages, some of which depart radically in concept. One of these is NUFORM, offered by A.S. Thomas Inc (Westwood, Mass), which uses numerical input in a fixed format and is a multi-user interactive system implemented on DEC PDP-11 minicomputers. A three-dimensional interactive graphic capability is to be made available for NUFORM users in June.

Oriented or directional geometry forms the basis for Datamat Programming Systems' (New York) GTL and Weber NC Systems' (Milwaukee) PROMPT. The latter system, implemented on an HP-9835A minicomputer with a CRT, literally asks specific "what next?" questions of the programmer, who then selects one of the specific responses from a menu of alternates on the scope, or keys in a numerical value.

Selecting a language to suit the needs of any given shop—with its unique assortment of NC equipment and mix of workpieces—is not a task to be taken lightly, nor is it a simple one. Most experts recommend that anyone shopping for a programming system—both the hardware and software—should try to project what the plant's needs will be five years into the future. Once a company's programmers have become fluent in a particular NC language, it may not be easy to switch. Still it isn't impossible, and progressing from one APT-based system, for example, to another may not mean much more than learning some added tricks. Also, of course, many of the time-sharing services offer software that is essentially, if not totally, transportable to in-house computers.

Language studies available

For any firm faced with the problem of language selection, two special studies are available and are recommended. Both were prepared under contract from the US Army Communications R&D Command (Ft Monmouth, NJ) and were done by the same principal investigators, James J. Childs, Joseph Harrington Jr, and Peter D. Senkiw. First of these is the *Numerical Control Language Evaluation*, published in March 1974, which covered seven programming languages in their application to workpieces that would typically be machined on a machining center. The second is *Numerical Control Lathe Language Study*, published in November 1979, which compares 15 languages as they apply to turning.

Although both represent excellent work, it must be said of the second that the authors learned a great deal from the preparation of its predecessor. Also, although the first volume is still a valuable document in showing the capabilities of the languages studied, it is beginning to show its age. NC is a dynamic technology, and the capability of most of the languages studied has since been extended—both by updating of the soft-

Tracing flexible rule, templet, or part model with stylus of Alden Automatic Parts Programming System (APPS) captures coordinates, which are converted by computer to linear/circular-interpolation commands shown on CRT. These may be punched in tape or fed to behind-the-reader NC interface for machine control

ware itself and by progress within the hardware-supplying industry as well.

The second volume is an up-to-date work, with the possible exception of some of the prices it quotes, and provides considerable insight into the languages as they might be applied to machining operations other than turning. Essentially the same evaluation technique was used in both reports—ten sample parts were designed and then programmed by specialists in each of the languages under study—but the resulting data is pre-

sented in the lathe report in a manner that facilitates comparisons.

In both cases, the authors note that the statistical base is minimal, but they are careful in providing the details of their methodology. These reports are available from the Numerical Control Society (519 Zenith Dr, Glenview, Ill 60025) for $65 per copy ($55 for NCS members) plus $2 for postage and handling, or $115 for the set ($100 member price) plus $4 for postage and handling.

HANDLING NC PROGRAMS

Early in the NC era, the media on which part-programs were stored were many and varied. They included punched tape ranging from less than an inch wide to perhaps 7 in. wide, as well as reel-to-reel magnetic tape and even 35-mm photographic film. From this melange emerged a standardization effort that settled on the now familiar 1-in.-wide tape with the asymmetrical sprocket holes flanked by eight rows (or levels) of coding holes of specified diameter, spacing, and pitch. Details can be found in Electronic Industries Assn Standard RS-227A. EIA Standard RS-244B defines the most commonly used character code for NC, and other EIA standards define vari-

ous formatting schemes and aspects pertinent to NC programs and programming.

A free list of these NC standards and the standards themselves can be obtained from EIA, 2001 Eye St NW, Washington, DC 20006. More-comprehensive standards indexes, which include references to standards and specifications issued by other organizations as well as by EIA, are available from the National Machine Tool Builders' Assn, 7901 Westpark Dr, McLean, Va 22101 (at $4 per copy), and the Numerical Control Society, 519 Zenith Dr, Glenview, Ill 60025 (at $12 for nonmembers or $8 for members). Other pertinent literature is also available from these sources.

These and other standardization efforts brought considerable order to the programming field. Some experts believe that additional efforts would have produced still more benefits—such as greater standardization in NC systems themselves that would reduce or eliminate differences in required control inputs or postprocessors.

But standards, even though they are constantly being updated, have a way of being bypassed by a technology that is advancing as rapidly as that of electronics and computers. Today, for example, there is increasing use of the ASCII character code (American Standard Code for Information Interchange) because of increasing data transmission with computers. Indeed, most of today's controls accept either EIA or ASCII code at the flip of a switch—and many of them will automatically recognize which code is being used and literally flip their own switches.

Although they have progressed a long way in terms of reliability—from star-wheels mechanically making electrical contact through the holes in punched tape to beams of light in today's photoelectric types—tape readers have long been considered one of the weaker links in the NC chain of command. Attempting to reduce the physical wear on the tape itself and the preventive maintenance necessary to ensure reliable reader operation, designers and users of NC systems have long sought alternate means of storing part-programs.

Memories built into NC and CNC systems for part-program storage greatly reduce tape and tape-reader problems because they allow a single pass of the punched tape through the reader for loading and subsequent machine operation from the memory.

Direct substitution of floppy disks or digital magnetic-tape cassettes are another means of eliminating punched tape. In addition to the advantage of magnetic data storage and reading, these media also offer the advantage of reduced physical volume for library storage of programs. A reel of 1-in. tape is a lot smaller than pre-NC jigs and fixtures, but a program library of hundreds of tapes can become formidable.

It should also be noted that the EIA

committee on NC standards is currently at work on floppy disks with respect to their size, format, track allocation, protocol, and other characteristics pertaining to NC use.

Store it at the computer

Direct numerical control (DNC) is another concept that bypasses punched tape. Initially at least, this concept involved generation and storage of part-programs at a plant's central computer facility with a number—dozens—of NC machine tools hooked up to the computer and receiving part-program commands in a real-time mode. Because a computer or transmission failure could result in downtime for potentially dozens of individual NC machines, tape readers on each control were typically provided for a backup mode of operation.

As enlarged memory capacity was added to control systems themselves, however, the tie to the apron-strings of the host computer was loosened, and whole part-programs were transmitted into CNC memory at each machine on a non-real-time basis. This avoided the danger of an immediate shutdown of numbers of very expensive machine tools in the event of a computer outage.

Flexibility of shop management in such a system is enhanced by use of those control systems incorporating a self-postprocessing capability. Provided that a particular workpiece can be machined on any of several different machines, the central system can transmit a CL-file to any suitable machine that happens to be available, and the

CNC itself will convert this into usable commands.

Although self-postprocessing capability is primarily of benefit in larger NC installations, typically those of the aerospace industry, the use of program-transmission capability seems to be filtering down into much smaller NC installations. This even includes some that are using the computer-assist of the CNC's computer for programming manually.

Programming hardware seems to plug together almost with the facility of hi-fi music systems built of individual components, the result of such interface standardization as EIA's RS-408 and RS-232C. The former concerns parallel binary-data interchange as in a behind-the-reader (BTR) connection between an NC system and a separate data source. The latter concerns serial binary-data transfer and is currently being phased out in favor of newer standards (RS-422A, RS-423A, and RS-449). Application notes on interconnection of equipment meeting the old and the new standards are available from EIA (*Industrial Electronics Bulletin No. 12*, priced at $4.25).

How a system can grow

Much of the programming or tape-preparation equipment in the listing that starts on the next page is available in a basic, minimum version—typically with alternate choices of input keyboard units and output tape punches at increasing price and capability—which then permits a variety of add-on units to be plugged in later as increasing capacity and sophistication are required.

One example is the NC HQ introduced last year by Computer Operations Inc (Lanham, Md). The basic box incorporates microprocessor-based electronics, a floppy-disk unit, and input and output ports. In its minimum configuration, a keyboard/printer (Teletype, DECwriter, TI Silent 700, TermiNet, etc) is plugged in for input, and outputs are connected to up to eight CNC machines for direct memory loading from the manually prepared (and edited) programs stored on the floppy. Programs prepared or edited by MDI at the machine's control system can also be transmitted back to the NC HQ for storage in edited form. Each 5¼-in. floppy can store up to 99 individual programs totaling the equivalent of 800 ft of punched tape, and any one can be accessed in less than 1 sec.

The system can be upgraded by plugging in a CRT/keyboard, a plotter, a printer, a tape reader and tape punch even though the basic concept is to avoid the use of punched tape, or a modem to put the system on-line to a time-sharing service, or it will accept input from an in-house computer.　　[Text continues]

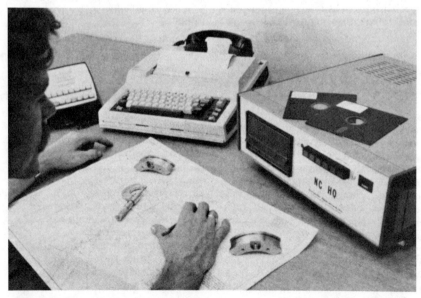

Microprocessor-based device (NC HQ by Computer Operations Inc) can be used for manual proramming or as terminal for local or time-shared computer. Programs are stored on floppy disks and may be edited, then they are transmitted to memories of up to eight CNC machines. Programs edited at CNC can also be saved

DIRECTORY OF
HARDWARE, SOFTWARE, SERVICES

The following is a listing of some companies offering representative products or services involving various aspects of numerical-control part-programming, preparation of machining tapes or other media (such as floppy disks or magnetic tape), storage and editing of part-programs, and other related items. The listing is alphabetical by companies, with no attempt to classify products or services by type. Not all companies offering NC-related products or services are listed, and product/service listings of individual firms are not complete listings for each company.

Company	Products/services
ABR Corp 262 Mott St New York, NY 10012 212/431-7820	Control tape, patches, splicers, reels and adapters, tape filing cabinets and systems, tape reproducers, EIA/ASCII converters, card-to-tape converters, tape-perforating equipment (including Flexowriters, Teletypes) with modular plug-in accessories for punch-tape editing, copying, code conversion, etc
Alden N/C Div Alden Self-Transit Systems Corp 2 Mercer Rd Natick, Mass 01760 617/655-6610	Computerized programming and tape-preparation and -editing systems in several configurations; stored-program editors; stand-alone memory systems (floppy and solid-state) for retrofit to hard-wired NCs; NC-program-transmission system (Computer Network System) for transmission from mainframe host to intermediate mini to CNC memory or retrofitted memory on NC
Applicon Inc 32 Second Ave Burlington, Mass 01803 617/272-9345	Interactive computer-graphic system for CAD/CAM applications. Automatic surface labeling, tool-path generation, APT source or CL-file output. Each CPU supports 4 graphics terminals and 1 program-development terminal, master/satellite link provides database access to as many as 20 graphics terminals; plotters, peripherals, many configurations
Applied Digital Communications 214 W Main St Moorestown, NJ 08057 609/234-3666	Stand-alone NC-tape-verification system incorporating plotter, software, and interface to DEC PDP-8 mini, for plotting EIA-coded machining tapes for NC punch presses to various selectable scales; custom software offered
Calma Interactive Graphic Systems 527 Lakeside Dr Sunnyvale, Calif 94086 408/245-7522	Interactive computer-graphics system for CAD/CAM applications. Up to 5-axis NC-programming capability; APT source or CL-file output; ability to write macros. Distributed processing capability. Color terminals
Centech Inc 511 Zenith Rd Glenview, Ill 60025 312/299-6788	ELAN part-programming language (software) and postprocessors for lathes, mills, machining centers, drills, grinders, wire EDM, flame cutters, punch presses, etc; runs on Hewlett-Packard desk calculator, high-speed plotter, tape punch
Computer Operations Inc 9700-B Palmer Hwy Lanham, Md 20801 301/459-2100	NCHQ device for program preparation (off-line manual or as time-share terminal), edit, storage, transmission to 8 machines (CNC or memory-NC). Stores 99 programs (800-ft-tape equivalent) on 5¼-in. floppy. Accepts programs edited at CNC. May be used with various inputs, including CRT; can output to printer, punch, plotter, modem, tape-reader
Computervision Corp 201 Burlington Rd, Rt 62 Bedford, Mass 01730 617/275-1800	Interactive computer-graphics system for CAD/CAM applications. 2- to 5-axis capability; can generate geometry for various source languages (APT COMPACT II, SPLIT), cutter-location file, or on-line NC postprocessors. System supports up to 8 interactive terminals for time-shared use. Color terminals
Datamat Programming Systems Inc 15 W 81 St Suite 7G New York, NY 10024 212/874-0309	GTL part-programming language and postprocessors (software); Olivetti P6060 desktop minicomputer with 32k memory, printer/plotter, display, 2 floppy-disk drives, tape-punch. Generates geometry; selects tools, feeds, speeds from stored material/tool data; generates multicycles (as: REAM calls for spot-drill, drill, bore, ream) and pocketing routines

Company	Products/services
Data Specialties Inc 3455 Commercial Ave Northbrook, Ill 60062 312/564-1800	LRP-300 perforated tape reader/punch with standard RS-232 and TTY current-loop interfaces for keyboard/printers and CRT/keyboard units; NC-30 portable tape-punch with multiple interfaces for various CNC systems (for punching out edited programs for archival storage, for example); other punch-tape equipment and computer peripherals
Digital Controls Corp 9031 Deerwood Dr Milwaukee, Wis 53223 414/355-3703	Super-Stor retrofittable program storage and editing system for updating non-memory NC system; includes photoelectric punched-tape reader, and I/O ports for plug-in video editing terminal, tape punch, or DNC. Firm also offers contract programming, time-sharing service, and software for NC, business, and engineering applications
Digital Systems Corp 223 Mall Office Complex Monroeville, Pa 15146 412/373-3310	QUICK-PATH (2- and 3-axis contouring lathes, mills, etc) and QUICK-DISC (punch-presses) part-programming languages (software); general-purpose DEC PDP-8A minicomputer with keyboard/printer, reader/punch, and following options: high-speed I/O, CRT, graphics CRT, plotter, mass storage (such as floppy disk), I/O interface ports
Digitronics Div Comtec Information Systems Inc 53 John St Cumberland, RI 02864 401/724-8500	Perforated-tape readers, punches, handlers, reader/punches with either 8-bit parallel or RS-232 interface, including desk-top and portable models as well as rack-mount versions
Dwight Instrument Co 593 New York Ave Lyndhurst, NJ 07071 201/438-3334	Program preparation, storage, editing, communication, and interfacing accessories and terminals, including retrofit items for updating hard-wired non-memory NC systems, such as Stored Program Buffer (SPB), which adds CRT/keyboard and memory to older NCs for program storage and editing
Encode Inc Dexter Industrial Green Perkins Way Newburyport, Mass 01950 617/462-8116	GENESIS part-programming language and postprocessors (software); Encode minicomputer programming system in four versions: for 1 NC machine, for 2 or more; for 2 or more with more-complex geometry; for implementing business/engineering routines in addition to NC. Various options can be retrofitted

TRAINING PROGRAMMERS

Skillful part-programmers are a vital requirement for effective utilization of NC machine tools. Upon their efforts depend the operational efficiency of those machines and the financial payback of the significant investment in the machines themselves, the plant's NC-support facilities, and the overhead costs involved.

Skillful NC part-programmers are scarce. This reflects not only the general shortage of experienced people in the metalworking industries but also the increasing demand for programmers as industry turns more and more to the use of numerically controlled machines to increase the capability, versatility, and productivity of manufacturing.

On an industry-wide basis, the obvious answer is to create new programmers by training them—and there are a number of sources for such training. But first, what qualifications should programmers have, and what must programming trainees learn?

According to the National Machine Tool Builders' Assn booklet *"Selecting an Appropriate NC Programming Method,"* the principal qualifications for manual programmers are as follows:

1. Manufacturing experience. Programmers must have a thorough understanding of the capabilities of the NC machines being programmed, as well as an understanding of the basic capabilities of the other machines in the shop.

They must have an extensive knowledge of, and sensitivity to, metalcutting principles and practices, cutting capabilities of the tools, and workholding fixtures and techniques. Programmers properly trained in these manufacturing-engineering techniques can significantly reduce production costs.

2. Spatial visualization. Programmers must be able to visualize parts in three dimensions, the cutting motions of the machine, and potential interferences between the cutting tool, workpiece, fixture, or the machine itself.

3. Mathematics. A working knowledge of arithmetic, algebraic, trigonometric, and geometric operations is extremely important. A knowledge of higher math-

Company	Products/services
General Electric Information Services 401 N Washington St Rockville, Md 20850 301/340-4000	Remote computer time-sharing service offering ADAPT, APT, APTURN, CINTURN II, GETURN, NCPPL$, HI-PRO part-programming languages and postprocessors. Processing can be either interactive or batch, immediate or delayed (for reduced charges). Graphics and plotting routines available for program verification
Gerber Systems Technology Inc 83 Gerber Rd South Windsor, Conn 06074 203/644-1551	Interactive computer-graphic systems for CAD/CAM applications. Up to 5-axis NC-programming capability, APT-equivalent statements created automatically, cutter-location file or on-line NC postprocessing. Each CPU supports up to 4 interactive work stations, DMS data-management system for distributed hookup of several CPUs, terminals, plotters, peripherals in many configurations
Manufacturing Data Systems Inc 4251 Plymouth Rd Ann Arbor, Mich 48105 313/995-6000	COMPACT II part-programming language and links (equivalent to postprocessors); remote computer time-sharing service offering COMPACT II; various time-share terminals and stand-alone computerized programming systems with options including video display, hard-copy outputs, plotters
Manufacturing & Software Services 6761 Bramble Ave Cincinnati, Ohio 45227 513/271-4900	TOOLPATH part-programming language and postprocessors; remote computer time-sharing service; MICROAPT stand-alone part-programming systems (incorporating DG Eclipse minicomputer) in single- and dual-user configurations (peripherals of latter include two CRT/keyboard units in addition to reader/punch, plotter, disk drive, printer)
Morcap Industries Inc 195 E Kehoe Blvd Carol Stream, Ill 60187 312/653-5840	SED-16 plug-in programming/editing unit provides 12-in. CRT, keyboard, 16k memory on wheeled stand for use at machine-tool site. Options include high-speed tape punch, digital magnetic-tape cassette recorder, and current loop or RS-232 I/O port
National Computer Systems Inc 4444 W 76 St Minneapolis, Minn 55435 612/830-7600	CompuTool CAD/CAM system includes CompuScanner 3-axis digitizer (coordinate measuring machine) for input of data (including free forms) into CompuScope computer graphics system for manipulation, scaling, modification with light pen, and eventual output of part-program on magnetic-tape cassette for NC CompuMill. APT postprocessors adapt output for other NC machines

ematics, such as advanced algebra, calculus, etc, is not normally required.

4. Attention to details. It is essential that programmers be acutely observant and meticulously accurate individuals. Programming errors discovered during machine setup can be very expensive and time-consuming to correct.

5. Desirable qualities. Programmers must be able to work effectively with other people. In some instances, another person may be required to act as an "insulator" between the programmer and the machine operator, shop supervisor, etc.

"Manual programming," the booklet notes elsewhere, "requires the programmer to have more-detailed knowledge of the machine and control, machining practices, and methods of computation than does computer-aided programming. Computer-aided programming, on the other hand, requires a knowledge of the

computer programming language and the computer system in order to process that language. In general, manual programming is more tedious and demanding because of the detail involved. In a computer-aided programming system, this detail knowledge is embodied in the computer system (processor, postprocessor, etc)."

Experts in the NC and training fields typically agree on these qualifications and requirements—adding such subsidiary details as a knowledge of blueprint reading, machinability of different metals, use of shop measuring instruments, tolerancing methods, and safety practices.

Where should you look for candidates? First of all, in your own plant— out on the shop floor. Edward F. Schloss, a Cincinnati Milacron sales vice president, puts it this way: "We've had excellent success with good lathe operators

and good boring-mill hands. They don't know it, but they've been programming most of their working lives, and they know basic shop math and trigonometry. You can teach them programming rather handily. Conversely, though, it's fairly hard to make NC part-programmers out of high-powered mathematicians. The path programming is easy. But what to do with it—the feeds, speeds, etc—that may take even more-extensive training."

With more-powerful computer-assist programming—such as Milacron's Cinturn II, which includes macros that automatically determine such cutting parameters as feeds and speeds—the need for metalcutting knowledge on the part of programmers is reduced. Through the use of this software, Cincinnati Milacron has been very successful in hiring new college graduates, including some with nontechnical degrees, and training them to be NC part-programmers, says Thom-

153

Company	Products/services
Numeric Micro Inc 2750 Northaven, No. 202 Dallas, Tex 75229 214/247-2767	Variety of tape-preparation units ranging from terminals for manual programming or use as remote terminals for time-sharing or computer hookup to floppy-disk editing units with CRTs and high-speed reading/punching/transmission. Options permit interfacing to variety of CNC systems, and time-sharing services
Numeridex Inc 241 Holbrook Dr Wheeling, Ill 60090 312/541-8840	NC tape, accessories, supplies, and tape-preparation equipment including LC-5000 and 9800 systems, both of which can be interfaced to CNC systems for direct program loading of CNC memory from remote reader of tape-preparation unit and for transmission of CNC-edited program back for punching new tape
Numeritronix Inc 2580 Azurite Circle Newbury Park, Calif 91320 805/499-2643	Exec 150 (portable, plug-in) and 155 (built-in) program-storage and -editing unit retrofittable to hard-wired NCs, accepts input from tape reader, keyboard, or DNC computer; allows machine operation from memory (60 to 940 ft of tape); interfaces to various tape punches; CRT version to be introduced
Structural Dynamics Research Corp Manufacturing Engineering Services Div 2000 Eastman Dr Milford, Ohio 45150 513/576-2400	APTURN (lathe), APTMIL (mill/drill), and APTPOINT (point-to-point) part-programming languages available on GEISCO time-sharing and stand-alone mini-computer systems; VERSIGRAPHICS interactive plotting program; HI-PRO punching software combines APTPOINT, VERSIGRAPHICS, and special program modules PAL (pattern layout) and PAM (path minimizer)
A.S. Thomas Inc 355 Providence Highway Westwood, Mass 02090 617/329-9200	NUFORM part-programming language for lathes, mills, machining centers, EDM, etc. Multi-user interactive system with keyboard/printers or CRT/keyboards. Available on various models of DEC PDP-11 minicomputer. 3-axis interactive graphics system scheduled for release in June 1980
Threshold Technology Inc 1829 Underwood Blvd Delran, NJ 08075 609/461-9200	Voice Numerical Control (VNC) accepts vocal input by programmer (in addition to keyboard alternate) using 89-word vocabulary. Implemented on DG Nova 3/12 minicomputer with 32k memory, 10-megabyte disk, tape reader/punch, and interactive CRT that confirms system's 'understanding' of commands
United Computing Corp McDonnell Douglas Automation Co 22500 S Avalon Blvd Carson, Calif 90745 213/830-7720	UNIAPT part-programming language, including extension modules for lathes, mills, etc, and postprocessors; can be extended for interactive graphics; implemented on DG Nova 3/12 and Eclipse S/230 with peripherals (turnkey stand-alone systems) and a variety of other minicomputers

as R. Caldwell, manager of manufacturing-engineering's programming and systems at the firm's main plant. Caldwell stresses that the trainees are given hands-on machine-tool experience in the plant before they are advanced to programming.

All suppliers of NC machine tools, of course, provide some sort of training in the programming of their products, and most offer formalized training programs. Milacron's sales department, for example, has 20 full-time customer-training instructors headed by Michael C. Ramundo, who expects that the company's 1980 program will top 3000 trainee-weeks for operation, maintenance, and programming courses. That number is up from 2060 student-weeks in 1979 and 1320 in 1978, and it is expected to include about 1000 NC programmers.

The task of Ramundo and his staff, of course, is to teach the programming of Milacron-built machines and to do it, in most cases, in a week. Thus, the company's prerequisites for programmer training include the following:

"Participants must have knowledge of general machine-shop safety procedures and be able to read detail prints, sectional views, and NC manuscripts.

"Knowledge of plane geometry, right-angle trigonometry, dimensioning conventions, and fundamentals of tolerancing is required.

"Knowledge of NC manual part-programming, NC machine-tool setup and operating procedures, part processing, metalcutting technology, tooling, and fixturing is also needed."

Sending people with that kind of background to school, Ramundo notes, will ensure that users of the NC machine will get the maximum benefit for their training dollar—the cost of a week of the trainee's time, travel, and living expenses, even though the training fee is waived with the basic purchase of the machine tool.

Both Schloss and Ramundo stress that these are not snap courses and that there is a formal evaluation of the students upon completion of the course to indicate any areas in which they need additional work. Copies of this go to both the students and their immediate supervisors. This is important because of the programmers' considerable effect on the productivity of the NC machine and on the safety of its operation.

Strongly contrasted on the basis of company size and the specialization of its products is Moore Special Tool Co

Company	Products/services
University Computing Co 1930 Hi Line Dr Dallas, Texas 75207 214/655-8886	UCC APT part-programming language with special modules for turning, milling, point-to-point, etc, and postprocessors; remote computer time-sharing service; NC software for both large-scale and minicomputer in-house systems; stand-alone in-house programming system (based on DEC PDP-11)
Unitech Inc 1005 E St Elmo Rd Austin, Texas 78745 512/444-0541	Media Processing Systems (MPS) for program preparation (tape or other), editing, duplication, verification, and transmission (may be used as terminal for remote computer time-sharing system); options include choice of keyboard/printer unit, CRT, floppy disk, plotter, direct connection to machine tool
Weber N/C Systems Inc 11601 W North Ave Milwaukee, Wis 53226 414/453-9511	PROMPT interactive part-programming language for lathes, machining centers, EDM, flame-cutters, point-to-point machining (including punch-presses), etc. Software runs on HP 9835A desktop mini with video display, plotter, tape punch, and peripheral options, including printer, floppy-disk drive, tape reader. Cassette programs available for additional business routines
Westinghouse Electric Corp Industry Systems Div 200 Beta Dr, O'Hara Township Pittsburgh, Pa 15238 412/782-1730	Computer time-sharing services offering APT, WESTURN, CINTURN II, cam-design macros, FMILL: APT preprocessors and postprocessors; stand-alone computerized (Westinghouse Series 3200) programming and tape-preparation center (with APT capability) accommodating up to 4 part-programmer stations and capable of incorporation in DNC system
Wiedemann Div Warner & Swasey Co 211 S Gulph Rd King of Prussia, Pa 19406 215/265-2000	Wiedepoint IV tape-preparation system for Wiedematic CNC turret punching machines. Includes DEC minicomputer plus mass storage for up to 1920 part-programs averaging 100 points; optimizing routine for programs of up to 1500 points; full edit capability. Accepts Wiedepoint language or tape-image data. Graphic plotter. Outputs EIA or ASCII tape
White-Sundstrand Machine Tool Controls & Data Systems Div 3615 Newburg Rd Belvidere, Ill 61008 815/547-5321	Remote computer time-sharing accepting inputs in SPLIT (including SWIFT turning module), APT, CONAPT, NC-tape data, card image; Omniprep stand-alone programming and tape-preparation units (based on DEC LSI-11) with various optional keyboard/printers, CRT, plotter, floppy-disk drive, readers, punches; Omnicontrol DNC systems

Gordon Lumley is one of 20 full-time instructors at Cincinnati Milacron. Here he makes a point for class of customer part-programming personnel

(Bridgeport, Conn). Running Moore's NC-training facility is Stephen Liscinsky, who says, "Some of the people who come to the Moore school use the programming themselves. Others take the information back to train other people in their companies. When I'm asked who make the best programmers, I say that it's usually the people who have a decent knowledge of jig grinding and shop math. The important thing is knowledge of the machine."

The Moore school follows an individualized education philosophy, holding classes sometimes for only one person and sometimes for as many as six. Often the students are all from the same company; or they may be from different firms doing similar types of work. Prior to the start of a class, Moore sends out questionnaires to determine students'

Basic training for NC

Programmer-training courses offered by machine-tool builders, control manufacturers, computer time-sharing services, and software houses naturally tend to concentrate on the particular company's products or services. And with good reason. Courses are short—typically a week—and the object is to teach customers how best to use some particular piece of equipment or software system. The more knowledge that students bring into this kind of learning environment, the more they can appreciate the specifics of that hardware or software, and the better they can learn to use it.

But, if these are "graduate" courses, where do the individuals gain "undergraduate" training? This includes basic shop skills, understanding of machine tools and metalworking, and a general knowledge of what an NC machine does and how it's programmed.

Literally dozens of colleges, universities, and technical institutes offer courses in numerical control—including programming. A few of these worth noting are Bradley Univ (Peoria, Ill), Brigham Young Univ (Provo, Utah), New Haven (Conn) Technical College, Northern Illinois Univ (De Kalb), and the State Univ of New York at Stony Brook.

A considerably more extensive list of educational institutions offering NC courses is available from the Numerical Control Society (519 Zenith Dr, Glenview, Ill 60025), which also offers a publication list including pertinent materials for individual reading. For companies establishing their own training programs, NCS also offers an NC-training course (for $30) that was developed and donated by Caterpillar Tractor Co. Correspondence courses are available, including one from Brigham Young Univ and another on APT language from NCS.

Self-taught programmed-learning courses are available from *American Machinist*/Beckwith Training Programs Inc (3620 Walnut Hills, Cleveland, Ohio 44122). Three such courses are offered: (1) Introduction to Numerical Control, (2) Operating an NC System, and (3) Introduction to NC Programming.

In charge of Moore's NC training facility is Stephen Liscinsky, who sends questionnaires to determine experience level of trainees prior to class startup

level of experience with jig grinding, NC equipment, and the type of work to be done. "We treat our customers on an individual basis," says Liscinsky, "according to their level of experience and the type of machine work they do—whether it's a mold work or tool-and-die work, for example."

Most classes for the NC jig grinder are five days; for the more complex CNC jig grinder, they can run up to eight days. "The pace of the course varies according to the speed with which the students pick up the work. If they're slow to get it, I go slow; if they're fast, I move fast," says Liscinsky. "I keep them interested in what they're doing."

A measure of Liscinsky's success at "keeping them interested" is that, even though many arrive at Moore with little confidence in their ability to learn the tricks of programming, by the time they've completed the course, most "can't wait to get back home to try what they've learned on their own machines."

"We don't just teach them to program," says Liscinsky. "We also teach them everything the machine can do. And many, seeing the applications, recognize jobs similar to ones they may previously have had to pass up. Now they know how to do it, and they're anxious to get back to uncover opportunities they've been missing."

One of Liscinsky's graduates is Dale Miller, president of DMC Jig Grinding (Detroit), a small job shop specializing in cams and employing about a half dozen people. The firm installed a Moore G-48 jig grinder in October 1977. Liscinsky remembers him as initially leery of programming but quick to pick it up.

Miller subsequently attended class at Manufacturing Data Systems Inc (Ann Arbor, Mich) to learn the use of the COMPACT II programming language, which DMC is currently using on MDSI's time-sharing service.

MDSI and other time-sharing services and software houses, of course, are another source of programmer training, naturally specializing in the software that is their product and in the hardware needed to run it.

Miller, who is now considering the purchase of an in-house computer system for NC programming, makes some direct and interesting comments: "The average person seems to think that a doctorate in mathematics is necessary for programming. That's ridiculous. It's really quite simple.

"I learned manual programming first, because I wasn't going to a computer system until I knew what I was doing manually. You can't use a computer to add and subtract if you don't know how to add and subtract yourself. Computers aren't foolproof; they only give you back what you put in. And the only way to know what to put in is to know what you're doing—then verify what comes back out. You have to know what the tape should look like.

"Then it's worthwhile to use the computer for the time savings it makes possible. It becomes very fast after a while. When I first got into programming, it cost $472 for the program for one particular workpiece. About six months later, I wrote an almost identical program for $27." ∎

CHAPTER IV

Computer Simulation for Manufacturing

First, choose an FMS simulator

Asking a computer 'what if' before you buy the hardware for a manufacturing system can save millions. These programs can help

THE IDEAL COMPUTER simulation for a flexible manufacturing system (FMS) has not yet been written. Such a simulator would accurately model any conceivable FMS, run on any available computer, and be used by persons completely unfamiliar with computers and simulations.

Instead, a number of less ambitious FMS simulators have been created; these have been the subject of a study carried out by our organization for the US Army's Tank & Automotive Command (Warren, Mich).

Some simulate a single, specific combination of machine tools, work-storage and -handling equipment, and supervisory computers. These are usually written by FMS owner-operator companies. Others model the operations of a family of systems and are usually written by machine-tool builders for their own use in equipment proposals. Still others simulate a variety of FMS types and are usually written at universities and research organizations.

The prospective FMS buyer will find that a simulator designed to investigate a wide spectrum of machine-tool/conveyance-system configurations is the most useful. However, the few simulators in this class are not as general as one would like, and, since they are complicated, they tend to be more difficult to use, modify, and debug than those designed for specific FMSs.

Requirements are more modest for owners of existing FMSs. These people want the computer program to investigate the consequences of machine failures, of changing the part mix, of adding a machine to the configuration, etc. But they are not, for example, interested in comparing the performance of different materials-handling systems. Typically, they have purchased the simulator to run with an FMS, and it may run "in background" on the FMS control-system computer, on a backup control computer, or in the corporate data-processing center.

By John Patrick Bevans
Charles Stark Draper Laboratory Inc
Cambridge, Mass

For a simulation to be portable—able to run on different computer makes—it must be written in a popular high-level language, such as FORTRAN, or in a simulation language, such as ECSL, GASP, or SLAM, that is itself "written" in FORTRAN.

Some non-FORTRAN-based simulation languages, such as GPSS and SIMSCRIPT, are also said to be portable, and simulations written in those languages would not be bound to a specific type of computer.

In addition to portability, a simulation written in FORTRAN usually has modest memory requirements and fits into a small computer. However, it is considerably more difficult to write, debug, modify, and maintain a simulation written in FORTRAN than it is to do the same for the equivalent written in a language designed for simulation work. A minor drawback of simulation languages is their cost, anything from a few hundred dollars to more than $10,000. This is usually in addition to the cost (if any) of the simulation itself. For reference, the table lists a number of discrete-event simulation languages and systems that can be used to model FMSs.

How close to real life?

The simulation must model the FMS in question with an appropriate accuracy. Unfortunately, this is not an easy task. In some cases, a simulation designed for a certain type of FMS provides reasonable results when simulating a different type of FMS, but confidence in the results is usually low unless they can be confirmed by some other data or method.

For example, a simulation that models a loop-conveyor materials-handling system (MHS) might be used to simulate a cart-type MHS, but the results would be suspect because the model ignores the potential for cart congestion.

Likewise, if a simulation de-

picts the transit times between work stations merely as fixed numbers and the actual MHS is a conveyor, the simulation results may be far from the truth. In this case, depending on the FMS controller's operating policy, parts that cannot enter a full work station either impede other parts or are "sent around the block." Either alternative creates substantial variations in the interstation transit times, which are unaccounted for in a simple model of the MHS.

This last example also points up the importance of ensuring that the simulation accurately reflects the operating policies that are, or will be, used. Such policies as part-introduction rules, rules for reacting to failure conditions, etc, are embodied in the control-system software. [continued]

Simulation languages

Name	Contact
CAPS/ECSL (Computer-Aided Programming System/Extended Control and Simulation Language)	Prof G.K. Hutchinson Univ of Wisconsin School of Business Adm PO Box 742 Milwaukee, Wis 53201
GASP IV (General Activity Simulation Program)	Pritsker & Assoc Inc PO Box 2413 West Lafayette, Ind 47096
GEMS (Generalized Manufacturing Simulator)	Prof D.T. Phillips Indus Engrg Dept Texas A&M Univ College Station, Tex 77843
GPSS (General Purpose Simulation System)	Wolverine Software PO Box 1251 Falls Church, Va 22041
INS (Integrated Network Simulation Language)	Dr S.D. Roberts Regenstrief Institute 1001 W Tenth St Indianapolis, Ind 46202
SIMSCRIPT II.5	CACI Inc 12011 San Vicente Blvd Los Angeles, Calif 90049
SLAM (Simulation Language for Alternative Modeling)	Pritsker & Assoc Inc PO Box 2413 West Lafayette, Ind 47096

First, choose an FMS simulator

Simulator name	Carts On Line (COL)	General Computerized Mfg System Simulation (GCMS)	General Flexible Mfg Systems Simulator (GFMS)	HABMS (Advanced Batch Mfg System Model)
Latest revision and date	6, 1981	9, 1981	11, 1981	8, 1979
Computer language	Extended control & simulation language (ECSL)	FORTRAN, GASP IV	FORTRAN-77 GASP IV	ECSL
Source statements	700	2500-3000, excl comments	5000	350
Environment	Will run on most computers having a FORTRAN compiler and an ECSL compiler	CDC 6500/6600 requires 40K 60-bit words; has been transferred to other computers with FORTRAN and GASP capability	Requires approx 600K bytes of memory on IBM-compatible computers; will run on most computers having FORTRAN-77 and GASP IV capability	ECSL compiler; needs 16K words, FORTRAN IV, and backing store. Will run on Z80-based microcomputer
Types of FMSs that can be simulated	FMSs with multiple work and load/unload stations served by one or two carts moving bidirectionally on a common track	With (1) conveyor, cart, crane, forklift MHS; (2) unidirectional and bidirectional MHS; and (3) temporary storage capability	FMSs with multiple work and load/unload stations connected by a conveyor network or robots. Stations can have shuttle queues	Unlimited, from job shops through transfer lines, but object of program was ease of use and quick answers. 15-20 cards input for typical model
Level of detail	There are no shuttles at stations. Tools are not modeled. Station failures are modeled as well as details of cart movements including conflicts	Part/cart congestion can be shown; tool movement is not modeled; decision rules for six operational decisions can be specified; can model station and cart failures	Station failures, as well as materials-handling-system, congestion are modeled. Tools are not modeled	Macro level. Materials-handling systems simulated as organizational delays but not technological; average travel times are used
Documentation	User's guide	NSF Grant APR74 15256, Report 7 (262 pages)	User's guide	Papers include sample run
Cost and availability	Program can be put on tape provided by user	Program can be put on tape provided by user	Program can be put on tape provided by user	Free to research groups. Will discuss with others
Contact	C.S. Draper Laboratory Inc Mail station 71 555 Technology Square Cambridge, Mass 02139	Prof J. Talavage School of Ind'l Engrg Purdue Univ W Lafayette, Ind 47907	C.S. Draper Laboratory Inc Mail station 71 555 Technology Sq Cambridge, Mass 02139	Univ of Wisconsin School of Business Admin PO Box 742 Milwaukee, Wis 53201
Additional comments				Good planning tool for sizing systems, evaluating feasibility. Quick and easy to use

FMS policies can often be changed without machine or computer-hardware changes, but the modifications have to be performed very carefully. The same is usually true in the case of operating-policy changes in a simulation; the software must be rewritten, and the task is complicated enough to require the services of a skilled programmer familiar with the simulation.

Leading operator through

A truly user-friendly FMS simulator would ask of its user, seated at a computer display terminal, questions about the characteristics of the FMS to be simulated. Then, after performing the simulation, it would immediately display the results. The user could, in response to additional prompting, change system parameters—such as the number of carts, the part operation times, "next-machine" selection rule—and obtain new results.

Unfortunately, today's simulators fall

short of that level of friendliness. The cost would likely prohibit (indeed, if it were possible) creation of an interactive and truly general simulator, one that can be used by non-programmers, can run on virtually any type of computer, and can simulate the entire spectrum of FMSs.

Instead, existing simulators encompass only a limited number of FMS types and can be used only by computer-knowledgeable persons. Some are "data driven": that is, the data input directly specifies most of the characteristics of the FMS, and the remaining characteristics are embedded in the simulator. Others require the user to assemble "building blocks" of software to model a specific FMS. In this latter case, the simulator can be thought of as a high-level language.

Information needed

The data requirements of most FMS simulators vary slightly from one to another. But some types of data are typically needed by all.

These requirements can generally be grouped according to whether they deal with the machine tools, the materials-handling system, the parts to be processed on the FMS, or the way the factory schedules people and materials.

Machine-characteristic information usually needed includes the number of each type of machine, the number and type of queue positions at each one, queue-servicing policies (whether first-in-first-out or some other scheme), the transfer time between queues and machines, what happens when machines fail, expected failure rate, and whether parts assigned to a failed machine can be processed off-line.

Additionally, it is useful to be able to input tool-storage capacity of each machine, whether machines can share tools and how, the time required to move tools, and the time needed to set up tools on each machine type.

Materials-handling information needed by simulators includes the type of

K&T FMS Simulator	MAST (Mfg System Design Tool)	SPEED (Trademark)	Variable Mission Simulation Model	Simulator name
8, 1981	8, 1981	1.2, Oct 1981	1.0, Dec 1979	Latest revision and date
SIMSCRIPT 1.5	FORTRAN	FORTRAN-66	Digital Equipment FORTRAN IV-PLUS	Computer language
10,000	7000, 4000 excl comments	5000	5800 incl comments	Source statements
Univac 1108, using EXEC II or EXEC VIII Operating System	Suitable for IBM, Amdahl, CDC, Univac, or most other mainframes. Special version of MAST is available for DEC PDP-11 computers	Can run on HP-1000 minis as well as mainframes with ANSI FORTRAN-66 compiler; requires approx 150K bytes on CDC Cyber 176 or 65K overlay on HP	Requires 60K bytes on DEC PDP-11/44 or 11/70. Transferrable to VAX or IBM. PDP-11 can be same computer that controls Variable Mission System	Environment
Model is configured for broad application. In addition to most FMS types, transfer lines, manufacturing cells, etc, can be simulated	MAST can simulate any number of machines, a variety of part types and mix, in-process storage at machine, dedicated facilities or in-transporter, and conveyor or cart MHSs	Most easily models FMSs in which parts are on carts, although some conveyor transport can be modeled	Variable Mission systems with cart, conveyor, or transfer-line materials handling. Stations with or without queues. Station and cart failures. Machine- and load-station groups	Types of FMSs that can be simulated
Extensive. Physical activities are simulated in detail, especially for material-transportation functions. Control-system algorithms are simulated. Extensive user-oriented reporting is provided	Each part in the system is tracked in each movement from machine to storage to transporter to machine. All aspects of congestion are included	Part congestion at stations, machines; transporter breakdowns, operating schedules; probabilistic part routings are modeled	Congestion on MHS as option. Queuing dynamics at all station types. Multiple options for defining production schedules	Level of detail
Computer-user documentation is available	100-page user's manual includes sample system	100-page user's manual includes output from sample	100-page user's manual includes sample run	Documentation
Proprietary software	$4125 incl mag tape; $25 each add'l manual	$18,000 incl installation and training	Proprietary software	Cost and availability
John J. Hughes Special Products Div Kearney & Trecker Corp 11000 Trecker Way Milwaukee, Wis 53214	CMS Research 945 Bavarian Ct Oshkosh, Wis 54901 Attn: J.E. Lenz	John F. Ippolito Horizon Software Inc 97 Strathmore Rd, No. 3 Brookline, Mass 01246	Machine Tool Div Cincinnati Milacron Inc 4701 Marburg Ave Cincinnati, Ohio 45209	Contact
The K&T FMS simulator was originally developed in 1971. Extensive validity tests have been conducted. The model has been continually updated and improved over the time span of its use	MAST Simulations have been performed for Allis-Chalmers (Milwaukee), Caterpillar (Peoria and Aurora), Ingersoll-Rand (Roanoke). Incl such vendors as K&T, Sundstrand, Giddings & Lewis	SPEED requires no programming by user and is entirely input driven. Interactive model generator can be used to build models and train new users. Available on United Information Services timesharing network	Defining model options rather than programming logic facilitates use and speeds response. Designed for user with little or no formal simulation education. Simulation model provides basis for Variable Mission Batch Scheduler Model	Additional comments

system (conveyor, robot, cart) and a dimensioned layout of the network showing machines, load stations, storage areas, and queue positions. For conveyor systems, the simulator needs to know speed and direction and the position of stopping places. This information is also needed to simulate cart systems, and the model also requires the protocol for advancing carts, cart-carrying capacity when more than one type is used, transfer times into and out of load stations, and where failed carts are repaired.

The simulation model also needs a description of the failure behavior of the materials-handling portion of the FMS: how often is a failure expected, and how soon can it be expected to be fixed?

Part-characteristic information needed includes a complete description of the elementary operations for each setup of each part type. Assuming that tooling exists at the machines, the simulator must be fed a list of all the machines that can perform each required operation, the time (including tool-change time) needed for each, the tool required, and the sequence.

Other part-related questions that need to be answered include the precedence in setting up parts, the number of fixtures available for each setup, the time needed to fixture and remove each setup type, and the inspection requirements: frequency, duration, and location.

Other information required to perform a computer simulation of how a flexible manufacturing system will operate includes projections for how the FMS will be used: what number of hours per shift, shifts per day, days per week? what scheduled maintenance? will parts be cleared away at end of shift? will part types be batched? how many workers?

Some simulator programs might be able to use prognostic data, such details about possible future changes as addition of new machines. Whether these changes would stay in compliance with existing protocol for machine and system use is also needed information for proper simulation.

Acquiring all the information needed to properly fill in the blanks in a computer simulation might, at first, appear to be a tedious task. In fact, however, a simulator merely organizes questions that will be asked during setup of an FMS. So there is no duplication of effort; indeed, going through a simulation actually streamlines the move into acquiring an FMS and can lend a sense of direction to the project of installing such a system.

Best of all, simulations can point out pitfalls and new avenues to explore before any money is invested in machinery or control hardware. Their proper use can, quite literally, save a manufacturer millions of dollars in improperly specified equipment. ∎

This article is adapted from one of the appendices to The FMS Handbook, *published this month by Draper Lab under contract to the US Army/TACOM.*

Simulation helps minimize WIP

Excess work-in-process is often used to solve breakdown problems.
This study helped design a more efficient production line

FREQUENTLY, an old job shop must be pressed into service to meet an unforeseen heavy demand for a product. Turning such a shop into a production-line facility, however, is fraught with potential problems. Not the least of these is the tendency of shop personnel to anticipate the frequent machine breakdowns associated with an old facility by stockpiling large in-process inventories.

Although such a strategy may seem logical to the operators and line supervisor, the existence of large quantities of work-in-process (WIP) inventory can quickly turn what, at first, looked like a perfectly good solution to a manufacturing problem into an economic disaster. In fact, just such a situation did arise at one of the facilities of Israel Military Industries when a new weapons component was developed.

Development and initial production of the new part, the receiver for the Galil assault rifle, took place in an existing multiproduct job shop. As soon as demand for the part increased significantly, the job shop was reorganized into a single-part production line, and special jigs and fixtures were installed. The line included a series of work stations linked by manual transfer of parts.

As expected, the old machines, which range in age from two to more than 20 years, break down frequently and take an average of three to four days to repair. To keep the production flowing and the workers busy, the supervisors used to stock up about three production days' worth of parts ahead of each work station. This practice did indeed increase production rates and improve work-force utilization, but at a price: an unacceptable level of work in process.

The CAM/CAD Research & Development Center of IMI was given the task of analyzing the production line and recommending a redesign of the operations to minimize WIP while effectively utilizing the same equipment; no additional capital investment was allowed. As a result, the number of operations was reduced from 58 to 23, WIP was reduced by 75%, and the production rate was also increased significantly.

A two-step study

To accomplish its objectives, the study team worked in two steps. First, methods engineering was applied to design an efficient, well-balanced production line. Second, a detailed analysis using a computer simulation was performed on the improved line in order to evaluate alternative operational schemes.

Methods engineering produced a redesigned line capable of producing 100 parts per day. A number of operations were combined, and others were resequenced to improve the flow and to save on setup times; the 58 operations listed in Fig 1 were reduced to the 23 operations listed in Fig 2.

In addition, a press operation (not listed) was transferred from the middle of the line to the end of the line. This operation is performed on a batch-lot basis at a remote location. Moving it to the end of the line, therefore, simplifies the whole operation. Other improvements include the elimination of operation No. 6 (side grinding), which was found to be unnecessary, and the combination of several operations at one work station.

A better-balanced line

The new line is far better balanced than the old. One way of expressing line balance is in terms of the coefficient of variation (COV) of the operation times, or the ratio of the standard deviation of operation times on a line to the mean operation time. The smaller the coefficient of variation, the less variation there is among the operation times on a line. The new line has a COV of 0.29 whereas the old line had a COV of 0.43.

A further improvement was achieved by transferring parts between stages more frequently: twice a day instead of only at the end of the day.

Simulation centers on three issues

The evaluation of alternative operational schemes of the improved line centered around three interrelated issues: the amount of WIP, the repair policy regarding machine breakdowns, and the work force required for machine operation and supervison.

In an ideal production line, where there are no breakdowns and work progresses smoothly, there is no need for planned in-process inventory. If some WIP does accumulate, it is due to only the occasional waiting between work stations because the process times at the various stations are not equal. In practice, however, machines break down at random times, and the time required to repair them also follows a random pattern. A buffer stock of partly processed parts from a machine that has failed provides work for the next station, and, consequently, the line can continue to operate productively.

The question is, how much in-process inventory should be available at any time? A directly related question is, how long should a repair operation take, including waiting time for maintenance personnel? The latter question, in turn, depends largely on the repair policy established by the shop. The simulation study attempted to analyze these questions. To do such a simulation, it is first necessary to define the nature of the part flow of the line. The following assumptions were made in this connection:

■ The parts are processed in sequence at each station.
■ A sufficient number of parts wait ahead of the first stage so that it is alway busy.
■ An initial inventory of parts is established ahead of each station at the beginning of the line operation.
■ After being processed, parts accumulate at a station until they are transferred to the next (daily and twice-daily transfers have been studied).
■ A station can operate if the buffer serving it is filled sufficiently to allow a full period (a shift, for example) of work.

By Dr S.Y. Nof, School of Industrial Engineering, Purdue Univ, East Lafayette, Ind; and **Dr Gideon Halevi** and **M. Bobasch,** CAM/CAD R&D Center, Tel-Aviv, Israel

1. Initial production line

Station No.	Operation	Operation time (minutes)	Breakdown (historical) No. per year	Breakdown (historical) Duration (days)
1	Width milling	2.5	6	4
2	Face milling	3.65	3	4
3	Slot milling	2.5	2	6
4	Width grinding	3.0	4	7
5	Milling of step	2.4	2	6
6	Side grinding			
7	Planar milling	3.3	3	4
8	Milling of step in slot		3	4
9	Deep drilling	5.64	20	2
10	Milling of long slot		8	1
11	Angular milling (rough)	2.45	2	4
12	Angular milling (fine)		2	4
13	Milling of forward plane	2.55	4	6
14	Milling of rear angle		4	6
15	Rough boring	17.03	6	5
16	Milling of pocket	3.93	3	4
17	Milling of relief			
18	Rough milling of rear relief	2.87	6	4
19	Width milling of slot	4.0	8	4
20	Final milling of corners inside slot	2.7	6	4
21	Final milling of slot	3.55	4	6
22	Milling of aperature on slope	2.0	8	5
23	Rough milling of counter-slot	2.8	6	4
24	Final milling of counter-slot	3.9	4	6
25	Face turning	5.4	6	4
26	Milling of slot in rear slope (rough)	7.8	4	6
27	Milling of slot in rear slope (fine)			
28	Drilling of upper slot			
29	Milling of upper slot	5.4	12	3
30	Milling of corner inside the upper slot			
31	Milling of rear pocket	4.8	2	6
32	Milling of slanted aperture	2.7	6	4
33	Milling of longitudinal inner slot			
34	Widening of inner slot (rough milling)	7.8	6	4
35	Widening of inner slot (fine milling)			
36	Milling of outer right slot			
37	Lower profile milling	4.6	6	4
38	Milling of upper plane	3.3	3	4
39	Milling of rear slot across	2.65	2	3
	Milling of forward slot across		6	3
40	Milling of lower pocket forward	4.5	12	3
41	Milling of outer left pocket	5.3	12	3
42	Widening of lower slot milling	4.0	12	3
43	Milling of inner guide	4.1	12	3

Station No.	Operation	Operation time (minutes)	Breakdown (historical) No. per year	Breakdown (historical) Duration (days)
44	Milling of inner slants forward (rough)	1.9	2	3
45	Milling of inner slants forward (fine)	3.95	12	3
46	Milling of relief for inner slot	1.44	6	3
47	Fine boring	4.57	12	3
48	Milling of rear side pocket (rough)	3.0	6	3
49	Milling of rear side pocket (fine)		2	4
50	Drilling of hole in the bottom	5.8	2	3
51	Drilling of 4 holes (right side)	3.35	3	2
52	Drilling of 4 holes (left side)	2.5	2	3
53	Drilling of relief in upper slot	2.33	8	4
54	Lengthening of bore (left)	2.4	1	3
55	Milling of dovetail (right forward)	3.4	2	3
56	Milling of relief in dovetail	1.82	2	3
57	Milling of tooth for lower slot	2.0	4	2
58	Grinding of upper plane	2.66	5	1

2. Redesigned line

Station No.	Original Station No.	Operation time (minutes)	Breakdown at stage Mean duration (days)	Breakdown at stage No. per year
1	1 + 2 + 3	3.6	2	6
2	4 + 58	5.0	2	4
3*	5 + 7 + 8	3.3	2	3
4	9 + 10	5.6	2	20
5	11 + 12 + 13 + 14	5.0	2	4
6	15	17.0	2	6
7	25	5.4	2	6
8	16 + 17 + 38 + 39	6.5	2	3
9	18 + 23 + 24	9.1	2	8
10	26 + 27	7.8	2	6
11	28 + 29 + 30	5.4	2	12
12	21 + 31	7.2	2	2
13	32 + 33 + 37	7.3	2	6
14	34 + 35 + 36	7.8	2	6
15	40 + 46	5.9	2	12
16	41 + 19 + 20 + 22	12.0	2	12
17	43 + 44 + 55	6.0	2	12
18	45 + 48 + 49	6.4	2	12
19	47 + 54	6.5	2	12
20	42	4.0	2	12
21	50	5.5	2	2
22	51 + 52	5.8	2	2
23	53 + 56 + 57	5.8	2	2

* Original Station No. 6 eliminated

Simulation helps minimize WIP

If the part inventory is not sufficient for a full period, then a half period can be started. Work for less than half a period is not permitted.

■ When a buffer has been filled to capacity by a work station (the station has produced sufficient parts for the next station to work a full period), the stage is blocked and will not start processing another part until the next work period.

■ The last work station is never blocked because completed parts are removed from the line.

■ Processing time at each station is known (Fig 2). Processing time is considered to be constant but may vary according to efficiency factors.

■ Machine-failure frequency and repair times are known from historical data (Fig 1 and 2) and are randomly generated in the analysis according to these data.

■ A machine can fail only when it is processing a part, not while it is idle or blocked.

■ Where several machines operate in parallel at one work station, all of them cannot fail at the same time.

■ All machines are repaired independently; repair times are based on historical data (Fig 2)

The analysis program, written in FORTRAN, is based on simulation of the production flow along the line for a given set of operating conditions. Basically, it advances parts from station to station and, following the rules set forth above, determines whether a work station is idle, blocked, or under repair.

A flow diagram for the logic simulation is illustrated in Fig 3. After the buffer stocks for each station have been determined, the program calculates the required production quantity (PQ_i) at each work station (i) per work period in accordance with the input data:

$$PQ_i = \frac{\text{Work period (min)}}{\text{Process time/part (min)}} \times \text{No. of machines at } i \times e_i$$

where e_i is the efficiency of station i.

The buffer capacity, BC_i, for station i (ahead of station i) can then be expressed as follows:

$$BC_i = PQ_{i-1} \times \text{repair time at } i-1 \text{ in period} + \text{initial inventory at } i$$

This total quantity of buffer stock must guarantee sufficient parts for regular production at station i, for production at station i while station $i-1$ is under repair, and for a minumum stock level at station i to accommodate certain production and efficiency imbalances among the work stations.

In order for station i to work on parts during a full work period, the actual amount of BC_i must be equal to at least PQ_{i-1}. Alternatively, if BC_i is less than PQ_i but BC_i is greater than $\frac{1}{2}PQ_i$, then station i is allowed to work for half a work period; otherwise, stage i is idled. On the other hand, if BC_i is greater than the amount specified by the above equation, stage $i-1$ is blocked to prevent excessive production. This approach attempts to eliminate excessive accumulation of WIP by keeping it between an upper and lower limit.

The breakdown logic of the simulation works as follows. When a breakdown is generated at station i it always occurs at the beginning of a work period. The program, therefore, checks the status of station i in the previous work period because breakdowns are allowed to occur only at a station that is working. Therefore, if station i had been idle or blocked or possibly already under repair during the previous work period, the new breakdown event is postponed; the program ignores the breakdown call. When a legitimate breakdown occurs, the program generates a repair time, and the station is scheduled to return to operation after the repair is completed.

After each work period, the program computes the number of additional parts produced at each station and, as a result, the new work-in-process stock at the next station. The value of

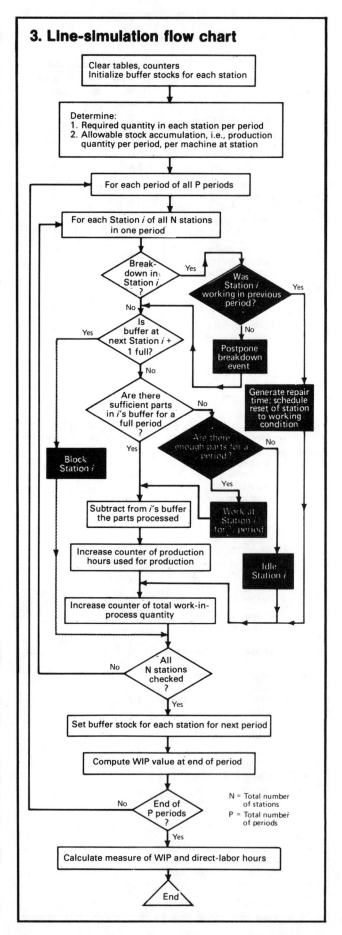

3. Line-simulation flow chart

4. Effect of WIP on production

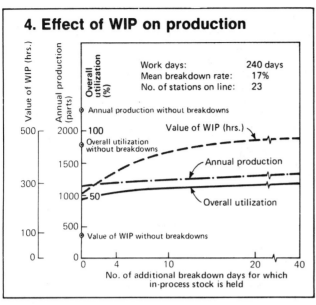

Work days:	240 days
Mean breakdown rate:	17%
No. of stations on line:	23

Annual production without breakdowns

Value of WIP (hrs.)

Overall utilization without breakdowns

Annual production

Overall utilization

Value of WIP without breakdowns

No. of additional breakdown days for which in-process stock is held

5. Effect of WIP on production ratios

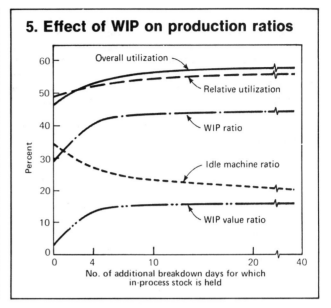

Overall utilization

Relative utilization

WIP ratio

Idle machine ratio

WIP value ratio

No. of additional breakdown days for which in-process stock is held

6. Effect of breakdowns on production

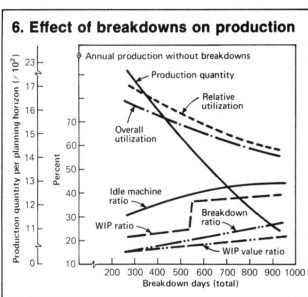

Annual production without breakdowns

Production quantity

Relative utilization

Overall utilization

Idle machine ratio

Breakdown ratio

WIP ratio

WIP value ratio

Breakdown days (total)

7. Work-force requirement vs WIP

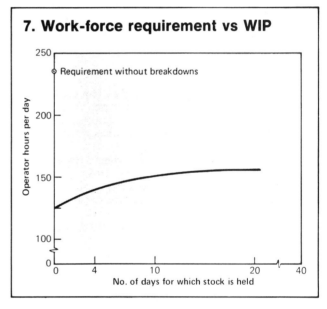

Requirement without breakdowns

No. of days for which stock is held

8. Work-force requirement vs breakdown

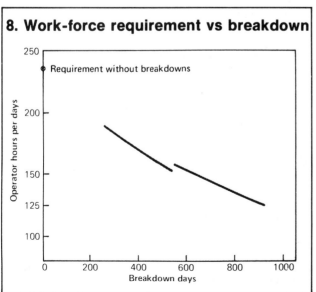

Requirement without breakdowns

Breakdown days

Analysis factors

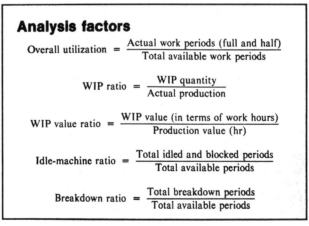

$$\text{Overall utilization} = \frac{\text{Actual work periods (full and half)}}{\text{Total available work periods}}$$

$$\text{WIP ratio} = \frac{\text{WIP quantity}}{\text{Actual production}}$$

$$\text{WIP value ratio} = \frac{\text{WIP value (in terms of work hours)}}{\text{Production value (hr)}}$$

$$\text{Idle-machine ratio} = \frac{\text{Total idled and blocked periods}}{\text{Total available periods}}$$

$$\text{Breakdown ratio} = \frac{\text{Total breakdown periods}}{\text{Total available periods}}$$

Simulation helps minimize WIP

WIP at each station in terms of work hours expended for parts in buffer storage is computed by taking the difference between the total number of work hours available per work period at the station and the work hours that have been expended on parts that have been completed and forwarded to the next station. The total WIP is calculated by summing the individual WIP calculated for each station. At the end of the whole planning horizon, the program computes summary statistics of WIP—both in number of parts and value (hours), and the actual production quantity.

Several WIP schemes simulated

A number of different schemes for establishing allowable work-in-process inventory and alternative machine-breakdown and repair situations were examined. For reference purposes, a simulation was also run for a line with no breakdowns and with no planned in-process inventory.

Based on historical data on breakdowns and repair times, WIP plans were simulated to cover the following conditions:

■ WIP to cover breakdowns. Accumulate in-process inventory between stages on the line to provide work during the anticipated repair days for one breakdown at a previous stage. For instance, if station No. 17 is programmed to process 100 parts per day and the expected repair time for a breakdown at station 16 is three days, then the buffer between stations 16 and 17 should hold 3 x 100 = 300 in-process parts. Therefore, station 16 will be activated to process up to 300 parts for buffer storage plus its production goal of 100 parts per day before it is idled.

■ WIP for additional delays. Accumulate in-process inventory between stations to provide work as above for the expected breakdown duration plus some stock for additional repair days. The additional stock will provide work when repair durations turn out to be longer than expected.

For realistic simulations, the following breakdown and repair-condition combinations were considered:

■ Historical breakdown frequencies and repair durations.
■ Half the historical breakdown occurrences, each requiring the historical repair duration.
■ Historical breakdown frequencies requiring only half the historical repair duration.
■ Half the breakdowns, requiring half the repair duration.
■ Historical breakdowns, all requiring exactly two repair days.

The various combinations actually represent, in turn, policies of improved preventive maintenance, improved repair service, and controlled repair activities. In essence, each combination implies a different total number of breakdown days per year. As an example, the historical data called for 900 breakdown days while using half the historical breakdown occurrences produced only about 270 breakdown days per year.

The analyses represented in Fig 4 through 8 provided some valuable information for the design of the line. (See box for the definitions of the various factors analyzed.) Without any breakdowns, the line can produce about 2300 complete parts per planning period at an overall utilization level of 89% and a WIP of about 120 parts valued at 87 hr. The idle-machine ratio, an indication of how often machines are blocked because of full buffers or idled because of insufficient parts, for this reference condition is only 2%. These values of the reference analysis provide upper limits for comparison purposes. It is clear that, if the demand for this part exceeds 2300 per planning period, then additional capacity must be provided.

Fig 4 and 5 clearly support some intuitive observations: As WIP is increased to cover additional potential breakdown days, the benefits in production and utilization start to decrease. In other words, increasing amounts of WIP start to have decreasing effects on production and utilization. For instance, the addition of WIP to cover four breakdown days beyond the expected breakdown days increases production by about 6% and overall utilization by about 15% (Fig 4). To achieve another 6% increase in production would require another 15 days' worth of stock; to achieve another 15% increase in overall efficiency is virtually impossible by increasing WIP.

The effect of breakdown days (Fig 6) appears to behave in a similar way: an increasing number of breakdown days has a slowly decreasing rate of effect on utilization. The reason for the discontinuities in some of the curves is the difference in breakdown parameters. The jumps occur at the point where the breakdown duration is historical and the breakdown frequency is half the historical one and at the point where the breakdown duration is two days and the breakdown frequency is historical. However, the number of breakdown days is nearly the same.

Labor cost must be considered

In the ideal case, where there are no breakdowns, the line would require about 240 worker-hours per day. When breakdowns do occur, this figure decreases significantly, to about 125-190 worker-hours per day because direct labor is idled.

The amount of WIP apparently has a smaller effect here: there is an increase of 26% when stock is added for an additional 40 breakdown days. A controlled-repair policy that cuts the number of breakdown days to one-third of the historical figure implies a 50% increase in the work-force requirements. This also corresponds to about a 50% increase in utilization in the latter case, compared with an increase of 26% in utilization in the former. Thus, the added cost of labor also has to be considered when various designs are evaluated.

The significance of each operational variable with regard to its contribution to productivity is also an important factor. Just what are the maximum effects that can be accomplished by each factor? The highest production level per planning period when WIP is added to cover 40 additional breakdown days is about 1300 parts. This is a higher rate than can be achieved without any additional WIP and operating on the basis of historical breakdowns and repair times.

On the other hand, any of the policies of improved maintenance will raise the level of production about 14,000 or 15,000 parts per planning period. When the total breakdowns are reduced to 270 days, the production level increases to more than 1750 parts per planning period! Obviously, improved maintenance has a significant effect.

Balanced line no better

When a hypothetical, perfectly balanced production line of the proposed system was analyzed for comparison, there were no significant improvements. Because the processing times on such a line are equal, the line could not recover from any interruptions caused by machine breakdown; it could never fill the buffers ahead of each work station. A full extra shift would be required just to fill the buffers.

The addition of more parallel machines was also found to be an unreasonable approach to the redesign of the line. This would require a large number of mostly idle machines and a very high increase in WIP. These major guidelines were followed in the redesign of the job-shop line:

■ Design an effective, coordinated flow line, with fewer work stations and a low coefficient of variation of processing times.

■ Control maintenance and repair activities: limit repair duration to two days; halve breakdown occurrences through better maintenance.

■ Do not increase in-process inventory beyond that needed to provide work during breakdown periods. If additional WIP is accumulated, it should not exceed four days' worth of stock at each station. ■

CHAPTER V

Justifying Computers in Manufacturing

Machine-tool justification *8,672*

Hidden savings brought to light

A new machine tool seldom gets credit for all the savings it produces, especially the indirect savings, but this new justification procedure shows how to track them down

s *170*

facing, boring and
g tips   s *9,100*

threading, and other   *11,000*

d other semi-perishable
d replacement   *1,320*

            21,420

RECT SAVINGS

g   s *12,300*
        6,000
        7,030
          320
          400
         9,600

ciency   Total

Z B, page 1)

Hidden savings brought to light

Justifying the purchase of a new machine tool—proving in dollars and cents that the investment would be a sound one—is one of the most exasperating, and sometimes frustrating, tasks for the engineer or manager at the shop level.

It's obvious to him that the new machine ought to be bought. Let's say it's a numerically controlled lathe that would replace a manual lathe—or, more likely, two manual lathes. He knows the new one will produce twice as much, and that the pieces will be more accurate and more consistent. But when he tries to put it down on paper, the figures just don't add up to the benefits he knows are there.

It could be that he's missing something. And there may even be benefits he's never thought of.

Warner & Swasey has tackled this problem and has gone a long way beyond the usual methods for machine-tool justification, into categories of savings that have not been given adequate attention before. These are the indirect savings: reduced cost of carrying inventory, reduced tooling costs, and a variety of others, including reductions in cost of operator training and cost of inspection.

At first glance, it might seem that these categories are only the fringe areas, with little potential for helping to justify the purchase of a particular machine tool. In several years of working with this procedure, however, w&s has found that indirect savings amount to a significant percentage of direct savings. On the average, inventory savings have been 12.5% of direct savings, tooling savings have been 26.7%, and miscellaneous savings 19.7%—altogether, a handsome 58.9% added to the direct savings that are often depended on to justify an investment.

But does a new machine tool *really* save inventory expense, for example, simply by producing pieces faster? It certainly does. If it works faster, it is producing less-expensive pieces, and, for the rest of the time spent by these pieces in additional manufacturing operations, or in storage, less money is tied up in them. Until now, this saving has usually been overlooked, along with a lot of others.

Furthermore, w&s has developed a detailed set of worksheets for identifying and evaluating these savings. The worksheets take into account the usual direct savings, as well as the indirect savings, and they supply a logical, step-by-step method for working the calculations. In effect, they force the user to think about all the potential savings.

At the same time, the company points out that machine-tool justification is more an art than an exact science, and should be treated that way. Nobody should expect two-decimal-place accuracy from this or any other justification procedure used in planning capital investments.

This is especially true of some of the indirect savings, which are very hard to measure. In fact, they can only be estimated—but that doesn't mean that they should be ignored. These savings do exist, and, if the estimates are not made, they are being assigned a value of zero, which is almost certainly more incorrect than even incorrect estimates would be. The important thing is to make the estimates reasonable.

w&s developed the new justification procedure as a way to explain and evaluate all the benefits of replacing manual turret lathes with the company's numerically controlled SC lathes. This does not, however, limit the procedure's usefulness. With only a few modifications, which have been made in the following example, the worksheets should serve equally well for any kind of machine tool.

Putting the procedure to work

The example necessarily deals with a specific problem in a specific shop, of course, and many of the figures would be different in some other application. Nevertheless, it illustrates how the concepts are put into practice.

This shop is a machine shop that operates two shifts a day, with 50 employees on each shift. It has already had experience with NC machines, and it is considering an NC lathe for several parts that are now machined on manual turret lathes.

From the machine-tool builder, the shop has learned that the new lathe will cost $160,000, plus $4000 for installation. The question is: Will there be enough savings to justify the purchase? The calculations will determine, first of all, how many of the present machines can be replaced by the new one and what the direct savings will be. Following this, the various indirect savings are calculated in what constitutes the major portion of the procedure (it takes 13 worksheets in the original form). To help keep things organized, this text will use outline-type letters and numerals on the section headings.

A. Direct savings

The tabulation below assumes that separate calculations will be worked out (not on the worksheets) to compare the operator-hours required for producing parts by the old method. However, Warner & Swasey suggests that this be done on a sampling basis, especially when it involves a large number of different parts.

The shop in the example has 200 parts that could be run in small lots on the new lathe, and it would be clearly impractical to make a complete before-and-after analysis of every part. Instead, this can be done for only a representative

Direct savings—first-year summary

1. From production estimates on typical pieces, or other information, determine the time needed to produce by:

   a. New method — *3hr.*

   b. Old method — *6hr*

2. Production advantage (b ÷ a) — *2*

3. Annual hours on new equipment at normal load — *3400*

4. Equivalent hours on old machine(s): (2 x 3) — *6800*

5. Deterioration factor for old equipment. You may subtract, from 100% efficiency, 1% for every full shift year of machine use. Enter no less than 75% unless additional substantiation is supplied — *80%*

6. Total old hours being replaced, including deterioration: (4 ÷ 5) — *8500*

7. Total hours saved: (6 − 3) — *5100*

8. Value of hours saved: (7 x $____hourly rate) — *$51,000*

9. Add other significant annual savings because of method improvement, including elimination of secondary operation — *$3500*

10. Subtract any significant additional annual operating costs because of new equipment. (Include job turnover tape cost)

    50 tapes/yr x $60 — *$3,000*

11. Total first-year direct savings: (8 + 9 − 10) — *$51,500*

Three who had a chance to try it

During the time this program has been developing, Warner & Swasey has been preparing proposals for customers that include some of the indirect calculations described here. Here is how three of these prospects reacted:

Hal Brown

. . . is chief industrial engineer for Baker-Perkins, Saginaw, Mich. The company produces food and chemical-processing equipment, both batch and continuous. Many of the parts are large; most of the quantities are small.

The plant has nine NC machines: three drills, two large boring mills, three machining centers, and a two-axis NC turret lathe. Lathe justification was based on a study of 11 parts.

Although indirect savings were originally proposed, these were not included in the final proposal on which the purchase was based. However, some of these savings can now be documented, especially on tooling.

On the conventional lathes in the plant, positive-rake tools must be used; on the NC lathe, the spindle hp and mass of the machine permit negative rake. This means six or eight cutting edges from carbide inserts (triangular or square) instead of three or four. The cost is about the same for inserts with positive or negative rake, but the latter give twice the life.

The plant's special-tool catalog shows about 2000 specially ground form tools for conventional machines. These form tools are not required with the NC lathe. In the same way, the use of standard carbide threading inserts instead of high-speed chasers and threading tools is giving better-quality threads and reducing tool cost.

With the data he is collecting, Brown thinks he will include tool calculations in the next machine-purchase proposal.

Jerry Poss

. . . is plant manager of Northwest Engineering, Green Bay, Wis, a company that builds heavy construction equipment. Poss is an enthusiastic supporter of the concept of indirect savings. He studied each of the proposed indirect savings and, with some modifications in the calculations, accepted about two-thirds of them for his own proposal.

That proposal brought two four-axis NC lathes to Northwest Engineering. Because the company is on piecework, and therefore the conventional machines are more productive than in day-work plants, it is more difficult to justify an NC machine on the basis of direct savings.

It was the prospect of substantial savings in inspection, in lead times, and in tools that made the purchase possible. And it has since been possible to confirm many of these savings.

Poss cites a part formerly requiring a lead time of 12 weeks because of secondary operations, which is now produced complete on an NC lathe in two hours.

Elimination of form tools was a major saving that was anticipated. But the elimination of a second-floor machine shop in one building was a ben-

efit that was not anticipated. That change alone cut four indirect jobs (a trucker, an inspector, an inspector-helper, and a tool superintendent).

Because Poss had been involved in the acquisition of NC machines before (though not for this company), he did not make the mistake of underestimating the tape-preparation and start-up costs.

Poss likes the organized approach to checking indirect savings. "It forces you to take a look at every area you should consider," he says. "That way you don't forget something. You will be able to use some of them."

Tom Preston

. . . is NC coordinator for the Schrader Fluid Power Div of Scovill Mfg Co, Wake Forest, NC. The plant manufactures air and hydraulic components, including cylinders, valves, and regulators.

When it considered the purchase of its first NC machine, a two-axis, slant-bed turret lathe, the company presented a justification that included calculations for indirect savings. However, Preston says, the greatest benefits were in the direct area, in cycle time and setup time. He was dubious about the indirect savings and did not use them. "The cycle and setup savings were enough," he says.

Schrader has since bought two column-type turret lathes and two machining centers. One lathe was expected to eliminate extensive use of form tools, and this saving was included in the calculations.

---

sample of typical parts. The parts *must* be typical, however, and they must represent the full range of work. Then, based on weighted averages of the time required to produce parts by both methods, you can establish how much faster the new equipment will turn out the full range.

The tabulation at the left shows that the new lathe would take a total of 3 hr to machine one each of the 13 parts that make up the sample, and that the old equipment requires 6 hr to do the same work. The number of hours the new equipment will operate per year at normal shop load (line 3) is based on 50 weeks a year, two shifts a day, five days a week, at 85% uptime.

Line 5 may prove debatable. It makes an allowance for the fact that machines deteriorate in use. W&S says a good approximation of this deterioration is 1% for each shift-year, which is 2% per year for a machine that operates on a two-shift basis.

Therefore, if you have used standard times for calculating operating costs of the old equipment, and if those standard times were established five years ago when the equipment

was new, you should increase the time required, as shown, to correct for deterioration.

If you have used current, realistic times for the old method, you may want to skip this factor. But Baxter Fullerton of Warner & Swasey points out that there are effects of deterioration not measured by the calculated operating cost of old equipment. Cycle-time comparisons are usually based on the standards of several machines, whereas it is the oldest machines that actually will be replaced. Operators may tend to leave additional stock on a turned part with an old machine. If the piece is to be ground, inspectors will usually pass it, but the extra time spent in grinding does not get charged to the old lathe. Fullerton argues that there are effects of deterioration that are not measured by before-and-after cycle times, and that some allowance for this factor is appropriate.

The hourly rate for line 8 is the operator's pay plus fringes. No overhead is added, because the saving here is a reduction in direct labor cost only.

The line for other significant annual direct savings (line 9) makes sure that, if the new method eliminates the need for

1. Inventory life cycle of a workpiece turned by old method

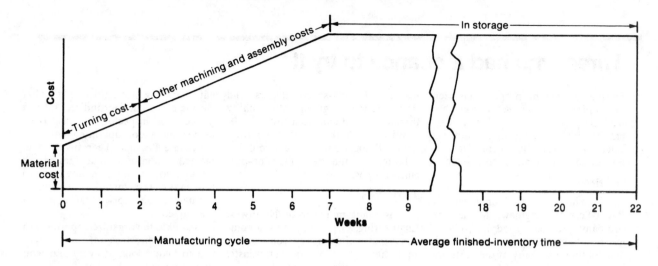

Indirect savings—first-year summary

1. Inventory-expense savings from faster floor-to-floor times

   a. From reduced turning lead-time $ 1,000

   b. From reduced piece cost   6,650

   c. From better scheduling decisions   1,022 $ 8672

2. Inventory-expense savings from eliminating secondary operations

   a. From reduced lead-time $ 170

   b. From reduced piece cost   275

   c. From better scheduling decisions   30 $ 475

3. Tool-cost savings

   a. Standard turning, facing, boring, and chamfering cutting tips $ 9,100

   b. Grooving, radius, threading, and other form-cutter tips   11,000

   c. Cutter shanks and other semiperishable tool inventory and replacement 1,320 $ 21,420

4. Miscellaneous indirect savings

   a. Operator training $ 12,300

   b. Inspection   6,000

   c. Scrap and rework   7,030

   d. Trucking   320

   e. Floor space   400

   f. Department efficiency   9,600 $ 35,658

   Total first-year indirect savings $66,225

As indicated by line 10, the change in direct costs between the old method and the new should also include any added costs imposed by the new method, not just the reductions. For example, if it is an NC machine and if there is a significant turnover of jobs that will require new programming and new tapes, this cost should be estimated. Thus, if the machine will work on 200 parts, and if 25 of these will be replaced with others during a normal year, there will be a tape cost for the 25 new parts. In this example, the average cost per tape is $60, so, if the average part requires two tapes, the added cost per year is $3000.

B. Indirect savings

Now we start on the interesting part of the analysis: indirect savings. This has been a large gray area in most justification procedures. The savings here have been difficult to identify and difficult to evaluate; therefore, they have often been ignored. However, as noted earlier, these savings can be important, especially when a drastic change is made in manufacturing methods, such as is involved with a change to numerical control.

The big contribution of the W&S justification procedure is that it goes through all the potential indirect savings, step by step, and provides a logical way to evaluate them. You may not agree with the procedure at every step, and you may even decide that certain of the savings really have no value in your application. If so, feel free to use or adapt the procedure as you wish. But the worksheets do make sure you won't overlook anything.

As shown by the summary at the left, indirect savings are divided into four groups. Two are savings in inventory expense; one is the saving in tool cost; and the third contains various miscellaneous indirect savings. All are difficult to estimate with any degree of precision—but precision isn't really necessary. In fact, you should not mislead yourself by trying to be too accurate; the goal should be reasonableness rather than precision.

B.1. Inventory-expense savings . . .

The savings in inventory expense can be substantial, and they come largely from the fact that, with less machining time per piece, the pieces you carry in inventory (in-process inventory and finished inventory) have a lower value. Additional savings are produced if the pieces are in process for a shorter period of time.

In any calculation of the expense of carrying inventory,

any subsequent operations, this saving will be included in the total. The figure of $3500 shown here is somewhat premature, because it hasn't been worked out yet. This will be done a little later in Section B, where the same basic figures are used for another calculation.

2. Some indirect savings from use of new turning method

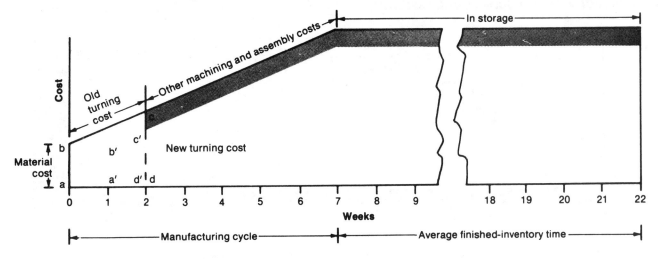

three factors are involved. One is the value of the inventory; the second is the length of time the inventory is carried; and the third is carrying cost as a percentage of inventory value. This third factor includes the cost of money and the costs of storage, handling, damage, loss, obsolescence, and taxes. In the accounting profession, this factor is generally acknowledged to be 2% per month, so an annual rate of 24% is used in this example.

Thus, if you are carrying $100,000 of inventory for six months, the expense should be very close to 12%, or $12,000. And if you can achieve a 10% reduction either in the value of the inventory or in the length of time you carry it, your annual saving should be $1200.

The diagram in Fig 1 illustrates how the inventory value is generated during a typical manufacturing cycle, a 22-week cycle in this example. The vertical scale represents the cost of the average workpiece, starting with the cost of the material (casting, forging, barstock) and rising from there as the piece goes through successive operations in the manufacturing cycle. The horizontal scale represents the time in weeks through the manufacturing cycle and then for the average length of time that finished pieces spend in storage until they are shipped.

However, if you think of the horizontal scale in terms of the average number of pieces worked on or in storage during each week of the complete cycle, then the total area of the diagram can represent the total value of inventory—work in process and finished pieces—at any given time. And for any week, that week's worth of pieces (350 in this example), multiplied by the average value of the pieces during that week, equals the week's share of the inventory.

By extension, the area can also represent the cost of *carrying* the inventory, because this cost is simply a percentage of the inventory value. Thus, the annual cost of carrying this 22-wk cycle would be the total area x 24%. The *weekly* cost of carrying the same 22-wk inventory would be the total area x 24% x 1/52.

Now, if we say that Fig 1 is the diagram for the old method in our example, then Fig 2 compares the inventory costs of the old and new methods. The only change reflected in Fig 2 is that the new NC lathe can produce parts twice as fast as the old manual turret lathe can. All other factors are the same: material cost, subsequent operations, and length of time in storage.

(Normally, in a direct replacement, the new lathe would have the same output as two old lathes. However, for purposes of illustration, this diagram makes the additional assumption that there is only one old lathe, and that it has to work two weeks to generate a week's worth of parts for subsequent operations.)

As the diagram shows, the total area has been reduced considerably. This means that the total value of the inventory has been reduced, and that the cost of carrying the inventory has been reduced in the same proportion.

The larger saving has come from the reduced cost of the pieces produced (the shaded area from week 2 to week 22), and the other saving has come from reduced lead-time (the shaded area from the start of the cycle through week 2). Now for the calculations that will put a money value on these—and other—savings.

B. 1.a. . . . from reduced turning lead-time

In chronological order, the first inventory-expense saving under the heading of faster floor-to-floor times is the one produced by the shorter lead-time. This is calculated as follows:

1. One week of production on new machine:
   _80_hr x $_30_/hr departmental cost $_2,400_

2. Equivalent production on old equipment:
   _2_weeks:_160_hr x $_24_/hr dept cost $_3,840_

3. Average number of pieces per week, new machine   _350_

4. Average material cost $_5_/pc x _350_ pcs $_1,750_

5. Old method, weekly inventory expense:

$$\left[\frac{\$\underline{1,750}\text{(line 4)} + \$\underline{3,840}\text{(line 2)}}{2}\right] \times \frac{\underline{2}\text{ weeks (line 2)}}{52\text{ calendar weeks}} \times 24\%$$

    $_34_

6. New method, weekly inventory expense:

$$\left[\frac{\$\underline{1,750}\text{(line 4)} + \$\underline{2,400}\text{(line 1)}}{2}\right] \times \frac{1}{52} \times 24\%$$

    $_14_

7. Weekly saving: (line 5 − line 6) $_20_

8. Operating weeks   _50_

9. **Annual saving:** (7 x 8) $_1,000_

3. Effect of better scheduling decisions

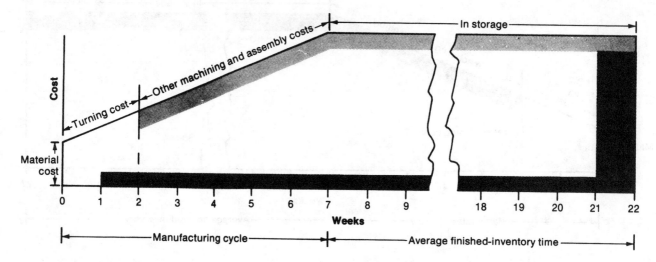

In this calculation, the departmental cost for the old method, which is figured at $24/hr, includes the $10/hr labor cost used earlier, plus $14 for overhead. As the new machine will entail a higher cost and a larger depreciation charge, the departmental cost for the new method is estimated at $30/hr. The earlier analysis estimated that the new machine would produce 350 pieces in an average week, and a similar estimate gives average material cost of $5/piece.

Next, the calculation of the difference in inventory expense during production is done simply by filling in the blanks on lines 5 and 6. In effect, we are calculating the average value of the completed product on hand during the production period (the average is one-half completed), and then finding the weekly cost of carrying this inventory under each method: $34 for the old method and $14 for the new, which comes to a difference of $1000 in a 50-wk year.

(Note that, under the old method, the production period is two weeks, again assuming that only one old lathe is being replaced. If the production period was one week for both methods, the annual saving would be $150.)

B.1.b. . . . from reduced piece cost

When the turning operation has been completed, the pieces go through the subsequent operations and then into storage, to wait until they are shipped. Obviously, the cost of carrying this inventory will be lower under the new method than under the old, because of the difference in the cost of the pieces produced.

Cost of material can be ignored, because it's the same for both methods. Thus, the difference in inventory value of a week's output depends only on the number of hours worked and the departmental cost. Here, the difference is $1440.

Then, as there are 20 weeks of product in inventory at any one time, and as we want to find the weekly saving, we multiply by 20/52 before applying the annual-cost figure of 24%. Finally, multiplying by the 50 operating weeks in a year produces an annual saving of $6650.

B.1.c. . . . from better scheduling decisions

The final saving in inventory expense under the heading of faster floor-to-floor times is the saving attributable to better scheduling decisions. If you have shortened the manufacturing cycle, you should be able to reduce your protective stock somewhat. The amount of improvement shown here is 2.5%, a figure that isn't too difficult to accept if you admit that there is, in fact, some saving in this factor. Furthermore, even though Fig 3 illustrates it as potentially a shorter period of storage *and* a lower inventory value, it is actually calculated as a simple 2.5% reduction in inventory expense after completion of the manufacturing cycle—15 weeks instead of the full cycle.

1.	Cost of one week of production on new machine	$2,400
2.	Cost of equivalent production, old equipment	$3,840
3.	Reduced cost of inventory: (2 − 1)	$1,440
4.	Weeks remaining before average piece is shipped	20
5.	Weekly saving in inventory expense: $\$1440$ (line 3) x $\frac{20 \text{(line 4)}}{52 \text{ weeks}}$ x 24%	$133
6.	Operating weeks	50
7.	**Annual saving: (5 x 6)**	$6,650

1.	Material cost per week	$1,750
2.	Operating cost of one week's output	$2,400
3.	Cost of remaining operations on same pieces	$7,660
4.	Value of one week's inventory: (1 + 2 + 3)	$11,810
5.	Average time in finished inventory, in weeks	15
6.	Estimated improvement in scheduling decisions	2.5%
7.	Weekly inventory expense, finished inventory: $11,810 (line 4) x $\frac{15 \text{(line 5)}}{52}$ x 24%	$818
8.	Operating weeks	50
9.	Annual finished inventory expense	$40,900
10.	**Annual saving: (9 x 6)**	$1,022

170

4. Added savings from reduced secondary operations

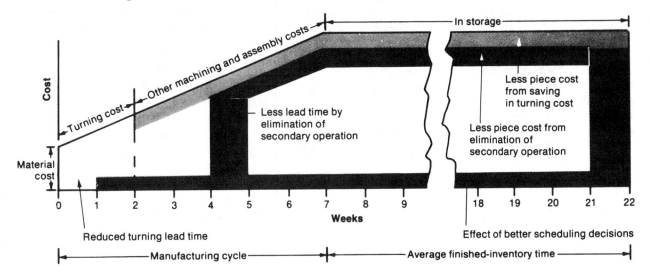

The tabulation determines, first, the total value of the pieces added to inventory each week at the end of the manufacturing cycle. This includes cost of material, cost of production through the turning operation, and cost of remaining operations (which must be estimated).

Next, it determines that the weekly expense of carrying 15 weeks' worth of finished inventory is $818, which comes to $40,900 for the full 50-wk year. Since we are going to save 2.5% of that, the annual saving is $1022.

B.2. Eliminating secondary operations

Very often, a new, modern machine tool, especially an NC machine, can perform operations that previously had to be done on more than one machine. Obvious possibilities for an NC lathe are threading and contouring, and the new machine may be accurate enough to eliminate grinding or polishing. Other possibilities: back-boring, sizing, and deburring.

In this example, a complete operation will be saved on 20 of the 200 parts that are expected to be run on the new machine. Therefore, on the average, one-tenth of an operation will be saved per part. At this point, we calculate the *direct* savings from elimination of secondary operations.

1. On average, how many secondary operations will be saved on each part	1/10
2. Total annual piece production, new method	17,500
3. Total number of operations saved: (1 x 2)	1,750
4. Average production/hr, eliminated ops.	10
5. Average dept cost/hr, eliminated ops.	$ 20
6. Cost per piece, eliminated ops.: (5 ÷ 4)	$ 2
7. Annual direct saving: (6 x 3) (Enter in summary of direct savings)	$ 3,500

And now, back to the indirect savings. Fig. 4 shows the familiar diagram, now augmented by the effects of eliminating operations that would have taken place in the fifth week. The diagram exaggerates the savings, because we don't save on all parts, only 10% of them. The calculation of these savings follows the same pattern as those from faster floor-to-floor times, and totals $475.

B.3. Tool-cost savings

Next on the agenda are savings in tool costs, and these are a good deal larger than the savings in inventory expense. Since a numerically controlled lathe is replacing a manual turret lathe in this example, the new machine will, of course, operate with fewer tools. With NC, the tools can be manipulated more readily than they can on a manual lathe, and one tool can sometimes do the work that would otherwise require two or more.

B.3.a. Standard cutting tips

It is estimated that the new machine will handle its workload with five standard turning, facing, boring, and chamfering cutting tips, whereas the old machines need seven on each machine. On the average, however, tools on the new machine will be replaced at the end of three hours of machine time (not time in the cut), and the tools on each of the old machines last for five machine hours.

1. Production advantage, new method vs old	2
2. Av number of standard cutters, new machine	5
3. Av number of standard cutters, old machine(s)	7
4. Av edge life in calendar hours, new machine	3
5. Av edge life in calendar hours, old machine	7
6. Av tip-replacement cost per cutting edge	$ 2
7. Operating hours per week	80
8. Cost per week, new method: (7 x 2 ÷ 4 x 6)	$ 266
9. Operating weeks	50
10. Annual cost, new method: (8 x 9)	$ 13,300
11. Cost per wk, old method. (7 x 1 x 3 ÷ 5 x 6)	$ 448
12. Annual cost, old method: (11 x 9)	$ 22,400
13. Annual saving: (12 − 10)	$ 9,100

Hidden savings brought to light

It turns out that, even though the tools have to be replaced more frequently on the new machine, it still has a large advantage in this example, inasmuch as it will remove the same volume of metal per week as the two older machines do and will wear out 40% fewer inserts. As shown, this yields a saving of $9100 a year.

B.3.b. Form-cutter tips

The cost of grooving, radius, threading, and other form-cutter tips can be reduced considerably with NC because a contouring numerical control can guide a simple, indexable cutting tip through many a cut that would require a specially ground form cutter when made on a manual lathe. Therefore, this tabulation (a continuation of the previous tabulation) shows that two form cutters will be needed on the new machine, and that four are needed on each old machine.

14.	Av number of form cutters & tips, new machine	2
15.	Av number of form cutters & tips, old machine	4
16.	Av cutter life (calendar hours), new machine	8
17.	Av cutter life (calendar hours) old machine	16
18.	Av cost to regrind or replace per edge (new)	$ 5
19.	Av cost to regrind or replace per edge (old)	$ 8
20.	Cost per week, new method: (7 x 14 ÷ 16 x 18)	$ 100
21.	Annual cost, new method: (20 x 9)	$ 5,000
22.	Cost per week, old method: (7 x 1 x 15 ÷ 17 x 19)	$ 320
23.	Annual cost, old method: (22 x 9)	$ 16,000
24.	**Annual saving: (23 − 21)**	**$ 11,000**

Note also that the form tools for the new machine should be less costly to regrind or replace. The reason for this is that the new tools will be less complex, because NC will eliminate the need for some of the features required on a form tool for a manual lathe. Putting it all together, we find there's an annual saving of $11,000.

How it developed

About six years ago, Baxter Fullerton, now a vice president of Warner & Swasey, began visiting people who had bought NC turning machines, to check on their experiences. In some cases, savings in inventory were greater than those in direct labor. Thus began the search for a regular method of estimating indirect savings. About four years ago, Fullerton began trying it out on groups of W&S salesmen. Some salesmen began using elements of it with prospects. A format gradually developed, which is now in wide use within W&S. The authors have adapted that format so it can serve broadly in evaluating indirect savings that may result from the introduction of an NC turning machine or machining center of any make.

Shanks required for new machine

1.	Variety of standard shanks needed	12
2.	Quantity of each	2
3.	Cost per shank	$ 35
4.	Inventory of standard shanks: (1 x 2 x 3)	$ 840
5.	Variety of form-cutter shanks needed	5
6.	Quantity of each	2
7.	Cost per shank	$ 50
8.	Inventory of form-cutter shanks: (5 x 6 x 7)	$500
9.	Variety of all other semiperishable tools and holders (bars, chaser holders, etc.)	25
10.	Quantity of each	2
11.	Cost per semiperishable tool	$100
12.	Inventory of semiperishables: (9 x 10 x 11)	$5,000
13.	Total shank inventory, new machine: (4 + 8 + 12)	$6,340

Shanks required for 2 old machines

14.	Variety of standard shanks needed	30
15.	Quantity of each	3
16.	Cost per shank	$ 18
17.	Inventory of standard shanks: (14 x 15 x 16)	$1,620
18.	Variety of form-cutter shanks needed	50
19.	Quantity of each	1.5
20.	Cost per form-cutter shank	$ 20
21.	Inventory of form-cutter shanks: (18 x 19 x 20)	$1,500
22.	Variety of all other semiperishable tools	50
23.	Quantity of each	2
24.	Cost per semiperishable tool	$ 50
25.	Inventory of semiperishables: (22 x 23 x 24)	$ 5,000
26.	Total shank inventory, old machines: (17 + 21 + 25)	$ 8,120
27.	Reduction in shank inventory: (26 − 13)	$ 1,780
28.	**Inventory-expense saving: (27 x 24%)**	**$ 430**
29.	Av shank-replacement cycle, in years	2
30.	**Annual replacement-cost saving: (27 ÷ 29)**	**$ 890**
31.	Total annual saving: (28 + 30)	$ 1,320

B.3.c. Cutter shanks and other semiperishables

If we're going to need fewer tools, we can get along with a smaller inventory of shanks and other semiperishable tooling, and we'll also save money, because the replacement of such tools will cost less.

Thus, the estimates in the example above assume that, if the average number of standard cutters on the new lathe will be five, as was estimated in B.3.a., then, to cover all possibilities, the toolcrib should have an assortment of 12 shanks for such tools, plus an equal number in reserve. Similarly, for the two grooving and other form cutters, the crib should have five shanks and five more in reserve. And for all other tools and holders, there should be 25, plus backup.

A similar line of reasoning is used for the old machines, except for two things. A greater variety of shanks and other tooling is needed, and the cost per item is lower.

Overall, the calculation shows that the tooling inventory will be reduced by $1780 with the new machine, and that the yearly saving in inventory expense will be 24% of this, or $430. If shanks last two years, saving on replacement is $890 per year, bringing the total to $1320.

B.4. Miscellaneous indirect savings

Savings involving operator training, inspection, scrap and rework, materials handling, and floor space are sometimes considered too vague to bother with. However, there are important savings under the miscellaneous heading.

B.4.a. Operator training

As everyone knows, operator training is a continuing cost, because of normal turnover. In this example, the turnover rate is 20% per year. Under the old method, it takes 30 weeks to train a new operator, and the average loss of efficiency during this period is 50%.

For the new method, the turnover is the same, but there is only one operator per shift instead of two. In addition, because there is less to learn about operating a numerically controlled machine, and because less depends on operator dexterity, it takes only 15 weeks to train a new one, and the loss of efficiency during training is only 25%.

Training cost, old method

1.	Annual rate of operator turnover	20%
2.	Operators required: (2 x 2 shifts)	4
3.	Operators to train annually: (1 x 2)	0.8
4.	Training time in weeks	30
5.	Average efficiency loss during training	50%
6.	Cost per week: ($30/hr x 40 hr)	$1,200
7.	Annual training cost: (3 x 4 x 5 x 6)	$14,400

Training cost, new method

8.	Operators required: (1 x 2 shifts)	2
9.	Operators to train annually: (1 x 8)	0.4
10.	Training time in weeks	15
11.	Average efficiency loss during training	25%
12.	Cost per week: $35/hr x 40 hr)	$1,400
13.	Annual training cost: (9 x 10 x 11 x 12)	$2,100
14.	**Annual saving: (7 − 13)**	$12,300

Departmental costs under old and new methods are estimated at $30 and $35, respectively (up from $24 and $30 for normal production), because the training will require the help of higher-paid personnel. As the calculation shows, there will be an annual saving of $12,300.

B.4.b. Inspection

The reduction in inspection cost is based on the fact that an NC machine can be depended on to produce more-accurate

---

pieces. Thus, the inspection burden is reduced, because fewer pieces have to be inspected, or because fewer dimensions on each piece have to be inspected. In this example, it is estimated that the inspection cost will be reduced by 50%, and the rest of the calculation merely establishes the dollar value of the saving.

1.	Number of machines being replaced	2
2.	Number of machines per inspector, old method	10
3.	Inspectors needed per old machine (1 ÷ 2)	0.2
4.	Cost per inspection hour	$15
5.	Hours per years: (2000 x 2 shifts)	4,000
6.	Annual inspection cost: (3 x 4 x 5)	$12,000
7.	Estimated % saving with new method	50 %
8.	**Annual saving: (6 x 7)**	$6,000

B.4.c. Scrap and rework

Scrap and rework costs should also benefit from the greater accuracy of an NC machine. How much benefit? That depends on the present percentage of scrap and rework, but it's not unreasonable to expect an NC machine to cut the reject rate in half. That's what happens in our example; the reject rate drops from 4% to 2%. The rest of the calculation uses familiar figures to determine that the annual saving will be $7030.

1.	Number of machines being replaced	2
2.	Av material cost/wk: ($5/pc x 350pcs)	$1,750
3.	Av % of scrap and rework, old method	4 %
4.	Av % of scrap and rework, new method	2 %
5.	Hours per year: (2000 x 2 shifts)	4,000
6.	Departmental cost per hr, old method	$24
7.	Departmental cost per hr, new method	$30

Scrap and rework cost, old method

8.	Annual cost of production: (1 x 5 x 6)	$192,000
9.	Annual cost of material: [(line 2) x 50 wks]	$87,500
10.	Annual scrap and rework cost: [(8 + 9) x 3]	$11,180

Scrap and rework cost, new method

11.	Annual cost of production: (5 x 7)	$120,000
12.	Annual scrap and rework cost: [(11 + 9) x 4]	$4,150
13.	**Annual saving: (10 − 12)**	$7,030

B.4.d. Trucking

Materials-handling within the plant will be reduced by any elimination of operations, of course. The following calculation is based on the estimate that, of the 200 parts to be machined on the new lathe, 20 will no longer require one of the secondary operations performed under the old method.

1. Number of parts on which operations will be eliminated	20
2. Av number of times each part is run per year	4
3. Av number of operations eliminated, each part	1
4. Number of trucking moves for average job	4
5. Av number of moves per hr per truck	12
6. Trucking cost per hr	$ 12
7. Moves per year eliminated: (1 x 2 x 3 x 4)	320
8. Cost per move: (6 ÷ 5)	$ 1.00
9. Annual saving: (7 x 8)	$ 320

B.4.e. Floor space

The cost of floor space will also be reduced. The new machine will need more space around it for parts, but, as there will be one machine instead of two, the net reduction will be 200 sq ft and an annual saving of $400.

1. Number of machines being replaced	2
2. Space required for each machine and parts, old method, in sq ft	300
3. Total sq ft required, old method: (1 x 2)	600
4. Sq ft required for new machine and parts	400
5. Sq ft saved: (3 − 4)	200
6. Annual cost per sq ft	$ 2
7. Annual saving: (5 x 6)	$ 400

B.4.f. Department efficiency

And finally, there is a potential saving in what Warner & Swasey calls the general rise in department efficiency. When a more productive machine is installed in a department, w&s claims, it can have a stimulative effect on the workers not assigned to the new machine. According to w&s, these other workers take a look at how fast the new machine can turn out parts, and they go back to their old machines and work a little harder. If they work even a tiny bit harder, the saving can be significant. As shown here, a 0.2% improvement in efficiency in a department employing 50 operators per shift amounts to $9,600 a year.

1. Number of employees in department per shift	50
2. 2000 hr per year x 2 shifts	4000
3. Departmental cost per hour	$ 24
4. Annual cost: (1 x 2 x 3)	$4,800,000
5. Estimated % improvement in efficiency	0.2%
6. Annual saving: (4 x 5)	$ 9,600

This completes the miscellaneous savings, which add up to $35,658, producing a grand total of $66,225 for indirect sav-

ings—a larger amount than usual because, in this example, savings have been developed in every possible category. As a percentage of direct savings, they come to 128.6% (vs the average of 58.9%), including 17.8% for inventory savings (vs 12.5%), 41.6% for tool-cost savings (vs 26.7%), and 69.2% for miscellaneous savings (vs 19.7%).

Adding it all up

Now for the final summary. As noted earlier, equipment and installation costs have been supplied by the machine-tool builder. Start-up training is based on the figures in B.4.b.: Two operators will work at 75% efficiency while being trained for 15 weeks at a cost of $35/hr—$10,500. Then, 400 tapes (average two tapes per part for 200 parts) at $60 per tape will cost $24,000. Adding these costs to the installed cost of the new machine and deducting resale value of old equipment, net installed cost is $188,500.

Final summary of replacement analysis

I Equipment to be replaced
2 manual turret lathes

II Proposed equipment
NC lathe

III Cost

A. Equipment	$ 160,000	
B. Installation	$ 4,000	
C. Plus one-time costs: Start-up training	$ 10,500	
Tapes for full machine load 400 tapes @ $60	$24,000	$198,500
D. Less resale value of old equipment		$ 10,000
E. Net installed cost		$188,500

IV Estimated first-year savings

A. Direct savings	$ 51,500	
B. Indirect savings	$ 66,225	$117,725

V Gross first-year return:
(IV ÷ III)   63%

Then we transfer the total direct savings and the total indirect savings from their summaries to find the total savings figure of $117,725. And the final figure—total savings divided by net installed cost—shows that the gross return on the investment will be 63% in the first year.

Most NC installations result in indirect savings. When they can be documented in this way, they may justify an investment that direct savings alone do not justify. ∎

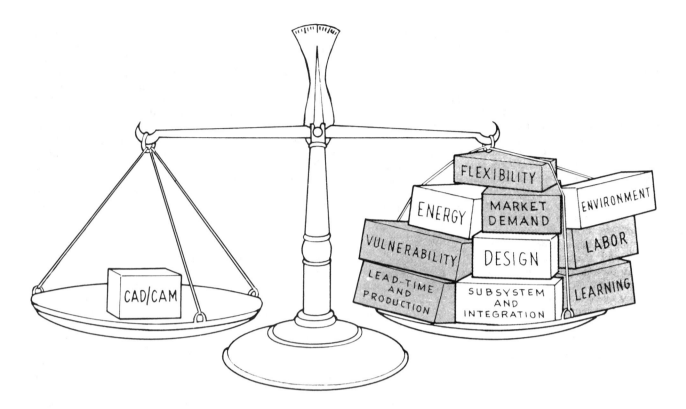

CAD/CAM justification needs balance

Implementation of CAD/CAM must be based on its far-reaching
effects, rather than on narrow economic justifications

A LONGER-TERM, strategic view of investment in computer-aided-manufacturing technology — as opposed to the more prevalent short-term, cost-justified view — holds the potential for significant changes in important investment decisions by both the public (military) and the private (corporate) sectors. Such changes are necessary if the full potential of computer-aided-manufacturing (CAM) technology is to be fulfilled and US industry is to be revitalized, a national goal that has gained widespread support from all sectors of US business and government in recent years.

The benefits of computerization are potentially greater than the benefits of discrete, particularized innovations; yet current management approach is unlikely to recognize the full range of possible benefits or to make decisions that will take advantage of them.

Clearly, computer-aided manufacturing may be applied beneficially to particular operations. Its major potential, however, is in optimizing operating conditions not only within individual operations but also between successive operations and among all parts of an integrated system. Developing and using computer-integrated manufacturing effectively will require a comprehensive view that expands the potential to broader groups of operating units and longer periods.

Investments in CAM technology are typically cost-driven. Most investments in technology are justified by first-order

By William K. Holstein, PhD, professor
School of Business, State Univ of NY at Albany

savings, capacity increases, or other benefits (such as improved reliability) that can achieve a short-term cost saving or cost avoidance with little or no change beyond the introduction of a new machine or system.

Other powerful motivators of investments in technology, however, are based on non-cost or strategic issues and goals and may not, at least in the short term, produce direct economic benefits or cost savings. These "strategic investment drivers" or "non-cost drivers" or "capability considerations," along with more-traditional cost/benefit considerations, must have a part in investment decisions concerning computer-aided-manufacturing technology.

Strategic factors are vital

A strategic factor is a motivator, or driver, that indicates that a new technology should be developed or installed even though it will not necessarily reduce costs in the short-term and may even increase short-term costs. Strategic factors significantly affect a company's products, processes, or methods of operation, exerting important influence over future profitability, market viability, and competitiveness.

In some instances, the cost implications of a strategic factor simply cannot be determined or cannot be reduced to "controller's terminology." Some rough estimates may be possible, but, frequently, future costs and cash flows are so uncertain that estimates are not reliable. Despite these difficulties, strategic factors should be important to the investment decision and should get explicit, careful (although non-cost-based) consideration.

CAD/CAM justification needs balance

The strategic factors chosen for discussion here should exert important influence on investment decisions but are not presented in order of importance or weight in the investment decision.

Vulnerability to short-term shortages in critical materials. A short-term shortage in materials, such as cobalt, chromium, and titanium, or in difficult-to-manufacture items, such as very tightly designed integrated circuits, could leave the US in a vulnerable military position. As an overly simple example, imagine the implications of a technological breakthrough permitting aluminum instead of titanium to be used for aircraft landing gear. Even if aluminum gear cost more but could be rapidly produced in sizable volume, adoption of the new technology would solve critical supply and processing problems of titanium alloys.

Flexibility and surge production capabilities. The ability to meet large increases in demand or sudden shifts in product mix is obviously desirable for US manufacturers serving the US military (and competing in the private sector). However, the military's historical proclivity for lowest-cost procurement without regard to lead-time has placed many manufacturers in a difficult position. In a time of mobilization, though, when cost considerations are tossed out and lead-times (surge capacity) are the only criteria, responding to surge demands may be impossible with the wrong technology. A different technological approach might provide inherently superior product-mix flexibility or surge capability. If flexibility and surge capability were given substantial weight in the capital-investment decision and were allowed even to dominate cost-based criteria, dramatically different equipment and scheduling approaches might now be available for many critical parts that currently create substantial risks in the event of military mobilization.

Market demand. The traditional capital-budgeting (cost-driver) approach involves a systematic search for alternatives to reduce the cost of existing product technology through product design or process changes. The strategic approach involves the adoption of new technologies that will result in new products or features or processes that, in the long run, will change the market and, therefore, the long-run cost structure of the market. To be competitive, then, manufacturers will have to take account of the intangible long-term benefits and develop technologies that permit them to do things that they couldn't do before—to market more-diverse, custom products, create new markets, build and successfully defend new market niches, etc.

Energy and related resources. The rapidly increasing cost and ever more risky supply of energy must affect future investment decisions involving new technology. The adoption of new materials, design, and manufacturing technologies that significantly reduce energy consumption or reduce dependence on certain types of energy or materials is already desirable. However, unless non-cost considerations enter the decision or very long-range cost and supply estimates are used, many worthwhile investments may be postponed or disregarded. Furthermore, the trade-offs among cost elements must be carefully handled. If strategic objectives are to be met, a significant shift in cost structure might be required even though it means organizational adjustment, re-evaluation of cost controls and incentives, and, of course, higher short-run costs.

Design. A difficult problem in the defense industry and in several non-defense industries is what might be called "unmanufacturable designs." More-aggressive decisions and investments in new design and manufacturing technologies, particularly computer-integrated technologies, offer the promise of critical product or system functions that cannot be obtained with conventional technologies. What is needed is the foresight, the tolerance for risk, and the strategic investment analysis to

stimulate the initial investment. Again, government policy can help to influence or change the criteria that determine management's tolerance for risk.

Environment. Federal and state government pressures have led manufacturing companies to make large investments in new technologies in order to meet environmental standards. Much of the investment being made is defensive, however, and designed to solve a specific problem with present product or manufacturing technology. A more comprehensive approach that integrates design and manufacturing technologies, materials and methods, planning and control might lead to environmental *and* other savings.

Labor. Larger, more integrated approaches to investments in new technology can affect labor in several ways. Computer-aided manufacturing can replace or supplement critical skills in short supply and can yield quality and consistency improvements, reducing inspection requirements, assembly interruptions, and maintenance problems. New technology can change the nature of tasks in the workplace to reflect the changing nature of the work force and to alleviate problems caused by shifting demographics. New technology can remove manufacturing and assembly workers from hostile or unhealthy environments, free needed human resources for more-productive tasks, reduce errors, and free administrative and clerical personnel for more-productive assignments.

The continued development and refinement of new technologies can assist in attracting and retaining highly qualified, aggressive, innovative technical personnel who wish to retain technological currency and who will not remain in a work environment that is static or falling behind competitors' technologies.

Learning. Investments simply to advance in knowledge of a new technology are imperative in some instances. One example is the emerging field of robotics. Despite early leads in the development of robots, US industry has fallen well behind West European countries and the Japanese in installing robots on the shop and assembly floors. Experience gained with first-generation technology helps companies as they adopt increasingly sophisticated systems and integrate new technologies more fully with other subsystems.

Although it is indeed possible to move directly into more-advanced technology without first participating in rudimentary developments, history teaches that experience early on the learning curve is vital. A short-term, cost-based view, however, hinders justification of initial expenditures. What is needed is a willingness for investment for learning's sake. That is a tall order for a manager who will be paid on the basis of this year's bottom line or who must compete for resources with other, smaller cost-justified investments.

Lead-time and production. Conceptually, many managers would be willing to trade (somewhat) higher costs for reduced lead-time or speedier production. Many would also trade higher costs for faster adoption or development of a technological innovation. Practically, however, determining the cost savings of shorter lead-times offered by computer-integrated design and manufacturing is very difficult. The question is how can lead-time effects be built into the decision criteria?

Subsystem integration. Integration potential per se should be an important factor in investment decisions. Investments in planning and control systems or manufacturing that help to integrate other subsystems should get more-positive weighting simply because they contribute to a more integrated system. This too is a difficult objective to build explicitly into investment decisions, but procurement policies and investment criteria must reflect these important factors if significant progress is to be made.

The US Air Force Integrated Computer-Aided Manufacturing Program (ICAM) has the clear and practical objective of greatly shortening the implementation period for incorporation of computer-integrated-manufacturing technologies into US industry. The output of ICAM will be systematically related modules for efficient manufacturing management and operations and for unified direction for US industry.

The ICAM program has funded several research and demonstration projects to develop a unified "architecture" of manufacturing, standards and definitions of subsystem elements, and modules that fit into a computer-integrated-manufacturing environment.

Almost every aspect of the ICAM program's work relates to the strategic issues discussed here. Yet many of the ICAM program's most useful technologies and subsystems cannot be justified solely by the use of short-term, cost-based criteria. Present US government procurement policies, focusing on annual buys, permitting capitalization of only short-term investments, and giving primary emphasis to lowest-cost initial bids, also impede adoption of ICAM technology.

High-level commitment needed

Industry and government managers responsible for capital-investment decisions involving new manufacturing technologies should find methods of incorporating consideration of strategic factors into investment decision-making.

The methods chosen and the strategic factors to which important weight must be given vary from situation to situation. There are, however, common elements in virtually all capital-investment decisions in new technologies: future cash flows that are highly uncertain, implementation lead-times and problems that are difficult to forecast, and long-term benefits that are almost impossible to state or to quantify. Despite these difficulties, managers should try to become sensitive to the important strategic factors in investment decisions and to develop a tolerance for risk and a willingness to invest in corporate learning when the strategic factors clearly suggest it.

Assisting management in developing this sensitivity to and awareness of strategic factors is a very appropriate role for corporate boards of directors. Corporate directors or board subcommittees now review major capital-investment programs in most large corporations. If board members would review such programs more carefully, raising questions about strategic factors, future competitive capability if the investment is not made, present technological effectiveness vis-à-vis competition, etc, significant changes in investment analysis might be accomplished.

Concerted, sustained high-level board and management interest and action would be required, but, unless the motivation and goals are clearly established at the top, significant change will not occur.

Government policy lacking

Several of the strategic investment factors we have identified relate to US government policy and views on such matters as military preparedness, defense readiness, surge capability, systems-performance characteristics, strategic-materials availability, etc. Managers responsible for capital-investment decisions in industry cannot make decisions based on these factors *in vacuo*. Unless the important strategic factors are clearly expressed in government policy and reflected in bid specifications and cost negotiations, industry cannot be expected to make investment decisions based on those factors.

This observation leads to several questions. What is the country's defense-readiness posture, and how is it reflected in government procurement policies? How much extra short-term unit cost would the government be willing to absorb for significant additions to surge capability, reduced reliance on critical materials, shorter implementation time for new tech-

nologies, or greatly expanded processing capability or flexibility? A more specific administrative issue is this: who in the Department of Defense is responsible for reviewing these issues and suggesting executive or legislative approaches for dealing with them?

The answer to most of these questions at the moment is "we don't know." What is necessary is much more explicit treatment in government procurement policy of the type of strategic factors discussed here. Industry needs a clearer statement of goals and objectives and an indication of the government's willingness to invest and assist in meeting those goals. Lowest unit cost per se is no longer a sufficient criterion. Much more thought and discussion must be directed toward the concept of lowest unit cost *given* that certain strategic objectives are obtained.

The Air Force and other government agencies should encourage the incorporation of long-range investment analysis into government contracts and should allow a looser interpretation of forecasts, risks, and future cost savings.

The government's role in helping to develop a strategic view of investments in new technology need not be restricted to relationships with military suppliers. Taxation and depreciation policy, investment credits, non-military procurement policies, trade policies, loan guarantees, joint ventures, access to government laboratories, antitrust immunity, and a host of other approaches are available. This does not mean that the government should insert itself into corporate decision making. Rather, government policy should be directed toward motivating appropriate corporate strategic responses to the changing economic environment and to strengthening and toughening the competitive capability and long-term responsiveness of US industry.

If government policies can assist senior corporate managers to view investments in computer-integrated-manufacturing technologies as part of comprehensive long-range business plans rather than simply as one of many independent capital-investment or equipment projects, many benefits of national importance can be obtained. These benefits will accrue to corporations as well in terms of future profitability, world market share, productivity, and efficiency.

For a long-term view

A major barrier to the incorporation of a strategic view in investment-decision making is the fact that most proposals for changes in manufacturing technology flow up from managerial and technical specialists in fairly narrow subsectors of the business. Recognizing that a top-down flow is not likely to develop, a company's top management should find ways to stimulate innovation at lower levels. Programs are needed to provide seed money for high-risk projects, to encourage a project "champion" to persevere in the face of discouraging short-term results, and, most important, to invest in learning and in integration.

This is nothing more than a point of view, a perspective in which long-term capabilities and cost structures clearly dominate accumulated short-term benefits accruing from more-conservative investments. It is not easy to develop and reward people, both in government and in industry, who can see that vision, but it holds the promise of rewards far greater than now imagined. ∎

This article is based on a paper presented at a colloquium on The Strategic and Organizational Implications of New Manufacturing Technology, held under the auspices of the Manufacturing Studies Board, which was established by the National Research Council in May 1980 to examine leading manufacturing issues for policymakers. The National Research Council is the operating arm of the National Academy of Sciences.

Buying CAD/CAM graphics

CAD/CAM productivity is enhanced with interactive computer graphics, but choosing a system is tough. Here is some help

SUCCESS IN THE MARKETPLACE can place exceptional strains on any manufacturing operation. This is particularly true for medium-size companies, which frequently sport rather lean design/engineering/manufacturing staffs. Today the capabilities of such an operation can be greatly enhanced with the introduction of a turnkey interactive computer-graphics system to provide CAD/CAM (computer-aided design/manufacturing) capability.

The requirements of fast engineering turnaround needed to capitalize on today's commercial opportunities; the increasing workload of a successful and growing company; the high cost of real estate; the time-consuming, costly recruiting and training of designers and manufacturing engineers with relevant experience and product knowledge—all these factors combine to make productivity improvements offered by CAD/CAM computer graphics very attractive. But choosing an appropriate computer-graphics system also has its pitfalls and requires careful consideration before a purchase order can even be considered. There are many decisions to be made.

Lease or purchase?

To begin with, CAD/CAM computer-graphics capability can be purchased or leased in a number of different ways from very different sorts of vendors. For casual users, there are service bureaus that specialize in CAD/CAM: Structural Dynamics Research Corp (SDRC, Milford, Ohio) is an example. SDRC offers walk-in access to its Applicon systems located at offices in Cincinnati, San Diego, Paris, London, and Wiesbaden. Similar services are offered by general-purpose timeshare networks, such as Control Data Cybernet and others, that provide access to their computers and software via telecommunications links and lease display stations, plotters, and digitizers.

In both these approaches, the costs consist of some or all of the following: equipment rental, terminal-connect time, telephone-line charges, data-storage charges, software-use charges, a charge for computation, and sometimes charges for custom programming and training. However, for more than casual use, these charges grow rapidly, and users whose bills exceed $5000 per month generally find it more economical to acquire an in-house system.

Acquiring an in-house system, too, takes a number of different approaches. Some users prefer to integrate their own system. They buy software and hardware from different vendors, put the various elements together, and make them work themselves. For example, a company may purchase CAD/CAM software, such as the AD2000 package from Manufacturing & Consulting Services Inc, computers from Digital Equipment Corp, display stations from Tektronix Inc, plotters from CalComp, and digitizers from Summagraphics Corp and then assemble the pieces into an integrated system.

A variation of this approach is to add CAD/CAM software, terminals, and ancillary hardware to existing corporate computer-center facilities. IBM, Honeywell, Control Data, and other general-purpose mainframe manufacturers offer software and hardware to do this to some extent. Of course, giant corporations with a vital interest in maintaining a position of technological leadership in their industry develop CAD/CAM systems entirely in-house at a cost of literally millions of dollars. Lockheed Corp, General Motors Corp, and McDonnell-Douglas are some that did this in the 1960s.

Doing it yourself is costly

Self-integration and particularly self-implementation obviously require a great deal of user know-how, money, and time

By Charles M. Foundyller
Daratech Associates
Cambridge, Mass

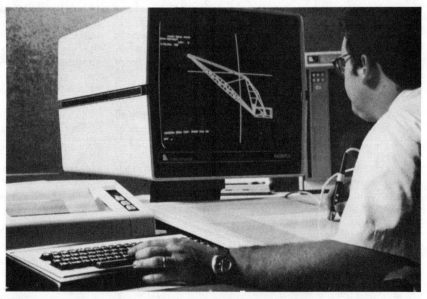

Designer IV terminal of Computervision interactive graphics systems is used to generate NC toolpaths. Part of tablet is reserved for symbolic and menu entries

One of two work stations of a Gerber IDS-80 system is equipped with a digitizing tablet. Processor is under table between operators; other output stations are in back

IBM 3250 graphics work station is used with CADAM system developed by Lockheed Corp and marketed by IBM. Light pen, function keys are used to interact with image

What hardware do you get?

Most vendors of CAD/CAM computer-graphics systems supply all the necessary hardware. This includes work stations, graphics processors, output stations, and local interconnecting cables and equipment. However, it is important to know in advance just exactly what you can expect, and a checklist like the following can be very helpful.

Work stations
Graphics displays
Alphanumeric displays
Keyboards
Cursor-control devices
Function-menu devices
Hard-copy units
Work-station processors
Special furniture

Graphics processors
Computer
Main memory
Cache-memory hardware
Memory-mapping hardware
Virtual-memory hardware
Memory-parity hardware
Memory battery back-up
Floating-point-processing hardware
Real-time clock
On-line disk storage
Off-line magnetic-tape storage
Work-station interfaces
Output-station interfaces
Telecommunication interfaces

Output stations
Pen plotters
Electrostatic plotters
Photo plotters
Perforated-tape punches
High-speed printers

Interconnecting cables
Local data-interconnecting cables
Power cables

Initial consumables
Disk packs
Magnetic tape
Paper tape
Drawing vellum
Plotter pens and ink
Electrographic paper
Electrostatic-plotter toner
Hard-copy unit paper
High-speed printer paper
High-speed printer ribbon
System console paper
System console ribbon

Buying CAD/CAM graphics

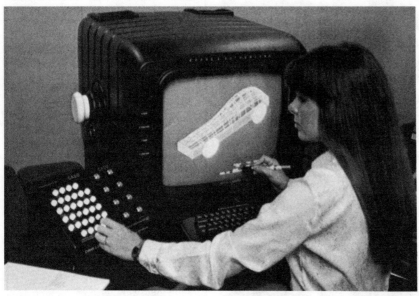

An Evans & Sutherland work station is used with MCAUTO's CADD system, which runs on a large mainframe and is shared by many users with diverse requirements

to carry out. Thus, for almost all users, self implementation can be ruled out: the enormous risks, costs, and time are simply too great to justify this approach.

Self-integration makes sense for an increasing number of companies with CAD/CAM experience and the in-house software and hardware expertise to see it through. When it is undertaken with the help of a major supplier of mainframes, such as IBM or DEC, the risks are smaller; but, *caveat emptor*, most mainframe manufacturers are new to CAD/CAM, and even IBM, which, like other mainframe suppliers, markets CAD/CAM software developed by third parties, "does not guarantee [software] service results or represent or warrant that all errors will be corrected."

Thus, most engineering managers prefer to focus responsibility for CAD/CAM on a single vendor and purchase ready-to-use systems supplied by established CAD/CAM companies, such as Applicon, Calma, Computervision, Gerber Systems Technology, M&S Computing, Summagraphics, and others, which will take responsibility for the hardware, software, installation, maintenance, training, and applications: the so-called "turnkey approach."

But what exactly is the turnkey approach, and how much responsibility will a turnkey vendor take?

One popular concept of a turnkey system is that the user need only turn it on to make it work. Obviously, this is not a realistic view. Most turnkey purchases involve both vendor and user in a close working relationship that will require both commitment and performance by each side for the system to succeed.

In industry parlance, a turnkey CAD/CAM system customarily includes four components: (1) an integrated set of hardware, (2) software, (3) vendor services, and (4) a commitment by the seller and the buyer to make the system work. The hardware includes work stations, a system processor, output stations, their interfaces, and interconnecting cables. The software includes all the general-purpose programs and application software needed to operate the system. The services include installation, maintenance, and an undertaking to look into and fix software bugs (software maintenance).

In addition, many vendors provide management education, training for operators, help with application and special-purpose programming. However, the implicit, or explicit, commitment made by both sides to work together in good faith is the crux of a turnkey purchase—especially for users with no previous CAD/CAM experience.

There are, of course, variations, and some vendors supply more or less of these components with their turnkey offerings. It is, therefore, important that buyers examine the nature of each turnkey package and carefully evaluate system, services, and commitments in the light of their particular needs.

A turnkey vendor undertakes a number of responsibilities vis-à-vis a buyer that have an important bearing on the overall value of the offering. Implicit in any turnkey purchase is the vendor company's promise to use its best efforts to provide the buyer with a working system having functional capabilities appropriate to the buyer's expectations of

Buying the auxiliaries

Although many turnkey-systems suppliers provide all the hardware, there are still some items that they do not customarily furnish, and you will have to make sure that such auxiliary equipment is available by the time the CAD/CAM system arrives. Here is a checklist of the kind of hardware you will probably have to purchase independently.

Climate-control equipment

Air-conditioning, heating, and humidity-control equipment is usually purchased independently by the user to specifications provided by the CAD/CAM turnkey-system vendor.

Telecommunications equipment

Leased telephone lines, in-house wiring, and data-transmission devices (line drivers, modems, or data sets) are acquired by the user directly from the telephone company or other source. CAD/CAM vendors often supply guidance in this area.

Power-conditioning equipment

Most CAD/CAM systems cannot tolerate wide fluctuations in voltage or high-frequency disturbances on power lines. When the power supply is irregular, power-conditioning equipment will have to be installed, and this is customarily the user's responsibility.

Furniture

To a certain extent, vendors supply tables and racks with their equipment but usually only when their equipment is built in. For the most part, the buyer will have to purchase additional tables, chairs, and storage cabinets for disk packs, tapes, maintenance manuals, spare parts, and other supplies.

Expendable supplies

Except for a minimal amount of initial supplies of printer paper, ribbon, pens, ink, paper tape, disk packs, magnetic tape, etc, the buyer will have to purchase these items independently from the CAD/CAM vendor or from a third party.

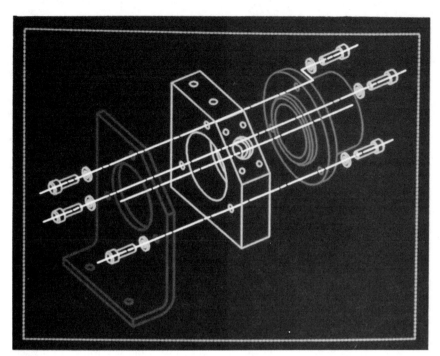

Ability to develop a three-dimensional color exploded view of an assembly is one feature of Calma's CAD/CAM graphics system. Line resolution is 1024 x 1280

What software do you get?

Software is what makes your system functional and is, of course, provided by the turnkey vendor. But is it tailored to your applications? Usually, the vendor supplies an appropriate selection from a list of stock software products. Make sure you get what you need.

Operating software
Control-store microcode
Operating system
Device drivers
Data-management system
Power-fail and -restart software
Telecommunications drivers
Network-support programs
System-to-user interfaces
System-to-mainframe interfaces
System-use accounting software

Utility software
Copy programs
Programming-language processors
Program-debugging aids
Data-conversion software to support off-standard output stations
System-update software

CAD graphics software
Basic graphics
Advanced graphics
Advanced-graphics editors
Drafting software
Hidden-line removal
Finite-element-model creation
Finite-element-model analysis
Bill-of-materials extraction
Area, volume, mass extraction

CAM graphics software
APT interface
NC basic software
NC drilling support
NC flame-cutting support
NC machining-center support
Sheetmetal pattern layout

Special applications
Bottle-design package
Piping layout
Structure-model building
Special analysis programs

Manuals and logs
System operators' manual
System supervisors' manual
Tutorial manuals
System-maintenance manuals
Software-source listings
System log
Work-station logs

improved productivity, management control, and payback. While this promise is seldom explicit, and some contracts go so far as to specifically exclude it, it is an inseparable feature of the turnkey approach and the basis upon which many other responsibilities of the vendor rest.

Vendor responsibilities cover activities both before and after the sales agreement is concluded, and it is important that the buyer evaluate them beforehand.

Vendors must study user's needs

Prior to making a proposal, the vendor is responsibile for studying and understanding the buyer company's application, its organization, its abilities, and its limitations to judge whether the system will do the job. The better vendors also determine whether the buyer company is willing and able to adjust its organization and operating procedures to make the system work. The vendor company must also set reasonable expectations of performance, benefits, payback, and service and make sure that it will be able to provide the level of support required by the user.

After the sale, the vendor generally assists the buyer in planning the installation and advises on the purchase or lease of ancillary equipment and supplies. Such matters as planning computer-room layout, work-station areas, electric power, etc are typical of the things that must be planned in advance in conjunction with the vendor. Most vendors also provide buyers with advice on purchas-

ing air conditioning, telephone-line leasing, modem-purchasing or -leasing options, power-conditioning equipment, as well as other technical matters that buyers may not be used to dealing with.

Also, many vendors feel responsible for educating the buyers' management on the impact CAD/CAM might have on their organizations and what to expect and plan for in the future. Training for operators and supervisors to prepare them to use and manage the system is also provided by most vendors prior to installation. Organizing engineering data, scheduling and controlling access to the system, and providing for the security of its data are all part of this training.

Of course, the vendor is responsible for delivering the system, uncrating and erecting it, and then bringing it on line according to a prearranged delivery schedule.

After the system is up and running, the turnkey vendor provides preventive and remedial maintenance for the hardware and debugging and fixes for the software. Some vendors' technical and support people monitor each new installation and provide advice on how to correct any problems they recognize. It is here that the vendor must work to make good on the promise to fulfill the buyer's expectations of functionality, productivity improvement, and payback.

The leading vendors also consider it their responsibility to provide an orderly plan for each user to expand its system as its needs grow. Implicit in this under-

Buying CAD/CAM graphics

Services are what count

A key advantage of a turnkey CAD/CAM graphics purchase is that the vendor offers comprehensive CAD/CAM expertise based on its experience. This is particularly helpful for a novice company buying its first computer-graphics system. Five basic types of services are commonly provided:

Hardware maintenance

Usually, the seller undertakes to provide renewable, yearly remedial and preventive maintenance contracts. Some vendors guarantee a maximum response time: this is usually the maximum time for a service person to leave for the user's site after receiving a call. Others guarantee a specified uptime over a designated period—95% for Computervision. Implicit in such a guarantee is the availability of spare parts.

Software maintenance

Typically, the seller undertakes to locate and correct bugs, usually on a "best-effort" basis. The ability and qualifications of the vendor to provide this service is extremely important; malfunctioning software can disable the system just as much as a hardware failure. Some vendors agree only to examine the problem and provide "fixes" when (and if) they become available. This means that service results are not guaranteed and that there is no guarantee that bugs will be corrected. Because of the effect that this can have on the success of a system, software-maintenance arrangements should be examined carefully prior to purchasing a system since this can have a bearing on a system's fitness for a particular purpose.

Applications assistance

The seller provides the buyer with assistance on how to get the most out of its system. Ideally, the seller's applications people are familiar with the buyer's industry, the particular design and drafting operations, and the company's product, and they are, therefore, able to provide appropriate advice. Services offered generally include both on-site and telephone consulting.

Management assistance

The seller provides the buyer's managers or high-level supervisors advice on matters of system management, such as access control, scheduling, and selection of personnel. In addition, advice on start-up planning, how to hire and train operators, wage scales, career paths in CAD/CAM, etc, may also be provided.

Education

Training for all levels of personnel is provided by most of the established vendors. Usually, basic, intermediate, and advanced operator courses are available. Some vendors also provide courses on special software packages and programming, as well as a course for key operators. Seminars for management are also given by some vendors. Courses are generally structured as one- or two-week affairs and consist of laboratory and class work.

bought, the cost (in addition to the purchase price of the system itself), and the effort that will have to be made to ensure that the installation is a success. In this regard, it is the buyer's responsibility to make a commitment to a partnership with the seller. In fact, many installations have failed because the buyer did not, at first, understand what would be required and later was not prepared to bear the costs and make the necessary effort.

Just as it is the vendor's responsibility to study the buyer's application, organization, and limitations, it is up to the buyer to judge whether the seller really understands the particular situation. Without this understanding, the seller will, of course, not be in a position to prepare a suitable proposal.

Often, it is left to the vendor's salesperson to convince the buyer that the company is familiar with the buyer's situation. But the buyer is well advised to look beyond the salesperson to the seller's management and applications-support people for this assurance.

After the sale, the buyer, working with the vendor, must plan the installation and must order the required ancillary equipment and supplies in a timely manner. It is also up to the buyer to see that the computer room, air conditioning, humidity control, conditioned electric power, leased telephone lines, data-transmission equipment, proper lighting, etc, are in place according to schedule.

The buyer must make available management, supervisory, and technical staffs for the various training seminars recommended by the vendor. The buyer must also work with the vendor to organize the data, set work schedules for the operators, set a system-access policy, and provide for security of the system and its data. The buyer must also be prepared to make procedural and organizational changes to accommodate the requirements of running the system.

It is also the buyer's responsibility to plan, with help from the vendor, the switch-over to CAD/CAM and to see that it is done in an orderly way, avoiding overdependence on the system in the early stages before start-up difficulties have been ironed out and the staff is fully conversant with the system.

Once the system is delivered, the buyer is responsible for seeing that the vendor's personnel have adequate access to the facilities and are given the appropriate support to see that the system is erected and on-line as planned.

After the system is running, the buyer is responsible for seeing that the vendor is provided with enough information on any malfunctions that develop and for giving the vendor sufficient access and

standing is a commitment not to render their customers' systems obsolete and to provide, with each new product introduction, reasonable means of transferring data, programs, and operator skills from the older to the newer systems. This is called "upward compatibility" and is very important to the buyer. Clearly, a buyer cannot afford to invest thousands of worker-hours in a soon-to-be obsolete technology.

Lastly, many vendors feel responsible for keeping abreast of new developments, continuing their research and development programs so that they can upgrade their products and make available to their customers timely, new applications and other CAD/CAM innovations.

To this end, many vendors establish and support user organizations. These groups are a vehicle for disseminating new ideas, sharing user-developed software, discussing common problems and needs, and collecting field-experience data so vital to vendors for upgrading their products.

On the buyer's part

The buyer's responsibilities toward the seller are no less important than the seller's responsibilities to the buyer. Indeed, the way they are discharged has an important bearing on the relationship between the parties and, ultimately, on the success of an installation.

Many buyer responsibilities correspond to those of the seller and so cover activities both before and after the sales agreement is signed. In the first place, the buyer must understand what is being

support to correct them. The buyer should also be prepared to discuss problem areas frankly and constructively and to act promptly on reasonable suggestions made by the vendor.

The buyer company must also ensure that its expansion plans will be supported by the vendor's plans for improving the system. In addition, the user should participate constructively in user-group activities and share its experiences with the vendor and other users, while learning from theirs.

Finally, during the course of the relationship, the vendor will disclose to the buyer proprietary technical information as well as plans for the future. It is up to the buyer to keep this information confidential and not disclose it to others so that a close working relationship with the vendor can be sustained.

Most turnkey vendors supply all the system hardware. This includes work stations, graphics processors, output stations, and local interconnecting cables and equipment. Work stations often come complete with graphics displays, alphanumeric displays, keyboards, cursor-control devices, and function-menu hardware, and they are frequently supplied with, or built into, special furniture. The output stations are sometimes built into racks or are complete floor-standing units or table-top units.

Many vendors also provide a small quantity of such supplies as disk packs, magnetic tape, paper or Mylar tape, drawing vellum, and pens and ink for plotters.

Software is, of course, also provided by turnkey vendors. This gives the system the functional capabilities required. In addition, the vendor normally supplies several sets of reference manuals and tutorial materials. As a rule, the software provided is tailored to users' applications; that is, the vendor supplies a set of off-the-shelf software selected jointly by the buyer and seller from the vendor's list of stock software products. Typically, this software is delivered in object (working) form and not in source (modifiable) form, although some vendors make both forms available.

All software not included

Some software is *not* usually provided by the vendor. For example, special-purpose programs, such as those used to create families of parts are normally developed by users after the system is delivered. This is because these programs depend on the users' product parameters, and most vendors generally avoid custom-programming assignments. However, this kind of software is not immediately essential: it characteristically makes using the system more convenient or broadens the scope of what the system will do.

Services provided by the vendor company based on its comprehensive CAD/CAM expertise are a key advantage of a turnkey purchase—particularly for first-time users that need a single unambiguous focus of responsibility for their CAD/CAM hardware, software, and applications. In addition, the coordinated education and consulting programs covering system management and applications provided by turnkey vendors have proved to be less confusing for beginners than independent programs that tend to advocate conflicting philosophies. Five basic types of services are provided: (1) hardware maintenance, (2) software maintenance, (3) applications assistance, (4) management assistance, and (5) education.

Piecing together and understanding the many components of a turnkey purchase is, of course, necessary before criteria for evaluating systems and vendors can be set. *Turnkey CAD/CAM Computer Graphics: A Survey and Buyers' Guide for Manufacturers* (Published by Daratech Associates, PO Box 410, Cambridge, Mass 02238, 370 pages, $153), from which the material in this article is excerpted, discusses the setting of system- and vendor-evaluation standards and includes a detailed net-present-value financial justification, with illustrated explanations of contemporary CAD/CAM technology and its merits. Also available is a US Directory of Vendors.

Although the turnkey approach may not be for everyone, it can be an ideal solution for users that have outgrown service bureaus but are not up to integrating a CAD/CAM system themselves. ∎

Turnkey CAD/CAM graphics vendors

These companies offer CAD/CAM computer-graphics systems with application support for manufacturing processes, including NC-tape preparation:

Applicon Inc
32 Second Ave
Burlington, Mass 01803
617/272-7070

Auto-trol Technology Corp
12500 N Washington St
Denver, Colo. 80233
303/452-4919

California Computer Products Inc
 (Calcomp)
2411 West La Palma Ave
Anaheim, Calif 92801
714/821-2011

Calma (GE)
5155 Old Ironsides Dr
Santa Clara, Calif 95050
408/727-0121

Computervision Corp
201 Burlington Rd
Bedford, Mass 01730
617/275-1800

Control Data Corp
8100 34th Ave South
Bloomington, Minn 55420
612/853-8100

Gerber Systems Technology Inc
83 Gerber Rd
South Windsor, Conn 06101
203/644-2581

IBM Corp
Data Processing Div
1133 Westchester Ave
White Plains, NY 10604
914/696-1900

Information Displays Inc (IDI)
709 Westchester Ave
White Plains, NY 10604
914/761-1144

Intergraph Corp
1 Madison Industrial Park
Huntsville, Ala 35807
205/772-3411

McDonnell Douglas Automation Co
Brown Rd at Lindbergh
St. Louis, Mo 63166
314/232-6963

Manufacturing & Consulting
 Services Inc
2960 South Daimler Ave
Santa Ana, Calif 92705
714/540-3921

Manufacturing Data Systems Inc
4251 Plymouth Rd
Ann Arbor, Mich 48106
313/995-6000

National Computer Systems Inc
Computool Div
4444 West 76th St
Minneapolis, Minn 55435
612/830-7600

Redac Interactive Graphics Inc
1 Redac Way
Littletown, Mass 01460
617/486-3529

Tektronix Inc
4900 S.W. Griffith Dr
Beaverton, Ore 97005
503/644-0161

CHAPTER VI

Metalcutting Applications of Computers

Preparation of

Microcomputerized tape-preparation system keeps nine NC machines running on two shifts and making profits for this 50-worker plant

J.F. Fredericks Tool Co is a modern, 50-employee job shop with an annual volume of about $2-million. The company is housed in a modern, 16,000-sq-ft plant in park-like surroundings in Farmington, Conn. The word "modern" is emphasized because the company prides itself in keeping up to date and its management is firmly convinced that a major share of the credit for its success and expansion has been due to a policy of investing in modern equipment.

Fredericks Tool seeks out high-precision jobs, and most of the work it machines ends up in the aerospace field or in machine components. Among its customers the company lists such firms as Pratt & Whitney Aircraft, Polaroid, IBM, Xerox, Honeywell, and Raytheon.

The firm was less than half its present size and doing less than a quarter of its present volume in the early 1960s when it first dipped its corporate toe into the numerical-control waters—at a time when NC was a relative rarity on the manufacturing scene. The first NC machine was a Bridgeport mill retrofitted with a Colemaster control for X-Y positioning of the table.

From that initial retrofit, the NC complement at Fredericks Tool has grown to nine, three of which have computerized NC (CNC) systems.

Split almost equally between machining centers and turning machines, the company's NC inventory consists of two Burgmaster turret-type Econ-O-Center machining centers with Westinghouse two-axis positioning controls, a Burgmaster Econ-O-Center VTC with a 20-station automatic toolchanger and a General Electric 550 three-axis contouring NC, a Matsuura MC-660V machining center with a 15-station toolchanger and Fanuc 3000C computerized control unit, one Jones & Lamson 4512B TNC Combi lathe (4½-in. bar capacity, 12-in. chuck)

tapes in a precision job shop

with a Bendix 892A NC system, one J&L 312B Combi (3-in. bar, 12-in. chuck) also with a Bendix 892A, two J&L PTL 550 chuckers (1-in. bar, 5-in. chuck) with Autonumerics controls (one a hard-wired Positool 900, the other a Positool CNC), and a Mori Seiki chucker (5-in. capacity) with a Yaskawa Yasnac CNC.

Tape preparation at Fredericks Tool has paralleled the job shop's growth in NC. Programming and tape-punching for the original Colemaster/Bridgeport were done at the machine—and were redone at the machine if corrections were necessary. That meant, of course, that the machine wasn't cutting chips and wasn't earning profits while it was being used for preparation of tapes.

With the subsequent installation of additional NC machines, Fredericks Tool acquired a used Flexowriter for tape preparation. This permitted tapes to be prepared off the shop floor and without interference with machine operation. But correcting new tapes or converting proven tapes for use on different machines continued to be somewhat tedious.

Coping with NC growth

Addition of four more NC machines in 1977, bringing the total to the current nine, put too much of a strain on existing tape-preparation facilities at Fredericks Tool, and the company tried a computer time-sharing service on a trial basis. Perhaps uncharacteristically, this trial did not suit the company's particular requirements, and the time-sharing approach was not adopted.

What Fredericks Tool finally did acquire for tape preparation was an NC-23 microcomputer-controlled tape-preparation and editing system built by Four-Data Inc (Plantsville, Conn). All of the job shop's tapes are now programmed manually with this equipment.

Principal unit of the modular system (at left in Fig 5) incorporates a tape reader, a tape punch, the electronic brains (including Intel 8080A microprocessor and memorized software), input/output communication ports, and a function keyboard for control. Various peripheral modules can be plugged into this, including the following: a teletypewriter/printer (as in Fig 5); a visual display unit, such as a CRT; a mass storage unit, such as a floppy-disk system; a plotter; an acoustic coupler for telephone linkup with a time-sharing computer service; and a direct input/output to an in-house computer system. In

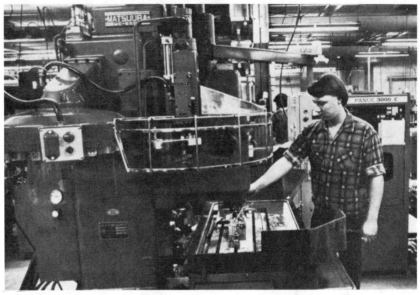

1. Used primarily for contouring operations on relatively small workpieces is this Matsuura MC-660V machining center with computerized Fanuc 3000C control

2. Fixturing on table of Matsuura machining center holds four stainless-steel aircraft components in different attitudes for a variety of machining operations

all, the system architecture allows up to eight input/output ports.

The built-in microcomputer integrates the 8080A microprocessor with 4k bytes of read-only memory (ROM), of which 3k is available for specialized software—generally called "firmware" when incorporated in ROM.

Software for the NC-23 has been "designed to meet today's needs," according to FourData, but modification to suit specific requirements or for future updates is easily handled by reprogram-ming the ROMs, which are actually EPROMs (erasable programmable read-only memory). If the user of an NC-23 system wants a function or a code changed, FourData will furnish a newly programmed set of EPROMs in return for the old set at a charge only for time and handling.

The Fredericks Tool installation consists of a central NC-23 with a peripheral 60-character-per-sec typewriter/printer—representing a purchase price of well under $10,000 or a monthly rental of

Preparation of tapes in a precision job shop

3. Hard-wired NC system (Bendix 892A) on J&L Combi bar and chucking lathe is equipped with semiconductor memory for tape storage and editing

4. Operator inspects workpiece from J&L chucker. Control is Autonumerics CNC, which features CRT readout, part-program storage, and full editing capability

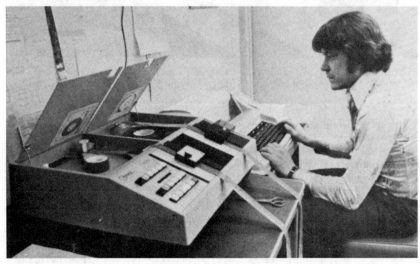

5. Tape preparation for all Fredericks Tool NC machines is done by programmer with FourData NC-23, which provides program editing and communications features

$320. The basic capability provided is tape (either paper or Mylar) punching from the keyboard in either ASCII or EIA coding, block-by-block editing (the system is buffered), copying tapes (including conversion from ASCII to EIA and vice versa), and search-and-edit of existing tapes. Punching speed is 75 characters per sec, read/print/punch is at 60 cps, and maximum tape-reading speed is 120 cps. A number of automatic checks are made, including a parity check that is either odd or even depending on whether the system is in EIA or ASCII mode.

A little bit of DNC

One of the features of the Fredericks Tool installation is that the NC-23, which is located off the shop floor in a small programming office, is remotely connected to three of the NC machines in the plant: the Matsuura machining center with Fanuc CNC, the small J&L chucker with Autonumerics CNC, and the J&L Combi 4521 lathe with Bendix 892A control (which incorporates the optional program-storage memory feature).

All of these controls provide both the program-storage and the RS-232C interface (the plug is visible in Fig 3 on the side of the control) necessary for transmission of tape data directly into control memory. A selector switch determines which machine link is activated.

With this setup, the NC-23 can also be used as a peripheral tape punch for any of these three machines, and the CRT readout of the Autonumerics CNC system works essentially as a peripheral to the NC-23. Thus it is possible to do editing at the machine while tapes are punched remotely.

Because the plant's other hard-wired NC systems do not feature program-storage capacity, a direct linkup would have little point, and the Yasnac CNC system on the Mori Seiki lathe, which does provide program storage, does not offer a compatible interface.

One frequently used capability at Fredericks Tool is the use of master tapes for part-family programs. The shop often produces runs of similar parts; the master tapes—initially punched and edited on the NC-23—are simply re-edited on the system to make dimensional modifications and to add or delete part features as required.

What are the basic benefits? According to Roger Fredericks, company president, "We buy equipment to keep us on top as a job shop. NC gives us a completed part except for deburring, and, without NC, our operation would be a disaster. The NC-23 enhances our flexibility and helps keep the NC machines running for two shifts—and that makes it a lot easier to pay for them." ∎

Machinist Bob Kelly checks path of profiling end mill on an experimental stainless part programmed with VNC

Voice commands produce NC tapes

**A speech processor that converts a programmer's analog
voice signal into the digital language of the computer
permits part-programs to be generated by vocalizing the data**

Business was progressing at such a rate for Plainville Machine Works (Plainville, Mass) that its one programmer couldn't maintain the production schedule any longer. Plainville is primarily a jobbing shop, specializing in one or two custom parts at a time, and Ed Thayer, NC programmer, found himself making as many as 1500 tapes a year.

"And, I'd say, 75% of them were for one or two parts," Thayer states. "As fast as I'd make them, the job would be done on the machine." He was programming manually, and, at this rate, more programmers would have to be hired.

That was about mid-1978. Thayer is still the only programmer at Plainville,

but he now produces up to 2000 tapes a year for some 15 NC machines and spends only 5 hr a day programming, with another 3-4 hr available for coordinating things on the shop floor.

Tape preparation by voice

A voice-input NC-tape-preparation system is a large part of the reason. By entering data vocally, he saves the time previously spent writing tape manuscripts; computer processing power reduces the calculation time necessary to produce the tapes; and the system's interactive/prompting and part-program-software features further speed the tape-preparation process.

There are actually three plants in Plainville, constituting three separate companies under the ownership of one

man. In addition to the Machine Works, there is Plainville Products, which primarily does production jobbing; five NC machines form the heart of its production machinery. Plainville Hydraulics Corp is a high-production machining facility making hydraulic rotary actuators that can be found in such products as backhoes, material-handling systems, and robots. Thayer programs for all three metalworking companies.

Late in 1978 the Machine Works bought a Voice Numerical Control (VNC) tape-preparation/manufacturing-control system from Threshold Technology (Delran, NJ). The VNC-200 is the third generation of voice-input equipment to be offered by Threshold.

The interactive/prompting system permits a worker to enter data by voice

Voice commands produce NC tapes

directly from a part drawing or blueprint. Shop language is used, and, once spoken, voice commands are processed and formatted, re-presented for verification to the programmer, and then entered into the NC processor. The prompter then requests the next bit of information; eventually, a complete part-program tape is punched.

Plainville had investigated time-sharing as an alternative to manual programming but concluded that, for its applications, the service was too expensive. Thayer felt that it might have been suitable if he were doing very intricate parts all the time, but, "for a lot of our tapes, I just wouldn't call up for it."

That would leave him doing most of the tape preparation manually, which was what he was doing anyway. Now, with an in-house unit, Thayer can do everything on it.

Of course, the company also considered a computer-based keyboard system. (The VNC-200 does use a keyboard for various functions.) But, as Thayer tells it, "I'm the kind of programmer who came out of the shop, involved with the mechanical aspects of metalworking; I just hunt-and-peck when I type. With this unit, all I have to do is talk in the data. With the keyboard, I would be taking the time to write out a manuscript prior to keying it in." All Thayer writes down now is a list of the tooling to be used for the job.

He also likes the system for working with large blueprints. He lays them out across his desk and stands over them, calling in the numbers and the machining steps to the VNC as he decides how the part should be made.

Steps in preparing a tape

Here's how Thayer makes a tape. First, he types in "PO," and the CRT (optional with this system) displays several options: activate, edit, print, or create a postprocessor. This last option is an interesting feature of the unit, in that it allows the user to create a postprocessor in the event of new machine acquisitions or format changes.

Thayer relates that Hank Fredericksen, the company's owner, is especially enthusiastic about this feature, since it means that specially written postprocessors don't have to be purchased for every new machine. That can be expensive, he says.

Thayer has made postprocessors, or "posts," for all the plant's machine tools, which include a variety of NC lathes, mills, drilling machines, and machining centers; several manufacturers' control systems are involved, including both NC and CNC.

He checks machine-tool manuals for coding specifics and creates the program that corresponds to each machine's particularities: for example, the number of digits used before and after the decimal, whether the mode is incremental or absolute, or the number of feet of tape that must be used for a leader.

After pulling out the postprocessor, he retrieves his already entered voice commands. The voice system had been previously "trained," in this case by repeating each word of the vocabulary five times to provide a reference-set of features. The vocabulary consists of 89 words—for example, *thread, angle, turn,* etc.

How words are 'understood'

The reference-set, which involves converting the operator's analog voice signal into the digital language of the computer, is created in this way. The operator wears a close-talking, noise-canceling microphone on a lightweight headband; this is designed to reduce interfering acoustical signals and background noise.

The extraneous signals caused by breath noise must also be accounted for. A strong tendency exists to exhale at the end of isolated words and to inhale at the beginning, and exhalations can produce signal levels in a microphone comparable to speech levels.

However, the actual beginning and ending of a word, its "boundaries," must be determined for it to be stored accurately. And so pattern-recognition processing, which discriminates between speech sounds and the frictional breath noises, is used.

What this amounts to is that, from the microphone output, a wave spectrum of human speech is produced. A spectrum analyzer derives features from these signals to indicate the overall spectrum shape. Combinations and measurements of these values are then processed in the hardware to produce a set of 32 significant acoustic features.

One of these features is an initial estimate of word boundary. The word boundary is further refined by separating speech from the breath noise. This is accomplished by using a so-called "variable-backup" technique, which involves hardware processing to account for the duration and overlapping between the speech and the breath noise (you are *backing up* through the breath-noise signals to return to the actual word boundary, and the distance and time is *variable,* dependent on the sound of a word and the speech/breath relationship involved in its pronunciation).

A total of 512 bits of information are required to store the feature map, or reference pattern, for each utterance. In training the machine, the system extracts a feature-matrix for each repetition of a word. A consistent matrix of features is required before those features are stored in memory.

And a threshold factor is chosen, which means that a feature of voice being entered is considered valid only when it occurs a minimum number of times relative to the training samples.

Once the parameters of recognition are set, a spoken word is digitally compared with each reference-matrix. Similarities and dissimilarities are appropriately weighted, and the stored reference word producing the highest overall correlation is selected as correct—provided, of course, that it exceeds the minimum threshold value.

Inadvertent message entry is prevented both by the fact that the words in the limited system vocabulary are not generally used in ordinary conversation and also by formatting the data-entry

With headset on, programmer Ed Thayer selects data from part print and enters machining steps; prompter display at right is asking for part coordinates

Acramatic two-axis NC directs boring bar moving in to finish-machine hot-rolled steel tubing that has been welded to the workpiece plate

sequences so that, after a block of data has been entered, a verification word is required before the entry is considered valid by the speech-recognition system.

Software helps preparation

But back to programming NC tapes. After Thayer selects a postprocessor for the machine that the part will be run on and retrieves his voice reference, he then keys the command "IN," which means that data is to be entered, and begins to give the vocabulary and information appropriate to the part and its machining steps (see AM—Feb'80,p125 for an example of an interactive "conversation" between the programmer and the VNC).

As the data is entered, the entries appear on the CRT, and verification commands necessary for the prompter to move to the next step help the programmer to check what he is doing. A plotter provides an added visual verification of the part-program; scaling of particular sections permits close examination of complex or intricate cuts.

Recent innovations by Threshold allow words to be entered at rates of up to 180 per min, more than fast enough for programming situations. When all the material has been entered and checked, a tape is ready to be punched. The part-program can also be stored on a 10-megabyte disk, and a line printer provides added verification and a hard copy of the program.

Thayer makes extensive use of the VNC's software features to prepare Plainville's tapes. For example, he uses a program called Sysmac: essentially, macroprogramming.

"I enter certain 'arguments' into the computer, such as speed, Z data, and so forth. Then I can call them out when I want them repeated; it saves my having to call up some 6-7 lines of information, and it eliminates mistakes you could make by leaving out some G or M functions, since less information has to be put into sequence."

Pattern storage is another feature he uses often. For, say, a set series of holes, a pattern can be stored. Then such codes as tool, feedrate, speed, and other variables can be entered as needed, and the pattern is called up to define the configuration.

Offsetting allows, for example, the same slots or milled pockets to be machined in varying locations by offsetting the X and Y coordinates. Vertical-to-horizontal movement can also be effected by calling for a 90° rotation of the pattern.

Thayer found this particularly useful for a part being produced on a machining center at the plant. The workpiece was the same size as the width of the table, and the full machining width of the table was required for the necessary operations to be completed.

He brought the tape back into his office, meanwhile instructing the machinist to flip the part on its side with a crane hoist. "I pulled out all the sources, the X, Y, I, and J values, and used the 90°-rotation command to turn them. By the time the machinist had flipped the

part, I was walking out with the edited tape to finish the job."

The editing capability makes his work a lot easier, Thayer points out. "In one line, I can tell the VNC to 'mass-edit,' say, all of the feeds throughout the program. Also, if I realize, 'hey, I should have done *this* operation first,' then I can move a group of lines to another location."

Interestingly, the programmer doesn't do a tape check on some 25% of his parts; he just sends the tape to the machine and lets it go. Both his experience and the extensive verification procedures within the system permit that, he explains. Running the part-program tapes without verification checks saves a lot of time.

MIS capability

Thayer is extremely pleased with the unit and honestly admits to considering it a "toy," although, in the same breath, he characterizes it as a significant production tool. He estimates, that, on the average, he now makes tapes 50% faster than previously. This is very important, not only for the productivity increase but also because Thayer has supervisory duties. Additionally, a part-time worker who had typed in the earlier, manually prepared programs has been transferred to other work.

He describes programming by voice as "relaxed, very natural. I don't have to look away from the print, and, when I was writing the tape manuscripts before, my mind was always one line ahead of my actions. Now I move much quicker, and with less chance of error."

Threshold's support services are very helpful, he adds. In addition to a training session, the supplier provides a disk change twice a year, and "they're always updating down there."

The VNC-200 incorporates a Data General Nova 3 minicomputer, with 32k-word memory expandable to 128k words. Combined with the 10-megabyte disk storage, it makes a lot of processing power available to the user.

Threshold, in fact, now calls the unit a manufacturing-control system, to distinguish it from more-dedicated, microprocessor-based tape-preparation systems. The firm offers such optional software as real-time reports on new orders, work-in-process tracking, analyses and reports on finished-goods inventory, accounts payable and receivable, and payroll. (The Nova minicomputer is programmed in FORTRAN.)

Plainville is considering the wider aspects of a management-information system, but, for now, the VNC is dedicated to preparing tapes for its NC machines. ∎

Machining new life into jet engines

A computer-controlled machining center demonstrates its speed and versatility in this jet-turbine-rebuilding operation at Eastern Airlines

Rebuilding jet-engine parts, we've found, is one of those jobs that seem to have been made for computer numerical control. Each part we work on may be a little different from the last, even though they are of the same type. Some require more metal replacement than others, and some are warped or bent slightly out of line. Accommodating these variations through simple editing procedures and skip sequencing is the forte of the newest addition to our shop: an Ex-Cell-O Workcenter 408 controlled by a Bendix System 5 CNC.

The parts we're rebuilding are from the Pratt & Whitney JT8D engines used on some of our aircraft here at Eastern

By Ted W. Davidson
Project technical specialist
Eastern Airlines Inc, Miami, Fla

Airlines. The engines are rebuilt at our Engine Service Center in Miami, where we have responsibility for maintaining 750 JT8D and Rolls Royce RB211 engines used in Eastern's aircraft and where we also service and repair parts for engines of 14 other airlines. Compressor stators, gearbox housings, and housing covers are typical of the parts we rebuild.

Weld metal restores surfaces

Each of these parts goes through a careful inspection procedure; then, if it's acceptable for rebuilding, it gets a weld-metal buildup on the worn surfaces and is machined back to its original dimensions. We did the machining on a shopful of conventional machine tools before we got our machining center, and some of the parts, such as the gearbox housing, had to be refixtured several times on different machines. The housing was

worked on a radial drill, a jig grinder, and three different milling machines—a process that demanded 0.0003-in. tolerances and required 36 hours of machining time. Clearly, there had to be a better way.

A better way, we felt, would be a numerically controlled machining center, one that would hold the tolerances we need, accurately locate workpieces, and handle a large number of tools automatically. Repeatable accuracy was a key requirement, since, in our business, a scrapped workpiece means more than wasted material; it means the loss of an expensive machined part. And a versatile control, one that would allow us to adjust the basic program to the needs of a particular workpiece, was essential.

One particular gear housing, for example, might require a few machining steps or more than two dozen, depending

Newest addition to Eastern's 'fleet' has a rotary pallet changer for fast part changeover

Compressor stator, gearbox housing, and cover are currently machined on the Workcenter. DC-9 longerons (left) and other parts are candidates

Back-boring bar indexes radially, permitting automatic insertion of tool

on how much rebuilding the part needed. If we let the whole program run on a part that needed machining on only a few surfaces, the machine would spend a large part of its time machining air.

Skip sequencing was vital

The control we needed would allow us to program the steps separately and skip over the ones we didn't need, without having to rewrite the whole program or punch a new tape. And it would have to allow quick editing of the program in order to accommodate those workpieces that are slightly warped or bent in noncritical dimensions.

The Ex-Cell-O 408 we purchased meets our requirements for workpiece capacity and accuracy. Our machine has 48 in. x 48 in. x 36 in. X, Y, and Z travel, enough to handle our largest pieces in one loading. Automatic leadscrew compensation, one of the options we ordered with the machine, gives us the locating accuracy we need in certain operations.

Other options were specified to help reduce setup and machining times. These included a rotary pallet changer, which enables us to load a second part while another part is being machined; a 48-station tool conveyor; fixture offset on all three linear axes; and a special mist-coolant nozzle. A precision presetter, which accurately sets tool lengths and diameters before the tools are placed in the automatic toolchanger, was ordered as an accessory.

The control we ordered with the machining center has the features and capabilities we were looking for. This unit, the Bendix System 5, has enough memory to store complete part-programs, which is the key to achieving the flexibility needed in our application. It is equipped with a CRT that shows program and tool position, and it has the ability to skip sequence. Combined, these three

features provide quick access to any part of the program for editing or for bypassing unwanted operations. One special programming twist was necessary to take full advantage of these capabilities: those operations we wanted to be able to isolate, and skip if necessary, had to be programmed as a unit, with all required toolchanges occurring within that program segment. Usual programming practice would be to perform all operations with one tool before going on to the next.

Our machining personnel were involved with the machining center since early in the purchase decision and, before we accepted the machine, went through a training program—with great interest and cooperation—conducted by the builder at our Service Center. During that time, we went through runoff and accepted the machine two months after delivery.

89% of machining time saved

Here's how the machine handles that gear-housing job:

The tower-shaft snout is first bored with a hollow mill, then further machined and finished with five other hollow, end, and form mills. Dimensions are held to ±0.001 in.

Following the installation of the oil-pump-cavity liner, the liner is bored to remove 0.030 in. of stock.

The main oil-screen cavity is milled and bored, then the oil-screen stud holes are drilled and tapped.

The rear bearings for the starter-drive gearshaft, the gearbox-drive gearshaft, the main accessory drive, the fuel-pump-drive gearshaft, and the accessory-drive gearshaft, as well as the upper bearing liner of the gearbox-drive shaft, are all machined and finished to ±0.0003 in.

All together, 28 steps, using the same number of different tools, are used to

machine this part. The whole job takes four hours, 89% less time than it used to, and accuracy is excellent.

The machine's part-locating ability is put to the test on another job: machining the stators for the JT8D engine. This operation has always been an especially tough one to do with manually controlled machine tools. A total of 51 antirotation and locating slots are equally spaced around the circular stators, and each one must be precisely located and finish machined to a ±0.003-in. tolerance. This job used to take 8-12 hours, but now it's completed almost as fast as the machine table can index. Leadscrew compensation gives us dependable accuracy (we've checked it with a laser), and machining time is reduced to seven minutes.

Besides the slots, we machine the vane roots on these parts to ±0.002-in. tolerances and finish the inner air-seal ring. Total machining time for the part has been pared to 75 minutes from the 16-20 hours it took before.

The machining center is now performing a total of over 50 separate machining operations on five different JT8D engine parts made of a variety of materials: carbon and alloy steels, stainless, titanium, and aluminum and magnesium alloys. And we're working on programs to machine the diffuser, inner combustion case, front fan case, turbine-stator support, and six sizes of rings and seals for the stator, in addition to the parts already described. We haven't overlooked the possibility of making new parts on the machine, either; manufacturing DC-9 longerons is one such job that is under consideration.

We'll be turning more jobs over to our new machining center, and, judging from its performance so far, we anticipate that our Workcenter 408 will pay for itself within a year. ∎

Grind end mills with 8-axis NC

One setup and one wheel are all that's required for grinding flutes, gash, end teeth, and OD—including both primary and secondary reliefs—with 8-axis CNC grinder

More cutter life per grind, more grinds per tool, improved surface finish on milled parts, and improved utilization of multispindle machines as a result of more uniform tool life are some of the benefits Rohr Industries has cashed in on with an eight-axis end-mill-grinding machine operated by a computerized numerical control system. One quick example: the company has cut end-mill inventories from 50,000 to 25,000.

Automation of end-mill regrinding is expected to save Rohr more than $180,000 a year—easily justifying the purchase of a CNC machine tool with a base price of about $180,000.

Rohr's installation is, in fact, the first anywhere of a Huffman Model HS-4 NC grinder. Developed by S.E. Huffman Corp (Clover, SC), the HS-4 is capable of grinding the flutes of an end mill, gashing the end teeth, relieving the end teeth (primary and secondary), chamfering or radiusing the corner (up to a full ball-end configuration), and relieving the outside diameter (again both primary and secondary). It can do all this in a single setup and without changing the grinding wheel. Further, all of this is accomplished with preprogrammed speeds and feeds to precisely controlled geometry under flood coolant—the operator doesn't have to see what's going on—yielding a better finish on the tool being ground, with increased wheel life, and in reduced grinding time.

CNC controls eight axes

The complexity of end-mill grinding—actually the HS-4 is capable of working on a wide variety of cutting tools—is demonstrated by the fact that the Huffman machine provides eight axes of full numerical control, plus two more of manual adjustment. Five of the NC axes are linear and three are rotary; both manual adjustments are rotary. Axis nomenclature is standard, though somewhat difficult to visualize because of the machine's capability to rotate several of the linear axes out of their "standard" orientation.

Mounted on a horizontal slide atop a vertical column, the wheelhead is provided with three NC axes and one adjustment (Fig 2). The Y-axis is the horizontal slide, providing 12 in. motion in and out toward the work. The vertical Z-axis provides 10 in. of up and down motion to the wheelhead, which is mounted on a rotary b-axis that gives full 360° rotation in a vertical plane perpendicular to the Y-axis. The column itself can be adjusted ±45° about its vertical axis.

Five NC axes articulate the workholder. Fixed to the machine base is the X-axis, with 12 in. of horizontal travel perpendicular to the Y-axis (at its zero rotary adjustment). Mounted on the X-slide is a rotary table (c-axis) providing +40° (away from the wheelhead) and −160° of rotation. On top of the rotary is a horizontal table-and-saddle arrangement for U- and V-axes, U giving 12 in. of motion parallel to X (at zero, of course) and V 8-in. perpendicular to U. Mounted on top of the V-axis is a trunnion (manually adjustable ±20° for tilt) that carries the workholder, which itself provides the a-axis rotation and indexing of the end mill being ground.

All linear slides are solid cylindrical bars with preloaded ball-type bushings and are driven by preloaded recirculating ballnut leadscrews. Resolution of

1. Complete grinding of an end mill is possible in a single setup and without any change of wheel on CNC grinder. A 1-in., four-flute mill takes 6 min

By Hal Kasten
Manager, manufacturing engineering
Rohr Industries Inc, Chula Vista, Calif

these axes is 0.0001 in., and feedrates range from 0 to 150 ipm (programmable directly in ipm). Rotary-axis resolution is 0.01°, and rotary feedrates are programmable from 0° to 1224° per min. Closed-loop dc servos power all axes.

Coordinating the motions of this complex geometry is an Allen-Bradley 7320 computerized numerical control (CNC) system that is capable of simultaneous positioning of all eight axes, simultaneous contouring (linear interpolation) in all eight axes, and switchable-plane circular interpolation in X-Y, Y-Z, or X-Z with simultaneous linear motion of the third axis.

Other features of the CNC unit include program-storage and -edit capability (32k memory with battery backup), cathode-ray-tube (CRT) readout, inch/millimeter capability (selected by g-code), compensation for leadscrew and reversal errors, backlash takeup, cutter compensation, and fixture offsets that provide a compensation system for grinding-wheel wear.

The 2-hp wheel spindle is direct-driven by a self-contained ac motor hooked up to a solid-state variable-frequency power converter providing continuously variable spindle speeds from 720 to 7200 rpm. With a 6-in. grinding wheel (wheels from 1 in. to 8 in. can be mounted), this provides peripheral speeds of 1130 to 11,300 sfm.

Quick-change adapters are used in the workholder, and tools to be ground are preset in the adapters off the grinding machine so that spindle downtime is minimized. Normal time to change end mills in the workholder is 15-30 seconds.

Shanks from 1/16 in. dia to 2 5/32 in. dia can be accommodated. Cutters up to 12 in. dia are within the machine's capacity, with a maximum overall length of 20 in., a maximum flute length of 12 in. for square-end cutters, and a maximum flute length of 6 in. plus the radius for ball-end cutters.

Stan Huffman, president of S.E. Huffman Corp, credits the long-wearing properties of cubic-boron-nitride abrasive grit—General Electric's Borazon—with making the CNC grinder practicable. The minimal wear of Borazon wheels in grinding high-speed-steel cutting tools—aluminum-oxide and silicon-carbide wheels wear 20-30 times as fast, Huffman states—ensures holding tool geometry very precisely throughout the complete grinding of an end mill because the change in grinding-wheel geometry is minimal. "We can hold concentricity within 0.0002 in. on a given end mill," he notes. And the same factor greatly simplifies the problems of wheel-wear compensation.

Dish-shaped wheels are used with a 30° angle at the periphery and with a 1/2-in. or 1-in. width of abrasive on the periphery. The wheels used at Rohr are Borazon CBN Type II, 180-grit, 100-concentration, resin-bond wheels with a 6-in. diameter. Diamond wheels can be used for grinding solid-carbide end mills. At present, Rohr is running the Borazon wheels at 55% of maximum spindle speed, or about 3960 rpm and 6200 sfm. Investigation of grinding performance at the machine's higher spindle speeds is a future project.

Software is available and is being expanded. The postprocessor, written in FORTRAN IV and occupying about 100k of memory, is currently available for use on IBM 360 and 370, Minneapolis Honeywell 6000/66, and Univac 1108 computers—either in-house or time-shared. It is currently being implemented on a 16k minicomputer with peripheral disk memory. Discussions are also currently under way with Manufacturing Data Systems Inc (MDSI) on implementation in the COMPACT II system.

End mills, of course, constitute a definite family of parts, and family part-programming is used to simplify the job of producing tapes for the eight-axis machine. With this technique, the programmer's job is largely one of putting specific numbers to the geometric variables of an end mill—there are about two dozen, such as diameter, flute length and helix angle, end radius, and the various relief angles—and to several setup and wheel variations.

To simplify the user's programming task still further, Huffman supplies three grinding tapes with the machine—one each for a square-end, radiused, and ball-end end mill—and will quote on supplying others. One Huffman-supplied tape is programmed for a 1-in. end mill, right-hand helix, 29.5°, right-hand cut, 2-in. length of cut, 12° rake, with end teeth, two flutes to center and two off-flutes, with 10° primary relief and 20° secondary. Surface finish on the primary is guaranteed to 16 μin. on M42 steel. Total grinding time for this program is about six minutes.

Rohr's initial investigation of numerically controlled end-mill grinding was with a Huffman HS-1 grinder while the HS-4 was still under development. The HS-1 provided seven NC axes with two hard-wired GE Mark Century 550 NC systems, one a four-axis contouring unit that controlled the actual grinding operations, the other a three-axis control primarily for positioning the end mill with respect to the grinding wheel.

Primary objective of the NC end-mill-grinding project was to extend the life of end mills by flute-sharpening rather than by OD grinding. This was quite successful, extending the regrind life typically from about eight resharpenings up to as many as 27. Excluding cases of severely chipped cutters and depending on the size of the wear-land to be removed, diameter reduction of flute-ground end mills, in some cases, ranges from unmeasurable to about 0.0008 in.

But, as the company became more

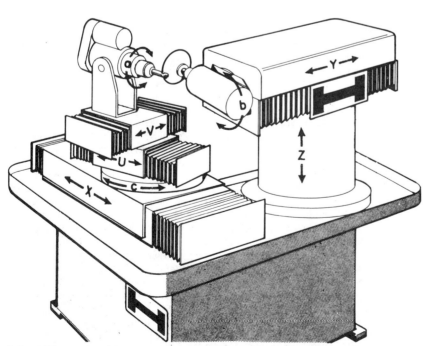

2. In addition to the eight axes under numerical control, there are two axes of manual adjustment: ±20° tilt of the end mill and ±45° of the Z-axis column

3. Among the advantages of NC-grinding of end mills is the ability to do the job under flood coolant

aware of the accuracies and capabilities of the grinder and its Borazon wheels, objectives were revised to include the total grinding of end mills. The company is now purchasing (at 60% of the cost of ground cutters) blanks that are made of M42 cobalt high-speed steel, have been milled and heat treated, and have had the shanks ground.

A blank is put in a toolholder, and the toolholder, in turn, is placed in the presetting fixture. Tool length and radial flute position must be correctly set in order to grind a quality end mill, and this is virtually the only operator-controlled function that is at all critical. After presetting, end mills are checked for runout, with ±0.0005 in. the maximum permissible. The company has two sets of toolholders to allow time for presetting the next blank while the machine is in its grinding cycle.

After insertion of the end mill into the quick-change holder on the HS-4, the operation is fully automatic. Flutes are ground; end-teeth are gashed and given both primary and secondary relief; radius or chamfer is ground; and both primary and secondary relief are ground on the OD. Flood coolant is used (Huffman recommends Shell's Garia D, a heavy-duty sulfochlorinated mineral oil), and there is no heat buildup in the

end mill; even immediately after grinding, it's possible to hold one in your hand with no discomfort whatsoever.

Grinding is always away from the cutting edge, which produces a better edge and avoids "pulling heat out to the cutting edge." Surface finish on the Rohr-ground end mills is between 8 and 16 µin., eliminating any need for hand polishing the flutes of end mills to be used for machining titanium.

Accuracy and repeatability are excellent. Helix angles are within 0.01°; tooth-to-tooth indexing is within 5 min (arc); runout between cutting edges and shanks is held to 0.0002 in. to 0.0005 in.; and diameters are held to within 0.0005 in.

Tool life is improved

The HS-4-ground end mills are yielding significantly improved tool life per sharpening. In machining 4340 and D6AC steels, the Rohr-ground tools are outlasting purchased end mills by a factor of four to one. Tool life in machining titanium has been doubled. And, in milling Inconel, the Rohr-ground tooling equals the tool life of any end mill the company has used.

Most of the machining of these metals at Rohr is done on two- and four-spindle machines, which demands the use of matched sets of cutters—new or re-

ground. Reduced diameter reductions as a result of flute sharpening have allowed Rohr to overcome problems in this area, and the close repeatability of NC grinding has provided improved performance in multispindle milling.

Rohr's NC cutter-grinding capability also opens up the possibility of using nonstandard end-mill geometry, which it has done so far in only one aspect, OD relief. Instead of the conventional primary and secondary, the company is now grinding its end mills with eccentric radial relief. This provides a slightly stronger cutting tooth, results in a better surface finish on the mill's OD, and eliminates two grinding operations (the roughing and finishing of the secondary relief). Together with flute grinding, this method has also helped to cut down on the diameter reduction in resharpening cutters.

Although this is Rohr's only departure from conventional end-mill geometry so far, further modifications are in the cards—for test purposes at least. The current helix angle, for example, is 27°, but the company wants to know whether 25°, 29°, or 32° might yield improvement. Another question still to be answered is whether 6° eccentric relief would be better for cutting Inconel than the present company standard of 7.5°. ■

On-line computer aids manufacturing

**From order entry through manufacturing to customer service,
this on-line computer system helps hold down costs
and boosts productivity by providing up-to-date information**

Successful injection molding depends almost exclusively on correct setup of the many variables that control the process, such as heat, time, fill cycle, etc. Often it is considered a form of black magic, relying on the experience or, rather, the memory of the operator. When factors affecting the parameters change, it can spell trouble. Littlefuse Inc (Des Plaines, Ill), a manufacturer of electronic products, has found a way to prevent such trouble.

When it is time to set up a new production run, an operator makes a simple entry on a computer terminal near the work station, immediately gets a printed process sheet for the part to be produced, and quickly sets up the machine, following precise instructions for materials and process steps.

The information from this process sheet is always the most current, even though material or routing changes might have been made only a short time before. In that event, company engineers would have entered the change via on-line terminals to quickly update the product-structure and routing files.

Costs are held down

On-line computer applications like these are helping to hold down costs and boost productivity in Littlefuse manufacturing operations. They are among many advanced applications in the firm's comprehensive data-processing system, which lends strong support, both in the plant and in the front office, to a fast-paced, diversified business.

Littlefuse is a subsidiary of Tracor Inc and the largest of that corporation's components group, which enjoyed sales last year of more than $63-million. It operates four manufacturing plants in Illinois and one in Mexico, producing a sophisticated and diverse product line, including a variety of fuses, switches, indicator lights, buzzers and flashers, TV components, appliance relays, and fuse-mounting accessories.

Host computer for Littlefuse's data-processing system is an IBM System/370 Model 138. Linked to the computer for on-line data processing and information exchange are some 30 visual display

Operator inspects parts from injection molding machine that is set up using process sheet generated by on-line computer terminal nearby. Information is always up-to-date

Stockroom clerk uses an on-line terminal to create a move ticket. The system tracks materials moved from receiving dock to stockrooms and to the various work stations

On-line computer aids manufacturing

terminals, several printer terminals, and data-collection units out on the shop floor. The system is, as data-processing director Bill Masloske puts it, "involved in virtually every aspect of our manufacturing business, saving time, trouble, and money and contributing to both better management and better customer service."

The system begins where business begins: with customer orders. Incoming orders, about half by telephone, are entered on-line, totally bypassing keypunching and speeding orders into the manufacturing cycle swiftly and accurately. Order entries, which average about 250 a day, are handled by two employees. Actual order-entry time, including the validation of customer and product numbers and a check for stock availability, has been halved with the on-line terminals.

Improved customer service

Customer service is better because of the system in other ways than swift order entry. Service personnel using the on-line CRTs can determine in moments, for example, whether a product a customer is inquiring about is available from stock. "This is a big plus, because much of our sales volume moves through distributors. We sell to them mostly off-the-shelf from inventory, which makes fast information about stock availability the name of the game," notes Paul Miresse, distributor-sales manager.

However, Littlefuse also does a lot of business with OEM accounts, and here, too, the on-line system's customer-service advantages are very important. Customer-service people can quickly answer a customer's order-status inquiry, for instance, by accessing the active order file via a terminal. This is done by keying in either the customer's own purchase-order number or the Littlefuse manufacturing-order number, which brings up a terminal-screen display, including full order details: parts, quantities, specifications, quantities shipped and pending, and shipment dates and modes.

Customer-service personnel also have terminal access to information on any of the company's 4600-plus distributor and OEM customers. In addition to customer names, billing and shipping addresses, and identification-code numbers, this information includes the customer's recent purchase history and credit limits. Incidentally, customer payments are applied on-line as received, thereby ensuring that up-to-date payment status is always available when a terminal inquiry is made.

"Ours is a dynamic business, and our customers usually need information in a hurry," Miresse points out. "The on-line system ensures that they get information fast and that the information is current and accurate. In addition, the system has clamped a lid on what had been fast-rising costs of customer service. Although our business has been growing by 50%, our customer service staff has only grown by 10%."

Contributions of the system to order entry and customer service are important and impressive, company officials admit. However, they are even more impressed with the advantages the system brings to manufacturing-related functions. "All facets of manufacturing, from materials-requirements planning (MRP) to finished-product costing, benefit from the on-line data processing and ready information," declares Charley McNerney, production and materials manager.

"The key factor here is the ability to continually update our product structure and to route database information on-line as changes occur," McNerney explains. "Because of this, all manufacturing departments and functions now draw upon the same, single, always-up-to-date and accurate information source regarding materials used and process steps required to produce any given Littlefuse product. Any user in any manufacturing-related function can, at any time, utilize the on-line terminals to obtain process-sheet information anytime they need it."

This is quite an achievement, McNerney notes. "We have some 16,000 process sheets (materials, routings, and operations sequences) to cover our extensive product line, and we used to have a lot of problems keeping them all current for all manufacturing departments. In fact, process-sheet data used by one department was rarely identical with that used by another department, and the data was not always consistent with the materials and process steps in actual use.

"The on-line system has totally eliminated problems like these. Now, when a bill of materials or a shop routing or a process-sequence change is required, as they repeatedly are, our engineers use their terminals to enter the change, and the change is reflected throughout the product structure and routing file the same day the change is made. It used to take ten days or more for this to happen," McNerney emphasizes.

Once the change is in the system, the updated process-sheet data is available via terminal inquiry wherever it is needed. How important is this? Consider the setup for a production run of one of the Littlefuse injection-molding machines. "These machines are vital to plant performance and productivity,"

says McNerney, "and setting one up to run a job is anything but simple. Critical variables of pressure and temperature settings, cycle times, and curing sequences must be taken into consideration, and these machine adjustments change as materials and/or process steps change.

"With the current process-sheet information readily available from the printer/terminal on the shop floor, the operator has no trouble making those critical machine adjustments. Machine setup is faster, and the production run is smoother as a result. In effect, the system controls the production environment for each job and lets us use the injection-molding machines the most efficiently," he sums up.

Process-sheet data is only one of the invaluable information flows supported by the on-line system. Another is cost-bulletin data. Product-structure and -routing changes inevitably trigger changes in the material and production cost of a product. Indeed, it is more often than not the other way around: changes in materials costs and inherent economies in changing product routings, as well as associated process steps, trigger changes in materials purchases and process sequences.

Whichever way it occurs, changes affecting costs occur so frequently that Littlefuse is forced to revise some 100 cost bulletins every day. "Our ability to display cost bulletins on-line saves a great deal of paper and printing time, not to mention filing of all this paper, and makes retrieval of cost data much easier and faster for our cost-accounting department," says Phil Blake, the company's assistant controller. "More important, we have much tighter control over cost changes, and everyone is alert to the current cost situation," he adds.

System prints move tickets

Still another important contribution of the system is on-line data collection, which records all raw-material movement, keeping inventory status current with plant performance. This recording of material is comprehensive, starting with the receipt of purchased materials at the plant receiving dock. It then records movement from the stockrooms to work stations, printing move tickets on-line as the transfers occur.

"In a business like ours, with its diversity of materials, process steps, and products and its strenuous service demands, assistance from the on-line computer system has become indispensable," states data-processing director Masloske. "The system is paying big dividends for Littlefuse now, and we expect it to continue to pay big dividends." ∎

NC router and CAM cut cost

Computer-aided manufacturing methods and a revolutionary approach to routing stacked sheetmetal parts make great improvements over existing line

Operator inspects part produced on DNC routing/drilling/riveting machine. Stack of nested parts is held with rivets that are removed after drilling and routing

For a long time, production engineers at McDonnell Aircraft division of McDonnell Douglas Corp (St Louis, Mo) were unable to justify replacing the manual routing of sheetmetal parts with numerical control. Not that they didn't carefully scrutinize the possibility. After all, McDonnell Douglas has always kept up with the latest in machine-tool technology, particularly as it applies to NC, and sports one of the earliest and most extensive DNC (direct numerical control) facilities, bar none.

"In fact, we frequently studied the feasibility of NC routing over the past eight or ten years," says Richard F. Mueller, branch manager of equipment and process engineering at McDonnell Aircraft. "We kept looking at our manual routing operation and thinking that there must be a way to apply NC. But, for years and years, we felt that we couldn't justify the relatively high cost of an NC router or the programming time, considering the relatively short time required for machining individual sheetmetal parts." Besides, the manual routing operation was arranged like an assembly line and, therefore, was already extremely efficient.

No time for programming

In typical aircraft profiling work, where NC machining has been so prominent, it may take anywhere from 10 to 100 or more hours to machine the part, and, therefore, a reasonable amount of programming time can be justified. "But, when it takes only a few minutes to rout a whole stack of sheetmetal parts, you can't afford much programming

time," Mueller points out. "You might spend as much on programming as would be required to do the manual routing on all the parts required for an entire lot."

The introduction of computer-aided manufacturing (CAM) technology has changed all that. Now the required data is digitized from master templets or drawings, an appropriate nest of parts is automatically arranged with the aid of interactive computer graphics, and a control program for NC machining of the entire nest of parts is automatically generated through special software. Future plans are for direct access to the engineering database, entirely eliminating the digitizing process and the need for master templets.

New router is key

A key to the application of such CAM technology to the manufacture of aircraft sheetmetal parts at McDonnell Aircraft is the introduction of a new DNC routing/drilling machine that provides a revolutionary approach to NC routing of stacked aluminum sheets. McDonnell Aircraft's Trumpf Trumatic Model 3000

BFZ CNC drilling and milling center is the first such machine in operation in the US and the second ever built—number one went to a small aircraft company in Switzerland. The machine, first demonstrated at IMTS-78 before delivery to McDonnell (AM—Sep'78,p191), eliminates much of the manual labor previously associated with the routing operations and provides an effective work center for a DNC hookup.

The parts under consideration are what McDonnell engineers sometimes refer to as pork-chop shaped—relatively small flat patterns in any alloy of aluminum sheet in either the O or T condition. They range in thickness from about 0.020 to ⅛ in., and the majority will fit onto an 8½ x 11-in. sheet. Typically, these parts become interior structural details, such as ribs or framers making up the shell of an airplane. They are usually formed after being routed and, therefore, contain various pilot and tooling holes to work with the forming dies.

Parts routed in stacks

An ever-changing array of such parts is required during the production run of

For manual routing, stacks of blanks, each with its drilling templet or routing block, are mounted down on plywood backing plate for travel to drillpress and router

Operator uses overhead-arm router on nest of stacked parts. Stacks are held to ⅜-in. height, and reach is limited to prevent excessive operator fatigue

any particular aircraft. The chances that the same group of parts is required over again are very small—each release of parts brings a new grouping. But individual parts are made in multiples, and practice is to stack-rout as many parts as are practical. This holds true for both the manual and the new DNC routing operation. But, from there on, the methods differ drastically.

For manual routing, the maximum stack height is about ⅜ in. A greater stack height is precluded because it would cause excessive operator fatigue. The Trumatic can handle stack heights up to ½ in. The manual routing operation has been organized around a palletized but relatively labor-intensive manufacturing line.

Sheet stock is first sheared into small rectangles that approximate the shapes to be cut. This stock preparation is performed in the stores department, and the blanks, with the appropriate drilling templets and router blocks, are delivered to the routing department, sorted by material type and thickness. The operator then chooses parts based on the production schedule and makes up a routing pallet.

Stacks are fixed to backup plate

Stacks of blanks are laid on a plywood or composition backing plate, and the matching drill templet is placed on top of each stack. The operator then fastens each stack, with its drilling templet, to the backing plate, using lag screws and toe clamps. This work is done at one end of a roller conveyor used to move the nested pallets first to the drilling station and then to the manual router.

Once all the tooling and pilot holes have been drilled, with the drilling templets used as a guide, these templets are removed and replaced with the appropriate router blocks, which are fastened to the backing plates with lag screws through the tooling holes.

The pallet of parts is then moved along the conveyor to the router, where the operator guides the overhead-arm routing head to follow the individual routing blocks that act as contour templets. The pallets are then rolled to an unload station, where an operator removes all the screws and clamps to release the parts. From there, the pallets are returned to the head of the line by a roller conveyor running underneath the production line.

The pallets are 4 x 6 ft, but only about ½ to ⅔ of the depth is used, because it was discovered to be difficult for operators to reach across a full 4-ft range and still have sufficient muscle power to operate the router properly. The line is very productive because all the setup work—mounting the stacked blanks with drill templets and routing blocks—is performed away from the drilling and routing stations, which can be kept busy on a continuous basis: while one operator loads or unloads the pallets, another can be drilling or routing. This highly production-oriented setup has been in use for about 20 years—a fairly efficient method for performing a manual operation, making justification of NC that much harder. But it involves a great deal of manual work.

No templets or router blocks

The new method eliminates the need for drill templets and router blocks and even does away with all the lag screws and clamps. There is also no need to prepare the rectangular blanks of material. Instead, large sheets of aluminum, either 4 x 6 ft or 2 x 6 ft, are used. In one setup, an aluminum baseplate is hydraulically clamped in the Trumatic's coordinate positioning system, and then several sheets—a stack up to ½ in. thick—are automatically riveted to the baseplate. The rivets are strategically placed to secure the entire nest of parts during the subsequent routing operations.

Once the sheets have been so secured, all the holes for the nested parts are drilled automatically. Then the outside or inside contours are routed as required. All these operations—the initial riveting, the drilling, and the routing—are performed under NC. Then, still under NC, the rivets securing the stacked parts to the baseplate are drilled out, and the parts are released.

The Trumatic 3000 BFZ is constructed more like an automatic punching or nibbling machine than like a conventional drilling/milling machine. No wonder, for that's what Trumpf does best. "Our original approach for improving the production of aircraft sheetmetal parts was rather standard practice for us: a combination of high-speed nibbling followed by a milling operation to achieve the necessary aircraft quality," recalls Phillip H. Haynes, vice president at Trumpf America Inc (Farmington, Conn) a wholly owned subsidiary of the German machine-tool builder. "That approach will make parts, but it's also rather slow."

A better way

Trumpf engineers decided that there must be a better way to utilize their existing technology for fast positioning of sheetmetal, such as is used on their punch-presses. "Being sheetmetal people, we have always moved the material rather than the cutter, as is done in more conventional gantry-type machines," remarks Haynes. The result is a

On either side of the central C-frame of the Trumatic BFZ 3000 is an integrally mounted fixed table to provide support for the moving stack of aluminum sheets

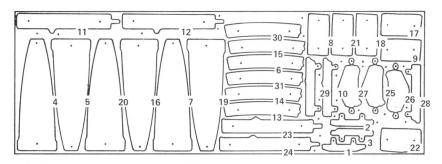

Typical nesting arrangement produced by computer graphics includes sequence of routing moves. Diverse path is intended to prevent buckling of stacked aluminum sheets

lightweight high-speed positioning system combined with a multiple-head work station to provide drilling, riveting, and milling functions under NC.

The machine frame is basically a C-shaped weldment that carries the various work stations (spindles and riveting device). Mounted in the throat of the machine is a cast-aluminum carriage that moves longitudinally to establish the machine's Y-axis. Mounted perpendicular to the carriage is a hardened and ground steel rail that moves transversely to establish the machine's X-axis. Both the carriage and the rail are supported and guided by five bearing points each. The throat, with its coordinate measuring system, is tilted 10° toward the front of the machine to assist in chip and scrap removal.

On either side of the central C-frame is an integrally mounted fixed support table, also tilted 10° forward, to provide support for the moving stack of aluminum sheets fastened to the positioning carriage. The table surfaces are constantly lubricated with a thin film of coolant under pressure so that the workpiece stack is, in effect, supported by a hydrostatic bearing.

The baseplate with its stack of aluminum sheets is fastened to the machine's

positioning carriage by six hydraulically operated clamps. Each clamp provides 1.5 tons of clamping force and adjusts automatically to any baseplate thickness. A manual, rack-and-pinion-operated manipulating device helps with alignment of the stack, prior to clamping.

The C-frame carries the following five work stations:

■ One routing spindle for cutters with a maximum diameter of 1.18 in. and an infinitely variable spindle speed of 3000 to 15,000 rpm.

■ One combination drilling and routing spindle for cutters with a maximum diameter of 0.3125 in. and drills with a maximum diameter of 0.413 in. and an infinitely variable spindle speed of 6000 to 18,000 rpm.

■ Two drilling spindles for drills with a maximum diameter of 0.42 in. and an infinitely variable spindle speed of 6000 to 18,000 rpm.

■ One riveting station with automatic feeding system for insertion and compression of 3/16-in.-dia aluminum rivets.

Each work station is provided with a "presser foot," which compresses the stacked sheets during drilling, routing, or riveting operations and thereby prevents the formation of burrs and keeps chips from being pushed between individual layers of the stack. The presser feet can also be used to hold the stack stationary while the clamping carriage is repositioned in order to provide an extended working range in the X-axis.

The machine is also equipped with an integral automatic chip conveyor for positive removal of chips. The chips are separated from the coolant and conveyed to a swarf box that comes with the machine.

As furnished by Trumpf, the BFZ 3000 came equipped with a Bendix System 5 CNC control unit. McDonnell Douglas, however, replaced this with its own Actrion III (specially modified for the company's DNC system), and future machines now on order are being furnished with these controls. "Our service record with Actrion units has been extremely good, and, considering the need to tie it in with our in-house-developed DNC system, we felt that it would be better to stick with a control with which we were thoroughly familiar," comments Mueller.

Nesting is automatic

NC-program development starts with arrangement of an appropriate nest of parts. This nesting is achieved by first loading the digitized data for individual parts into a database working in conjunction with a mainframe computer at McDonnell Douglas Automation (McAuto), the headquarters for all high-powered computers at the company. Production planners then access the nesting database through an IBM 2250 graphics terminal that displays a computer-generated nest intended to achieve maximum material utilization of the basic 4 x 6-ft sheet of aluminum.

The planner, using the graphics nesting processor (software), can get a reading of the actual material utilization and, if this falls below about 80-85%, will attempt to rearrange the nest better. Individual part outlines can be moved and rotated as desired, via light pen and associated function keys on the graphics terminal. The nesting software package will also automatically establish a preferred sequence of machining—the drilling and routing of all the parts in the nest and the necessary riveting pattern.

Once the planner is satisfied with the nest and the prescribed sequence of operations, a postprocessor run is invoked to convert the nesting data into an NC part-program for the entire nest.

Programs stored at host

The program is then stored in an object file at the host computer until it is required for manufacturing. At least 24 hours prior to the time it is needed to control the machine, the program is transferred to the IBM 1800 that acts as DNC computer. That data transfer takes about 5 min. Once the data is at the 1800, it is also instantly available at the IBM System 7 computers that perform the data transformations (interpolation and conversions) for the individual machines (each System 7 handles up to eight machines).

To bring the program to the System 7 for operating the Trumatic 3000 BFZ, the operator punches up the job-identification number for the nest to be routed. A voice communication link with the computer room is also available to the operator in case there is a problem or delay with the data transfer.

Everyone seems pleased with the new routing approach. McDonnell Douglas engineers figure that they have achieved a 4:1 improvement over the manual methods. Comparing the present method with a straightforward NC approach with individual programming for each part makes the advantages look even better: a nest of 50 parts takes about 1 hr of programming time; conventional programming might take as long as 2 hr to program an individual part.

And Trumpf reports that prospects for 1980 "look just excellent." Two additional machines for McDonnell Douglas Corp are scheduled for delivery before the end of the year, and machines have also been sold to Lockheed Aircraft Corp and Grumman Corp. ■

Six hydraulically operated clamps (cube-shaped units at left) are used to fasten the baseplate with its stack of aluminum sheets to the machine's positioning carriage

Operator changes tool at one of six working stations. Each station is provided with a presser foot, which compresses the stacked sheets during machining operation

Sculpting via computer optics

NC contouring of busts is the early, consumer application of Solid Photography, which acquires data about 3-D surfaces. Industrial on-line inspection jobs are next

In a back room at the Long Island plant of Solid Photography Inc, past rooms crammed with film-processing tanks, computers, specialized electro-optical equipment, and home-built numerically controlled milling machines, there is a studio where a dozen artists put finishing touches on individual pieces of machine-generated sculpture.

Most of the 100-or-so sculpted busts being worked on are one-of-a-kind, but there are several copies of a 10-in.-high head-and-shoulders sculpture of actor Telly Savalas, a demonstration bust used for studio display. "We're giving that one just a little bit more polishing," notes Arnold Weinstein, senior vice-president of Solid Photography Inc (SPI). The polishing, however, is merely cosmetic; the off-the-machine bust is perfectly recognizable.

Busts of people are far from the only items that can be replicated at SPI. Weinstein holds up an engine-exhaust manifold and a modified-hourglass NC proofing shape that had been milled out of the solid from data acquired by computer from a camera array. SPI recently installed a specialized 3-D inspection system that will check small diesel-engine blocks, and a modification of the Solid Photography process has been used to "photograph" the front end of a Volkswagen Beetle.

Subjects of the trademarked three-dimensional copying process—whether a person in the flesh or a plaster cast of an aircraft part—go through the same "sitting." At either of two studios in mid-Manhattan or in a shopping center in suburban Huntington, NY, subjects pose motionless for 0.9 second while series of linear light patterns are projected on them and special photographic equipment records their image from different

positions. Exposed film is shipped to the Solid Photography Inc plant in Melville, NY, where the replication process is performed.

After photographic processing with conventional equipment, the 35-mm-film reels are loaded into specially constructed scanning machines that optically encode portions of each photographic frame. Digital information from each frame is then fed into computers that match different views of the subject and synthesize the information into tool-path instructions used to program the milling machines.

In practice, most actual cutting is done in a substance SPI calls Paralene, an easily machined mixture of wax and plastic, although the shop has the capability to cut directly into metals and

stones. Machine sculpting is performed in a two-step roughing/finishing sequence for a Paralene figure that will be hand finished or used to form a casting mold for a more durable bust in bronze, pewter, cast marble, etc. For materials like solid marble, wood, and glass, which will bypass the casting step, machining is performed on a rigid, highly modified knee-type mill.

More than just figures of people

Most of the sculpting that the three machines currently perform is dedicated to reproducing the human head. But Solid Photography, which has cost an estimated $5½-million in development money since SPI President and Chairman Paul DiMatteo began working on the technique in 1971, is also applicable to

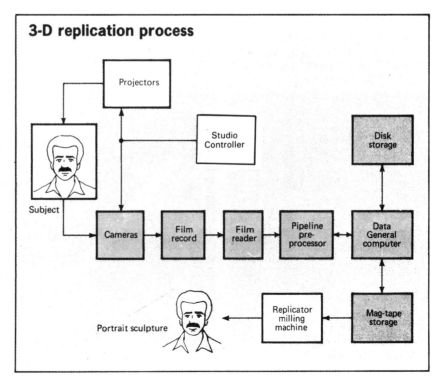
3-D replication process

Sculpting via computer optics

virtually any X-Y-Z shape, and the company is currently seeking to expand industrial, medical, scientific, and other uses of its proprietary electronic system.

Solid Photography Inc has worked with orthodontists and orthopedic surgeons in developing models of what a patient will look like after surgery and in creating molds for and actual parts of prosthetic devices. It has also copied a number of statues by famous artists.

A great many potential applications lie within industry. Generation of electrical-discharge-machining electrodes, casting molds, and prototype parts are all possibilities. Since it is relatively easy to electronically manipulate tool-path data to enlarge or reduce the finish-machined shape, models to be used for, say, wind-tunnel testing can be quickly manufactured.

Even without machining, there remains the important ability of a three-axis optical sensor to digitize a surface. This makes a potentially powerful tool for inspection, measurement, and incorporation into a hierarchical computer system for CAD/CAM.

Yet most of these industrial applications have been relatively underdeveloped in the brief history of the firm, the result of an initial concentration on consumer portraiture.

The application of machine technology to the creation of sculpted busts is far from new. Various attempts at using pantographic tracing devices to reproduce sculpture were made as far back as the early 17th century.

It was in 1804 that James Watt, whose steam-engine patent some 35 years prior had begun to revolutionize manufacturing, made the first of two proportional sculpting machines. That version rotated an original statue master between horizontal centers and traced it while a copy was made by a reciprocating cutting device that sliced into the workpiece. An improved version some five years later stood the master vertically and could duplicate statues in the same size.

Subsequent development by British inventor John Hawkins and his colleague Benjamin Cheverton and in France by inventor Achille Collas concentrated on pantographic tracing devices. Later, American sculptor Joel Tanner Hart's pointing machine (about 1852) held an array of more than 100 blunt pins, adjustable inward and out, to surround a model with what looked like a acupuncturist's fixture. When a model was extricated, the fixture could then be closed around a lump of soft clay, thereby imprinting 3-D shapes into the clay, which was then carved away. The process, called "spotting," was widely used in industry to make special cams.

Photo-sculpture, started in 1860 by Frenchman Francois Willeme, placed a subject in a circular room on a central platform surrounded by 24 cameras that snapped in unison. Each resulting photograph was traced in silhouette sequentially on a revolving clay block until all that was left to do was to smooth the sharp edges.

Still, the labor involved in photo-sculpture was no less than that required for an original work, observes art historian Michele Bogart, writing in last June's issue of *Smithsonian*, and the process—with a minor revival in 1921 by H.G. Edmunds—died out slowly.

Numerically controlled milling machines, capable of contouring in multiple axes, may have eliminated most of the manual effort in sculpting objects out of the solid, but there remains a series of steps necessary for programming it. What the Solid Photography process does is to streamline those steps via a computer.

Solid Photography Inc started in 1971 as a division of its then parent company, Dynell Electronics Corp, a small aerospace firm organized by DiMatteo and Weinstein in 1960. Dynell unveiled its proprietary division, called "Project East/West," in mid-1976 and subsequently set up a studio in New York City for photographing posed subjects (AM—Apr'77,p35). In late 1977, Dynell merged with the Norden Div of United Technologies, and Solid Photography Inc was spun off as an independent corporation. A $2-million loan from United Technologies went a long way toward capitalizing the infant company.

Computerized 3-D measurement

Solid Photography is distinct from stereoscopic photogrammetry, a process traditional in aerial reconnaissance and mapping of contours. Simply stated, that process extracts 3-D information about an object from a set of photographs of that object. Photos are taken from at least two vantage points, and the data observed in each of these two-dimensional photos is reduced into data of the actual three-dimensional object.

Close-range stereo photogrammetry of the human body has been performed manually for the past 11 years by a team of doctors led by Dr Robin Herron at Baylor Medical School, Houston. A dot pattern is projected in horizontal bands on the body, and a pair of photographs are taken. Using conventional map-plotting instruments, the doctors work out a set of X-Y-Z coordinates that accurately describe the shape of a person's body. As a diagnostic technique, the doctors can

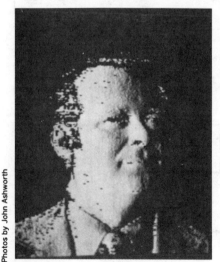

CRT display checks out computer-generated bust before cutting starts

Parallel light-beam sequence projects onto subject's face in rapid progression. Exposed frames of film from each camera are later read by computer scanner

Photos by John Ashworth

During fine-cutting, both ten-spindle toolheads sweep back and forth in X, cutting during each pass. Table indexes about 5° and moves up or down in Y about 1½ in. between passes. Each spindle contours independently, moving in and out in Z-axis

compare the "maps" of people over a period of time, and NASA has used the technique to study the effect of extended weightlessness on astronauts' physiques.

Solid Photography departs from conventional techniques, such as photogrammetry or optical ranging. It digitally encodes surface contours of the scanned object, providing *direct* readout of unambiguous X-Y-Z coordinates.

Where photogrammetry resolves the 3-D problem by parallax correction, SPI's process takes a different tack. The system uses film or direct video scan to record changes in projected light patterns that have known properties.

Subject sensors—cameras with associated projectors—can measure the X-Y-Z locus of all points within the field of view of a single lens. Multiple lenses acquire better resolution.

The portrait photographs are taken by a cluster of eight cameras and associated lighting equipment. The projectors throw changing stripe patterns of white light on the subject's face while each camera records coded photographic information on film. All of four quadrants are photographed simultaneously, compared with the 24 sections used by Willeme a century ago.

The original subject-sensor equipment made by SPI required the subject to remain motionless in a darkened room for 1.9 seconds while the camera and lighting equipment operated. Completed in 1976, its field vision is a cube measuring approximately 13 in. on edge, and the calculated resolution for the appara-

tus is better than 0.050 in. in each of the three axes.

A second-generation subject sensor encompasses a slightly larger field of vision, permits shorter (less than one second) exposure times, and has enhanced accuracy. Its camera array aims eight lenses: numbers 1, 2, and 3 are at the top, bottom, and middle of a stack that is 45° to the left of the subject's front; 4, 5, and 6 are to the right of the face; 7 and 8 are high-mounted and cover the right and left rear of the person's head and shoulders.

This apparatus, like the original, exposes photographic film, which then has to be "read" into a computer.

An alternative approach is to bypass the photographic stage with its requisite film processing and data transfer. This is the idea behind SPI's third-generation system, which includes solid-state TV cameras coupled directly to a high-speed processor that processes the data "on-site."

Direct processing is the technique used to check engine-block castings moving on a conveyor at Cummins Engine's diesel-engine foundry in Columbus, Ind.

Small-scale, large-scale

It's a relatively simple matter of arranging the photographic equipment to change the capability to see smaller or larger objects with proportional resolution. Although Solid Photography Inc's production-use subject sensors are tuned for objects the size of the human head, engineers there have also experimented

with microscopy and larger-image acquisition.

One array, consisting of two cameras and an associated projector, is manually operated and requires a 2-min exposure. This so-called micro sensor can view a cube measuring about 0.6 in. on edge to a resolution of 0.001 in. It can acquire information from one portion of the total subject at a time, with the subject mounted on a turntable or accurately translated before the cameras.

Another experimental camera system, called a macro sensor, can view objects measuring up to 10 ft on a side.

Output of photographic film that has been read by the optical digitizer (or direct output of the third-generation real-time TV system) is a stream of digital words representing the X, Y, and Z coordinates of the location of each surface-resolution element. For subjects that fill the entire viewing area, several hundred-thousand discrete surface-resolution elements are located.

Proprietary computer programs merge individual camera views into a composite database. The merging is crucial, says Senior VP Weinstein, to ensure that all quadrants meet at the same central apex, a vertical axis that runs through the center of the subject.

That stream of information is used to direct machine-tool movements. "The computers talk directly to the milling machines," says Weinstein. "We bypass conventional programming languages."

In production of a typical sculpted bust, a cylindrical block of Paralene is

203

Sculpting

mounted on the rotary table of an SPI-built rough-milling machine. A single horizontally mounted tapered endmill performs peripheral cutting on the workpiece. The crude approximation that is left is called a coarse cut and is transferred to a "fine-cut replicator," the next machine in the sequence.

20 spindles run simultaneously

The fine-cut machine, like the roughing machine, was built by SPI's machine shop. It consists of a fixed bed with a rotary table installed in the center of its square-shaped top. Two pairs of cylindrical ways, each pair with a central ballscrew, are located on either side.

Mounted on each pair of ways is a toolhead, and each toolhead holds ten thin tapered milling cutters.

Each of the 20 spindles is individually advanced in the Z-axis. As the rough-cut sculpture indexes through the rotary B-axis and is raised and lowered through Y, the cutter heads sweep back and forth in X, making many passes and removing small amounts of the workpiece in each pass. During a pass, each cutter contours through the 180° portion of the sculpture it sweeps past.

A third machine, heavily modified by SPI, is based on an Ex-cell-O knee-and-column milling machine and is used to replicate directly into metal, wood, and hard plastics. It is fitted with stepping motors and mounts a high-speed spindle or an ultrasonic machining head used for ceramic, glass, and stone.

When busts are unloaded from the 20-spindle machine or from the rigid knee-type mill, they are moved to the finishing room, where they are deburred, smoothed, or antiqued directly. Paralene sculptures may, depending on customer order, have a finish put directly on them, or they can serve as casting-mold masters.

At present, most of the price difference between sculptures is based on the extent of hand finishing. An unfinished wax bust in $\frac{1}{3}$ scale costs just under $100. At the pricey end of the scale, a full-size stainless-steel bust with a smooth facial finish is nearly $1400.

Most of the hand finishing work on statues goes toward artificially enhancing hair into the locks traditionally associated with sculpted busts.

Hair, lacking density, posed a problem for the sensing equipment. Now a computer algorithm effectively stretches an imagined cap over the hair outline without mussing the style.

It's unlikely that that particular algorithm will be used in industrial applications, however. Fortunately, not many machines grow hair, even though they may present "hairy" problems. ∎

1. All-aluminum, all-welded truck cab nears completion as welders join floor and upper section

Building aluminum truck cabs

**Ford's new all-aluminum, all-welded truck cabs are built
with the best available technologies — in material
selection, cleaning, forming, tooling, and assembly**

A new linehauler-truck cab, Ford's Model CL-9000, demonstrates how far the forming and welding of aluminum have progressed. Now moving off the assembly line at the Norwalk, Ohio, plant of Toledo's Sheller-Globe Corp, at better than 25 per shift, the cabs are the end product of research that has resulted in several technological "firsts":

■ A new high-style design that makes maximum use of extrusions and stampings for both structural and decorative functions. William P. Gobeille, Sheller-Globe's vice president of technical operations, says that this should boost the potential for lightweight transport vehicles. Energy-saving implications are obvious. Payload increases are substantial as a result of saving in cab weight.

■ Use of a new aluminum alloy for exterior body panels requiring severe draws. It was incorporated into the company's production operations on a demanding time schedule. An intensive materials-investigation program, in which the alloy was a key factor, ensured that every alloy proposed for the truck

Building aluminum truck cabs

cab had the desired forming properties and also met specifications for strength, surface finish, and weldability.

- Improved designs for tooling. Experience with steel forming was the base point from which successful modifications were made to form aluminum. It was pioneering, with a hefty trial-and-error component.

- A computer-controlled welding system, said to be the first of its kind, ensures a quality level so high that destructive-inspection techniques should no longer be necessary to ascertain weld characteristics. It also orchestrates an entire plantful of welding stations to ensure their efficient operation.

To these should be added such accomplishments as damage-minimizing handling methods for aluminum sheet and formed parts, more-efficient inspection and quality-control procedures, and a particularly important contribution by Ford: a monocoque-type cab design that not only enhances the cab's appearance and lowers air resistance but makes Sheller-Globe's job both easy and challenging at the same time.

From the manufacturing viewpoint, all these triumphs in aluminum will be extremely beneficial to many companies. Sheller-Globe and Ford, working together on a three-year development program have, in the words of Donald J. Mason, general manager of Sheller-Globe's City Machine & Tool Div, "obtained more engineering information about the drawing and forming of aluminum alloys than has been produced by any other single program in history. The materials, tooling, and production technology that we acquired could be successfully applied to other areas of the automotive industry," he continues.

The feasibility of producing exterior components for the truck cab was the primary concern in the development program. There were two main problems: (1) availability of aluminum alloys that could be drawn to specified shapes free of fractures and (2) obtaining such alloys that would be free of a condition known as "Lüder lines" throughout the visible exterior surfaces. Such lines form under certain conditions of elongation during fabrication of the metal and have the appearance of deformation in the metal surface.

Quarter panel is key component

A major materials-evaluation program, conducted by Sheller-Globe in cooperation with Ford and aluminum suppliers, resulted in the determination of the best available alloys, and their temper, for all cab-exterior body panels, particularly those considered the most difficult to produce. The right and left quarter panels were picked as the toughest assignment, being the most difficult to draw and possessing the greatest potential for Lüder-line formation. Its most challenging features were a recess for a vertical grab handle, a recessed rear window, a depression for a storage-compartment door opening in the lower part of the body, and several of the cab's structural framing members.

At the start of the program, 5052 aluminum alloy with an H-111 temper was thought to be the most suitable for the quarter panel. This was considered to be an acceptable compromise between the harder H-32 temper and the softer 5052-O temper. All of Sheller-Globe's preliminary tooling involved the use of this material to determine such tooling details as basic blank holders, blank size, and minor changes in punch and die radii. But the Lüder lines showed up,

2. **Engine-cover panel for medium-size cab** is carefully removed from stamping press (at rear) and inverted on "saddle"-type stack. After more forming processes, including trimming and piercing, it will be ready for shipment to assembly plant

3. **Cab panel,** mounted on checking fixture, waits in City Auto's inspection area for inspection of Ford-requested change in mounting holes for headlamps

A control system for resistance welding of aluminum

In block form, the diagram below depicts the complete system for control of a number of stations that perform resistance spot welding of aluminum at Sheller-Globe's Norwalk (Ohio) Assembly Div. Within the dashed lines is a complete, self-contained unit that is duplicated at each of 50 stations. The system is a product of Medar Inc (Plymouth, Mich). Welding guns are from Martin Electric Div of Thompson Industries Inc (Detroit), and the welding-transformer systems, providing 65,000 A dc at the electrodes, are supplied by Progressive Machinery Corp (Pontiac, Mich).

Control of the system involves monitoring the electrical characteristics of the weld, taking instantaneous readings from the monitored parameters every half cycle, then analyzing the readings to determine whether they represent satisfactory weld growth. If they do not, then corrective action either increases the weld heat or lengthens the welding time. At the completion of a weld, if corrective action has not brought the monitored variables within an acceptable range, the part is identified for rework.

Voltage and current are the principal parameters. Voltage is measured across the weld electrodes, and this requires a connection on the inside and outside electrode holder in close proximity to the electrodes.

Current is measured as a function of the voltage drop in the secondary of the welding transformer. It requires two connections along the welding horn, and the readings from them determine the impedance—or dynamic resistance—of the weld. This impedance is critical in evaluating weld-nugget growth, and its measurement throughout the weld correlates closely with weld-nugget size.

For sensing impedance in aluminum welding, high thermal and electrical conductivity requires a high value of current to be applied for a relatively short time. Furthermore, the limited plastic range of aluminum increases the difficulty of maintaining consistent nugget size without expulsion.

These are some of the more important factors in the technology of aluminum-welding control. Another might be added: in a production environment, an operator or setup worker can't be expected to set proper limits on a quality-control device that will identify material to be scrapped or reworked.

The system shown in the diagram overcomes the problems by requiring only one of the operators on the CL-9000-truck-cab line to produce good welds at the start of a production run. All normal setup procedures, including welding schedules and electrode dressing, are maintained. The one exception is the activation of a button or key switch that permits a new setup. When this control is activated, the weld-control system monitors all sensors for the first five welds. It monitors the sensed parameters and establishes new limits automatically. After the first five parts (assuming one part per weld) have been made, the stored information is analyzed and used to determine an acceptance region based on the first five weld samples.

Adaptive control is a key function of this system. Another important capability is load scheduling by means of a scanning feature. The central control can hold a weld-initiation signal for a particular welding station until the demand for current from other stations drops to an acceptable level, thus limiting the demand load on the entire system. Priorities can be assigned to particular weld stations, if desired, for increasing production efficiency at bottleneck stations, for instance.

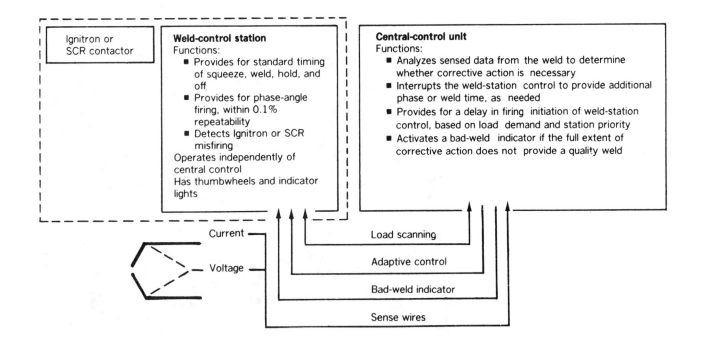

Building aluminum truck cabs

even though the quarter panels were produced without fractures from the 5052 H-111.

More experimentation—based on advice from aluminum-industry metallurgists and using Kirksite, a short-run tooling material—produced acceptable quarter panels from the new alloy designated 6009-T4. The material also provided improved physical properties, not the least of which was higher scratch- and dent-resistance than offered by other alloys.

Later on, in the early production phases of the truck cabs, Sheller-Globe engineers found that some of the stampings could be successfully made from 3004 aluminum alloy, which is less expensive than the 6009-T4 and has lower physical properties.

This extensive program and evaluation of materials was not the first at Sheller-Globe, however. The CL-9000 truck cab's design required it, but, as Gobeille points out, his company conducted extensive research several years ago to find the best aluminum alloys for truck-body panels. It also determined ways of modifying existing tooling for steel stampings so that similar parts could be produced from aluminum alloys.

The line starts at the mill

The production line for the new truck cabs starts at the mills of several sheet-aluminum suppliers and the shops of a number of extruders of aluminum structurals. Their shipments go to Sheller-Globe's City Auto Stamping division, in Toledo. (Its nearby City Machine & Tool division builds and maintains all the tooling.) The cab components—more than 350 of them—come together at the firm's Norwalk Assembly Div.

In several bays, City Auto operates stamping presses ranging in tonnage from 20 to 2000. On these machines, the blanking, drawing, piercing, and other sheetmetal processing produce the quarter panels and about 48 other components for the truck cabs. Some parts are currently purchased from a number of outside fabricators.

Outwardly, the presses look like those in any stamping plant. But John Beeler, the shop's production manager, explains that the tooling in the presses is a bit different and the way the components are handled is a lot different.

Beeler lists five important forming problems: the Lüder lines, springback, oil canning, flange tearing, and the sudden ruptures he calls "explosions."

The Lüder lines (named for the German metallurgist who discovered them in 1859) might appear anywhere across the face of a body panel, Beeler says. "Frequently, the metal on the back

side of a line will actually flake off. This could be across a deep-formed section, although it could be in any surface area that is subject to plastic deformation." Prevention of this problem starts at the mill, he says, explaining that, once the lines are detected, depending on how severe they are, the affected cab component may be rejected.

The phenomena of springback and oil canning are related, Dan Hojanacki, die-shop superintendent, points out, noting that the behavior of aluminum is different from that of steel. "Certain alloys, especially the ones we use, have more springback. We've had oil-can problems in the past. So we've experimented with various amounts of crown in our punches, trying to get a flatter panel. You see, aluminum hasn't been used much for automobiles, and so we're on a big learning curve."

Hojanacki continues on the subject of flange tearing: "Where flanges go around corners, it's necessary to build more relief in the die than you would if the material was steel. Although you might say that the job should be done in a few stages, I say that the fewer operations the better. In steel, you usually don't get a 90° flange with a 90° bend unless you design the tooling for it. Aluminum gives you the same [tearing] problem, only worse. It flares out more than steel does. What we do is work with somewhat thicker material for some of the components."

Beeler and Hojanacki agree that the

aluminum sheet that the shop uses is, in general, thicker than they would like it to be. (It ranges between 0.050 and 0.090 in., depending on application.) But, at the moment, the thickness minimizes flange-tearing problems and the rupturing that can occur anywhere across the face of a panel. Beeler predicts, "In a few years, aluminum will be as ductile as steel, and then the gage will come down."

Handling with no dents or dings

By the time thinner aluminum is formed in City Auto's shop, the methods for handling it should be refined to considerable degree. Currently, the only part-handling mechanization at each stamping press is a powered, mobile conveyor fitted with special rollers. Otherwise, the transfer operations, in and out of presses, are manual. The obvious reason: aluminum scratches more readily than steel.

"One of our major efforts here," says Quality Control Manager John Waltzer, "is to handle the aluminum gently. I say talk to the workers kindly and say 'please.' I tell them how much it costs and ask them to place it in the press dies carefully. When it comes out of the press, they could throw it on the stack, but they don't. If you've got a saddle fit and the part doesn't nest when they drop it, there'll be a ding somewhere."

Waltzer explains that the conveyors run only when their buttons are pushed and that they're not used for surge

4. Initial-run production samples of stamped truck-cab components are inspected in this area, which is responsible for contour and dimension control

storage between presses. This minimizes the possibility of dumping—and denting—a part as it tumbles off the end. The Neoprene rollers, he says, are worth every dollar of their high price.

Multiplant shape control

Augmenting these efforts to build correct tooling and handle the parts carefully is a part-shape-control system that spans plants in three locations. City Auto, the Norwalk Assembly Div, and Ford's Kentucky Assembly Plant, the destination of the cabs when they leave Norwalk, each possess one exactly on-spec representative of every critical component that makes up the cab. After Ford and Sheller-Globe have agreed that the contours and dimensions of a part are correct in every detail, Ford supplies a control part to each plant. If a dispute arises over a panel, during the course of the contract, the people involved at each facility can check the standard. "The portions of each control part that are especially critical are painted black," says Beeler. "By means of fixtures, we can check to see if a part that has just started on a run through the presses is on target or not."

Part configuration—its dimensions in three planes—is a major phase of Sheller-Globe's quality-control program. But part integrity—including absence of tears, dents, and "explosions," plus adequate thickness and surface finish—are of equal concern. Waltzer carefully checks the quality of all incoming aluminum. "Getting it with a defect-free surface has been a major problem," he says. "We've seen pits, occlusions of foreign matter, laminations, Lüder lines, and, just recently, some material that was 0.063 in. thick when the specs said 0.071. That's an 11% drop. Very likely, that difference could give us problems in the drawing operations. But we wouldn't let that happen!"

Assembly at Norwalk

Sheller-Globe's contract to produce the new Ford cab meant major changes and new investments at the company's Norwalk Assembly Div. The building was enlarged, a modern resistance-spot-welding system was installed, and the latest in immersion-type metal-cleaning facilities were added. Understandably, more employees were hired, and the plant's operations were put on a 24-hour-per-day basis when necessary.

The contract for which all this was required involved the production of five cab models—all in Ford's CL-9000 Series. Designated by overall length, there are 54- and 64-in. nonsleeper models and 76-, 88-, and 110-in. designs that accommodate various widths of bunks.

5. Main assembly fixture, rigidly built yet adjustable, grips cab's front panel and "U" assembly (rear and quarter panels) as crew of welders join them

All cab assemblies leave the plant in "white" condition, Sheller-Globe's term for bare, high-surface-quality aluminum. They're shipped to Louisville, to Ford's Kentucky Truck Assembly Plant, which adds primer, trim, and all accessories and then incorporates them into the total truck assembly.

A chemically clean start

The stampings from City Auto (as well as those from other suppliers) begin their trip through Norwalk at the new chemical-cleaning area. Extruded structurals from outside suppliers also come in at this location.

Bernard Dent, Sheller-Globe's director of manufacturing services and the man chiefly responsible for engineering the Norwalk line for the Ford cab (AM—Sep'77,p68), describes the cleaning system. "It cost us more than $100,000, but, without its efficient action, the rest of the process here wouldn't be very effective. We use the DuBois system—each firm's cleaning chemistry is proprietary. The DuBois is an acidic-activation system that involves a hot alkaline solution and a sequence of water and acid rinses. Two of the six tanks hold the same solution, because we need their holding capacity to keep the process flowing smoothly. Each part is date-coded as soon as it's cleaned. If seven days go by and it hasn't started through assembly, then it must go back and be cleaned again."

For most of the truck-cab components, assembly actually starts in the sub-assembly area. Later, everything comes together on the body bucks composing the main line. In either assembly area, there is no riveting staccato, only the quiet hiss of resistance-welding guns.

The new welding system at the

Norwalk plant can be thought of as comprising three major divisions: the power supply, the guns, and the controls. It was developed by Sheller-Globe, with help from Ford and the welding-equipment suppliers.

Sheller-Globe was well-prepared to undertake the task, after 15 years of successful resistance and fusion welding of aluminum and steel in the production of other models of truck cabs. So, when the Ford contract for the CL-9000 cab was awarded, Sheller-Globe's engineers had no difficulty launching a major study of aluminum-resistance-welding techniques and equipment to determine the ultimate performance requirements for the cab.

They concluded that spot-welding guns, for instance, would have to be much heavier than those they had been using. Cab design indicated that guns with throat depths as great as 38 in. would be required. But throat depth wasn't the only consideration. Engineers for both buyer and seller worked closely to achieve the maximum strength and rigidity of gun design for proper tip alignment and easy tip replacement.

Sheller-Globe's engineers found that throat depths greater than about 15 in. make direct-current power supply a necessity to achieve reliable welds and conserve energy at the same time. That narrowed the choice of power and control equipment and led to the purchase of a 65,000-A, single-phase, full-wave, dc power supply operating on 440-V, 60-Hz primary power and developing a 29.33-V secondary output. According to Dent, these are more powerful than any other portable-welding-gun transformers in existence. As a result, a new 10,000-kVA power-distribution substation was constructed outside the plant's walls, replacing the

209

Building aluminum truck cabs

1500-kVA substation that had been adequate. Another big Sheller-Globe investment was the closed-loop water-cooling system for the welding systems. It provides chemically treated cooling water of uniform temperature for welding cables, gun tips, transformers, and the computer.

Solid-state and scanning

The third major component of Norwalk's new welding system is the most sophisticated, Dent says. "Resistance welding of aluminum requires 3-5 times more electrical current, for about one-third the time, than is necessary for welding steel," he points out. "These high peak-current demands must be controlled so that they can be distributed in such a way that an extremely large power system is not needed."

Even though the new 10,000-kVA substation boosted the Norwalk plant's power capacity more than sixfold, a system of load scanning was required to further ensure welding reliability. And that required a computer.

In the system purchased for welding the CL-9000 cabs, all 50 welding machines are connected to the computer, each providing four inputs. Two inputs record electrical current being used at any instant. Two others record the voltage across the electrodes. Consequently, the load-scan system in the computer receives an analog signal that tells it how much electrical current is being used at any time.

With this information, the computer can delay the firing of any particular welding station until sufficient current is available to ensure satisfactory completion of a weld. Voltage drop is thus limited to about 8%. (If necessary, each of the resistance welders in the system can be operated independently of the computer.)

Dent explains the operation: "When a welding cycle is started at station A, the station automatically and electronically signals the computer that adequate current is needed to complete the weld. But, if welding cycles are in progress at stations B, C, and D, enough current may not be available for station A. So the computer automatically delays the start of the weld cycle at A until one of the others is completed; then it allows the weld at A to be completed.

"All this happens very rapidly," Dent continues. "In this operation, where we're resistance-welding aluminum and the total, actual welding time is perhaps 5-10 cycles, any corrective action to bring the impedance—that's voltage divided by current—path back within preset limits must occur before 3 or 4 cycles of weld time have elapsed. The

computer in our system looks at this impedance path during each half-cycle of welding time and makes corrections each full cycle to bring the impedance path within established high and low limits. If the computer senses that total weld time should be increased a few cycles to ensure a good weld, it can do it. If it can't, then it will shut off the system and indicate, on the panel at the particular weld station, that an unacceptable weld has been made because of a defective condition. This could mean replacing an electrode, correcting some problem in it, or cleaning the weld sealer from the electrode tip."

Dent claims that, because of the control system's scanning, demand for current never exceeds the system's capability, the plant's energy costs are substantially lower than if no scanning system were in operation, and the capital investment in power plant (the substation and all that goes with it) is proportionately lower. "Most important," he says, "weld quality is ensured."

Putting it all together

The buildup of a truck cab brings no less than 360 components together in the subassembly and main-assembly areas. Sides and underbodies are built up independently, then brought together in a main framing buck that acquires the rest of the components as it moves down the line. Rear panels join body sides and result in what is termed a "U-assembly." Engine tunnels mate with floors, containing some precision-engineered-and-built structurals, and become underbody assemblies. On the main-line bucks, these are joined to the U's, and the roofs are spot-welded on. Doors move in from their subassembly area and are bolted on and adjusted for a perfect fit.

Generally, all the other components fit perfectly, too. When all stampings and extruded sections arrive at the plant, they're checked with templets and special gages and by layout to be sure they fit together. This mockup is performed on a surface plate, flanked by a Model 72A PDQ Portage layout machine made by Bendix. The cab that's put together on it is composed of random-selected parts from incoming shipments. A special fixture picks up the zero points, and then the location of each key area can be read. Templets are on hand to check such features as windshields and door openings.

Throughout the assembly areas are a number of procedures developed by Sheller-Globe:

■ Cab doors are made so that no welding is performed on the exterior surfaces. The aluminum skin is mechani-

cally rolled and clenched around the entire periphery.

■ Although the truck cab is made from several different aluminum alloys, this makes no difference in the welding procedures. Several of the highly formed body panels are 6009 aluminum alloy (which takes a deep draw), others are 5052, and the roof is 3004. The extrusions are primarily 6061.

■ The design of the cabs is, in one respect, compatible with the production line and the outsize guns that are used throughout most of it. Working spaces for the welding guns, clamps, etc, are of reasonable size; edge distances and spot-weld spacing are feasible; and there's good access to the interior and other recesses.

■ Assembly of the upper cab to the floor, which includes the engine tunnel, takes place on a tilt-up fixture (see Fig 1), the only place on the main line where the work is elevated. This is the last welding station; beyond it are the buffing and surface-inspection areas, plus the station where doors and miscellaneous hardware and trim are attached.

■ Hand-held motorized buffers put the final sheen on the cabs. The buffing compound is a very fine grit, backed by a soft pad and whirled at speeds recommended for aluminum.

■ The highlight area subjects each cab to the glare of strategically located, high-wattage lamps, and the scrutiny of an inspector. Minor dents and scratches are ground and buffed out. The main line splits into two branches here to accommodate the cabs waiting for inspection. If they pass inspection, they're sent out to the outdoor storage area, ready to be trucked to Ford's Kentucky plant.

■ An S-shaped extruded hat section, part of the cab-floor framing on the driver's side and actually a main mounting member, requires more than the usual amount of work. It's formed in batches of no more than 25-30, because variations in the metallurgy of the basic extrusions, plus other factors, may require a change in forming strategy for the next group.

First, the extrusions are 100% inspected for flatness, and, if necessary, off-spec pieces are struck on a press to bring them within 0.020 tir. Forming is performed with the help of micarta "snakes," which serve much the same purpose as sand in pipe-bending operations: in this case, keeping the legs of the channel in parallel planes. The finished piece must have the distance between its two centerlines accurate to within 0.020 in. and a flatness on both top and bottom of the channel within the same tolerance. ■

Perforating by computer

New press system can change punch spacing at every stroke, takes orders from simple pushbuttons, and feeds stock with an accuracy of ±0.003 in.

Standard Perforating & Mfg Inc (Chicago) has a new way to make see-through sheetmetal. A pressman pushes a few buttons at a free-standing console and a computer responds, producing whatever hole spacing is wanted—and even changing it with each press stroke. Customers get the hole patterns they need, rather than mechanically indexed compromises.

"It makes the impossible jobs possible, and the difficult ones easy," says Standard's president, Jerome (Jerry) Ferdinand (see p213), "We've made a dramatic breakaway from the limitations of conventional ratchet-and-pawl feed mechanisms. This new press gives us much more freedom and flexibility in our manufacturing operations."

One of Standard's products that benefits from this upgraded technology is an air-diffusion plate for electrostatic precipitators. A common size is 60 x 144 in., with holes spaced uniformly (at 2¼ in.) across the width and increasing by 0.146 in. with each row as the plate's leading edge advances through the press. In a precipitator, this pattern of holes, punched on ever increasing centers, produces an even, efficient flow of the air that is to be electrostatically cleaned.

In the past: approximations

The flow wasn't always so even. Standard used to make the plates in five separate pieces, each with a different pattern (and, thus, a different amount of open area), then joined them together—usually at the construction site—to make a 60 x 144-in. unit that was supposed to have 23.9% open area. Ferdinand relates how some perforating companies, using somewhat more modern presses than his old ones, punch several rectangular grids of holes in a 60 x 144-in. plate, one grid above the other; hole spacing, equal in each grid, increases from one to the next, thus providing an approximation of continuously variable spacing.

"No more such compromises around here," Ferdinand says. "With this new perforating capability, I see exciting

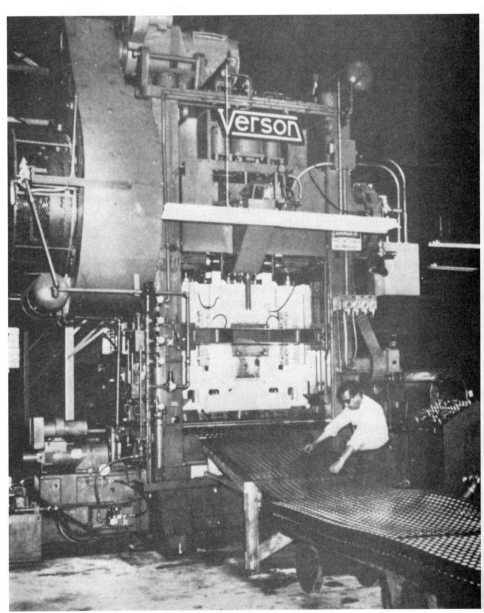

A digital computer programs sheetmetal perforating on this new 250-ton press. Output here is constant-spaced, but the system's flexibility permits endless variations

applications in the field of home appliances, home furnishings, heating and refrigeration, and certainly in architecture, where the combination of aesthetic and functional charateristics is very important. There is no other press

quite like it in the US. It's the hardware that can create entirely new markets, besides those I just mentioned."

But Ferdinand's pride goes further. Having seen tape NC perforators in Europe, and as an active member of the

Perforating by computer

Industrial Perforator's Assn, (he's currently its president), he set about to change the technology in this country a few years ago.

Technology 'back home'

The new system that he bought and that was ultimately lagged down in a cleared-out bay of his plant gives him the right to say to all who see it: "We've brought perforating technology back home."

Others helped the homecoming, shaping Ferdinand's ideas and suggestions into the machinery that is now in more-or-less steady operation. Neighboring Verson Allsteel Press Co provided a special machine, 19 ft tall above the floor, with an impressive docket of characteristics. Wegner Machinery Co (Long Island City, NY) gave it a special set of feed rolls. Unico Inc (Franksville, Wis) supplied the versatile computerized feed-roll drive, incorporating a Digital Equipment Co PDP-8 completely dedicated unit and an Allen Bradley Co set of electrical controls.

The roster of major partners in the installation won't be complete, however, until handling equipment is installed ahead of, and beyond, the perforating press. At the time of the installation's first demonstration, work had already begun on a stacked-sheet-delivery system. Soon a finished-product takeaway conveyor will replace the temporary runout ramp and wheeled cart.

When everything is in place, Standard's total investment could reach $500,000. Roughly $350,000 of this amount was spent two years ago when the press, its feed system, and its computerized controls were ordered.

Passing the pin-gage test

One yield from this outlay is accuracy. Hole-spacing pin gages—the go/no-go type—were pushed into randomly selected pairs of punched holes by Ferdinand's associates at the demonstration. The gages all went through, unaffected by the maximum feed tolerance of ±0.003 in.. per stroke, nonaccumulative. So accurate is the hole spacing that, if initially perforated stock is fed through again, with the controls set for a different spacing, one might believe that all holes were punched in a single pass.

"We don't intend to make parts that must be sent through more than once," says Ferdinand, "but this system is capable of repeat passes."

That kind of accuracy would not be possible without the Verson design know-how that was built into the new perforating press. Mel Verson, the firm's president, explains the key features: "The bed of a conventional perforating

Another perforator modernizes differently

David Hall, president of Diamond Perforated Metals Inc (Gardena, Calif), calls his new press "a high-precision performer." It gets commands from a digital control system that can produce as many as six different punched-hole spacings in one run, switching from one pattern to another without pause. Thumb-wheel-set counters on its roll-about control console permit presetting two kinds of input: (1) the desired number of "drops" (punches) in each of the hole patterns and (2) the number of "skips" wanted. (Up to 99 in. without holes can be skipped, useful for making the enclosure components that are one of Diamond's chief products.) Between holes, spacing is held to a tolerance between 0.002 and 0.003 in.

The company bought the press last year from Wegner Machinery Corp for about $250,000. Then it added a Niagara cutoff shear, together with a photoelectric encoder and two Durant counters; one counter measures correct length, and the other slows the stock-feed rolls at a predetermined point for better accuracy at cutoff.

The press handles stock up to 60 in. wide and from 0.015 to 0.1875 in. thick. Anything heavier than 14 gage—the maximum capacity of the shear—must be fed as precut sheet. Its integral feed rolls are actuated by the press crankshaft through a ratchet-and-pawl mechanism. Bowing of the rolls is minimized by two sets of small backup rollers, cushioned by air-cylinder action to maintain consistent friction coefficient regardless of stock thickness variations. A wide variety of metals—ferrous and non-ferrous, including titanium—are pro-

cessed by Diamond; all of them are run on the new press.

A few more press specifications: it's rated 250 tons and has a single slide (stripping action is provided by the tooling); it cycles at 100-300 strokes per min and is powered by a 50-hp, eddy-current-drive, variable-speed motor. The press is 12½ ft high.

The press is fitted with several hydraulic motors, in addition to the electric main drive. One adjusts the vertical position of the ram. A second motor adjusts the vertical position of the feed rolls to suit the height of a particular die. A third motor, through a ratchet, produces a skip in a hole pattern if such must be greater than the 2½ in. that is the maximum possible with the press's feed-roll indexing mechanism; holeless expanses up to 99 in. are possible.

Another hydraulic motor turns the press crankshaft, while the flywheel remains stationary, and is used for setting up a perforating project. It gives the setup person the necessary precise control. Since Diamond is a busy, 24-hour-a-day job shop, this feature is appreciated. Setup time is only about 30 minutes to an hour.

Diamond's chief engineer, Fabian Bogdan, designed a screw-conveyor punchings-removal system for the installation, plus electronic controls and mechanicals for the cutoff shear. In the photo, he's checking the startup of a run that will punch more than 1000 rectangular slots to make truck-radiator grilles from 5005-H14 aluminum, 0.10 in. thick and 48 in. wide. Measuring rolls (foreground) will signal—by encoder—the cutoff shear (lower left) to produce precise 34⅝-in. lengths for this assignment.

press is built to deflect no more than 0.0015 to 0.002 in. per foot. This one, with a bed that's 48 in. front to back x 64 in. right to left, plus a 4 x 64-in. slide, will move no more than 0.0008 in. per ft." He explains that the press's extra-heavy frame is of all-welded steel construction, stress-relieved, and pre-loaded with a tie rod in each of its four corners. The press is driven by a 150-hp, variable-speed motor with eddy-current control.

"The machine's frame is good for a 300-ton rating," Verson continues, "but its drive lowers it to 250 tons. Nevertheless, in stainless steel, it can punch holes that have a diameter equal to the metal's thickness. In conventional presses, the hole diameter must be at least twice the stock thickness." Under the most favorable conditions, holes as large as 3 in. dia can be punched, Verson says. The machine has five slides—a design that minimizes deflection problems; stripping capacity is 90 tons; and the machine is designed to use Standard's existing tooling, which can usually be changed in less than 20 minutes.

From 0.018 to 0.375 in thick

In hot- or cold-rolled plain carbon steel, stainless, or aluminum, sheet or coil stock as thick as ¼ in. (nominal) can be accommodated by this press. But Ferdinand explains that, under certain conditions, the machine can punch plate as thick as ⅜ in. At the other extreme, steel or aluminum as thin as 0.018 in. can ease through its rolls without slithering out of alignment. And, regardless of metallurgy and thickness, stock up to 60 in. wide can be handled.

Without the press's stopping momentarily, as much as 5½ in. of stock can be fed at 75 strokes per min, resulting in as many as 412 lineal in. per min through the press. At the other end of the performance curve, with a maximum feed of 0.6875 in. at 225 spm, the stock advances at a speed of 155 in. per min.

Air maintains roll pressures

The feed-roll system that moves sheetmetal through the press dies is a product of Wegner, a builder of perforating presses and related equipment. Absolute mechanical control of workpiece motion was the watchword when the system was designed. To maintain consistent coefficient of friction between the workpiece, the floating rolls above it, and the fixed-center rolls beneath it, the company provided an air cylinder to control the pressure exerted by each of the two floating rolls. Then it connected the cylinders by linkages to 2¼-in.-dia backup rolls, one contacting each of the floaters. If an especially tight squeeze on the

With this numeric keyboard, a key element in a new, computerized perforating system for sheetmetal, programming is as quick and easy as placing a telephone call

workpiece is required, the air cylinders working pressure can be increased to the limit of the plant air system, to provide approximately 3 tons of force.

The four working rolls in this system—a pair at the infeed and another at the outfeed 18 in. away—have hardened-steel faces, are 4.775 in. dia x 87½ in. long, and turn in antifriction roller bearings. A 10-hp dc motor, coupled to a precision gear train with two output shafts and with no perceptible backlash, powers the lower, fixed rolls. On the other side of the press, gearing transmits rotation of the lower rolls to the upper ones. The feeding action is brought to a precise halt by a full-regenerative braking system. There is no "dead" interval between driving and braking.

Closed loop keeps feed precise

The mechanical feed-roll system is only one reason for the high accuracy of this perforating press. Another is the computerized electronic-motor control system built by Unico. Output from the signal generator, determined by the setting on the 8k-capacity digital computer, is compared with rotary-encoder feedback pulses, generated at a rate of 1200 pulses per revolution, from actual stock movement through the feed rolls. A discrepancy indicates an inaccuracy in the feed system. The error signal is instantly processed by the computer, and correction signals are sent to the feed-drive motor's 1- to 35-amp silicon-controlled-rectifier (SCR) power supply. Thus, any inaccuracies in the feed action are detected and corrected as they occur.

Unico supplied its standard-model computer for this installation and adapted it to the perforating press. It's accurate to the third decimal place.

The other principal components of the control system are what Unico calls its System III digital numerical controller (DNC) and a 14-kVA, 240-V, 3-phase isolation transformer that keeps power surges off the line, corrects the power factor, and provides a stable flow of power to the feed-system drive. The system's conventional electrical controls, such as starters and disconnects, were supplied by Allen Bradley Co (Milwaukee, Wis). ∎

A chip for identical stretchforms

When Martin Marietta forms skins for jet-engine thrust
reversers, a microprocessor ensures exact repeatability

MICROPROCESSORS have pinned down the biggest variables in stretchforming: the proper amount of tension, elongation, and curvature for a particular part.

The process used by most aircraft builders to fabricate complex-contoured skins and structurals can now be controlled automatically by chips and tape memories instead of manually by artisans who are highly skilled but nevertheless susceptible to human errors.

The Baltimore Div of Martin Marietta Aerospace recently bought a sheet-metal stretchformer with that kind of control, reportedly the first of its type in the world, and along with it acquired greater confidence that stringent quality imperatives would be met. The most important requirements: repeatable close-tolerance dimensions (fit), dependable fatigue-life guarantees (vital information for aircraft owners), and satisfactory appearance (no wrinkles).

Sheetmetal skin sections for jet-engine thrust reversers take shape on this machine. Its microprocessor-assisted controls and solid-state memories ensure that each part in every batch is just like the others.

"We justified the purchase of the stretchformer mainly on its potential for upgrading quality," says John Meaney, the plant's manufacturing manager. He says that the complete thrust-reverser assembly, structurals and skin, must be built to a ±0.03-in. tolerance.

This potential means a lot to Martin Marietta because thrust reversers are one of its more important products. Averaging about 1500 lb each, with some measuring as long as 10 ft, they're likely to be incorporated as part of the General Electric jet engines that power much of the world's military and commercial aircraft. A low-volume product, they're usually fabricated in lots no larger than 100.

Several forming grades of aluminum are stretchformed to make the skin sections, the choice depending on such factors as location, type of aircraft, and customer: 2024 is commonly used; others include 2014, 7075, 7178, and 6061. Thickness of stock ranges from 0.012 to 0.250 in.

The process that forms these aluminum alloys is not new. Several decades ago, development engineers found that, when a metal sheet is stretched a specified amount, it can be shaped more severely without wrinkling than it could be by simple deformation under no tension. They developed a stretch-forming machine that gripped opposite ends of a sheetmetal blank, powered the jaws to exert a certain amount of tension on it, then forced the metal to wrap over a die with the desired contour.

This action stretched the outer fibers of the piece and compressed the inner ones. Because the latter were under considerable tensile stress prior to die forming, they simply returned to their original smooth, wrinkle-free condition when the machine relaxed the forming stresses and released the part.

It was a simple procedure, performed on a workpiece at ambient temperature, and it improved the metal's physical properties. But it took place on a not-so-simple machine that had to provide gripping, stretching, and wrap-forming actions to yield an acceptable complex-contoured sheetmetal part whose lines were not usually defined by basic cylindrical coordinates.

The challenge inherent in this method was to apply just the right amount of prestretch tension beyond the material's yield point without exceeding its ultimate strength or surpassing the critical elongation specified by the designer. Otherwise, premature metal fatigue could occur. Such control required experienced machine operators.

The microprocessor has now minimized that requirement. Its marriage to such a machine was arranged by Cyril Bath Co (Monroe, NC). The company's Versa Engineering Div and IMP Systems (Simi Valley, Calif) developed a control system with memory capability that can be programmed by first stretchforming a part manually and then, like certain models of industrial robots, can be "taught" to repeat its actions in a precise

Martin Marietta's new stretchforming press, the first with microprocessor control,
shapes sheetmetal into the contours of a thrust reverser for an aircraft jet engine

Operator Charles Kipp loads a tape cassette into deck of main control console to set up stretchformer for a production run. Facing him is a CRT display, banks of buttons and switches, and a keyboard. A microprocessor, with ROM and RAM, is inside

Workers carefully position sheetmetal blank between the machine's jaws and over its die, which is shrouded in slippery plastic film to help in the stretch-forming process

manner, producing any number of identical parts automatically. The stored program can be transferred to a magnetic-tape cassette to be used at any time and by an operator of any skill level.

For best workpiece loading and unloading, visibility during operation, and maintenance, the new stretchformer at Martin Marietta sits in a rectangular pit measuring about 14 x 20 x 8 ft deep. Its working components project adequately above floor level and are surrounded on three sides by a railing.

The builder, Cyril Bath, defines the machine as a Model VT400 and adds the designations 100CJ-120. This means that each of the machine's two jaws can exert a pull of 200 tons (thus the 400 number), its die table as well as its jaw width in the straight condition is nominally 100 in. long, and the maximum horizontal distance between its jaw faces is 120 in. Workpiece size is generally 48 x 144 in.

The machine has three basic moving components, all hydraulically powered, plus support beams, a main control console, and two local switch panels:

■ Each of the two gripping jaws, one at each end of the machine, is supported by a yoke on a carriage powered longitudinally by a pair of cylinders. A jaw consists of 12 segments, each powered by its own gripping cylinder. Other cylinders articulate and swing the jaw to the contour and position required for the specific job: each set of two segments is connected to a "curving" cylinder for vertical positioning; a wide variety of jaw

curvatures is possible. The segments on either side of the jaw center can be swung vertically, as a group, by a "swing" cylinder at either end of the carriage; the set of six segments can be tilted a maximum of 15° above horizontal. If the jaw must be skewed in the horizontal plane, the two jaw-carriage cylinders can be actuated to suit the requirements.

■ The hydraulically powered die table at the center of the machine is powered vertically by two pairs of cylinders and is kept in precise horizontal position by a vertical guided support tube. It does not rotate in a horizontal plane, but each pair of power cylinders can be actuated independently to tilt it in a vertical plane a maximum of 10° from horizontal. A T-slot on its centerline and a pattern of tapped holes on either side permit mounting of forming dies. Extension blocks, each 8 in. wide, can be fastened to the ends of the die table to lengthen it.

■ There are three different control panels. Most of the switches that trigger the various machine motions are mounted on the control console. Two auxiliary switch panels are mounted on the operator's end of the jaw carriages; they enable the operator to move the carriages and control the jaws when the workpiece is being loaded into the machine. The carriage-motion switches are duplicated on the main console, but the jaw open/close switches provided at the auxiliary stations are omitted; for safety, only the jaw-open switches are provided at the main console.

The main console contains the heart of the new stretchforming system: a Versamatic microprocessor-assisted control consisting of solid-state modular components. It does the required job with only 1K words in its random-access memory (RAM) and 10K words in its read-only memory (ROM). An analog/digital converter handles signals from the stretchformer's position transducers through an eight-channel multiplexer. Position information is sensed and transmitted by the transducers for the four jaw-carriage cylinders and the two pairs of dietable cylinders at the front of the machine.

Two digital/analog converters in the control console feed the signals from the microprocessor to the closed-loop servo circuits. A keyboard on the lower console panel permits editing the preselected limits of any given program, and a CRT in the console's upper center panel displays, on keyboard command, all stored data, including a table of limits, dwells, and sequencing information. It even flashes malfunction messages, setup instructions, and such machine-maintenance data as hydraulic low-level or over-temperature conditions. Flanking the CRT is a magnetic-tape deck for extracting all setup data.

Four basic control modes

The machine has four basic control modes: manual, automatic, read tape, and write tape. ("Automatic" relates only to the actual stretchforming stages; because the machine is loaded and unloaded manually, the entire operation is actually semiautomatic).

■ In the manual mode, all motions of the machine are regulated at the control-panel and can be effected between the preset limits shown on the CRT. When power is first turned on, the controls shift to this mode. At other times, the mode is selected via the scroll switch, which "unrolls" data on the CRT.

■ The stretchformer shifts to the automatic mode when any of the automatic switches are pushed: Load, Form, Post (postforming), Relax, Unload, and Cycle Start. Before the machine can perform a cycle automatically, it must first be programmed by the operator or by reading a taped program into the microprocessor memory.

■ The "read tape" mode permits programming information to be transferred from tape to the cycle-program memory. A printout is not considered necessary.

■ In the "write tape" mode, all information stored in the cycle program memory can be transferred to a magnetic tape for long-term storage.

When in "automatic," the control system allows the operator to fully program and/or edit the machine motion (or axis) for the eight other modes, those that directly determine machine operation—load, unload, pre (stretch), form, post (stretch, again), and relax—and two that move the die table—tilt and rate (up or down). These modes also permit adjustment of limits, dwells, and sequencing for all of the axes under the system's control.

With such a control system at their disposal, John Meaney and his staff can easily set up stretchforming programs that produce high-quality parts. Recorded on tape with help from the machine's microprocessor, the program becomes a "pedigree," as Cyril Bath calls it, for the particular part's quality specifications and other characteristics (AM—May'81,p65).

After setting the controls to the manual mode, the operator manually loads a blank into the machine, actuating the jaws in all their motions, their carriages, and the die table with the die mounted on it. As forming actions are initiated, position transducers transmit their signals to the microprocessor, which in turn develops a "table" in the RAM.

Parts are formed until a totally

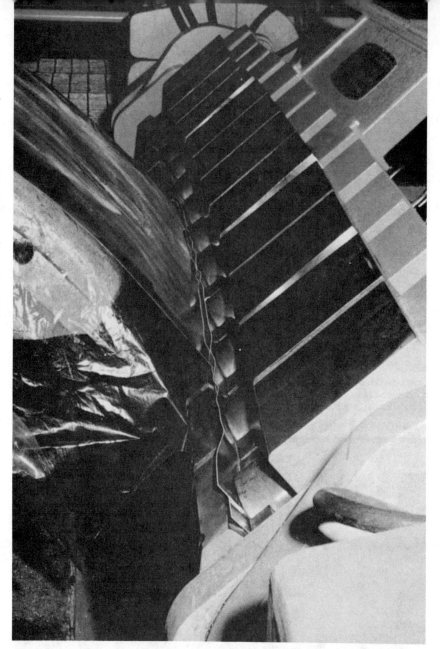

Segments of stretchformer's jaws can be individually positioned to accommodate the part's curvature. Each 12-segment jaw moves horizontally and can also be skewed

Forming dies await their turn in the stretchforming press. Each makes a different skin component. Press output, still protected by red film, sits in transfer cart, behind dies

Formed part, last of the run, is loaded on cart for trip to trimming press, in another department. Protective red film, a sprayed-on plastic, is then stripped off

Curved in two axes, stretchformed sheetmetal encases the interior of these partly assembled reversers. Microprocessor-aided control ensures high-quality forming

tains the software for using the tables, operating the tape cassette, controlling the displays on the CRT, and driving the operator-prompting sequence.

A simple record-keeping system

Soon after the machine went into full-scale production, Martin Marietta's stretchforming staff learned that other records were also required. A simple record-keeping system helps them select the tape cassette for a specific thrust-reverser component, choose the correct die (identified by a tool number), and set up the other controls on the machine. This accounting system has proved invaluable as the number of potential parts—and stretch-forming programs—has grown to at least 125. To date, Martin Marietta has actually run about 20 of them.

When a stretchforming job is ready to run and the correct tape is locked into the console, two employees pick up a flat sheetmetal blank from a pallet load and spread it over the machine's forming die. A magenta-colored plastic film, previously sprayed and later stripped off, protects the workpieces' top surfaces. Scratching or other kinds of surface damage cannot be tolerated. When the part has been trimmed in another plant area and is ready for assembly, this protective skin is peeled off.

Plastic of another type and color (green) covers the top of the forming die. Martin Marietta finds that a 2-mil-thick nylon film, extremely tough and thus suitable for the service, provides the necessary sliding, lubricating effect.

For certain stretchforming jobs, the operators apply a commercial lubricant made of petroleum jelly and No. 10 mineral oil to the bare metal surface of the die with a paint roller. When this lubrication method is used, the formed parts are subsequently vapor-degreased.

After the workpiece is gripped by the jaws, which are locally actuated by the switch panels at each side of the machine, the operator at the main console triggers the die table upward. At this point, the microprocessor and its memory take over, regulating the motions of the jaws and the die until the part is formed. Then the jaws are opened by the operators, who remove the part from the machine, place it on a cart for transport to the trimming department, and reset the stretchformer.

This is the way Martin Marietta stretchforms most parts for the thrust reversers—in one pass. However, a few, usually those with severe contours, are formed to their approximate shape and are then taken to an annealing furnace before being finish-formed in a second pass with another die. ∎

acceptable one is made. This usually requires no more than three trial runs. The CRT display on the console does much to expedite this procedure and, since part acceptance also includes tool certification, indicates tooling problems as well and states what must be done to correct them.

When the program is correct, the mode-selector switch is turned to the write-tape mode, and the program is transferred to a tape for permanent record.

At this time, a code word is automatically written on the tape to identify the start of the table. Then a check sum is calculated from the data flow and is written on the tape as a valid data check for future RAM loading. Thus, the control system sets up two checks on the tape. One determines whether the table is written into the tape correctly. The other sees to it that the RAM is loaded properly so that the table is ready for future production runs.

The ROM in the control system con-

CHAPTER VIII
Computers in Flexible Manufacturing Systems

FMSs for sheetmetal working

Two new manufacturing systems link shears, brakes, and
punch presses with loaders under a central computer

THE 'M' IN FMS originally stood for machining, but the
concept of linking operations into a flexible manufacturing
system has now gone beyond solely metalcutting. Two recent
announcements make it clear that the principle also may be
applied to fabricating sheetmetal.

An automatic fabrication cell, based on one right-angle-
blade shear and one turret punch press equipped for plasma-
torch cutting, was demonstrated at Westec 82 by the Wiedemann Div (King of Prussia, Pa) of Warner & Swasey. It forms
the basis of a more elaborate system that includes automated
materials storage and retrieval, off-line loading and unloading,
and additional shears, turret punch presses, and stand-alone
laser cutting machines.

Some 20 such full-scale systems have already been installed
in Japan by Murata-Warner & Swasey Ltd (Kyoto), the joint
venture company between Murata Ltd, a Japanese builder of
machine tools and robots, and the Cleveland-headquartered
unit of Bendix Corp. They vary in complexity, according to
Bradford L. Peck, Wiedemann marketing director, but most
are coordinated by a Digital Equipment Corp PDP 11 computer
and include automatic materials-handling equipment and more
than two machine tools.

Japan's Amada Co Ltd (Isehara) has been working on a
similar system for sheetmetal working of parts such as panels,
doors, and cases for cabinets, computers, etc. Under development for three years and first made public last November,
Amada's system combines an automated storage and retrieval
system (AS/RS) with one NC punch press, a blanking and
shearing press, and a press brake. A computer-controlled
loading system, a prototype palletizing robot, and another
robot that operates the bending brake can function as buffers
for material through the system, which includes controls by
Fujitsu Fanuc and Mitsubishi.

The system is aimed at small-lot producers rather than the
usual mass-production users of metalforming equipment, and
it's said to be attracting attention from Japan's major electric-
appliance and computer manufacturers. An Amada spokesman
reports that at least five or six systems per month—each
redesigned and modified in accordance with individual needs—
are being marketed. There are as yet no announced plans to
offer the system through US Amada Ltd (La Mirada, Calif)
because of international patent restrictions on the BLS6090
right-angle shear, a crucial component.

In the system that Amada demonstrated in its suburban-
Tokyo showroom, sheets are lifted, classified, and stored in the
AS/RS. A magnetic floater separates individual sheets for a
vacuum-cup loader, which locates the material for the first
machine, a 50-ton NCT-OOMA-557 turret punch press. The loader
next carries sheet to the L-blade shear, and sheared pieces are
then moved to a roller conveyor and picked up by a palletizing
robot, which orients pieces for pickup by a "colleague," a
second robot that places the punched-and-sheared sheet into an
RG-80 press brake that folds and bends the material.

Murata-Warner & Swasey systems operate in similar fashion, although brake-loading robots have not been a common
feature. Typically, raw sheet stock is automatically loaded on
the Wiedematic turret-punch-press table for punching of plasma cutting of multiple parts. The punched sheet is then
automatically transferred to the L-blade Optishear, loaded,
positioned, and sheared with the operator only sorting and
stacking finished parts.

An important aspect of the system, comments Wiedemann's
Peck, is the ability to have a single software package that
performs nesting functions in random patterns using nongraph
inputs, takes into account different blank sizes, allows for
required material-grain orientation, and still optimizes the
entire production operation. The firm is reportedly within a
few months of completing the programming link.

Emphasis for the Wiedemann system will be on improving
production rather than on being extremely flexible, according
to Peck, although, because of the modular approach, additional
machines can readily be incorporated and the entire system can
be operated under DNC.

Prices for such systems vary widely. Amada says that the
simplest version of its system goes for about $600,000 and that
any added sophistication can bring the price to $2-million.
Still, declares Tadashi Hirata, the firm's manager of punching-
machine sales, there is great interest, and 20% of his customers
are ordering a combination of a punching machine and a
bending brake. ∎

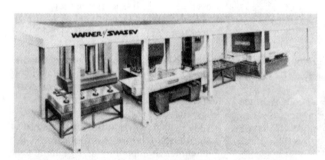

Concept drawings of Wiedemann linked-machine sheetmetal
system is patterned after similar systems installed in Japan

Demo FMS shown by Amada uses table-level materials-handling
system to tie shear, punch press together

Aiming
for FLEXIBILITYFLEXIBILITY

Manufacturers are beginning to combine metalcutting and other processes with materials handling under computer control. It's not yet the automated factory, but it's close

The survey, over a period of four years, brought out some interesting facts, and the most interesting of these, to us, was this: Of all the kinds of things manufactured in the United States, only 20% ever reach a production figure of 10,000. This 20% includes the commonplace things that we see. The remaining 80% are the less noticeable products of industry.

— *American Machinist*, 1947, reprinted in a DoAll handbook

In metalworking manufacturing, lot sizes are not less than 50 pieces for 75% of all parts so manufactured. Thus, any on-going opportunity to take advantage of economies of scale through mass production is severely limited unless new technology and worklife developments can be used.

— M. Eugene Merchant, director of research planning, Cincinnati Milacron Inc; from a 1976 presentation at the Tri-Service Manufacturing Technology Advisory Group

R&D comes up with the operating principle for a different kind of widget. Design sets to the drafting tables and graphics terminals and arrives at part prints. Sales takes a look and projects requirements of 1000 every year. And manufacturing, unable to economically produce the new widgets on presently installed machinery, tools up to meet the exciting demand by installing the latest in high-volume, hard-automation machine tools.

The widget in our story flops, however, as introductory products often do, and manufacturing faces the question "What do we do with all that dedicated machinery?"

It's an overly simplified tale, but something like it happens every day. The potential failure of a brand-new product isn't the only reason for worrying about digging in so deep that you can't climb out of the hole. Shifts in consumer preference, competitive strategies, availabilities of raw materials, different regulatory climates, etc, are all outside forces that are making metalworking manufacturers place renewed emphasis on holding open all possible options.

Insurance against unforeseen circumstances is a prime reason for the current craze for flexibility; it isn't the only one. Today's demanding customers want tailored products, often in quantities so small as to render them unacceptable for mass production. Mass production as a concept is becoming more and more passé, in fact. Even the automobile industry, which gave the world such things as the dedicated moving assembly line and the word *automation,* is now talking about "high-volume" manufacturing rates rather than "mass production."

Enter a brand-new series of terms like *flexible automation, families of parts, group technology,* and the rest, each irrevocably tied to developments in control technology, which have led the way for what has come to be called the Second Industrial Revolution. And enter, also, a single concept that tries to tie them all together: flexible manufacturing systems.

What is an FMS?

There is no generally agreed-upon definition for what have come to be called flexible manufacturing systems. Certainly, any operable factory can be termed a manufacturing system, and flexible is a relative adjective at best.

But there's no denying that, within the last five to seven years, a more responsive, yet automated way of addressing the needs of manufacturing has evolved. That new method relies on three distinguishing characteristics:
- Potentially independent NC machine tools
- A transport mechanism
- An overall method of control that coordinates the functions of both machine tool and conveyance system so as to achieve flexibility.

Within that broad scope, there are any number of individual approaches toward striking a balance between high

FLEXI in manufacturing systems

output (with minimal allowance for quick changeovers) on the one hand and great flexibility with concomitant reduction in output volume on the other.

This Special Report will examine some of the reasons manufacturers are looking for the capability of varying their production response, some of the strategies they've devised, and some of the pitfalls they've encountered. We'll look at the control function, advances in machine-tool design, material-handling systems, and the way they interact. The article will also explore an important facet of using flexible manufacturing systems: the relationship between the user of the system and the machine-tool builder that supplies it. Lastly, we'll see where some experts in the field think that the automated factory is headed.

The case histories presented are merely indicative of the ways that some manufacturers have attempted to juggle variability and productivity within their own product mix. The important thing to keep in mind is that, as the circumstances in

Eight 'wet' machines plus carts that tell DNC where they are

Almost six years ago, managers at International Harvester's Farmall plant in Rock Island, Ill, began thinking that a systems approach was the way to go for their machining operations. Two and a half years ago, the company started serious talks with Sundstrand Machine Tool (Belvidere, Ill) about such a system. This month, the $6.5-million system just installed at the I-H plant in Louisville, Ky, where the project was moved, is scheduled to undergo formal tryouts and acceptance tests, although the eight-machining-center grouping has been producing parts for tractors since November.

The installation came just in the nick of time, according to Lamont (Monty) Hoppestad, advanced-manufacturing-processes and facilities-planning engineer at the I-H Louisville plant. "Last spring, we introduced our new '2+2' vehicle," he says, referring to an articulated, four-wheel-drive tractor that's especially suitable for working row crops, "and it just took off in the marketplace."

Demand for the brand-new design, in fact, might have outstripped conventional capability to manufacture parts for the 2+2. But, when the I-H Louisville manufacturing system was designed, engineers for the farm-equipment company specified that it should be able to machine parts for the new tractor, as well as components for older-model farm vehicles. For I-H, it was a relatively simple matter to reschedule parts flow on the machining system to adjust for new-vehicle demand.

The manufacturing system comprises four 40-hp horizontal-spindle machining centers, four 25-hp machining centers equipped with tilt spindles that index to either horizontal or vertical orientation, a 240-ft-long pallet-shuttle system with two cars and 15 load/unload stations, and a measuring machine that is still being installed.

Its role includes roughing, finishing, finish-boring, tapping, and parts handling for five components on an older-series small tractor: the main frame, the clutch housing, two different spacer covers that fit between the frame and the front hydraulic lift, and a bolster that mounts to the forward end of the tractor.

When the machining system is doing nothing but cutting parts for the older series, it machines enough of those components to enable a subsequent assembly line (at the I-H Farmall plant in Rock Island, Ill) to build 12 tractors a day.

Harvester, in using the Louisville system for the older tractor model, eliminated the need for 78 machine tools in its Rock Island plant, opening up a lot of valuable floor space. But the company also hedged its bet on the Louisville system: the DNC-directed lineup also machines pump housings and transfer cases for the new 2+2.

Three levels of computers run the system's operation. There is an individual CNC at each machining center, the pallet-shuttle system is controlled by a microprocessor-based system (a micro rides on each cart), and both levels feed data into a supervisory computer, which also stores tool-path and machining-parameter information. In addition, the supervisory computer also schedules part mix and production via consoles at the load/unload stations.

"We just don't warehouse," Monty Hoppestad states flatly. Instead, the supervisory controller is programmed to attempt to achieve the correct balance of tractor components during their processing.

In typical operation, an empty shuttle car is driven to the loading station nearest the part bin where the required castings are stored. In the case of the five-part mix for the older tractor, the supervisory computer would sense that, say, a clutch-housing casting has to be loaded next in order to have the system producing clutch housings 25% of its operating time. A light atop the proper load station alerts an operator that that particular location is ready for attention. When the operator arrives and is

Cart travels on rails, signals position via mast

a plant can vary, so can the approach to solving the manufacturing puzzle.

Adapting to product mix

Before a manufacturing system can be designed, planning must take into account the type of production that will be accomplished. Prof K. Itomi, of Japan's Osaka Univ, differentiates between certain types of production in his book *Manufacturing Systems Engineering*. Production based on orders and for stock replenishment, he says, is characterized by firm requirements. He distinguishes this from jobbing or intermittent production, which is related to expected sales over a foreseeable time: "As economies grow and societies become more affluent, the desire of the individual to possess special goods different from those of other people rises, and the demand for specially ordered products increases, while the product life cycle decreases. This results in a wide variety of products with low volume.

"In addition, lead-time from the receipt of the order to the

ready to fixture a blank, station-console lights indicate which specific part to prepare for machining.

When this is done, the operator informs the central processor that the fixtured piece is ready for machining, and the casting is then taken for its ride, arriving at the machining center that has been tooled for work on it. The system is timed so that the fixtured blank arrives at a machine tool a minute or two before the cutting cycle stops for the workpiece already on the machine.

"We looked especially hard at the shuttle," says Hoppestad, "since we had heard from other flexible-machining-system users that it was a potential weak point in the hardware." He's happy with the shuttle-cart system on the White-Sundstrand system, however; it uses carts made by the machine-tool builder instead of outside suppliers, and both carts are driven by dc drives modified from table-drive designs for White-Sundstrand's machining centers—"proven designs," according to Hoppestad.

The carts have another feature that he likes. Each carries a pinion that engages a track-mounted rack in front of the entire line. The rack-and-pinion

arrangement operates a position encoder, which tells both the on-board microprocessor and the supervisory computer that the cart is accurately positioned and won't crash when the pallet swap is initiated.

Pallet exchanges between the cart and the machining center's table is done by a central pivot that is cantilevered out from the cart. The 180° swap is accomplished in less that a minute.

Each machining center is mounted on a sloping deck that dumps chips and coolant into a central flume. "We decided that we had to go with a 'wet' system, one that used coolant rather than machining dry," says Hoppestad. "Constant flushing is necessary to keep the tool clean when you don't have operators standing right there all the time—especially in precision-boring jobs."

The full line isn't even in operation yet—the inspection station is still being installed—but Monty Hoppestad is already thinking of ways to expand the IH system. "If demand for the new tractor continues to increase," he says, "we can dedicate the system to the more sophisticated jobs like precision boring, contour

milling, and trepanning, and we can do the less critical work like tapping at a manual machine or a head-changer that can be placed near one of the loading stations."

Hoppestad is pleased with the output of the new system. "It's just gobbling up the parts," he says. "It's a significant increase over the old lineup of conventional machines."

He's also pleased with the quality of the parts that the system produces. "I just don't think we'd be able to see accuracies like the line produces for the 2+2 parts from another machining center," he volunteers.

"In the event of a breakdown on one of the machining centers, there's no reason why we couldn't move the tools from the idled machine to another in the system," he says, pointing out that tools can be loaded into the toolchanger matrix of each machining center while the machine is running.

"And it would be very easy to add another machine, some more track, another pallet car, . . ." Hoppestad adds, his voice hinting of the enthusiasm of a seven-year-old pondering a new train set under the Christmas tree. □

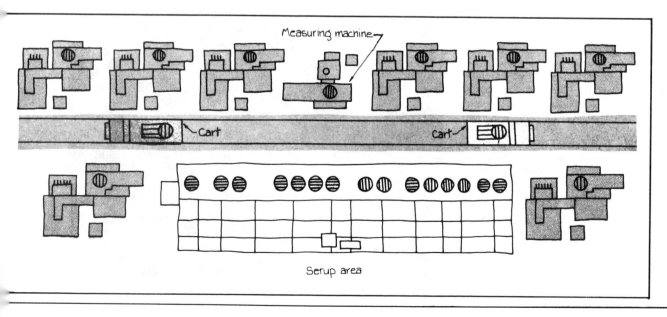

Measuring machine

Cart   Cart

Setup area

shipment of the product is expected to be as small as possible in order to win in a competitive situation," the professor observes. More-speculative production, intermittent by nature and tied to the marketplace, becomes necessary, he argues.

In adapting to product-proliferation demands in the marketplace, the factors of production are bound to be affected. When should a manufacturer switch from one of those factors of production to another? "In simplistic terms, one should substitute when the ratio of production to cost for one alternative is greater than the ratio of another," Prof George K. Hutchinson, of the Univ of Wisconsin — Milwaukee told the Numerical Control Society at its last annual meeting. But he immediately acknowledged that manufacturing advances — the performance of the digital computer — and the increasing cost of labor have made the decision more imperative, if less clear-cut.

Hutchinson set forward some ways of viewing manufacturing situations, especially as they relate to metalcutting. One useful view is to compare the number of different parts in a

Phasing in a flexible system by steps

At the Avco-Lycoming plant in Williamsport, Pa, manufacturing engineers are now working on the third phase of a machining-system installation that was begun back in 1975. The flexibility of the original line's design permits them to add a number of workpiece types with a minimum of current effort and expense.

Avco-Lycoming has built reciprocating aircraft engines since the 1920s and today supplies such builders of business, personal, and utility planes as Beech, Cessna, and Piper.

Machining the aluminum castings into finished engine crankcases is done on a line of about 80 stand-alone, manually controlled machine tools. But a new engine design, which substantially changed configuration and dimensions, precipitated a move to a flexible manufacturing system to do the metalcutting.

The new engine series, introduced in 1976, called for the accessory housing to become an integral part of the casting rather than a bolt-on addition. Because of a number of other design changes, the fixture and customized machines that had been used for the older engine series were no longer adequate.

"I suppose we could have bought additional new or used machine tools to expand our capacity," says Cliff McCracken, director of manufacturing engineering. "But that would have meant essentially duplicating our old line, and we decided to do it a bettter way."

The "better way" was to install a series of single-spindle horizontal machining centers, multiple-spindle indexing-head machines, and an in-floor towline cart transfer system for palletized workpieces, all operating under centralized control. J.W. Love, McCracken's predecessor, visited a number of other companies that were using similar concepts and, after a series of conferences and much analysis, Avco-Lycoming decided to work with machine-tool builder Kearney & Trecker (Milwaukee) to design and build its own FMS.

By the spring of 1974, the engine builder signed a purchase order for what was to become Phase One of the system. The machines — four traveling-table Moduline NC machining centers, one NC head indexer, and a manually operated material-handling system started producing crankcases for the new design in early 1976.

K&T provided much of the engineering as well as the machine tools, and it subcontracted the conveyor system to ACCO (American Chain & Cable, Bridgeport, Conn). Riggers from Avco-Lycoming did the actual installation, however, which included setting up provisions for a coolant/chip flume system that wasn't actually used until the second phase of the project. The coolant flume feeds into a central filtration and chip-removal system from Henry Filters (Bowling Green, Ohio).

With the system producing crankcases for one four-cylinder engine and one six-cylinder engine, Kearney & Trecker proposed an addition—

Phase Two—that was to incorporate more of the remaining four- and six-cylinder production. The second project, completed last November, added five more machining centers with 48-in.-sq pallet capacity, two more multispindle head indexers and another head-indexing unit to the first one to enable it to work both sides of the pallet at the same time. Additional in-floor towing-conveyor tracks were added to complete the system, and a pair of single-spindle machining centers (Milwaukeematic 800s) were added at the same time off the line for close-tolerance boring operations for gear centers.

Installation of the second phase of the system did not disrupt production on the original machines in the lineup, says McCracken.

An important part of the second phase was the installation of a centralized control system using two Interdata Inc Model 70 minicomputers. One, for DNC, governs machining instructions to each of the NC machines; formerly, the machine tool operated independently. The other controls material handling through

Work carts are towed by in-floor chain to machines

manufacturing situation with the production requirements:

Parts in system	Required production	System type
Low (1-2)	7000 and up	Transfer line
Medium (3-10)	1000-10,000	Special
Medium (4-50)	50-2000	Flexible
Medium (30-500)	20-500	Mfg cell
High (200 and up)	1-50	NC machines

Because transfer lines in this relative table are characterized by

high efficiency and dedication to production of a small number of parts, they rank at one extreme. At the other end of the spectrum, individual NC machines can be shifted to producing different models rapidly, but they lack, by comparison, the ability to capitalize on many production efficiencies brought by specialization.

It is within the mid-volume range of production, somewhere between the two extremes, that flexible manufacturing systems are designed to work best. [Continued]

coordination with more than 24 PCs; it records system performance and manages the functions of the DNC.

The current third phases involves adding drillheads to the head-indexing machines and adjusting some of the hard tooling to accommodate other engine designs. Avco-Lycoming lists many different engine models currently available, but some of those models are what McCracken calls "service types," virtually discontinued from a marketing point of view but still run in batches of two or three. Crankcases for these "service" engines, as well as those for rebuild jobs, will likely never be run on the flexible machining system. But the third-phase project for the FMS will allow most of the production-quantity crankcases to be processed under DNC.

In production, the system operates randomly on either four- or six-cylinder-engine crankcase-casting halves.

Left and right halves are fixtured onto each pallet at the cart-staging area, next to the two off-line machining centers. Line balancing, a function of the FMS minicomputer, is partially executed here as pallet carts are routed to the load area where proper castings are waiting. For a typical part, only five fixturings are required with the FMS, compared with 30 setups for the former line.

Carts are towed to the appropriate machine under computer control. "Some 81 limit switches in the floor feed information to the computer, which controls switching and stopping the carts," McCracken reports. When a cart arrives at the correct machine, a shark-fin-shaped plate rises from the floor and disengages the cart's chain drive. A pneumatic piston then pushes the cart against a hard stop for accurate positioning prior to unloading the pallet.

During debugging of the system,

some inaccuracies in cart location caused minor problems, McCracken says, but they were easily adjusted.

A pallet-shuttle table at each machine acts as an interface between the machine and the towline cart system and also banks palletized workpieces.

With a constantly expanded line of workpieces handled, the crankcase-dedicated flexible machining system, installed in phases over a number of years, illustrates a salient feature of such systems: production is not necessarily slowed by addition of other parts to the operating whole. One strong reason for that was the amount of planning that Avco-Lycoming put in from the start, with little major modification to existing machines during later phases. As H. Thomas Klahorst, manager for special-product sales at K&T, says, "If you keep ripping up an FMS, you might as well have bought a transfer line." □

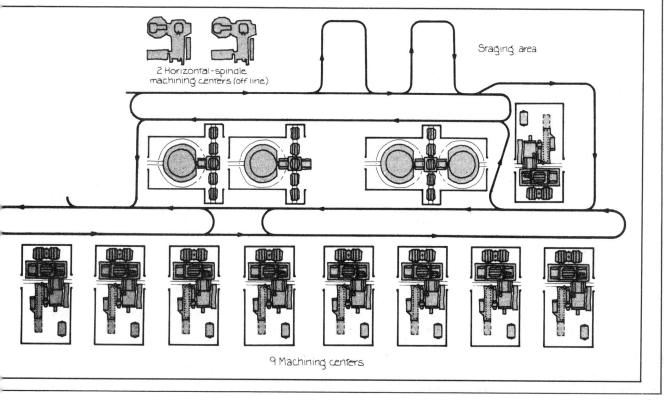

2 Horizontal-spindle machining centers (off line)

Staging area

9 Machining centers

FLEXIBILITY in manufacturing systems

That scheme essentially replicates the thinking of machine-tool builder Kearney & Trecker (Milwaukee). Thomas Klahorst, manager of special-products sales, further distinguishes among the manufacturing alternatives within that medium-diversity range. Eliminating transfer lines and stand-alone NC machining centers from discussion, he says that his division's experience has been that some 10% of mid-volume production applications call for installing manufacturing cells, 60% are best served with so-called flexible manufacturing systems, and the remaining 30% are best handled with what he calls "special systems."

A manufacturing cell, in the K&T concept, might consist of a machining center and one or two special machines clustered around a versatile handling system, such as a robot. Flexible manufacturing systems might include machining centers or more-standard, somewhat process-specialized machines, integrated into a control system that also governs material handling and parts flow throughout. So-called special systems are one step further toward transfer lines, comprising individual machines tailored to a fairly narrow range of parts.

Within that overall picture, there is a lot of room for argument about definition. When does a system become dedicated to a particular part family? At what point do production requirements for a single piece demand moving toward inflexibility? These and other theoretical questions are probably unanswerable, but the overall scale of volume vs diversity, of the trade-offs between efficiency and versatility, is useful to keep in mind.

Also a statistical problem

One indication of the confusion that exists over the definition of manufacturing systems is that they cannot be described adequately under current census-taking rules.

Metalworking-machinery shipments are reported by the Commerce Dept in its quarterly MQ35W Series of Current Industrial Reports. Each category of machine tool carries a notation of total shipments (units and value) within the reporting period. But the report lists only metalworking machinery and controls. What of the material-handling equipment, probes, etc, that are part of a manufacturing system but are not strictly included as part of a stand-alone machine that may be a functioning unit within that system?

In the hypothetical situation in which seven standard-design machining centers are linked with a pallet conveyor and placed under control of a supervisory computer, only the machining centers will be reported as metalworking machinery, according to Paul Berard of the Commerce Dept's Bureau of the Census, which collects the data. There may be a case for considering such a coordinated cluster under a general classification that includes station-type machines like transfer lines. But, Berard admits, the bureau is a little hazy on the subject since it is such a new field.

About a year ago, the National Machine Tool Builders' Assn (McLean, Va) addressed the problem of systems (and transfer machines) in a meeting of its marketing-statistics committee. Following that meeting, the association's current position is to report to its members shipments of individual machines, explaining with a footnote when they are part of overall systems.

Thus the hypothetical system comprising seven machining centers would appear in NMTBA internal statistics as seven individual machines; but a supplementary report would note that they were part of a single installation and that the total value of the system included additions for material-handling components, controls for the overall operation, and the value of the engineering that went into designing the system.

Molins system had right concept too early, was never built

"Still dead," reports John Bond, of Molins Ltd's American subidiary (Richmond, Va), about his company's ill-fated System 24 flexible machining system, which was formally proposed nearly 15 years ago.

In fact, the System 24 was never built, although half a dozen individual metalcutting machine tools that were to be linked into it were built and sold. One of them was used in making parts for the Concorde SST; others are in use in a couple of American computer companies.

The System 24 was not as early as the pioneering—and operational—lineup of machining centers the Sundstrand Machine Tool installed in its then sister company's aviation plant in Rockford, Ill, in the mid-Sixties. But the Molins system nevertheless gained widespread attention more than a decade ago as exemplifying a coming "new wave" in manufacturing.

Molins, a London-based manufacturer of cigarette-making machinery, engaged in a large-scale research and development effort that was partially

funded by the British government. It was to design and build a machining system that would be coordinated under computer control. The system, like present-day flexible manufacturing systems, addressed itself to the production of relatively modest lot sizes.

The demise of the proposed System 24 has been laid to a number of factors: the company found few customers ready to pay upwards of $1.5-million at the time for an integrated line of six or eight machines; the machines themselves were designed primarily to cut only easily machined aluminum (although subsequent units were made to machine ferrous materials); and software development by British controls builder Ferranti ran into snags. (Ferranti left the NC business seven years ago.)

But, at the time, the System 24 was seen as the next logical step beyond the multiaxis NC machining center, with a concept of "grabbing the workpiece once and not letting go until it is machined."

Its overall structure was to have been similar indeed to today's operational flexible system.

A row of modular, NC machine tools, with contouring capability, and inspection units formed the central line. These were not to have been identical, nor would they each have been capable of complete "machining-center" versatility. They were specialized: some were designed for optimum performance in drilling, some in three-axis milling, and perhaps one in six-axis operations.

The system was to be linked by an automatic transfer mechanism that would deliver workpieces—fixtured on 13 x 13-in. pallets—from setup, to storage, and then to as many of the machine tools as required. Storage during processing was in a rack system reminiscent of the wall in an Automat cafeteria.

An on-line computer would have controlled the overall operation, including scheduling. It was to have performed such functions as seeing that correct workpieces were deliv-

That information, however, is not made public. NMTBA economics-department staff member Joseph Franklin explains that a supplementary report is given only to that portion of the association's membership that contributes to it. Because there's no steady flow of shipments for manufacturing systems yet—they are often completed in clusters—monthly or even quarterly figures on the sale of these large installations can be "very misleading."

The matter is still very much up in the air, according to Franklin. "The committee's position could change in time," he says. "The reporting question is not solved."

If grasping the extent to which flexible manufacturing systems are being installed through machine-tool-industry statistics is an elusive task, getting users to talk about their installations is just as difficult. Competitive pressures that surround any new technology make metalworking companies often reluctant to discuss what may be their pride and joy. In responding to queries about installed systems for this report, for example, Ex-Cell-O Corp said that, while it was active in supplying such machinery, it had to respect the request of its customers not to reveal the concepts or actual hardware it has been developing.

As Prof Hutchinson pointed out to the Numerical Control Society, "At this point, an in-depth review of existing systems is not practical."

Developments abroad

Hutchinson, who has studied flexible manufacturing systems around the world, has some interesting observations about developments in other countries. "The German Democratic Republic," he says, "is clearly one of the leaders, if not *the* leader, in the field, when one considers either operational or planned systems and technology." He points to the PC-3 instal-

lation with its 14 work locations, the Prisma II with ten machine-tool stations, and the Rota class of systems for rotational parts as leading examples.

"In the Federal Republic of Germany, on the other hand," Hutchinson continues, "much of the developmental activity takes place in institutes associated with the universities." Not many systems are currently operational, by comparison with the United States, and emphasis in universities like Berlin and Stuttgart is on developing computer software.

Much attention has been focused on the Japanese MUM (or Methodology for Unmanned Machines) project, which has been succeeded by another government-sponsored developmental effort. The new project (AM—Jul'79,p81) will include blank fabrication, laser processing, and automated diagnosis.

Government support is also a factor in a developmental project undertaken recently by Britain's The 600 Group on a flexible manufacturing system pilot cell. The project (AM—Aug'79,p35) will concentrate on turned components and will use robots for loading small-size batches of parts.

In this country, the National Bureau of Standards maintains an interest in the developing technology of FMSs from a coordination point of view. Activities have centered around robotic cells, according to NBS's James Albus, and the bureau is "fairly well along in its proposal stage for a pilot cell." From his perspective, the NBS role would be to develop standards for interfaces between the control systems and the machinery they govern: items like software, the structure of data bases, even plug compatibility.

The National Bureau of Standards wants to develop a demonstration facility that could document steps taken and could be easily copied by other governmental agencies more directly involved in manufacturing. "We would provide an in-house government laboratory that would be available to

Scale-model mockup shows modular machines, parts-bank racks

ered to proper individual machines and that the desired tape program was automatically loaded.

Ferranti Ltd devised a "jukebox" for tape (magnetic, not punched) cassettes; it consisted of a drum containing up to 60 individual cassettes, each of which had a coded number read electromagnetically. Tapes were selected in ten seconds and slid into a turret that indexed it to a tape reader.

Another feature, available on the stand-alone machines even after the System 24 was abandoned, was automatic toolsetting by the machine tool. Individual machines were programmed to set their own cutters to length as part of the machining cycle.

Molins built a number of the modularized machines after the idea of linking them together was abandoned. Its Unit 1 was a twin-spindle, three-axis contouring machine designed for milling and drilling. Unit 3 was a twin-spindle, three-axis "hole-making" machine for drilling, boring, reaming, and tapping, Unit 6 was a six-axis contour-milling machine that would cut five faces of a cube-

shaped workpiece mounted on its rotary table. (Units 2, 4, and 5, which also were modular and designed for inspection and machining operations, were never built.)

Many of the System 24's concepts are, of course, in use in more modern manufacturing systems. Individual problems have been overcome, largely with the aid of new computer techniques and hardware.

But today's goals remain much the same as those of D.T.N. Williamson, Molins R&D director and manager of the System 24 project. "Primary aim of the system," he wrote at the time the system was proposed, "is the manufacture of a wide range of components, and to do so with a minimum of human intervention still retaining flexibility and the freedom to change."

One goal was to change factory operations so that one shift of setup personnel would be able to "load enough work pallets for three-shift operation of the machines. The line would then continue to operate through the night under computer direction with only a minimum of human monitoring." □

engineers within the Defense Dept, NASA, and other groups," Albus says.

Communication between builder and user

Should a governmental department set interface standards, it would go some distance toward streamlining installation of future FMSs, but most of the effort will still remain in the hands of the users and the machinery suppliers. As it stands, there has to be considerable give-and-take in the planning and design of these systems.

"You have to be able to define your objectives right from the start," says Thomas Shifo, general sales manager for White-Sundstrand Machine Tool Inc (Belvidere, Ill). Both the machinery user and the system supplier have to be willing to sit

Robots link cells of chuckers, shapers, shavers

The job done by a recently installed system for making pinions at Massey-Ferguson Inc's transmission and axle plant in Detroit might have been done by a dedicated transfer line or by hard automation linking separate machine tools.

Instead, the agricultural-equipment manufacturer decided to install a "flexible-automation" system, built around nine stand-alone machines joined into three "cells" by robots. With the new installation, the manufacturer produces four different sizes of parts in the same family: planetary pinion gears.

Boris Kelly, M-F facilities project engineer, was involved in the start-up planning that led to the flexible system's installation. "We were thinking in terms of hard automation—special loaders—for two dual-spindle vertical chuckers," he says. "New Britain Machine suggested a Unimate robot as an alternative to the special loaders.

"Delivery on special loaders at that time would have taken two to three times longer than for off-the-shelf programmable robots," says Kelly. "And cost would have been two to three times higher because the loaders would be custom designs."

At first, Massey-Ferguson felt that the proposed robots would be too sophisticated, but its engineers investigated the experiences of other users, reconsidered, and decided to automate the chuckers with a single robot.

Their experience was much the same when it came to specifying operating conditions for other machine tools they would need. "We asked builders of gear shapers to automate their machines for us," Kelly recalls. "Again cost and delivery times for hard automation were more than we had anticipated.

"At this point, Fab-Tec proposed a system to convey parts from one work cell to the next, leading us to a new approach: a 'flexible transfer line' instead of merely automated individual sections," he says.

In the resulting system, machine tools and robots are integrated into a flexible lineup that includes programmable controllers. The system includes the two New Britain Model 66 chuckers, a trio of Shear Speed gear shapers made by Ex-Cell-O's Michigan Tool operation, three National Broach gear shavers, and a Hammond deburring unit. Fab-Tec provided the conveyor system as well as a series of storage towers. All three robots are Model 2100s from Unimation Inc.

One Allen-Bradley programmable controller is assigned to the conveyor system; another, to the chuckers. A Texas Instruments PC provides interface control for the three gear shavers, the second and third robots, and a deburring station.

In normal operation, broached blanks are delivered to a pickup point near the chuckers, where the first robot loads two pieces at once to one of the lathes, which turns OD and face. Partially turned pinions are banked for redelivery into the other chucking lathe by the same robot, where a second face is turned.

Robot system was cheaper than custom-designed loaders

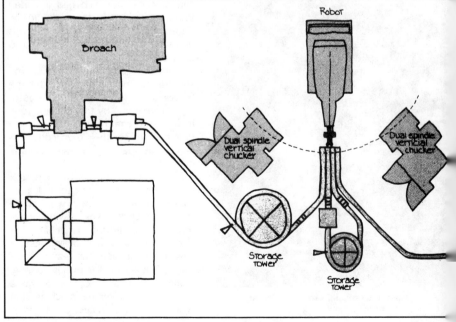

through a number of meetings to decide which available strategy to pursue, he says. "And it's important to get upper-level management involved from the start," he adds.

Fred Tatum, of Giddings & Lewis (Janesville, Wis), agrees, adding that the design of the system might well include a good deal of computer modeling. The computer, as an aid in planning work flow through a manufacturing system, affords more human input in that it hastens the evaluation of different ideas. "There's got to be a great latitude to brainstorm in coming up with the overall plan," he says.

Kearney & Trecker's Klahorst notes that his company's potential customers are becoming more willing to accept the challenge of installing a totally integrated manufacturing system. "Ten years ago, I'd walk in with a stack of prints for a

---

If either vertical chucker is shut down, the robot switches to an alternate loading program in its memory, and all turning steps are performed on the remaining chucker, which is reprogrammed. In that case, turning operations would continue at a slower pace, but the rate of subsequent shaping, deburring, and shaving operations would not be affected until a buffer storage of turned workpieces was exhausted.

This same alternative-program capability exists in the shaping cell, where pinion teeth are cut. If any of the three shapers are out of service, the second manipulator there continues to load partially completed blanks into available machines. This robot also supplies workpieces to a deburring machine, which has its own storage tower.

The third cell performs shaving operations on the pinions. The robot there loads and unloads the shavers with pinions delivered by the conveyor from storage towers.

The system is flexible to accommodate downtime for toolchange of any gear shaver. As with other operations, the robot continues to load and unload the shavers that remain operational, using its alternate program.

In loading the shavers, the robot must mesh the teeth in the pinion gear with those of the cutter. To ensure proper meshing during loading, the manipulator is programmed to loosen its grip on the pinion slightly, so that the workpiece can rotate on its own axis within the gripper until cutter and pinion teeth mesh.

Initially, the line was set up to run only one pinion size: 7 in. OD and 28 lb, the largest in the family. However, it was designed to handle three other pinion sizes, the smallest having a 3½-in. OD and weighing 8 lb.

Now pinions are run through the system in batches, grouped by size. Changeover from a batch of, say, 7-in. pinions to a batch of 3½-in. ones requires retooling and resetting each of the machine tools and retooling each of the robotic grippers. In the case of the robots, changeover time is reduced since commands for the grippers are stored in memory.

It is the memorized programs of the robots that govern system operations. Included at strategic places in the program, which is memorized as

the robots are led through proper sequences with a teach control, are commands to issue control signals to the machine tools and conveyors.

"From our experience so far in running parts, we find that the robotic manufacturing system is about as fast as manned operation on a short-term basis," says Boris Kelly. "But we estimate that the system is about 25% more productive over the long term because of consistency of operation."

Massey-Ferguson reports that the use of the robotized, conveyorized system has resulted in substantial savings in work-in-process inventory costs. "With a manual system," Kelly says, "when you have parts in individual containers, it is difficult to control workpiece inventory. With the new system, we know where each part is and how many parts are in the system at any time."

Projected pay-back for the entire automated grouping was to have been 1½ years under single-shift operation. With the saving in reduced in-process inventory, the economic justification becomes even more favorable. □

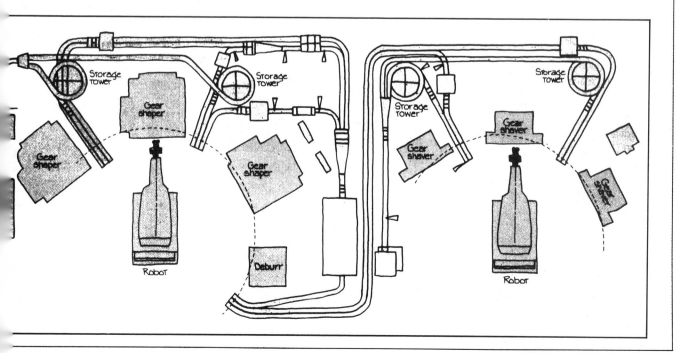

manufacturing system, and I'd be laughed at. Today people are conscious of their problems and come up with questions like 'what would you propose to manufacture this or that at such-and-such a rate?' "

At that point, K&T will develop two or three approaches, put them into a feasibility study, and present it to the prospective FMS user. A later discussion will zero in on one particular approach, and the idea will start to take shape. It may take months, or years, to get to the actual order.

With so much front-end engineering effort placed into

drawing up an FMS, the time spent is invariably longer than for most other machinery acquisitions. It's not uncommon for Bendix Machine Tool Corp (Warren, Mich), for example, to see 12 months elapse between the time a potential customer first becomes interested in buying a system and the order—or cancellation—date, according to Donald Lamb, the firm's vice president for special products.

One reason for that time stretch may be that a potential user simply does not have the standby engineering staff to quickly evaluate a large-scale operating system. By contrast, the auto-

Wire-guided carts would carry aircraft cylinder heads

It's not yet an operational system; it may never be. But the flexible machining system that Cincinnati Milacron is presently quoting for a large aircraft-engine manufacturer includes some interesting concepts in workpiece handling and in-process parts flow around 13 stand-alone machining centers and head-indexing machines.

Milacron is sworn to secrecy about the potential customer's name and certain details of the system operation. That is not unusual in the quoting and cost-negotiation interchange between a customer and a systems supplier. But, when engineers at the US's largest machine-tool builder describe some of the system's features, particularly the cart system, it is apparent that it's more than a speculative concept drawing.

Battery-powered carts (photo, bottom right) that follow wires embedded in the factory floor constitute an unusual feature of the proposed system. To the builder, they represent the latest in control and materials-handling technology.

"Fifteen years ago, you'd have used a conveyor," says D. Michael Clabaugh, manager of machine-tool products. "Ten years ago, it was tow chains or a railroad-track system.

"But those concepts had certain disadvantages," he says. With a tow chain, big in-floor pulleys located at corners might, for example, hinder tight-radius turns. There'd be inevitable stretching of the chain, and users would find that they'd constantly have to open up the towline and remove links to take up slack.

Last, but perhaps most important, says Clabaugh, is that rerouting to new machines would mean an extensive ripping up of the floor to install a new conveyor or towchain.

In the projected machining system, the randomly dispatched carts have on-board circuitry that both follows

the floor wire and communicates with a central interrogating controller via that wire, using a low-power transceiver.

In following the wire, which is placed in a shallow trench a few inches below floor level and covered over with an epoxy patching compound, the carts use one of two undercarriage antennas mounted toward each longitudinal end of the vehicle. "Actually, there is no front or rear," says John Lannom, manager of application engineering for Milacron's advanced-systems operation. "Each end carries identical bumpers, and the cart moves in both directions with equal ease."

A pair of drive wheels are mounted on a single axle, located midway down the length of the cart. Free-wheeling casters support each of the corners, so that the cart is free to rotate around a pivot point that lies at the center of the single axle.

In transit, the cart "sniffs" the underground wire that lies under the centerline of its forward directional-antenna array. The antenna senses a turn or bend in the route by detecting that the wire's signal gets stronger to the left or right of the antenna. That signal is processed by the on-board computer and is used to command one or the other of the drive wheels' servomotors to slow down, "effec-

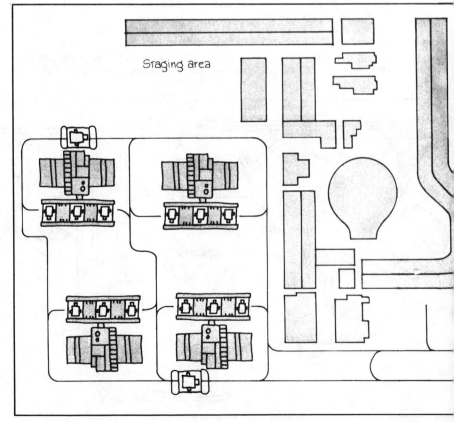

Staging area

mobile industry, Lamb says, will provide a supplier with a yes/no decision within two to three weeks of a preliminary quote. But more-flexible systems like the kind that Bendix is promoting are bringing transfer-line-scale investment decisions to industries that have been accustomed to buying production equipment on a one-at-a-time basis. So the selection inevitably takes longer as smaller staffs take a hard look at the proposed centerpiece of their factory.

By and large, the machine-tool companies that supply total manufacturing systems are more than willing to work with user staffs. Most even offer assistance in going through the accounting procedures necessary to economically justify installation of an FMS.

As K&T's Klahorst puts it, "We're not talking about machines selected out of a catalog; there's got to be a lot of negotiation."

Transport—whether it is the workpiece or the workhead that is moved—is one of the distinguished marks of a flexible manufacturing system.

Designers have a choice: moving the workpiece from one

tively turning the cart like a Cat tractor." The turn is stopped when the antenna again senses that it is centered over the wire. Each cart moves independently, under computer control.

"It's like a fleet of taxicabs rather than a rapid-transit railroad line," says Kendall Bone, engineering supervisor at Cincinnati Milacron.

Seven carts will service the 13 machine tools, although the number of carts is easily adjusted, says Clabaugh. When a cart arrives at a machine tool, it locates on hydraulic jacks connected to the queuing table of the machine. The workpiece carrier (dark green in the schematic below) on each cart is lowered hydraulically and slides into position in the waiting line.

Positioning tolerances for placing the pallet onto the queue are admittedly sloppy, but Clabaugh says that, when the 32-in.-sq pallet is moved by the machine tool onto its cutting table, V-blocks there permit accurate location.

The proposed VMM2 line (for Variable Mission Manufacturing, Milacron's automated-factory concept originally proposed in the 1960s) is dedicated to a family of parts: aircraft-engine cylinder heads. Each of the 11 traveling-column horizontal-spindle machining centers carries two tool matrices, each with 30 tool pockets, for a total of 660 individual tools available for processing.

In addition, there are two machines that index multispindle heads for gang drilling, tapping, and similar opera-

tions. These head indexers hold the preset tool clusters on a turret mounted on a central axis tilted 45° up from the horizontal; when called up, the turret swings the appropriate head down into a horizontal position, ready for Z-axis feed into the palletized workpiece.

"The head indexers are not what you'd call one of our catalog items," says a spokesman for the builder, "but we've had some experience in putting them together, and they are proven designs."

The builder will not say whether the plan called for operating the system on a batch basis or on a totally random basis within a certain parts family but does point out that the basic design would accommodate either form of operation. □

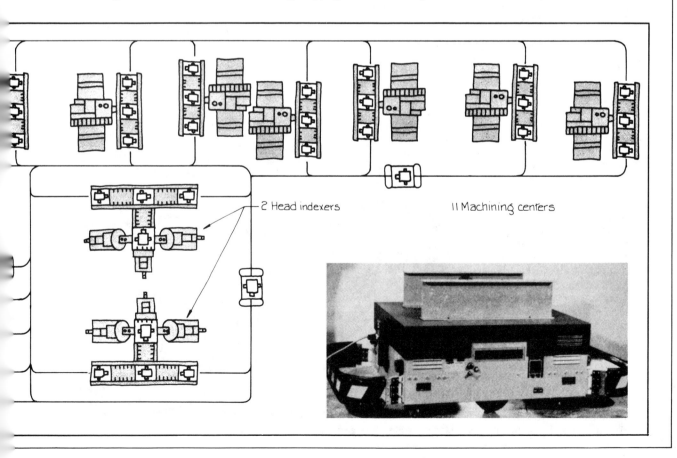

2 Head indexers   11 Machining centers

machine tool to a more dedicated one or bringing certain specialized elements of a machine tool to a stationary workpiece, as in a headchanger. Their choice is predicated on the shape and size of the workpiece, the degree of specialization of the machine, available floor space, and even just plain designer preference. And it's possible to mix the alternatives: to move the workpiece from one flexible, single-spindle machine to a headchanger where specialized spindle clusters are then sequentially changed.

Parts: round or prismatic

Starting with the shape and size, many systems designers draw a distinction between workpieces that are generally "prismatic," or cube-shaped, and those that require rotation, such as gears, disks, and the like.

Work that must be turned is almost invariable free-standing—that is, not bolted to a pallet. For these parts, roller conveyors are good transport mechanisms, and, by adding robotic manipulators to factory conveyor lines, many manufacturers achieve flexibility with fairly standard handling equipment.

"As it turns out in the real world of production, most 'parts of rotation' are well within the weight limitations of robots,"

says Mike Clabaugh, Cincinnati Milacron's manager of machine-tool products. "That fact, plus the design of the present-day slant-bed lathe, means that three-quarters of all rotational parts can be phyisically handled in a robot-centered cell."

A conveyor/robot/lathe combination forms the workpiece-processing system that has been under study at the Technical Univ of Berlin by a team headed by Prof G. Spur. Although it is relatively simple in its composition, the manufacturing cell is very flexible in its functions. It incorporates such features as automatic clamping a wide variety of workpiece diameters with controlled clamping force, automatic measurement of the finished part, and controlled toolchanges. Object of the test-bed cell is to develop the computer software to enable a group of such cells to be integrated into an overall system capable of processing short production runs and even single parts at random.

A robot-centered manufacturing cell drew widespread attention at the 1978 International Machine Tool Show, where, in the DoAll booth, a manipulator sequentially loaded, unloaded, and stacked parts going through several different machining operations, including milling and drilling. A robot cell does not necessarily constitute a manufacturing system, but it can go a

Paired headchangers give transmission line its flexibility

Tractor-transmission cases machined at the J I Case plant in Racine, Wis, don't move around much.

Instead, Case relies on the agility of a pair of headchanger machine tools integrated into a line to shuttle different specialized workheads to the parts.

The result is a fairly dedicated, yet inherently flexible line in which the 1300-lb gray-iron castings move through only six machines as they become cases for either 8-speed or 12-speed transmissions in high-horse-power agricultural vehicles.

Back in 1976, when engineers for the farm-implement manufacturer were planning a new series of two-wheel-drive tractors to be introduced two years later, they sought to incorporate other major components into the transmission cases. The resulting design, which won an award from the Iron Castings Society, included parts that were formerly bolt-ons: a rocker-shaft housing, a top cover, filter and brake housings. The new transmission-case design also called for more-intricate machining.

"We looked over various suppliers and went to Ingersoll Milling Machine Co," says Robert Riebau, vice president and general manager for J I Case's components division. The headchanger-machine concept then being developed by the Rockford, Ill, machine-tool builder was particularly appealing, he says. The concept was

incorporated into a machining lineup installed early in 1978.

Each of the two headchangers moves a series of machining heads that sequentially serve a single work station. The machines consist of palletized work fixtures, a load/unload pallet shuttle, a four-position index table, a feed slide with dual spindle drivers, and a recirculating head-transfer mechanism.

Twenty-two individual heads are

shared between the two headchangers, providing a total of 188 hole-making or similar operations in each workpiece cycle. Heads range in weight from 8000 to 12,000 lb. They roll along a rectangular track, driven by a towchain, rather than being suspended from an overhead conveyor.

Each headchanger is equipped with a Spaulding Instruments programmable limit switch that replaces many

One of two headchangers sequences heads to pallet, foreground

long way toward providing—through the programming of the robot—a lot of flexibility in operations.

Unimation Inc (Danbury, Conn), the pioneering robot producer that supplied the manipulator for that DoAll IMTS demonstration, apparently recognizes this fact. Last fall, the company replaced its internal-applications-engineering department with a new Applications & Systems Div. Its beefed-up staff will focus on the entire manufacturing process, says Unimation, rather than looking at isolated pockets for robot applications. The new division reportedly has already been besieged with consulting requests.

Robots obviously can handle boxy parts as well as they can handle round ones. But those prismatic parts are often likely to be larger and heavier than a robot can easily heft, and so they are candidates for palletizing. Transporting parts that have been prefixtured on pallets opens up a whole range of conveyance methods.

Move the palletized workpiece

One relatively simple method calls for use of roller conveyors like those used in robotics applications. Consider such a workpiece-transport system in use two decades ago in a Westinghouse turbine-engine plant, where Sundstrand machines were linked by a waist-high conveyor loop that carried turbine blades, grouped by families, through stations for different machining jobs. A continuously running drag chain led roller-supported pallet carriers through 16 stations. The system (AM—Dec9'63,p97) was sequential, not flexible, but it indicated what could be done to automate stand-alone machine tools.

Cincinnati Milacron, in developing the concept for its Variable Mission I manufacturing system in 1968, relied on waist-level roller conveyors that used pallets to take the workpiece to each station. In one proposed variation of the VMM, palletized parts flowed around a cluster of machine tools on what looked like, in plan view, a ladder, with individual machines located in the center of each rung and work flow moving up one side and down the other. Pallets were coded for each desired machine at the system's staging area, and workers at switching points along the route could move pallets toward their intended destination by switching a pallet to the correct "ladder rung."

Roller conveyors are not the only means of moving pallets around. They can be mounted on vehicles that ride on fixed tracks, on the factory floor, or on an air or fluid cushion. The vehicles may be self-powered like rapid-transit railroad cars, pulled along by underground tow-chains like cable cars, contin-

---

cam-operated mechanical limit switches and controls Z-axis slide motion to within 0.005 in. In operation, each head that is sequentially loaded onto the feed slide automatically selects its own preprogrammed rapid advance, feed, dwell, and rapid return. The head identifies itself by the configuration of four dogs located on an upper corner, signaling a computer to send appropriate signals to control the slide's rapid-advance/rapid-return motor and its feed motor.

In addition to the two headchangers, four other machine tools are used in processing the transmission cases. The workpieces, fixtured onto pallets, are moved from the first machine through the last by a series of nonpowered roller conveyors and conventional lifting mechanisms.

At the first machine, an Ingersoll traveling-table mill, locating surfaces on the case's top, bottom, and both ends are milled. Palletized workpieces are then transferred to a table-level roller conveyor servicing an Ex-Cell-O 508 machining center, which cuts both sides and front end.

The headchangers are next in line, followed by another Ex-Cell-O horizontal-spindle machining center, which performs boring, facing, drilling, and reaming jobs. Parts re-enter the conveyor serving the fifth machine and are rolled to the last machine, an Ingersoll shuttle-table boring mill that performs finish-boring.

JI Case has been running each of the two transmission-case configurations in rather large batches, more than 100 at a time in most situations, according to Riebau. "But the inherent flexibility imparted by the pro-

grammable controls on the headchangers as well as the CNCs on the machining center makes it easy to go from one transmission to the other," he says.

In the year and a half that the six-machine line has been operating in Racine, it has worked pretty much to specifications, according to Riebau. He quickly adds that, should one of the headchangers go out of service for a considerable period, it would be relatively simple to move heads to the other machine and operate at a somewhat reduced rate compared with normal.

Similarly, initial line setup and debugging went well, Riebau reports, but, in start-up production, "we found out that those machines generated a heck of a lot of chips." Case had to beef up the chip conveyors to handle the load. □

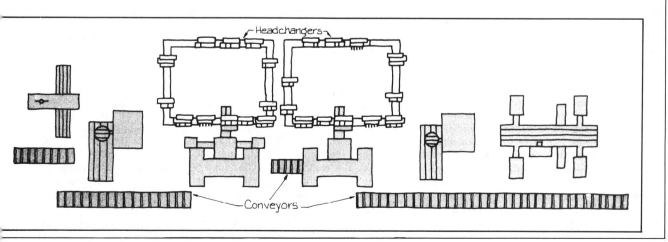

---

uously driven by track-mounted leadscrews like machine-tool slides, or indexed along a straight line as in a transfer machine.

The pallets may be positioned along their route by physical stops, by signals generated by encoders along the way to halt the drive motors, by signals from an implanted wire in the floor, or by special "smart" drive motors.

Naturally, there are tradeoffs to be considered in comparisons of all those options. Manufacturing-systems designers emphasize that the handling system must be tailored to the anticipated workpiece. In palletized, prismatic parts, weight becomes a prime factor.

The car in the pallet-shuttle used on typical White-Sunstrand Omniline manufacturing systems, for example, travels on a pair of track rails and is capable of supporting 8000-lb loads in transit, double that while stationary, as during a pallet swap at a machine or loading station. The 10,000-lb, 22-ft car consists of two major elements: an automatic rotary pallet changer and the powered transporter unit it is mounted on. A dc motor with a timing-belt drive moves the car, which is driven by a spur gear engaged with the gear rack mounted on the inside of one of the track rails.

The Omniline car (see p220) receives power and control signals via a mast from a free-standing bus-bar system, located 12 ft overhead. Sensing bumpers on each end stop the car when its path is obstructed, but normal stops are signaled from the controller, which determines the car's location by reading signals from an encoder connected by pinion to the track's rack.

A double-rail cart system is also the one favored by Giddings & Lewis Inc, which locates its manufacturing-systems program at its Gilman Engineering division. Fred Tatum, who manages the G&L systems operation, notes that, while it is a good idea to transport the workpiece on occasion, better economies can be obtained by keeping the workpiece reasonably stationary and moving it to a different machine only when necessary. He places great reliance on toolchangers, rather than pallet carts.

In one G&L-proposed manufacturing system, for example, a shuttle car rides back and forth on a straight track in front of five machine tools: a pair of VTLs (with toolchangers), a pair of horizontal-spindle machining centers (with toolchangers and rotary tables), and a single headchanger machine (which, in appearance, is mostly toolchanger).

The pallets-riding-rails approach appears also on an FMS at the Herbert Warnke machine-tool plant in East Germany, among other installations.

Carts roll along floor

Kearney & Trecker, too, has taken a cart approach in its flexible-manufactuing-system installations. But the carts that the Milwaukee builder has used are not run on railroad-type tracks; instead, they run on the plant floor, pulled by an in-floor conveyor.

There are a number of advantages to this configuration, not the least of which is an unobstructed floor where people and fork-lift trucks can move with ease.

An unobstructed floor is one of the prime reasons that Cincinnati Milacron is promoting the concept of wire-following battery-powered carts. The builder has done considerable developmental work in modifying Eaton-Kenway Robocarrier carts that use a pair of undercariage antennas to "sniff out" and follow a transmitting wire buried just under the floor. (The idea had been adapted to mail-delivery carts for office buildings, where the guidance wire is simply laid under the carpet.) In addition to the wire-guidance mode (see story, p176), a plug-in umbilical connects to a handheld controller to steer the carts off the floor wire.

The 32-in.-sq pallets that will ride these carts won't accom-modate the largest of workpieces, but they will carry some 80% of all workpieces normally cut on the machining centers that the carts are meant to service, according to Milacron's Clabaugh. "If we tried to address 100% of the part sizes possible," he says, "we'd lose part of our ability to standardize system components."

Pallets move on fluid stream

That's not to say that Milacron and other builders shrink from transporting huge workpieces when they have to. A case in point is the hull-fabrication line for the XM-1 Abrams tank that the builder has installed in the Chrysler-operated Lima (Ohio) Modification Center. That line, although not a true "flexible manufacturing system" in the sense that it is dedicated to only one workpiece, moves 40-ton workpiece/pallet combinations to each of four machining stations sequentially. It does this with a fluid transport shuttle.

Lifting heavy workpieces by a captive stream of air is not really new. So-called air casters, akin to Hovercraft, have been used for years in shipyards for moving huge sections of freighters and tankers, and a number of air-supported pallet designs have moved into the factory, where they have transported loads across relatively smooth floors.

Prisma 2, the early (begun in 1972) FMS used in the East German factory run by the Fritz Heckert Combine (AM—Aug'78,p153), uses a sophisticated air-cushion support and linear induction motors to transfer heavy milling-machine sections through ten machine tools and two wash stations.

"But we found out that air is too spongy," says Ken Bone, an application engineer at Milacron. For the Chrysler tank-hull line, a water-bag system—actually, filled with coolant—is used. Pallet transfer is nonsynchronous, although there is no real provision for queuing since the individual stations are well balanced to each other. During transfer, the water bag is inflated, lifting the pallet; one of four "rabbits"—one for each station—then lifts, tugs, brakes, and drops the pallet, allowing it to float down into proper position.

Accuracy for work location is not so critical on the tank line as on other systems, partly because a pair of headchanger machine tools can provide tight tolerances between hole centers in those situations where it is important. So final pallet positioning at each station in the transfer line is accomplished with hydraulic clamping and heavy-duty shot pins.

Accuracy of docking maneuver

In the XM-1 tank-hull line, the pallet shuttle becomes, in effect, part of the machine tool, since it serves as the machine table during cutting. But most flexible machining systems that move the work rather than the machine separate the conveyance mechanism from the machine's worktable. When that is the case, a docking maneuver is needed to shift the part from cart to machine table, and this raises questions about positioning accuracy: if the shuttle cart is misaligned with the table during the docking, the pallet is likely to crash during the workpiece swap.

System designers attack the potential problem in a number of ways, as might be expected. Hard stops with limit switches may be used, as in some K&T arrangements where a fin-shaped tab juts up from the in-floor tow-chain. In Sundstrand systems, engineers favor mounting an encoder to the car; engaged to a track-mounted rack, the encoder provides the line's controller with continuous information on its position, much like a DRO on a machine slide. Cincinnati Milacron won't specify the proprietary pallet interface it is developing between the wire-following carts it uses and the shuttle tables affixed to the machining centers in its proposed systems.

Although it is not yet serving that function, the new I-drive from Ingersoll Milling Machine Co might have some interesting applications for positioning shuttle-mounted work for loading on a machine table. The ac drive uses an integral microprocessor that not only "knows" its position at any time but can store movements commands for programmed acceleration, deceleration, and stops.

Move the machine, not the workpiece

Many manufacturing systems achieve flexibility by being able to move a workpiece from one stand-alone machine to another. But who's to say that the completely opposite approach is not just as efficient? Why not keep the workpiece in a fixed location, then move machine elements to it?

Single-spindle NC machining centers equipped with toolchangers do this to some extent. They usually can't provide the dedication of function—cluster drilling, gang tapping, etc—needed to efficiently handle more than low-volume production, hence can't really be termed manufacturing systems. But what of a stand-alone machine that brings *multispindle* heads to the workpiece, or one that can exhange toolchanger drums to automatically avail itself of a selection of single-spindle tools

Stand-alone system moves tool magazines, not workpieces

A flexible "system" need not have workpieces moving all over the factory floor; the tools, instead, can do the moving.

That's the principle behind the integrated YMS (for Yamazaki Machining System) soon to be installed at George J. Meyer Mfg in Cudahy, Wis. The manufacturing system is fitted with two tables (one rotates) so that setup can be done on one while machining is done at the other. But its flexibility is a result of moving tools: whole 30-pocket drum-shaped toolstorage magazines are exchanged onto the machine's central column, and the column also travels to a rack where it can accept multispindle heads.

Meyer Manufacturing, a division of A-T-O Inc (Willoughby, Ohio), makes automatic packaging and bottling machinery, labeling machines, and rinsing and inspection equipment for beverage-bottling lines. When it is installed, the YMS will be assigned a variety of metalcutting jobs, including fabrication of filler bowls and other large components of filling machinery.

Engineers at Meyer Mfg are understandably reluctant to discuss detailed plans for the machine, which, at press time, had just gone through tryouts at the Yamazaki plant near Nagoya, Japan, and was en route to Wisconsin. "It will actually be some time before we have good data to report on how it runs," says Jerry Rhode, manager of manufacturing and industrial engineering at Meyer.

The machine represents the first full-production use of the YMS in this country, but another, larger-horsepower machine has been operating in the Florence, Ky, plant of its builder, and a third has been running at a Norwegian shipyard. A fourth YMS is due to be delivered to Ladish Co, a manufacturer of specialty pipe fittings and large welding flanges that, coincidentally, is also located in Cudahy.

Meyer Mfg's machining system consists of three separate "corridors" that, respectively, are dedicated to machining, tool storage, and workholding. In the central corridor, a traveling-column, horizontal-spindle unit moves along an X-axis runway and "visits" various stations along the outer corridors.

The outer, workholding corridor faces the 30-hp machining spindle and consists of a workholding bedplate, another workholding station with an 80-in. rotary table, and a three-shelf rack that holds the multispindle heads.

At the rear of the traveling column, a tooling corridor supports four drum-shaped tool-storage magazines. Under numerical control, each carousel-shaped magazine can be shifted onto the machining column, where it then

rotates, as a normal toolchanger does, for access to individual tools.

The carousels can hold tools up to about 8½ in. dia (with adjacent pockets empty). When larger individual tools or multiple-spindle toolheads are required, the double-pillar column moves opposite the rack adjacent to the rotary table and extends through its Z-axis, engaging the heavier tools shelved on the rack.

So, although the typical workpiece on the Meyer Mfg machining system will not move, just about everything else will. Keeping the workpiece stationary, says Ted Niwa, director of Yamazaki's Mazak Machine Tool Div, which is setting up the Meyer system, is actually one of the biggest advantages of the machine, particularly when very large workpieces are involved. □

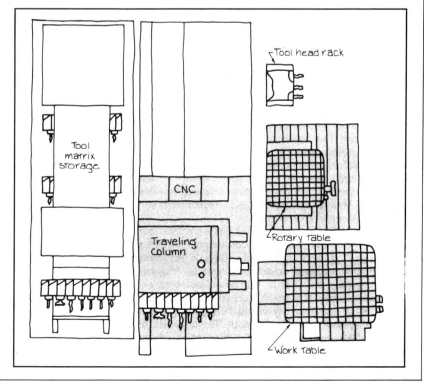

FLEXIBILITY in manufacturing systems

that quadruples or better the tools normally selectable on a machining center?

Among this class of machine system, Bendix Machine Tool Div (Warren, Mich) favors the headchanger approach. Two years ago, when that machine-tool builder unveiled its machine, its purpose was to "fit" halfway between single-spindle machines and big transfer lines. Since then, the concept has evolved into much more.

The Bendix flexible machining system is centered around a Z-axis slide that drives the working toolhead. When retracted, the slide accepts 2-ft-sq toolheads, which are loaded onto it with a transfer bar similar to one that shuttles workpieces along a transfer machine. Toolheads, which can carry up to 17 spindles, are swapped in under 3 seconds; physical codes on each head identify them to a CNC, which can shuffle heads past when they are not needed for a particular workpiece.

As in other headchanger machines, the Bendix design carries waiting heads around in a circuit. In this case, they are hung from a monorail conveyor, but other designs for the toolhead track are possible. Both the Cross Multi-Center and the Ingersoll headchanger, for example, use waist-level tracked tables that let the heads roll in a roughly circular loop; Cincinnati Milacron's headchanger also uses a table conveyor but minimizes floor space by stacking two straight conveyors one atop the other—one moving left, the other right—and connects the two with a pair of elevators at each end.

What makes headchangers true systems and more versatile than head-indexing machines is what is done with the heads while they wait for sequencing onto the feed slide to meet the workpiece. The conveyor permits them to be shunted on to spurs for tool resetting, rolled to other machines when needed, or just placed into temporary storage. It is relatively simple, for instance, to store a series of dedicated toolheads on a single "railroad siding" and to bring them into the main circuit—either by manual or automatic switching—when the part family that is being run on the machine is changed.

In the case of some high-volume industries like automotive, those sidelined heads could well be ones adapted from a transfer line that was disassembled at the end of a model run. Dedicated heads from many transfer machines could thus be held in storage on a single headchanger, waiting for batches of replacement or service parts to be run.

Link conveyor tracks together

When two or more headchangers are linked by tooling conveyors, a degree of insurance is built into the system: should one machine be taken out of service, the others have access to the tooling, and production can continue. A good example of this concept is the three-headchanger system being installed by Bendix Machine Tool at Deere & Co's Moline, Ill, plant. The three units, arranged in a U-shape around a central workpiece area, all share the common head conveyor, which carries as many as 90 toolheads. Each unit has a bypass so that the machine can work in any combination, selecting heads out of storage. Part of the unused toolheads are stored above the machining system to save floor space.

A variation on the headchanger theme exchanges not only multispindle toolheads but also tool-storage matrices filled with individual standard-shank tools. This is the Yamazaki Machining System (YMS) in which a traveling column with horizontal spindle can slide to face a toolhead-storage rack, where it can advance forward in the Z-axis and pick up heads. Alternatively, a rear shuttle system can bring up individual tool carousels filled with up to 30 tools each. The carousels, once in position on the machining column, then rotate to present individual cutting tools to an automatic toolchanger that inserts them into the spindle.

Although the system, which is designed to be installed

almost as a stand-alone machine tool, has appeared only in single-column configuration, it is designed to be able to share the column slideway among several machining columns, Thus, the tool carousels and multispindle tools can be shared among a number of maching stations.

Manufacturing systems, the organizing of productive machinery and other resources for efficient output, have been part of America's metalworking scene for a long time—they can be traced back to the New England armories of the early 19th Century. What is changing today is the way they are conceived and installed. The flexibility that remains the goal is made possible by changes in control technology and in the machine tools themselves.

Machine-tool-technology changes are coming fast. James A.D. Geier, president of Cincinnati Milacron, underlined that recently when he told a group of Cleveland financial analysts that, in 1978, about 44% of his company's sales were in products not made by Milacron five years prior.

What's ahead in systems

Where is that technology taking manufacturers? In 1977, the Society of Manufacturing Engineers conducted a Delphi-type survey among industry experts on the question of manufacturing systems. The resulting consensus forecast placed anticipated dates on the step-by-step acceptance of manufacturing systems with their characteristic flexibility.

About 10% of existing NC machine tools in 1982 will be connected to a dispatch or control computer, the survey predicted. That percentage will increase to 25% by 1987.

Two years hence, an estimated 10% of total machine-tool production will not have a stand-alone use but will be part of a versatile manufacturing system, with automatic part-handling between stations and control by a central computer. Seven years from now, the survey said, that percentage will increase to 15% of total machine-tool production.

Some 12% of the cost of new manufacturing systems will be allocated to automatic material-handling components in two years, the SME poll predicted. Five years later, 20% of total costs will go toward handling machinery.

The use of flexible machine-tool systems, ill-defined as the systems concept may be right now, will be of central concern throughout most of the metalworking community. It is for that reason that it forms a functional topic now being analyzed by the Machine Tool Task Force, a group of about 100 experts organized under the aegis of the Dept of Defense. That group's report, due in October, will devote approximately one-quarter of its scope to the management of machine-tool systems.

For most mid-volume manufacturers, installation of flexible systems is likely to raise brand-new questions: how do you direct traffic with independent carts moving freely about? how does warehousing fit in? optimizing feeds and speeds?

But there can be little doubt that flexible manufacturing systems are a reality, and on a worldwide basis. What these multimillion-dollar installations offer users is the opportunity to change rapidly with market demands, to built a manufacturing facility that can easily incorporate subsequent additions, and, for some, to remain alive in a competitive market-place. ∎

'NEW WAVE' in manufacturing

Visualize a conveyor-linked line of specialized, multi-spindle, contouring NC machines with automatic toolchanging—controlled by an on-line computer

By D T N Williamson, Director of Research & Development
Molins Machine Company, Ltd, London, England

The metalworking plant described briefly at the left is actually being built at the Deptford Works of Molins Machine Co. The installation is scheduled for completion and initial operation early in 1968. Not a far-out research project, the Molins 'System 24' results from hard-headed economics in building industrial machines for a profit. Furthermore, the underlying concept is not 'mass production.' The system has been conceived mainly for the production of relatively modest lot sizes.

Economic studies indicate the system will be able to reduce the cost of manufacturing machined components by a factor of between five and ten, as compared to con-

1. **Automatic transfer devices move palletized work** from setting stations to storage rack to NC machine tools. Scale model shows completely modular arrangement of computerized system

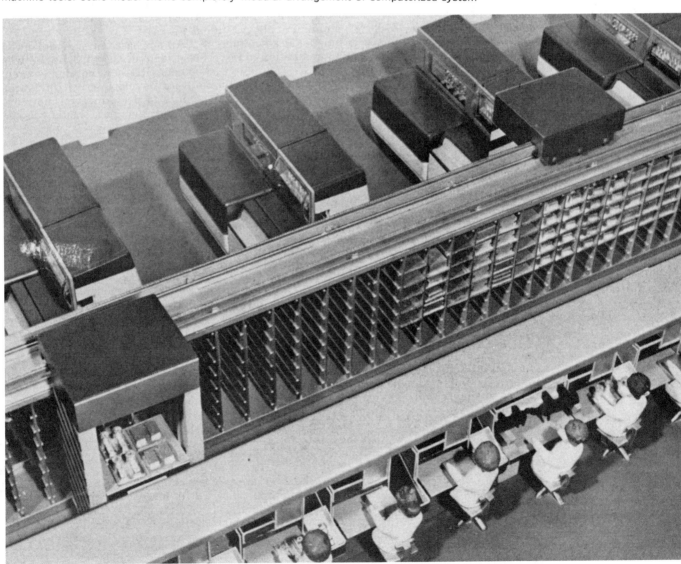

ventional methods. It will bring major reductions in requirements for floor space and personnel. And, most surprisingly, Molins anticipates no increase in capital investment for a given level of output.

Converting System 24 from an idea into a producing reality has demanded considerable new thinking and the development of new hardware components at virtually every step of the way. Basically, it is the next logical step beyond the multi-axis NC machining center, with its concept of 'grabbing the workpiece once and not letting go until it is machined.'

Briefly, a System 24 installation (Fig. 1) would consist mainly of:

■ A row of modular, numerically controlled machine tools with contouring capability. Say, six or eight of them. These will not be identical, nor will each be capable of complete 'machining center' versatility. Rather, they will be specialized in that some will be designed for optimum performance in drilling, some in three-axis milling, and perhaps one in six-axis operations. All but the six-axis unit will be twin-spindle machines for faster metal removal.

■ An automatic transfer mechanism that will deliver pallet-fixtured workpieces from setup, to storage, and thence to as many of the machine tools as are required.

■ An on-line computer that will control the overall operation, including scheduling. This will perform such functions as seeing to it that the correct workpieces are delivered to the proper individual machines (in the right sequence if more than one machine is required to complete the workpiece), and that the desired machining tape is automatically loaded.

Primary aim of the system is the manufacture of a wide range of relatively small machined components of varying complexity, and to do so with a minimum of human intervention, still retaining flexibility and freedom to change.

As an example of what this is likely to mean in factory operations, it is anticipated that one shift of setup personnel (probably female) will be able to load enough work pallets for three-shift operation of the machines. The line would then continue to operate through the night under computer direction with only a minimum of human monitoring.

The machines of System 24

Components to be manufactured with the system will primarily be of aluminum alloys. Molins' decision to design most machine parts in aluminum stems from this metal's excellent machinability, which provides production economies significantly outweighing the added costs of the material. Further, since materials are purchased on a weight basis and most often used on a volumetric basis, the light weight of aluminum tends to reduce this cost premium.

Some other industries have come to the same conclusion, especially manufacturers of computer equipment and business machines.

Internal surveys indicated that 70% of Molins' machined components were within a size of 12 x 12 x 6 in., and that between 80 and 90% of metal parts could, in fact, be made of aluminum alloys. In many cases, functional advantages could be gained in addition to faster machining.

Experience has confirmed the validity of this approach, and the metal components of Molins' new range of machines are almost entirely of aluminum alloy.

Thus, the machining envelope of the System 24 sub-units is defined, and the machines must be capable of high spindle speeds to take full advantage of aluminum's excellent machinability.

Limited 5-axis needs

Most industrial components are designed with relatively simple geometry and most machining can usually be done by a unit with three-axis capability. However, about 50% of potential NC parts at Molins require some five-axis capability. While this may consist only of a hole at some awkward angle or a tilted pipe-connection flange, a five-axis capability must be included in the system to avoid workpiece resetting. In general, such work accounts for considerably less than 10% of the machining on the part.

If a single machining center were to be used for machining all components, it would therefore have to have full five-axis capability. But this would necessitate some compromises in its design, as

well as increasing its cost. Three-axis machines are simpler, less costly, lend themselves more easily to greater rigidity (hence higher metal removal rates), and are much more easily designed with simultaneously cutting multiple spindles for even greater metal removal capability.

This introduces the concept of a group of specialized complementary sub-units, some with three-axis capability and perhaps only one with five-axis possibilities. As a further refinement, some of the three-axis machines are designed for optimum performance in milling, and others for hole manufacturing (drilling, reaming, boring, tapping). Thus, three basic types of machining sub-units have been developed: a six-axis mill-drill, a three-axis mill, and a three-axis drill.

All are based on a modular concept, and all accept the same work pallets. Further, nothing prevents future development of other machines to perform even more specialized functions, should the need arise.

Horizontal for chip clearing

Since the machines are conceived to operate with minimum human intervention—and to remove chips at a high rate—a horizontal spindle configuration was selected to allow chips to fall free of the machining area. An under-floor chip conveyor then removes the scrap.

The three-axis milling units (Fig. 2), which have an effective speed of about four times the metal removal rate of the six-axis machine, are intended specifically for high metal removal rates on aluminum alloy workpieces in combination with high surface finishes. They feature twin, horizontal spindles driven by Pelton-wheel oil turbines (Fig. 3). Speed ranges are between 8000 and 30,000 rpm, and up to 24 bhp is developed at the spindle.

The second type of three-axis machine, which may be called a drill for convenience, is intended primarily for hole production (drilling, reaming, boring, and tapping), but also includes a contour milling capability. Its twin

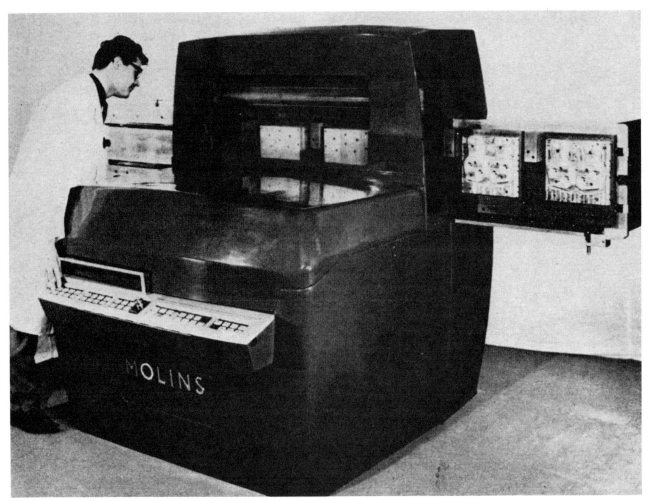

2. Modular twin-spindle NC milling machine has been running for three years. 'Wings' facilitate manual loading and unloading of pallets, which will be fully automatic in complete installation

horizontal spindles are driven by hydraulic motors through a two-speed gear unit in speed ranges of 0 to 1800 rpm (in either direction) and 2200 to 5200 rpm. At speeds above the tapping range, between 2 and 9 bhp is available at each spindle.

Aside from these details and some small differences in the hydraulic actuators for optimum performance in each machine type, the three-axis twin-spindle machines are otherwise identical.

Two Meehanite castings form the main frame. The rear casting houses the vertically moving Y-slide, which is an aluminum alloy casting carrying the twin vertical worktables, and a cutter magazine above. The X-slide, also aluminum, moves horizontally in the front frame casting, and carries with it the Z-slide (a Meehanite casting) mounting the spindles.

Slide motion is provided in all cases by a combined hydraulic ac-

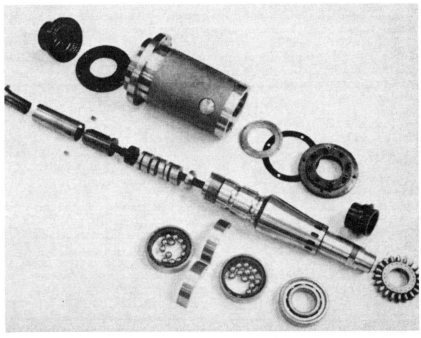

3. Pelton-wheel oil turbine (extreme right) drives milling spindle at 8000 to 30,000 rpm for high metal removal rate on aluminum alloy workpieces

tuator and hydrostatic slide (Fig. 4). A chrome-plated, ground rod with a larger-diameter section in the center (forming the piston) operates within a cylinder in the slide casting to provide motive force. The ends of the cylinder are fitted with hydrostatic bearings for the oversize 'piston rod.' A flat caliper-type hydrostatic slideway prevents rotation around the round slideway. Parallelism and perpendicularity are adjustable.

Rigidity, accuracy, and freedom from wear and maintenance are the prime benefits of the hydrostatic design. Round-the-clock operation must be trouble-free.

A remote hydraulic power supply provides constant-temperature oil to several machines.

Ferranti diffraction gratings provide feedback data to the tape control systems, also by Ferranti. System resolution is 0.0001 in., and overall accuracy over the entire table movement is 0.0002 in.

Automatic inspection

Automatic manufacture demands automatic inspection of the components produced, and a third type of three-axis machine fulfills this function. Essentially, this machine is identical to the three-axis mill except that cutting spindles are replaced by omnidirectional sensing heads with ball-end probes.

Normally, only the first pair of pallet loads in a batch will be inspected. In use, the probes are moved into contact with the workpiece at selected points and, if their feedback data indicates an out-of-tolerance condition, the control computer will print out the pertinent information. If this is the case, the deviating part will be transferred back to storage and the remainder of that batch will not be processed until corrective action has been taken.

The inspection tape is produced from the machining tape by means of a computer subroutine that 'substitutes' the probe tip for the geometry of whatever cutter was used to produce the surface being inspected. All the parts programmer has to do is indicate the inspection points on the program.

The six-axis mill-drill unit, bearing many similarities to the three-axis units, incorporates many more compromises in order to gain maximum flexibility in presenting the cutter to the workpiece. Only one pallet can be ma-

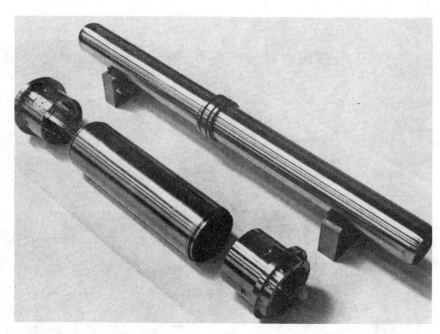

4. Combination hydrostatic way and hydraulic piston moves all slides, and allows fine adjustment of squareness of motion. Wear will be minimal

chined at a time, for example. The single spindle is similar to the design used on the three-axis drill.

In addition to the X, Y, and Z linear movements, rotary motions are provided for the worktable (R) and the spindle (A), and an independent axial motion (W) is provided to advance the cutter along whatever angle is dictated by the position of the A-axis. Thus, the six axes permit cutter access to any point on a workpiece except the surface contacting the pallet, permit swiveling the cutter about any point on its centerline without translation of that point, and permit accurate boring at odd angles.

Automatic tool setting

Provision is made on all three types of machine for automatic tool changing. Use of preset tooling, however, is avoided for two basic reasons: (1) the presence of a chip or other dirt on the adapter or in the spindle can destroy accuracy, (2) the cost of tooling components and presetting labor can soar, since there is a natural tendency not to break down tooling setups that will be used again. In the System 24 machines, each cutter is set to length automatically in the toolchanging cycle.

Each cutter is stored in a mating holster that grips the cutting end firmly. For each spindle there is a turret with five interchangeable magazines, or toolbars, each with

14 such holsters (13 is the maximum in the six-axis machine). A toolbar can be manually or automatically located in a slot on the Y-slide above each worktable, and is protected by a hinged cover that is closed during cutting and open during a cutter change.

To pick up a cutter, on tape signal, the slides operate at rapid traverse to position the spindles before the desired tools, opening the toolbar cover. Then the spindle advances until its hydraulically actuated collet is over the parallel shank of the tool (a slight chamfer on the tool shank facilitates this). The collet closes, the spindle withdraws the tool from its holster, and the Y-slide rises, closing the magazine cover and positioning the cutter in front of a Z datum pad mounted on the pallet. Alternatively, a previously machined surface on the workpiece may be used as a Z-axis reference, if this is more suitable.

Next, the collet is opened, and the Z-slide moves forward. As the cutter contacts the datum surface, it slides further back into the collet against a spring. Upon reaching the programmed Z position, the collet is again closed, and the tool is now set to machining length. For the next required tool change, the machine would first go through the motions necessary to replace this cutter in its holster, then follow the above sequence.

Loading the machines

For fully automatic operation, the machines require an additional unit to provide both fresh workpieces and new cutter magazines. This loading unit consists of a cast housing which sits alongside the machine and contains two rotating turrets. The upper one is a five-station unit containing five toolbars, and the lower one is a four-station turret in a cross configuration that can handle up to four pairs of pallets. The loading unit has six functions:

■ To raise the pallet from the horizontal position, in which it is stored, to the vertical position for machining.

■ To provide a buffer storage capacity of up to three pairs of pallets. This minimizes work changeover time and smoothes the demand on the conveyor system, and it also provides work for the machine in the event of a conveyor failure.

■ To provide a cleaning system after the pallets have been used by the machine tool, so that chips will not contaminate either the work area or the conveyor system.

■ To give automatic insertion and withdrawal of both toolbars and work pallets from the machine tool.

■ To provide a station for electronic pallet identification.

■ And to provide for automatic toolbar selection, storing 140 cutting tools per machine.

How changes are made

The toolbar turret is equipped with a reading head to permit computer selection of the proper toolbar. When selected, this toolbar is held vertically underneath the axis of the upper turret. Similarly, the pallet turret is equipped with two readers, and holds selected pallet pairs vertically above its axis.

Both pallets and toolbar are thus located in the same plane and in the correct relative positions required by the machine tool. The pallet pair is loaded first by a horizontally traveling arm, and while the pallets are being positioned precisely on the machine table, the arm goes back to get the toolbar. If additional toolbars are required during the machining program, they can be changed by a signal on the NC tape.

Pallets are fed to the loading unit at the rear horizontal platform of the pallet cruciform. When the machine completes the program on which it is working, the pallets and toolbar are ejected onto their respective turrets. The pallet cruciform then indexes forward through three 90° steps.

Chips blown off

The first step brings the newly machined pair of pallets face downward to the cleaning area, where chips are blown off by compressed air blasts. The second step rotates it to a vertical position beneath the cruciform, where further air blasts remove chips that may have remained on previously horizontal surfaces. And the third step brings it up to the rear horizontal position for removal.

This also positions a new pair of pallets for loading into the machine, but not the most recently delivered pair. The reading heads again identify the new pallets and relay this information to the computer. If this is a new part, the computer not only selects the proper cutter magazine, but also selects a new machining tape.

The numerical control systems

Control of the individual machine tools is by NC units specially developed by Ferranti, Ltd. Data input is on ½-in. magnetic tape in cassettes holding 300 ft, which are stored in a random-access file.

Access to a considerable number of tapes is vital to the system, since, depending on the type of work being done, as many as 60 tapes per machine may be required over a 24-hour period. The total active library may well exceed 20,000 programs.

Tapes changed automatically

A 'jukebox' for the tape cassettes was created. This consists of a drum containing up to 60 of the cassettes, each of which has a coded number that can be read electromagnetically along its upper edge.

Any cassette in the drum can be selected in less than ten seconds.

The cassette is slid from the drum into a two-position rotating turret, where its 'ready-to-start' status is confirmed by a rewinding device. When the previous tape on the opposite side of the turret has been run, the turret indexes to place the used tape in the rewind device and the new cassette into the tape reader. Once the previous tape has been rewound, it is re-inserted into an empty space in the drum. Thus, while selection takes as long as 10 seconds, interchange requires less than 3 seconds.

The controls provide contouring capability by means of linear interpolation. A medium-size computer is used in tape preparation. The computer's postprocessor program closely approximates the desired cutter path with small linear steps representing 25 milliseconds of slide motion. Step length is selected for the desired cutter feedrate, and acceleration is controlled by increasing and decreasing step length at start and finish of a cut. For accuracy, the postprocessor limits acceleration to a maximum of 4.7 ips per sec in a cut, but permits accelerations up to 75 ips per sec for fast movements in air.

The choice of three bit values is possible on the tape: 0.0001-in. for very accurate work, 0.0002-in. for faster motions when accuracy is not critical, and 0.0016-in. for fast traversing. Respectively, these provide maximum feedrates of 60 ipm, 120 ipm, and 960 ipm.

For straight cuts, a special format condenses the data on the tape. Another special format is used in situations where feedrates need not exceed 15 ipm with the 0.0001-in. bit size. 'Playing' time for a

300-ft cassette of tape varies from 25 to 75 minutes in machining aluminum, and two to three times as long when cutting at low feedrates. For a 2400-ft reel of tape, aluminum-cutting programs will run some three to nine hours, with the above multiplier for low feedrate programs.

Several automatic tape and internal checks are provided to assure reliability. Logic functions are performed by DTL (diode-transistor logic) integrated circuits, and conventional transistor circuits are used for analog servo control. The circuit cards have monitor points, and fault and indicator lights for troubleshooting.

Has manual override

A machine tool can be stopped manually anywhere in the program without losing position, and manual feedrate override from 100% down to 10% is also available. Also provided is a tape search facility to pick out particular programs.

The standard Ferranti PROFILE-DATA NC program is available for users implemented on IBM System/360 Model 40 and ICT 1904 computers. A special six-axis version of PROFILEDATA is also available in the IBM System/360. In addition to the PROFILEDATA postprocessors, fully implemented three-axis and six-axis postprocessors are available for the new APT, ADAPT, and AUTOSPOT as implemented for the System/360 Model 40 computer.

Work pallets and setups

Central to the System 24 are the 13 x 13-in. cast iron pallets (Fig. 5, 6) and the machine worktables on which the pallets are automatically positioned and clamped.

Precision pallets vital

Machines designed to run without supervision must obviously be capable of repetitive accuracy well beyond that of conventional machine tools. This applies to the work pallets no less than to other potential sources of machining error, and to the precision of automatically positioning the pallets in any one of several machines.

Front face of the vertical work-table presents a serrated (to minimize chip interference problems) alloy steel clamping surface to the rear of the 1.4-in.-thick pallet. Rollers engaging the top T-slot (of two such slots in the pallet rear surface) guide the pallet approximately into position as it is slid in by the loading unit actuator.

Two vertical and one horizontal sensing units detect the position of three stainless steel rings mounted in the rear of each pallet with a resolution of a few microinches, and activate small servomotors driving eccentric rollers. These rollers shift and rotate the pallet until the three sensors null out, which takes about 15 seconds, and hydraulic clamps (two in each T-slot) secure the pallet.

Sensors interlocked

At this point, four pneumatic sensors operating on ground pads in each of the corners of the pallet's rear face check that the two surfaces are in proper contact. These are sensitive to about 0.0002 in., and activate switches if the error exceeds tolerance. All seven of these sensors are interlocked to the tape start, so machining cannot begin unless all are correct.

In practice, this electronic location system has worked extremely

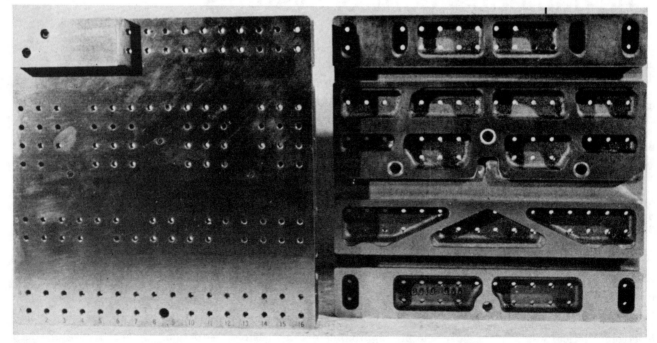

5. Standardized pallets are accepted interchangeably by all machines of the system. Block at upper left provides toolsetting datum. Three rings in rear face facilitate pallet positioning

well, and given an accuracy and reliability considerably better than would be possible with purely mechanical arrangements.

A 1-in. grid of tapped holes in the front surface of each pallet serves for work fixturing, and a tool-setting gage block in the upper left corner provides a Z-reference as previously described. The cutter setting method, of course, eliminates any need for precision in pallet thickness.

Pallets individually coded

Each pallet is identified by a binary reference number recorded as a series of holes on the upper edge, which can be read automatically by electromagnetic devices at various points within the System 24.

The pallets are also fitted with plastic carrying handles that interlock so that pairs are mechanically coupled in the automatic handling equipment and in active storage.

6. Aluminum fixture components are bolted to pallet according to image on slide projected from overhead. Trapped screws are then spun up into workpiece

Workpiece preparation

The most generally used material for System 24 manufacture is extruded aluminum alloy billet, followed by flat-rolled stock, and occasionally castings. The basic workpiece, then, is a cut length of a particular extrusion, a flat blank, or a casting.

Given the order for a particular part number, a plastic job envelope is taken from a file for use in the workpiece preparation center adjacent to the main System 24 workshop. This envelope contains the following previously prepared and checked items: (1) Drawing of the blank, (2) a drill templet (or punched card equivalent) for the pattern of tapped holes necessary to hold the blank on the pallet, (3) a worksetting drawing or photograph, (4) a worksetting slide transparency, and (5) a list of any necessary fixturing devices. If the particular workpiece also will require resetting (for machining the bottom), the envelope will also contain: (6) a resetting drawing or photograph, (7) a resetting slide transparency, and (8) a list of any necessary resetting fixtures.

Prepared workpiece blanks, set-up drawings or photos, transparencies, and any necessary fixturing devices are placed in bins. These are stored in racks, and are ultimately delivered by automatic conveyor to one of a line of modular worksetting stations that parallels the line of System 24 machine tools. When this happens, a coded number on the bin (keyed to the part number in the computer memory) is sensed, activating the conveyor to deliver the pair of pallets allocated for this job to the same worksetting station. Pallet arrival starts a real time countdown of the workset standard time for that part, which is displayed for the operator.

Each worksetting station is in the form of a bench three pallet-pitches wide (43 in.) and 58 in. deep. Pallets are delivered to the center and collected from the right-hand outer area. At no time do pallets have to be lifted, merely being slid along the bench surface or on rollers.

The bins with workpiece blanks, tooling components, and other items are delivered from the workpiece preparation center by a belt conveyor running above the pallet delivery positions at the rear of the bench. The bin intended for a particular worksetting station is deflected from this conveyor by a computer-actuated gate, which chutes the bin into a position flush with the bench top at the operator's left.

In addition to the time countdown, each worksetter is provided with an intercom and various other indicators and signals.

The operator's first action is to place the worksetting transparency in an overhead slide projector. This projects an image of the required tooling members directly onto the pallet. Additional information on the slide indicates to the operator which of a limited number of standard setup methods she is to use. She then uses a torque-limiting pneumatic screwdriver to spin the tooling hold-down screws into the pallet.

Next, the workpiece is positioned as indicated by the projected slide, and spring-loaded screws in the tooling are spun up into the tapped holes in the workpiece. Thus, the part is secured, but free access is allowed for the cutters on all surfaces except the one against the pallet.

The loaded pallet is now pushed onto the 'out' rack, where it waits until the second of the pair has been loaded and joins it. This signals the automatic conveyor to remove the loaded pair and deliver another empty pair. This procedure continues until all pallets for the particular job number and quantity have been delivered.

Worksetting capacity varies

Also of modular design, three worksetting stations are installed per machining unit in the System 24. Requirements will vary, of course, depending on the machining time required for the general run of parts produced in the individual installation. In general, however, the objective will be for worksetting capacity sufficient to provide in 8 hours enough pallet loads for that shift, 16 hours of night work unattended by worksetters, and a sufficient overlap so the machines can be kept running at the beginning of the next day.

For those workpieces which must also be machined on the underside, special resetting equipment has been developed to enable the job to be done rapidly and accurately. Initial fixturing for such parts includes a pair of columns positioned appropriately for the part in two of the pallet grid holes. Atop each of these is a conical diamond point which sits 0.004 in. above the level of the tooling. These provide precise locating points for subsequent resetting after the accessible surfaces have been machined.

Insofar as possible, scheduling by the computer arranges that work requiring resetting is completed during the day shift, and that both resetting and pallet unloading be performed by the same operator who did the setup.

Alternatively, it may be preferable to staff the resetting stations separately. In either case, the resetting stations occupy the same pitch as the setting stations, and the ratio of one to the other can be fixed to suit requirements.

When a reset is called for, an indicator in the girl's station lights up, and she steps over to the nearest resetting/inspection unit, where the pallets to be reset are automatically delivered.

The incoming pallet is located on the worktable of the reset/inspection machine, which is identical to the machine tool worktables, and the workpiece is removed. Microscopes incorporated in the unit are adjusted manually to position them precisely over the diamond points on the pallet tooling. Digital readouts indicate these positions, which will probably differ slightly from the true grid reference of these points, since the diamonds were only located to pallet grid accuracy.

The microscopes are now reset to the new position, as indicated on the resetting drawing, including a mirror-image correction for the original slight error. The fixturing on the pallet is now changed, if necessary, and the part can now be located accurately by aligning the two indentations with the microscope positions. The part is then clamped, and it can be accurate to 0.0002 in.

If a batch of identical parts is being processed, it is more convenient to leave two groups of pallets set up, one for original worksetting, and one for resetting.

The worksetters also unload pallets when the parts have been completely machined. In this case, the operation is essentially the reverse of loading—with loaded pallets and empty bins delivered, and an 'unload' signal being given in the station. Now the setup is completely disassembled and everything goes into the bin, which is routed out of the area by the conveyor and subsequently scheduled for additional operations, assembly, inventory, or whatever, according to the bin code number and the computer's program.

The automatic conveyor

From what has already been described it is obvious that another vital component of the System 24 is a complex of transfer devices, conveyors, and storage equipment.

A pallet storage rack stands between the row of machine tools and the row of worksetting stations (Fig. 7). Rack height provides eight pigeonholes on a pitch of 8.3 in., each supporting one pair of pallets on siderails. Horizontally, on the normal 129.3-in. spacing of the machine tools, the rack provides space for nine pallet widths. Thus, storage capacity is 72 pairs of pallets per machine, sufficient for 18 hours of continuous operation at a rate of four pairs of pallets per hour per machine on a 15-minute average cycle time.

Units chain-driven

Along each side of this rack runs an automatic conveyor, dubbed a 'MOLAC' (for Molins On-Line Automatic Conveyor). This is supported by a monorail at the top of the rack, steadied laterally by an angle at the bottom, and driven along the rack by an endless chain. Vertical and horizontal motion within each MOLAC is hydraulically actuated, and each contains a small hydraulic pump to power the actuators for these motions.

Travels at 10 fps

Longitudinal positioning is obtained from a coarse grating structure on the rack, which enables the MOLAC to be positioned within 0.8 in. At this point, a hydraulically driven fork locates on a roller mounted on each upright. A combination of high speed and accuracy is thus achieved. Maximum longitudinal velocity is 10 fps, and the MOLAC can accelerate to this speed in 1 sec. Vertical traverse rate is 1 fps, and the in-out rate is 2 fps, allowing a pair of pallets to be picked up and delivered in 3 seconds plus the longitudinal travel time.

The MOLAC adjacent to the worksetting stations, of course, transfers pairs of pallets between these stations and the rack, while the other unit performs a similar function between the rack and the machines. Each carries two pairs of pallets, which enables the worksetting MOLAC to pick up and de-

7. Modular spacing is 129.3 in. per machine tool. This provides space for three worksetting stations, and pigeonholes for 72 pairs of pallets for each machine. Just behind setup bench is conveyor from workpiece preparation center

liver pallet pairs simultaneously.

The machine tool MOLAC is equipped to handle cutter magazines, as well, and thus can deliver new toolbars in addition to workpieces. In operation, this MOLAC first collects an unmachined pallet pair from the storage rack, then moves to the machine tool to (1) pick up the machined pair, and (2) deliver the unmachined pair to the loader.

Each MOLAC is also fitted to read the binary number codes on both pairs of pallets. The first eight bits of each number indicate longitudinal position in the rack, and the next three indicate vertical location. Each pallet pair thus has a unique address and a specific pigeonhole.

Control by computer

It can easily be appreciated that overall scheduling and control of any system as complex as this one is beyond human capability. For example, a six-machine System 24 installation would be capable of producing between 2000 and 20,000 components per day—with wide variations in both configuration and lot size. Manual handling of just the information involved would almost certainly result in chaos.

Computers plus NC

In fact, it is the availability today of modern digital computers in addition to current NC technology that makes System 24 possible, and an on-line IBM 1130 computer provides this control function. A separate off-line computer is used for tape programming and overall system scheduling.

Frequent references and allusions have been made in foregoing sections of this Special Report to specific computer control actions, such as the routing of a specific workpiece blank via automatic conveyor from workpiece preparation to storage, to pallet preparation, to storage, to machine tool, possibly to a second machine (either before or after resetting), and then back to a particular operator for pallet unloading. These steps are all taken with automatic checks and double checks to make sure that the right machining tape and the right cutting tools are used on a specific workpiece. These are functions of the on-line computer.

Among the functions performed by the off-line computer, overall scheduling is perhaps paramount. Orders by part number and quantity for a period of, say, ten days or more can be input, and the computer will sort out those parts coded for System 24 production. The master file tape contains all needed manufacturing data, and is updated continually as new parts are programmed.

Data on printouts

Parts will be scheduled in groups providing suitably sized daily batches and reasonably uniform machine loading. The computer will print out a 'daily master file extract' (Fig. 8) with this data, and include such other information as workpiece blank codes and standard times for setup and machining. Separate printouts give a 'daily machine program list,' (Fig. 9) which lists the program tapes against the machines they're to be used on and a 'daily material schedule' (Fig. 10).

To enhance efficiency of opera-

DAILY MASTER FILE EXTRACT

PART NO	QTY	BILLET CODE	BILLET SIZE	PARTS/PAIR OF PALLETS	WORKSET NORM	FIRST OPERATION					SECOND OPERATION					THIRD OPERATION				CLEAN
						M/C	FIRST TOOLBAR	PRGM NO	RUN TIME MIN	RESET NORM	M/C	FIRST TOOLBAR	PRGM NO	RUN TIME MIN	RESET NORM	M/C	FIRST TOOLBAR	PRGM NO	RUN TIME MIN	
424760	24	006	240225	6	5	2	2	4764	5.2	0	1	1	4765	7.5	0					0
317298	12	002	190100	6	8	1	2	291	11.1	0	3	1	292	4.2	11	5	2	293	9.8	0
398712	64	011	270275	8	4	3	1	1090	4.9	0	4	2	1091	6.1	0	6	1	1092	7.8	0
471332	16	003	250150	8	6	2	2	2302	10.5	12	5	1	2303	6.7	0					0
388644	12	018	210200	12	6	4	1	1771	5.6	0	2	3	1772	13.8	0	6	1	1773	4.9	0
563233	80	007	185125	4	5	2	1	934	9.3	0	1	2	935	3.8	0					0
410869	28	006	290225	2	3	1	3	3827	5.4	0	3	1	3828	11.3	0					0
515423	96	012	200175	10	7	3	2	878	9.4	0	2	2	879	6.3	7	5	3	880	5.2	0
342453	16	008	280250	4	8	1	1	2791	7.6	0	4	1	2792	4.9	0					0
465772	22	011	265275	12	4	2	1	4621	6.2	10	1	3	4622	8.7	0					0
385491	64	012	290175	8	11	3	2	785	11.2	0	1	2	786	3.6	0	2	2	787	7.5	0
550762	6	007	250125	6	10	1	2	1616	4.6	0	3	1	1617	9.8	0	5	2	1618	3.9	0
419769	20	010	220250	10	9	4	2	2765	9.3	0	2	1	2766	5.5	16	6	2	2767	12.8	0
541198	36	004	195150	6	5	1	1	701	9.1	11	4	2	702	3.9	0					0
324878	48	018	260200	12	12	2	1	4030	3.6	0	1	2	4031	6.6	0	3	1	4032	5.9	0

8. Computer printout of master gives capsule view of total operations scheduled for the day

DAILY MACHINE PROGRAM LIST					
MACH NO.1	MACH NO.2	MACH NO.3	MACH NO.4	MACH NO.5	MACH NO.6
4765	4764	292	1091	293	1092
291	2302	1090	1771	2303	1773
935	1772	3828	2792	880	2767
3827	934	878	2765	1618	
2791	879	785	702		
4622	4621	1617			
786	787	701			
1616	2766	4032			
4031	4030				

9. Machining tapes are changed automatically by 'jukebox' device. Computer indicates tapes to load into each one

10. Material requirements for several days can be printed ▶ out by the computer as an aid for more efficient operations in separate workpiece preparation center

		DAILY MATERIAL SCHEDULE			
PART NO	QUANTITY	BILLET CODE	BILLET LENGTH	BILLET WIDTH	BILLET QUANTITY
424760	24	006	240	225	4
317298	12	002	190	100	2
398712	64	011	270	275	8
471332	16	003	250	150	2
388644	12	018	210	200	1
563233	80	007	185	125	20
410869	28	006	290	225	14
515423	96	012	200	175	10
342453	16	008	280	250	4
465772	22	011	265	275	2
385491	64	012	290	175	8
550762	6	007	250	125	1
419769	20	010	220	250	2
541198	36	004	195	150	6
324878	48	018	260	200	4

tions in the workpiece preparation center, a weekly material schedule can be printed out. With this, it is possible to group all requirements for a given extrusion cross-section so that all may be cut to length (which may also differ) at a single time.

Automatic rescheduling

Software provided for the on-line control computer includes an optimization measure so that, if a machine fails, this fact is automatically signaled to the computer, and it then rearranges the workload to make best use of the remaining facilities until the maintenance crew can return the machine to service. If a part had priority, it would be routed to a similar machine in the group, if one existed, and the workload would be rearranged. If no alternate was available, the pallets would be returned to the storage rack until the machine was repaired and back on the line.

When a machine fault signal is received by the computer, the maintenance staff is immediately alerted. A display at the machine indicates all likely faults, and the maintenance specialist will take appropriate action. He can switch the machine out of computer control for any tests he may deem necessary, and if he estimates the machine will be out of the line for more than 30 minutes, he signals the computer this fact for its rescheduling routine. When the machine comes back on the air, the computer reverts to its original schedule as far as possible.

Actually, priority has little meaning in a two-day cycle from workpiece preparation to final pallet unloading. Basic priority is established by the sequence in which the production control computer lists the parts. To give maximum flexibility, however, the software is arranged so that parts can be injected into the system at any time, merely by preparing a bin and reading the appropriate cards into the computer. Parts so injected are assumed to require priority, and they go to the head of the line.

It is mandatory, of course, that only jobs that are checked and debugged be fed into the system. Such checks can be made either on auxiliary machines, or on the automatic system at a time set aside for program proveouts (weekends). Any machine can be switched out of the computer-controlled setup for program testing, in which case the computer ignores it. Naturally, this is only practicable where the machine has a duplicate in the line.

Performance and economics

A computer can't cut metal. Neither, for that matter, can a numerical control system produce chips. Yet each can make a major contribution to the efficiency of metal-cutting operations. And, working together, the benefits are compounded. Inject the advantages of high-speed metal removal by multiple-spindle machine tools with specialized functions and the resulting combination is an entirely new breed of manufacturing facility.

Precise performance evaluations will have to wait for actual operation of the first System 24, scheduled to begin during the first quarter of 1968. But a considerable amount of data has already been accumulated in three years of operation of the twin-spindle milling machines on Molins components.

This experience indicates that milling jobs can be done in an average of one thirtieth of the time they can be done on manual machines, a productivity increase of

15:1 per spindle, including cutter changes and non-cutting motions.

The two-spindle drill, by virtue of its drill-bore-ream-tap capability, must be compared to a rather wide range of competing machines and processes. These range from manual drilling and tapping through NC turret drilling to jig boring. Holes larger than 0.6-in. requiring tolerances no finer than ±0.001 in. are usually produced by planetary milling on the twin-spindle mill, and, if necessary, are reamed to high accuracy at 20,000 rpm. Four accurately sized and positioned holes can be produced in a minute this way, which could take a good 20 minutes by traditional jig boring methods. A productivity ratio of 5:1 per spindle seems reasonable for the drill, if the alternative requires substantial jig boring.

Operations on the six-axis unit are the most difficult and expensive to do by alternate methods. Curved surfaces must be copied, and working at odd angles requires lengthy setups or expensive jigs. For this reason, a productivity factor of 10:1 should be easily achieved.

The conventional equivalent

A System 24 installation consisting of three mills, two drills, and one six-axis unit, can be shown to have a productivity factor of 11 over manual machines for the same jobs. If utilization efficiency of the System 24 is 0.8, it would require 145 conventional spindles (in a ratio of 5 milling for every drilling spindle) operating on a two-shift basis to match the output of the System 24. For round-the-clock three-shift operation, the requirement drops to 97 conventional spindles. But a more realistic comparison might even be a single-shift operation of 290 conventional spindles.

Giving validity to this comparison is the fact that most of the System 24 personnel are day-shift workers only. In any case, the number of machine operators for the manually controlled machines would be 290. Added to this would be supervisors and various other indirect-labor support personnel.

By contrast, the total personnel requirements for five days a week of 24-hr-a-day operation of a 7-unit System 24 (three twin mills, two twin drills, one six-axis unit, and one inspection machine) would be 45 to 51. This includes a control

11. Typical aluminum alloy machine parts produced on the twin-spindle milling machine. Bearing seats are end-milled orbitally, then reamed at high speed

supervisor and two assistants, 14 part programmers, eight in the materials preparation center, 12 to 18 worksetters, two inspectors, and six maintenance specialists.

For the two-shift conventional operation, floorspace required by the machine tools would total some 11,500 sq ft. The System 24 installation would require only 3500 sq ft—an area 85 x 30-ft for the machines, and one 70 x 15-ft for preparation.

Tooling costs cut

In the area of table tooling, the advantages of NC machines are well documented. System 24 machines are easily capable of producing any special fixture components of aluminum alloy, as the need arises. And, of course, the machines' cutter-setting capability reduces the need for stocking a large quantity of extra cutter adapters and holders.

Inventories of in-process parts and completed components are slashed drastically by the two-day manufacturing cycle. One can calculate the monetary worth of this by considering it against present practices and values in his own plant. But there is no way to calculate the dollars-and-cents value of the potential cut in leadtime to fill an order.

Now, what will it cost? Molins estimates the capital cost of installing the seven-unit System 24 in Britain at the equivalent of

$1,540,000. Again based on markets and prices in Britain, the capital cost of 290 machine tools to do the same job on a single-shift basis would be about $2,430,000: and of the 145 machines for two shifts, about $1,215,000.

Still using typical British rates for labor, rent, power, etc, and depreciating the capital cost over 10 years on a straight-line basis, the cost of operation for a year would be about $2.3 million for the conventional plant. Largely because of stiff night-shift premiums, this cost would be about the same for one-shift, two-shift, and even three-shift operation, though, of course, investment would be considerably reduced by two or three-shift operation.

System 24, on the same basis, would cost about $500,000 a year. ∎

'Variable mission' machining

**Into the production middle ground between low-volume
NC machining centers and high-output transfer lines
comes the new flexible, versatile Variable-Mission system**

Metalworking manufacturing executives and their process engineers have a problem—and it is a growing one.

They have the know-how and the tools to machine castings, forgings and weldments of average complexity at high production rates and relatively low cost when they are needed in large quantities on a regular basis. And they have various types of stand-alone NC machines and machining centers for similar parts needed intermittently in small quantities.

By Ben C Brosheer, senior editor
and **James C DeSollar,** vice president
Cincinnati Milling and Grinding
   Machines, Inc
Cincinnati

But difficulty is experienced in keeping costs low, quality consistent and production flowing smoothly in that middle-ground area where the parts must be produced at rates ranging in some instances from 5 to 50 an hour.

The proliferation problem

It is a growing problem—one that has been brought about by what is known in the automobile and truck industries as 'model proliferation.' Ten years ago, when new motor car sales were only 60 to 70% of what they are today, automakers had far fewer machining requirements in the range of 10,000 to 30,000 parts annually than they have today.

They are being forced by competition and the variable whims of an af-

fluent society to offer more new and improved models, with more choices of optional features, than ever before. And they are expected to do this at prices available only by mass-production procedures.

Similar machining problems are faced by many plants throughout the metalworking industry. These include makers of farm tractors and agricultural machinery, air compressors and industrial pumps, earthmoving machinery and industrial engines, power lawnmowers and outboard motors—to name only a few.

All of them have the added problem of economically machining replacements for out-of-date parts on a variable-need basis. This sometimes adds up to thousands of duplicate parts annually, espe-

1. Variable-Mission I (VMM I) manufacturing system is designed primarily to machine parts
in a random mix at rates ranging from 5 to 50 pieces an hour, and includes various
combinations of NC and automatically cycled units served by mission-address system, conveyors

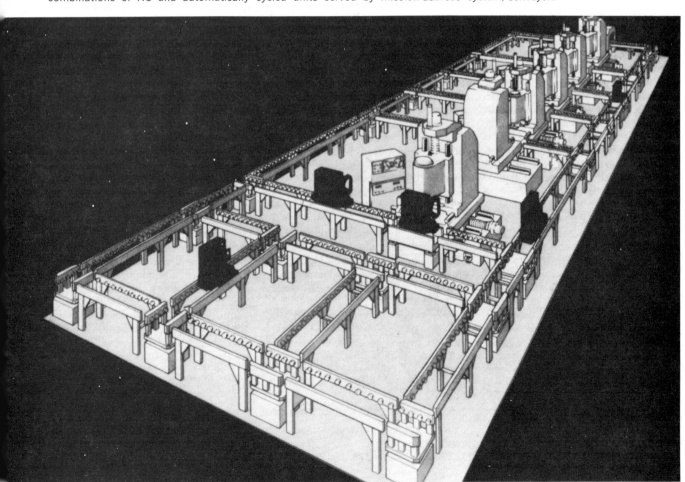

'Variable mission' machining

cially in the auto industry.

What is needed is a new concept in machining systems, one which can be operated economically in the neglected area between the low-volume capabilities of toolchanging NC machining centers and the high-volume capabilities of fixed-mission transfer line complexes. Such systems should be able to process a variable product mix, with minimum delays for setup changes and dulled-tool replacement.

A few years ago, a project team was organized by Cincinnati Milling Machine Co to analyze current machining systems and to identify, as precisely as possible, their deficiencies. The team agreed that the highest attainable level of system versatility would be automatic random-order machining of a variety of workpieces.

This would be accomplished by using a series of programmable work stations interconnected with a power conveyor and employing a workpiece address system that controls both work movement and station operation.

High cost-cutting potential

Much attention is being paid today to improvements in NC systems, to improving programming procedures, to direct computer control of stand-alone machine tools, and to developing adaptive control systems—and rightly so. But none of these developments alone has the cost-cutting potential of programmable random-order machining complexes, which combine the flexibility of NC machining centers with the cost reducing capability of the mass-production transfer line.

The Mill's studies formed a basis for projecting what would be required of tomorrow's manufacturing systems, and possibly of tomorrow's entire factories. Out of this came Cincinnati Milling's Variable-Mission I (VMM I) automatic manufacturing systems, a practical step toward the versatile machining complexes needed for medium output (say 5 to 50 parts per hour).

Arrangement of a typical VMM I system, as proposed by Cincinnati engineers, is shown in Fig. 1. It might be used for processing transmission gear cases, pump housings, and the like.

This line consists of six process-specialized NC machining units, four of them mounted on single-wing bases, and two on a duplex base, to provide five work stations. Non-NC, automatically cycled units can also be used.

Queuing conveyor lines and address-system controlled turntables connect the work stations with the main conveyor loop and the load/unload stations in the staging area.

The economic relationship of Varia-

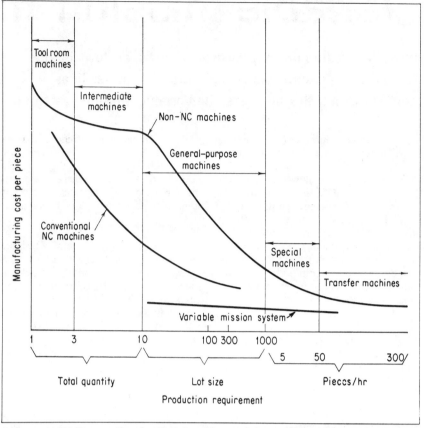

2. Parts of medium complexity, in lots of 20 to 1000 at rates of 5 to 50 per hour, are processed by Variable-Mission I system at very low per-piece costs. Above estimates are based on experience with a wide range of machining processes

ble-Mission systems to available machining systems is charted in Fig. 2. This graph, while highly generalized, reflects average experience with the various machine tools shown.

Prior to the introduction of NC machine tools, the cost per piece machined generally followed the upper curve in Fig. 2, as increased production requirements led to installation of more-sophisticated metal cutting systems with increased capacities. Cost reductions achieved with stand-alone NC units for small job lots are indicated by the middle curve. Results believed to be achievable with VMM I systems are indicated by the lower curve.

Cincinnati's Special Machine Division engineers have determined that VMM I automatic machining systems must have the following characteristics —none of them sensitive to control system characteristics:

■ A proper mix of mutually supported, process-specialized workstations to insure versatility.

■ A capacity for high metal-removal rates by employing properly designed, amply powered machining modules.

■ A higher degree of process spe-

cialization than has been economically feasible for either general purpose NC machines or time-locked multi-station transfer line modules.

■ Work station configurations that improve the efficiency and the effectiveness of workpiece delivery, registration, and ejection.

■ An improved locating and coupling method that will more accurately, more stiffly and more rapidly mate workpiece-supporting pallets (or special pallet-based fixtures), machine elements, and tooling accessories.

■ A versatile, programmable address system (encompassing both work station designations and workpiece identifications) that can be updated with ease to quickly accommodate the introduction of part design modifications or entirely new parts into the complex in any required mix.

■ A capability for expansion and for revision—to accommodate possible requirements for increased capacity, and to permit incorporation of possible technological developments.

The VMM I automatic manufacturing system concept appears to be most applicable where lot quantities are reasonably large, where the mix of parts to be machined at the same time is rea-

248

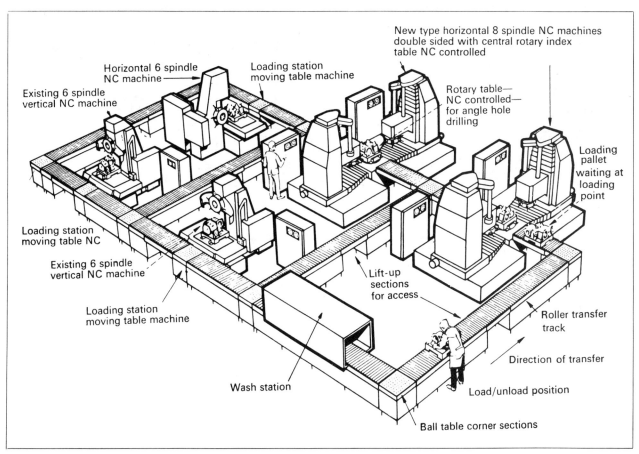

3. First-stage Variable-Mission I system planned for machining transmission cases at Borg-Warner
Corp's plant in Letchworth, England, will use manually transferred pallets during a tryout period
before installation of power conveyors and address systems. Additional NC units may also be added

sonably similar (preferably with some operations common to all of them), and where production requirements are somewhere in the range of 5 to 50 parts per hour.

The number of parts per hour that the VMM I system can turn out with economic advantage varies widely with part configuration and processing requirements. VMM I appears to be less applicable to small systems where the size and complexity of different parts vary considerably—particularly when the parts are to be processed in relatively small lots, when frequent changes in setup are required, or in low-production work where some or all of the parts are so complex as to require many cutting tools, some with compound-angle orientation.

Fundamentally, Cincinnati's concept involves a family of multi-station manufacturing systems, in which every station is integrated, functioning as an element of a composite system. The individual processing positions are designated as *stations*, rather than as machine tools, because the concept is not limited to metal cutting operations. Even electrochemical machining stations could be located within a VMM I system.

Automatic *interrogating stations* can be incorporated into a VMM I system —automatically recording any defective characteristics and automatically discharging defective parts.

Automatic assembly stations might also be included, possibly to press liners into drilled holes prior to finish-reaming or finish-boring operations, or to assemble subsidiary parts to the workpieces being processed and then bolt or weld them in place before the next cutting operation.

The VMM I concept is basically oriented to the use of NC work stations, with occasional use of non-NC automatically cycled units whose operations are initiated by the positioning of the incoming workpiece.

In all instances—except possibly for very infrequent use of a manually controlled machine for operations too difficult or too expensive to program—the concept involves work stations that function without the aid of operators. It also involves the interconnection of all workstations and one or more pallet load/unload stations in a staging area with a power-conveyor loop, along which the workpieces are moved automatically from any station to any other station according to a programmable

and easily modifiable production plan.

Complete flexibility and variability are inherent in the VMM I system's concept. So much so that a very effective NC machining center complex easily might be assembled by combining one or two workpiece holding center sections, a face milling unit, a horizontal-spindle turret module and, possibly, a vertical-spindle turret module, with some roller conveyor sections and a pallet load/unload station.

Even a powered conveyor system is not essential to the operation of a simplified VMM I system, such as the one sketched in Fig. 3. It shows the basic elements of a system currently being assembled for Borg-Warner's automatic transmission plant in Letchworth, England. The result of the combined efforts of engineers of Cincinnati Milling Machines Ltd in Birmingham, England, their counterparts in Cincinnati, and Borg-Warner manufacturing executives and engineers, it will rely in its first stage of evolution on manual transfer of pallet-supported workpieces to stations around the conveyor loop.

This simplified VMM I system will consist of seven NC units—two standard Cintimatic 3-axis, 6-spindle vertical turret drilling machines; a special Cinti-

'Variable mission' machining

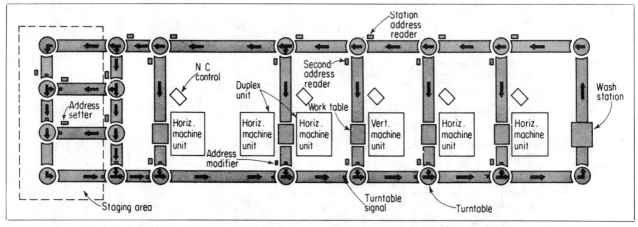

4. Coded addresses and workpiece identifications are applied to the pallets before they leave loading conveyor spurs in the staging area—to direct workpieces to various work stations for completely automatic processing with full line balancing. Concept is very flexible

matic 3-axis, 6-spindle horizontal turret drilling machine already in use in the Borg-Warner plant; and four 8-spindle horizontal turret-type machines specially developed in Birmingham for use with VMM I systems. These four units will be mounted on the wings of two duplex bases, as shown at the right in Fig. 3.

The Variable-Mission system became an obvious choice for machining low-volume mixes of different transmission cases when Borg-Warner calculated that the first-stage arrangement shown in Fig. 3 would require only 20% as much direct labor, 25% of the tooling cost, 10% of the setup changeover time, and 50% as much floorspace as competing systems. And the capital cost would be only 20% greater.

This first-stage arrangement will enable Borg-Warner to perfect its procedures before going on to the second stage, when the line will be rearranged for automatic machining of a random product mix. This revision will include installation of a powered roller conveyor system and a station address system. Additional NC units may be added eventually to increase the power of the complex.

Flexible work transport

A typical fully automatic VMM I system—with powered roller conveyor lines and automatically controlled turntables—will probably be arranged somewhat as indicated in Fig. 4.

The concept is very flexible. Conveyor loops can be added to incorporate more NC or automatically cycled work stations, inspection stations or assembly stations. Loops could also be added if needed to serve manually controlled work stations, or holding stations for off-line operations.

The conveyor sections may be waist high, as shown in Figs. 1 and 3, or the conveyor could be dropped to floor

level and the work elevated only at the workstations. An over-and-under conveyor system could be used, with shuttle-type or U-type conveyor spurs at each workstation. Then work could enter at one end of the line and leave at the other, and each machine would be readily accessible for maintenance, or control tape and cutting tool interchanges.

In any arrangement, a principal key to the economic success of any such automatic complex will be the pallet address system employed. Of equal importance will be the system used for queuing workpieces ahead of each work station and the arrangement for locating and locking the work-carrying pallets at each station.

The workpiece address system devised by Cincinnati engineers for use with automatic VMM I systems is unusual, but quite simple. It is designed to insure that each workload goes only to the proper work stations in the complex and, where necessary, in the proper sequence.

Each work station is assigned an identification code symbol different from that assigned to any other station —except that identical stations tooled for identical operations usually will be assigned duplicate symbols to permit sharing the workload.

Each pallet leaving the staging area is identified with a symbol indicating the workpiece it is carrying, and the address of each of the work stations to which it is scheduled. Addressing is done in the staging area, as indicated in Fig. 4. It can be accomplished manually, when different workpieces are loaded along the same conveyor spur, or automatically, when separate spurs are provided for each different workpiece.

The address system is so designed that work can travel from station to station in either a fixed or a random

sequence, depending on process requirements and station availability. This is accomplished by determining which operations can be performed in any sequence, and therefore can be assigned *independent* addresses, or which operations must be performed in a specified sequence and therefore must be assigned *dependent* addresses. The ability to distinguish between independent and dependent addresses is important for automatic load balancing.

When a loaded pallet passes the address setter in the staging area, it is coded to show all of the *independent* operations it will be seeking, but only the first of the *dependent* operations is scheduled.

After leaving the staging area, each coded pallet orbits around the conveyor loop until a queue line ahead of a work station to which it is addressed is free to accept incoming work. As each pallet approaches the loading end of a queue line (along the upper side of the conveyor loop in Fig. 4), a station address reader determines whether *any* address on the pallet coincides with the adjacent work station. If so, and there is room in that station's queue line, a turntable is actuated to shunt the fixture onto the queue line conveyor. There a second address reader checks the pallet to make sure it wasn't shunted into the line incorrectly.

If there is no coincidence of address, or if the queue line is filled, the turntable remains stationary to allow the pallet to bypass that station. It continues along the main conveyor loop seeking an addressed station that can accept it. This helps keep the workload at the several stations in balance, and eliminates pileups at some stations, while other stations are starving for work.

When work assigned to a station is completed on a workpiece, and the pallet is released to the discharge conveyor, an address modifier automatically erases the coded address of that station. If it was a *dependent* operation, the modifier replaces the address with the address of the next *dependent* operation on the schedule. If it is the last *dependent* operation, no new address will be applied.

A turntable at the end of the discharge conveyor returns pallets to the main conveyor loop when they have been released by the address modifier. When all addresses are erased from a pallet, it is returned to its proper spur in the staging area for unloading.

Since the sensors in the address readers can easily be moved from position to position, the address identity of each work station can be changed quickly. Thus, if a machine is deactivated temporarily for a change in setup, or for the replacement of dulled tools, removal of the sensor from the station address reader ahead of that station will cause pallets on the conveyor line to bypass the station.

Provision for standby machines

This feature permits standby machines to be included in a VMM I system for quick substitution for identical units should an abnormal shutdown be required. It is necessary only to install the proper tools, operating NC tape, and station address sensor to substitute a standby machine in the line. When changeovers must be made frequently, use of standby stations may be a profitable investment.

At each work station, an indexable locating table lies in the path of the queue-line conveyor, to receive, locate and lock in place the loaded pallet when it reaches the station. This machine center section is capable of no axial movements, can only rotationally index the workpiece. All traverses of the machine spindle are accomplished by moving the machine column or the spindle.

The work-locating table is an important element of the unique fixture-to-machine connector system devised to insure accurate and rigid support of the workpiece. The top face of each table carries a precision multi-tooth ring which mates with a similar ring on the under face of the pallet. Clamping force is equalized all around the mating rings to eliminate distortion.

To facilitate loading of workpieces into palletized fixtures in the staging area, the workpieces should be qualified before delivery to the VMM I system. In some instances, where qualifying operations are not difficult, and do not involve much time, the qualifying machine may be located in or near the staging area. In such cases, it is anticipated that the system's load/unload

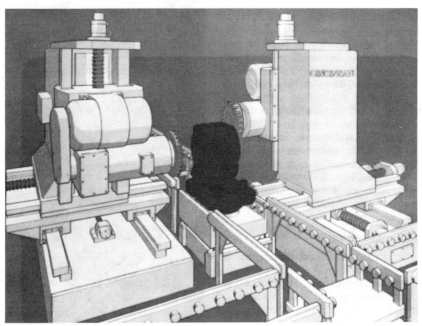

5. One or two heavy-duty face milling modules can be used at the face milling work station of a VMM I complex. Each is numerically controlled and has X, Y and Z axis traversing capabilities in front of its side of indexable table

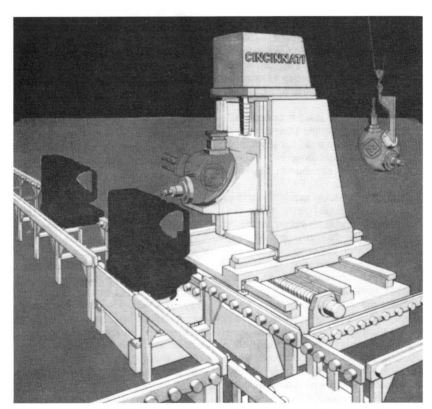

6. Pretooled four-station turrets can be interchanged quickly and easily on the tilted face of this heavy-duty NC turret station, designed especially for use with VMM I automatic systems. It can be used singly, as shown, or in duplex setups

operator will have ample time to mill locating pads or drill manufacturing location holes in the workpieces without falling behind the line's needs.

A major advantage of the Variable-Mission system concept is that, by dividing the work among several machines in the complex, each machine can be designed specially for the specific operations it is to perform. It is not necessary, for example, to provide a heavy-duty spindle suitable for rough face milling operations in a machine to be assigned only drilling, reaming, tap-

'Variable mission' machining

ping, counterboring and countersinking.

Occasionally, it may be desirable to include one or more NC machining centers, complete with tool storage magazines and automatic toolchangers, in a VMM I system. The machining centers would have to be so arranged as to work in conjunction with a fixed-position work support table, as do the other machines in the line.

Most VMM I systems, however, will be designed for maximum work station cycle times of only 4 to 5 minutes, and 6- or 8-spindle turret-type NC units are expected to provide more than enough toolchanging capacity at end-cutting-tool stations.

Stations, not tools

It is Cincinnati's contention that in the long run it will be better to add more stations to the line than to increase the number of tools available at individual stations. By dividing the work among several work stations, more spindles can be cutting chips at the same time, thus increasing output.

If 32 tools are needed for a job, say Cincinnati engineers, they should be divided among four 8-spindle turret units—making it possible to achieve four times as much production as with a single, toolchanging NC machining center that has the capacity to store 32 tools or more but which can use only one tool at a time.

Generally, a VMM I system isn't expected to provide the same degree of flexibility for very small lot production as a group of stand-alone NC machining centers that can handle the same number of tools.

If a plant needs to machine parts in very small lots, and must make frequent setup changes, it may pay to do the work with toolchanging NC machining centers. However, the economic situation is reversed in the 5 to 50 parts per hour range for which the VMM I system is designed.

The primary field for VMM I machine modules now being designed will be for the processing of castings, forgings or weldments that will fit within a 30 x 30 x 28-in. cubic envelope, weigh from 20 to about 150 pounds each before machining, and are scheduled in job-lots ranging somewhere between 20 and 1000 parts.

Production rates are expected to range from 5 to 50 parts per hour for workpieces of medium complexity that require a multiplicity of face milling, drilling, reaming, tapping, counterboring, countersinking or slot milling operations. Cubic parts can be machined on almost any vertical face, since they can be indexed about the vertical axis of the center support table in 5° increments, and on the top face. Flat parts could be supported in picture-frame fixtures for machining on opposite faces.

7. **Horizontal 8-spindle NC turret drill station** for VMM I systems is designed to eliminate interference of tools with workpiece or pallet (as sometimes happens with other horizontal-spindle turrets) when the turret is being indexed

Work station arrangement

Typical metalcutting work station arrangements currently planned for VMM I systems are sketched in Figs. 5 through 11. Any of the standard machine modules will be usuable singly or in duplex setups on one or both sides of standard work-support center sections. In all cases, all machine motions are accomplished separate from the work-support center section, which can only be indexed—not traversed.

The process-specialized face milling modules shown in a duplex setup in Fig. 5 are designed to perform only face milling operations—nothing else. Each of the NC heads may have up to a 50-hp spindle drive motor, and will drive inserted-blade cutters as large as 16 in. in diameter. Each head is arranged to feed the cutter past one face of the workpiece and then return. Depth settings for roughing and finishing cuts are made automatically according to signals from the NC tape. The tape also controls the number of passes, cutting speeds and the feeds.

Face milling stations in VMM I complexes will be usable for operations on a number of different workpieces processed through a line at the same time in a random mix. Incoming parts are identified by part number codes when they are transferred into the queuing conveyor. This gives the machine's control system time to search a looped tape for NC instructions while the pallet carrying the part is being located on the indexable table. The same tape carries instructions for address modifications when the pallet leaves the face milling station.

A unique turret-type NC machining module for end-cutting tools is shown in Fig. 6. Like the face milling module, it can be used singly or in a duplex arrangement as shown in Fig. 5. Here, the entire turret assembly can be exchanged for another one, preset in the toolroom, to process a different part or parts. The four registration faces on each turret are designed to permit quick interchanges of single- or multi-tool head assemblies, and the interchange of special bearing assemblies when necessary.

A radically different horizontal-spindle NC turret drill configuration is sketched in Fig. 7. Designed especially

8. Vertical 8-spindle NC turret drill station designed for use in VMM I systems also has light milling capability. Like other machining units in this series, it is designed to work on a 30 x 30 x 28-in. envelope.

for use in VMM I systems, it is believed by Cincinnati engineers to be superior to side turret mounting arrangements when horizontal spindles are needed. It keeps the tool from interfering with the center-section table, the fixture and the pallet when long tools must be indexed. Four of these traveling-column units are to be made for the Borg-Warner installation shown in Fig. 3.

The vertical-spindle NC turret drill for VMM I systems shown in Fig. 8 is of more conventional design. Like the units shown in Figs. 6 and 7, it is being designed to work within a 30 x 30 x 28-in. cubic envelope, and will have capacity to drive a 1¼-in.-diameter drill in cast iron or mild steel.

The machine modules shown in Figs. 5 through 8 all are being designed for use with some form of numerical control, so that the complexes in which they will be used can have the greatest possible flexibility and adaptability. The more-specialized units shown in Figs. 9 through 11 may also be numerically controlled, but for most applications it is anticipated that they will be automatically cycled units with the cycles initiated with precision limit switches when workpieces are locked in place. As with the four NC modules described above, these units will be

usable singly, or in duplex as shown.

Either three- or four-sided turrets can be used on the modules shown in Fig. 9, which will be used principally when VMM I systems àre expected to process the same parts repeatedly in fairly large job-lots, and in VMM II systems described below. Control of the Z-axis motions of the turret slides of these units can be achieved with NC tapes, or with cams associated with specific turret faces.

Turret indexing would bring the different cams into use. Normally, the different turrets for this type of module would be prepared and application-proven in the toolroom before delivery to the machine for a setup changeover.

When large hole patterns repeat frequently, and production quantities are large enough to justify the cost of special tooling, multi-spindle cluster heads for drilling and tapping operations can be used on the turret faces of the modules shown in Fig. 9, or directly on the heavy-duty slides of the modules sketched in Fig. 10. Quick-acting precision couplings are used for mounting the cluster heads to the spindles.

Station center sections, which locate and support the pallet-held workpieces, are designed to withstand cutting loads of 50 hp or more, so fairly heavy thrust forces can be applied when drill-

ing hole patterns with cluster heads.

While many precision finish-boring operations will be done off-line after other operations have been completed on a workpiece, there will be times when it is desirable to finish bores while the workpieces are still mounted on their supporting pallets—so Cincinnati engineers are designing precision boring modules for both VMM I and VMM II systems.

As shown in Fig. 11, it is anticipated that standard boring spindles will be mounted on adapter plates that will be precisely registered with the saddles of the boring machine modules. Mounting and preproduction testing of single-point cutter assemblies in the individual spindles will be done off-line in the toolroom before the spindles are delivered to the Variable-Mission lines.

It should be noted that the use of NC machining modules in the VMM I system complexes in no way changes their NC operating capabilities or characteristics. Programming for them will be accomplished in the same manner as if they were stand-alone NC units. The primary difference will be that, for the VMM I systems, operations requiring a large number of tools will usually be divided among several stations instead of being performed in the same setup on a toolchanging NC machining center. Existing and future programming techniques will be equally applicable.

As users gain experience with VMM I system complexes, it is probable that they will make frequent use of off-line computers to assist them in dividing the load among the several stations for random mixes of different parts being processed through a line at the same time. The better a line is balanced, the less idle time experienced at any of the stations and the higher the operating efficiency of the complex.

An important feature of the VMM I concept is the ability to use various combinations of machine modules in arrangements to suit different workpiece complexities and differing production requirements.

To cite a possible example—consider the case of a typical maker of truck transmissions. For some sizes, he will need to machine only 100 cases per lot; for others, lot quantities may run as high as 1000 or more. He could process a low-volume size and a high-volume size down the same VMM I system line at the same time, in any sequence.

Both sizes of cases undoubtedly would be processed through the face milling station, where faces would be rough and finish milled with the same cutters. And, probably, both sizes of

'Variable mission' machining

case would go to a vertical-spindle NC turret drill, for drilling and tapping bottom drain holes.

At this point, the paths would vary. The low-production cases probably would be routed to a series of basic NC stations (such as those shown in Figs. 6, 7 and 8), while the high-production cases could be routed both to the basic NC stations for some of the work, and to higher-production capacity, (usually non-NC) automatically cycled stations such as those in Figs. 9 and 10. In some instances, it may be desirable to route either or both types of cases to one or more precision boring stations such as the one shown in Fig. 11.

An important point to make here is that the paths for processing the different sizes of transmission cases are not separated physically. They can be mixed in the VMM I system in any convenient arrangement. It is only in the address instructions applied to each loaded pallet that the two lines can be considered divided.

Centralized control

With today's and tomorrow's dispersion of satellite plants around the globe, as in the cases of a growing number of metalworking enterprises, it is important to note that, if VMM I systems are duplicated (in principle if not in total detail) in some or all of these plants, distribution of setup instructions and control tapes from a central office make it possible for all such plants to quickly start production of identical parts. Or product modifications could be accomplished quickly, through the mails, without need for long-drawn-out committee meetings and protracted discussions.

Variable-Mission II

When parts production requirements are greater than the 5 to 50 parts per hour aimed for in the Variable-Mission I system concept, perhaps as high as the 100 to 300 parts per hour expected of transfer lines, what can be done to insure flexibility?

Assume, for example, that you are called on to tool up for a relatively high production rate on a fairly complex part, and that competition is so close behind you that you can't be sure your new product won't be obsoleted before you can amortize the cost of a new transfer line. What can you do to produce the needed parts at a reasonable cost, and at the same time insure that the equipment you buy will be usable for the next job?

The obvious answer is to start out with a highly flexible system that will machine parts at high rates for a reasonable price—one that can be changed over inexpensively and quickly to making another product.

Phase I of the concept, described above and referred to as the VMM I system, is aimed basically at the middle-ground production level, where it is desirable to be able to process a mix of parts in order to insure keeping the facility busy.

Cincinnati engineers responsible for the VMM I system have looked at the need for a flexible system capable of *high* production rates, and are convinced they have the answer. They call it the VMM II system. It is a flexible machining scheme with mass-production potentials.

VMM II systems, as now conceived, are aimed at machining the same part, or a family of several like parts, repetitively in larger job lots and at much higher hourly production rates than considered feasible with VMM I.

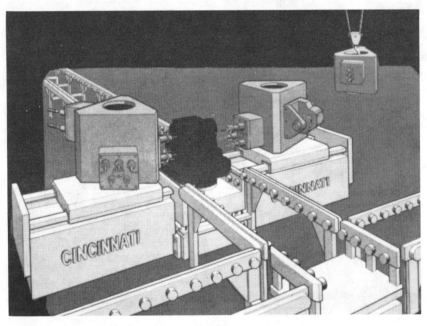

9. Three- and four-sided turrets, pretooled and tested in the toolroom, can be indexed or interchanged quickly when changing setups on this horizontal-slide automatically cycled station, which is usable for VMM I and VMM II systems

10. When large hole patterns are to be drilled repeatedly, increased production justifies the cost of quickly interchangeable multi-spindle cluster heads for this automatically cycled Variable-Mission I or II horizontal-slide machine

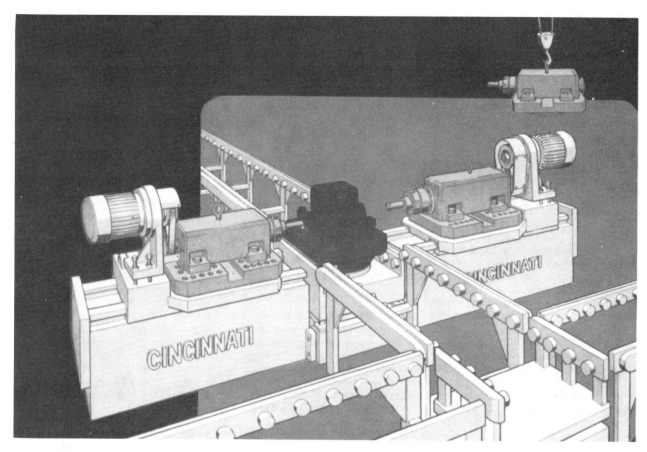

11. Pretooled precision boring spindles can quickly be interchanged on the adaptor plates of this automatically cycled specialized boring station for both Variable-Mission I and II automatic machining systems. As a rule, single-point boring tools will be used but cluster-type heads could be used

For some applications, a VMM II system might include some NC machining modules such as those employed in VMM I system complexes. One or more of the face milling assemblies might, for example, be used to prepare rough castings for operations further along the line.

But for the most part, the VMM II system is visualized as being made up primarily of non-NC automatically cycled units, possibly like those shown in Figs. 9, 10 and 11. Some could be in horizontal arrangements, as shown. Others could be constructed in vertical or angular arrangements if desired. Many of the stations could have pretooled three- or four-faced turrets which could be indexed automatically with selector switches if the line is revised for a different part—without a complete change in the production line arrangement.

When large cluster heads are needed for large patterns of holes, the arrangement shown in Fig. 10 could be used—possibly with modifications. Boring could be done with the units shown in Fig. 11, but where multiple arrangements of parallel holes are to be bored in the same part, cluster-type boring

heads could be used. When manufacturing and economic conditions warrant consideration of a VMM II system, other flexible cost-cutting units are sure to be developed.

The typical VMM II system now visualized by Cincinnati engineers would be arranged to process only one size and type of part at a time, and thus could be arranged for straight-through flow of workpieces. There would be no need for selective designations of stations and no need for the pallet address system so essential to the success of the VMM I. Each station in the line would be used in turn, or would be deactivated until the next set-up came along.

It would, of course, be possible to arrange a VMM II with a pallet address system, and possibly with a way of indexing turrets automatically with an NC system, so that different parts could be processed successively in a random mix.

In some mass-production plants it now takes several weeks to several months to change over a production facility for a new model—when it can be done at all without completely rebuilding the transfer lines. A VMM II

system, on the other hand, could be changed in hours, possibly minutes.

Spare turrets could be pretooled and pre-production tested, then stored until time for the model change.

A metalworking plant might have three, four, even half-a-dozen parts but not one of them alone could justify the installation of a transfer line. A VMM II system might be tooled to process these parts and possibly others, too. And it could be installed for little more than the cost of a multi-station transfer line suitable for only one of the parts. Not only that, the relatively small cost of some extra turrets would make it adaptable to many other parts on short notice. ∎

FMS transforms a creaky plant

Japan's Murata installed a ten-machining-center FMS of its own manufacture and halved its cutting-machine burden

ALONG-STANDING JOKE among the 850 employees at Murata Machinery's Inuyama, Japan, plant, which looks more like a weathered barn than a metalworking factory, has been, "Why doesn't our company keep milking cows here for us?" Yet, in what appears to be a farm building nestled into a vast, 106-acre tree-trimmed spread near Nagoya, the company has installed ten of its own machining centers and other machines linked to an automatic warehouse by an untended transport system.

The result is one of the most advanced flexible manufacturing systems in Japan, one that turns out 1500 different types of iron frames, gearboxes, and brackets for metalcutting machine tools and textile machinery.

Although the system originally was planned as a "pilot plant," more than ten metalworking companies have placed orders for similar installations, each priced at approximately $700,000, including computer programs. Dozens more companies are reportedly saturating Murata with inquiries, and nearly 3000 visitors, including a number of foreigners, have visited the country plant since it started operation a year ago.

By nine months after its opening, the FMS had already proven its efficiency to Murata's satisfaction. Explains Tadataka Shiomi, the company's Engineering Dept director, "This system makes 95% of work phases automatic. It used to cost ¥7000-8000 [$32.50-37.20] hourly, all inclusive, to run a conventional metalcutting machine. This new system has cut it down to half."

Under the old system, engineers say, a machine tool typically would be idle 65 out of every 200 working hours and, therefore, typically could not be generating revenue. Non-cutting time was attributable to scheduling, loading, or mechanical troubles. The new FMS has reduced this "dead" time to 15 hours out of every 200. The personnel required has dropped to 1/3-1/5 that of the old system, and productivity has jumped by 3.6

times, Murata reports. Furthermore, the integrated control of the automated warehouse eliminates the familiar scene of pallets piled up near machine tools, providing wider space and thereby helping improve safety.

Uses three computers

Making this FMS tick are three computers: a Panafacom U-100 minicomputer that governs only the automated storage-and-retrieval and workhandling system, an Hitachi L-330 directing the entire Inuyama plant scheduling, and, at the company's Kyoto head office, an Hitachi M-150 that programs Murata's five plants spread out throughout the country.

The host computer, the M-150, monitors inventory of each of the five plants and prints out what part or tool is short at what site and when to ship how many. The data is available through the L-330 at Inuyama, which is linked on-line with the host.

The plant computer controls operation of the workshops at Inuyama. The machining schedules that best suit required output are provided to individual work-area computers, such as the U-100 at the FMS site, through floppy disks.

From the data sent by the L-330, an operator enters machining schedules for each of the ten machining centers. In case urgent work is needed, the operator can override the program. The workshop computer, following the normal program, controls the following: a crane control and a traverser control for the automatic warehouse, a robotrailer control, chain- and roller-conveyor controls, work-transfer-equipment controls, and the CNCs on individual machining centers.

Untended workpiece handling

Materials and tools are brought to the entrance of the warehouse on pallets carried on fork-lift trucks driven mainly by the plant's 140 female part-time workers. Once a pallet is placed on the in-out station, the rest of the motions are untended.

A crane or traverser picks up the pallet and carries it either to one of the "stopover" stations or to one of the 284

storage-rack spaces in the automated storage-and-retrieval system (AS/RS). Location depends on how soon the pallet is required.

The crane and traverser move horizontally at two speeds—130 fpm or 15 fpm—and vertically at 40 fpm. The AS/RS has racks in two sizes: smaller ones are approximately 30 x 40 x 27 in., and larger ones are 30 x 40 x 60 in.

When the system operator initiates the process, an appropriately loaded pallet is carried out of the storage rack to a transfer station. There, one of two Digitron RT-1000 robotrailers pulls up to the station.

The robotrailer halts within 1-mm accuracy, and the pallet is loaded onto it by conveyor. The next computer signal tells the turtle-like, battery-powered vehicle to proceed to a particular machining center. The cart has three speeds—1.5 mph, 0.75 mph, and 0.45 mph—and selects one of three on computer instructions. For example, if a curve is sharp—with a 25-in. radius or so—the vehicle's sensor learns it from the configuration of iron signal plates placed on the floor. The cart transmits the information to the U-100 through cables embedded under the floor, and the computer tells the turtle to slow down.

As the robotrailer pulls up to the pre-programmed location beside the machining center, four "legs" that are usually retracted inside its belly are activated by hydraulic cylinders to match the vehicle's table level to that of the machining center's loader-feeder. The table can be lifted a maximum of about 4 in. As the work is set in place, the machining center begins operation, and the tools start cutting.

Once the machining is completed, the same sequence follows, but in reverse order. The robotrailer carries the work to the next machine, sometimes via a waiting station, or to the storage area.

Round-the-clock operation

In typical practice, the FMS operator programs the next day's schedule and double-checks the program at the beginning of the shift the next morning. Meanwhile, during the night, the FMS

By Naoaki Usui
AM Tokyo correspondent

keeps on working. But, in this case, all the completed parts are returned to the storage racks. Workers remove the work from the pallets the next morning.

What will follow the FMS? Shiomi and other Murata engineers aim at an expanded version of the system. Also considered are an automatic chip-handling system, improved toolchangers, and other refinements aimed at making the system more nearly "100% untended."

Murata's efforts to bring about the FMS started in 1975. The company, known in Japan for decades for its textile machinery as well as its machine tools, by then had started to feel the aging of its skilled workers, which made it difficulty to find night-shift workers. This coincided with the company's develop-ment of NC machines, and Managing Director Kiichi Okamoto led a team to design a flexible manufacturing system. In 1979, Murata, under a license from Digitron, started to manufacture the RT-1000 robotrailer. A similar agreement, announced late last year, gives Murata the rights to manufacture and sell eight models of Prab robots; some of these are used within the FMS.

The fact that Murata installed the FMS in an existing plant—with a rough and uneven floor—has aided the firm in promoting the new system, according to officials. Many visitors are owners of small- to medium-size machinery plants, and they are said to leave with a confidence that they, too, can install such a system in what may be a slightly run-down factory.

In addition to improving efficiency, the introduction of the FMS has motivated the employees, says Heiichi Ohmori, Inuyama's plant manager. "Workers used to wait until a fairly large number of parts were piled up and then move them for machining. They believed that was the only feasible way," he says. "But the FMS has proved that there is another way that works."

As a result, he contends, employees suddenly started learning harder than ever. A number of "voluntary study groups" popped up, some inviting college professors for weekly lecture sessions and others holding discussions based on books.

The FMS in a barn seems to have brought the plant and its workers something as useful as fresh milk. ■

Self-powered, computer-guided carts connect robot-tended cells of machining centers and stand-alone machines with palletizing stations (left rear) and the factory's automated storage-and-retrieval system (rear)

CHAPTER IX

Computers in Finishing, Assembly, and Inspection

Bar codes call auto parts to line

Bar-code stickers are slapped onto auto wheelwells at start of Datsun's Murayama assembly line. Codes then call up correct body parts at subsequent assembly stations

Optical bar-code scanning is the basis for an innovative control system for auto-body assembly, described by an American auto-production expert as "extremely interesting from a design point of view." Its developer, Nissan Motor Corp, is seeking international patents for it.

The producer of Datsun automobiles has been perfecting the system for the past three years at its Murayama plant in western Tokyo, where the claimed payoff has been elimination of 15 production-control jobs, reduction of errors from about 1% to virtually zero, and a 50% startup-cost saving over conventional central computer-based control systems.

Those centrally synchronized systems blindly furnish work stations with parts in sequence from a master list, but Nissan's decentralized approach scatters laser scanners along the line to read bar codes that are automatically affixed by magnetic tape to the engine compartment of every body. The codes, containing each car's chassis number and body and model type, dictate which particular door, for example, is to be called up automatically from a parts-storage area. The Murayama plant turns out 80 different model variations.

Won't interrupt flow

"It's like an earthworm," says Minoro Doi, general manager of the plant's production-control and engineering department. "Even if it's cut in half, it still moves." Doi explains that a mistake or pulling a car from the line will not disrupt or halt the entire operation, as can happen in centrally controlled systems. If a scanner breaks down, workers can read the bar codes and operate backup equipment manually. What is more, little computer reprogramming is necessary for model changeovers or other line reorganization.

As noted by the American engineer, who wants to remain anonymous, the system is "technologically trivial" because bar codes and scanners are hardly revolutionary. And he says few other plants could adopt it because they do not build up body sides independently from the main body line and "cherry pick" them selectively from a storage area, as the Murayama plant does. But Doi says a Nissan engine plant will soon start using the system for both assembly and distribution control and that the company hopes to extend it to such other operations as painting. And a Swedish automaker is negotiating with Nissan for a license on the system.

The assembly process starts when a computer, loaded with the day's production schedule on magnetic tape, calls up an engine compartment from among the six basic types and simultaneously transmits assembly instructions to a remote bar-code printer on the line. A robot removes the code from the printer and affixes it to the right-front wheelwell.

The code is then read at seven places by scanners, made by Matsushita Communications Industry Co, to determine the types of body side, roof, and doors to be called up. At one location, a scanner controls a robot that prints the chassis number below the windshield. At another point, a lamp connected to a scanner tells a worker which model card to attach to each body. The card tells workers down the line such things as where to make welds and drill holes. More than 100 bodies an hour go through the line.

Doi will not divulge the cost of the system but says it paid for itself in less than a year. The five basic patents would cover the total system design, the interface between the computer and bar-code printer, the chassis-numbering and lamp operations, and the door-distribution-control technique.

Besides efficiency and savings, the bar-code approach seems to enhance the Japanese emphasis on grass-roots decision-making. "Nissan apparently wants to maximize control over the individual workplace by workers," says the American auto-industry source. ∎

Robot affixes bar-code sticker, taken from printer to its left, onto wheelwell at start of Datsun assembly line. Later, code readers determine part delivery

258

Robots that paint can create jobs

Whether it's painting tractors or electronic hardware or selectively porcelainizing appliance components, robots need people

THE TURN TO ROBOTS for painting and related coating operations is on a broad front, judging by the recent achievements of giants in agricultural equipment and major appliances and by those of a small job shop serving the electronics industry. These achievements were reported at Finishing '81, the Oct 13-15 conference of the Society of Manufacturing Engineers in Detroit.

The aim, of course, is to increase productivity. But, contrary to what some may believe, workers are sometimes displaced rather than laid-off, and, in some instances, robots are actually creating jobs for factory workers.

Painting tractors

"With our growth in agricultural-tractor sales, so grew our facilities," began Robert E. Schuster, corporate staff engineer, Deere & Co (Moline, Ill). "By 1975, it was clear that we had to do something with the congestion of buildings in downtown Waterloo, Iowa.

"The answer was a new 2.2-million-sq-ft assembly plant northeast of the city, which was to include the leading edge of all technologies required. Since this would include painting, we were convinced that robots would be useful for this as well as for many other operations. We ended up with three that paint and two for water blow-off."

At present, the robots are handling 80-85% of the painting on each tractor—providing an annual labor saving of $300,000, he said. Two painters—one in a pit, the other above—handle the rest by touch-up. Paint consumption is reduced, too—about 13%, or $70,000 per year—because the robots apply paint more efficiently than painters. Energy conservation—from not having to heat spray booths—accounts for another $60,000, he estimated. This also avoids expenditures of $50,000 or so for air-heating equipment. Although Schuster couldn't estimate the saving from improved paint quality, which lessens rework, this is believed to be substantial, too.

This Waterloo success was not without thorns, however, he was quick to add. "Remember, this is a very modern plant; the entire operation is computer-controlled or computer-assisted. Interfacing all the computers, memories, and electronics was a monumental task. We were very fortunate to have the co-operation of union members who were willing to accept and learn the new technology. In the painting department, we now have one worker whose job it is to ride herd over all of the electronics."

When one of the 34 different model tractors is ready for painting, the main, or "host," computer puts it in a holding area. A worker punches in a particular paint code on the CRT of an Allen-Bradley programmable controller. Unless the wrong code is triggered, in which case the host rejects it and keeps the tractor where it is, the tractor enters the painting area and proceeds through in programmed fashion.

"The Allen-Bradley controller runs the mechanical equipment in the paint department," Schuster indicated, "but not the robots. It passes off the paint code to a Modicon programmable controller, which directs the robots when and how to paint. The robots have their own memory, and, based on the paint code in the Modicon controller, they select the proper program and paint the tractors." But, with only 64 min of memory per disk and 34 models ranging from 11,000 to 21,000 lb to paint, "we had to program painting individually by section: fronts, middles, and rears," then link the programs for each model.

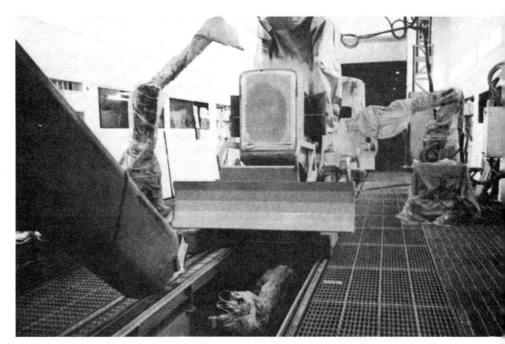

1. Three Nordson robots paint some 100 tractor models at Deere's Davenport, Iowa, plant. A Winchester disk system stores each unique 2- to 3-min paint program

259

Robots that paint can create jobs

Deere has since robotized painting at its Davenport, Iowa, plant (Fig 1), which produces as many as 100 more-complex tractor models in the 20,000- to 23,000-lb class. The goals, all of which have been achieved, were to eliminate the need for a painter in the pit (the least cherished of jobs among painters), trim painting time by one standard hour, increase paint-shop capacity, reduce energy needs to heat spray booths, lower paint consumption, decrease maintenance, and enhance quality.

From cassettes to disk helps

"This factory is not computer-controlled," he continued, "and so we didn't have the complex interfacing problems we had encountered at Waterloo." With so many models to paint and little assurance of model mix at any given time, however, program storage caused some problems. Although programs are stored in floppy disks at Waterloo, the Davenport programs were initially stored in cassettes. Storing several of the most common programs with some of the less common ones in the same cassette helped. Recently, however, programming was switched to a 5.2-Mbyte Winchester disk system having 42-hr memory, which is sufficient for storing all of the paint programs.

Unlike the more fully computer-controlled operation at Waterloo, the Davenport paint shop is a stand-alone operation. At the holding station, an operator punches in a particular paint code for the job at hand. After masking the tractor, another operator verifies the code, which allows the machine to enter the painting area. Robot electronics then take over—passing the code in sequence to the three robots that paint the tractor.

Waterloo chose DeVilbiss (Toledo, Ohio) Trallfas and Davenport Nordson (Amherst, Ohio) robots. Robot-teaching methods differ. The DeVilbiss technique, according to Schuster, "is to place the robot's hydraulics at zero pressure and take the manipulator through the paint routine while the robot records time and motion. The Nordson system uses a lightweight tube and wire simulator, which is run through the routine. Later, the manipulator is rotated back into the position that the simulator was in, and painting begins. Each plant believes its robots are best."

Schuster also suggested some guidelines for those who may be contemplating the use of robots for painting:

■ "The best jobs for robots are the bad jobs for painters"—those in pits, hot places, or cold places and those that are just barely meeting EPA and OSHA anti-pollution regulations. They are most effective for the more labor-intensive,

2. One robot with two spray guns selectively porcelainizes two washer covers simultaneously at General Electric's Major Appliance Div

repetitive applications and for those with a history of chronic quality problems.

■ Depending on the company involved, each robot can provide an annual labor saving of $15,000-$40,000. One robot is at least equal to one worker per shift. Using robots also reduces paint consumption—"we usually estimate 10%." And not having to heat spray booths is worth "one dollar for every 2-5 cmf/year saved." There's also a saving on rework, "but it's hard to quantify."

■ To estimate the cost of going to robots, he suggests a figure of $125,000 for the basic robot, $5000-$10,000 for setting up, $10,000 for engineering, and $10,000 for site preparation. Site-preparation cost, however, could swell depending on the particular site.

■ Will it be easy? Will you reduce labor as much as you thought? Will you have problems with electronics? No, he said. It won't be easy because it's a new technology. Unexpected problems will be encountered. "To date," for example, "we have not found a 'total-responsibility' vendor, one that will supply the machines and all their related software.

"You might think that you'll replace two sprayers but discover that you have to hire a robot technician." And chances are that "your engineers will spend more time with the robots than you thought."

■ Electronics are not a problem. "Much more common are the breaks in hydraulic lines, fittings, and seals and in electric wiring due to flexing."

■ And what about unions, aren't they hostile to robots? "We have had no negative experience," he noted. "If you're up-front with everyone from the start, you shouldn't have problems. The membership seems to like robots. They're proud to be associated with them. It's kind of like being akin to spaceships and in stride with the modern world."

Apparently some social scientists may not agree. But "it's obvious they have never sprayed the bottom of a tractor, the interior of a truck cab, or the inside of a refrigerator wrapper," he declared.

"Our company goal is to site as many robots as economics will allow."

Selective porcelainizing

Similarly, "open communication and integration with all parties affected" was the key to success with the first robotized operation (Fig 2) at General Electric's Laundry & Dishwasher Products Div (Louisville, Ky), according to James M. Bergant, advanced-manufacturing engineer. "Right at the start, we notified production workers so that they would have sufficient time to bid for other jobs. We didn't disguise the reason—the need for greater productivity. We were honest and up-front. To date, there hasn't been the slightest hint of tampering with the machine."

Off hand, the particular job involved might seem like child's play compared with painting tractors. In fact, however,

3. Only vertical portion of lid well, highlighted in white, gets reinforcing spray. Then entire cover is porcelain-enameled by electrostatic deposition

it was a precision application requiring imaginative systems engineering and skillful programming.

The company's porcelain-enameled components are finished by a rotating-disk electrostatic system in a fully automated line. Washer covers and lids and the tops of coin-operated dryers are conveyed on an overhead monorail at speeds of 11-19 ft/min with the components 42 in. apart center-to-center. The usual sequence is two racks or hangers of washer covers followed by a rack of lids. Dryer tops are run periodically as a batch. The hangers can accommodate two washer covers, two dryer tops, or four washer lids. The components hang symmetrically, back-to-back.

Because of the nature of the electrostatic process, however, the vertical lid-well surface of washer covers (artificially highlighted in Fig 3) cannot be porcelainized effectively in the continuous operation. Therefore, it receives a prior coat or "reinforcing spray" of porcelain before electrostatic deposition, but not along the front portion of the lid well (note break in highlight), which is tapered at 45° to the top surface This portion, in fact, as well as the entire upper surface of the cover, cannot receive more than a light dusting of overspray when the reinforcing spray is applied to prevent sagging during subsequent electrostatic deposition. Applying the reinforcing spray manually required one worker per shift over a two-shift

period. The worker would "float" with the line and then return upstream.

After considering several alternatives with robots, the scheme chosen was to mount two spray guns on a 24-in.-long shaft attached to the arm of a Trallfa and to use a servo that could provide a 420° roll for each gun. "Although we decided system requirements, systems engineering was provided by DeVilbiss," Bergant said.

A schematic of the layout appears in Fig 4. To identify the covers for the robot, a two-light photocell array is located within one hanger spacing (42 in.) of the robot's start-command limit switch. Another limit switch actuated by the upper rod of the carrier triggers an input signaling the programmed robot to paint. For color changes—five colors are used—a 30-gal pot is carted to the area, and hoses are attached manually. A gap of empty process racks provides time for changeover.

Programming the robot was the most challenging aspect of the project, said Bergant. The usual procedure of having an operator lead the robot through the sequence proved nearly impossible. "The leverage of the guns mounted 24 in. from the wrist of the robot arm made control difficult." To spray the two back-to-back covers precisely in the areas required, the rod had to be square to the workpieces throughout the spray pattern. Also tried, without success, was to place a pivot assembly on the end of the shaft and

have an operator guide the end of the rod while another worker programmed.

The method finally selected was to use a templet to guide and hold the rod. With the outer gun removed, a program could be generated with the front gun only. Then, if the rod was square to the covers, the other gun would spray the same pattern when reattached.

The templet comprised a short section of pipe welded to a rack so that the centerline of the pipe would coincide with the centerline of the washer covers. Since the guns rotate in a circular path and the surface area to be sprayed is rectangular, skillful manipulation of the robot's wrist was required to compensate for the varying spray distance.

After several weeks of running the robot in a shakedown mode, with two painters still in the area to oversee the operation and touch up the covers if necessary, the robot was released for production about two years ago, and the painters were transferred to new jobs. The single operator running the electrostatic-finishing system was put in charge of the robot as well. And, Bergant added, "the new duties—color change, start-up and shut-down, gun adjustment and maintenance—did not necessitate a change in job classification."

Substantial improvement in quality and productivity resulted. The greater consistency of the robot markedly reduced the amount of rework that had been associated with the manual operation, although maintaining spray consistency now requires greater care in rack maintenance to retain accurate positioning. Further, "annual labor savings amount to $51,000, and we've increased flexibility in scheduling. Since the robot can spray faster than workers, we can batch-run the washer covers and run the line faster than before. Best of all, we were able to transfer the workers to more-productive jobs with better working conditions."

It was, of course, important that this first application for robots work, Bergant remarked, since any first-time use of new technology "has a proportional impact on management confidence for subsequent applications. To date, 31 robots have been either installed or ordered for other areas of the division. One installation involves two finishing robots with a part-recognition system to provide a paint-reinforcing spray on six types of dryer components."

Robots add people

Obviously robots supplant people, all automation tends to, at least at first. But, like so many automation efforts of the past, robots increase productivity, which creates jobs in the long run.

Robots that paint can create jobs

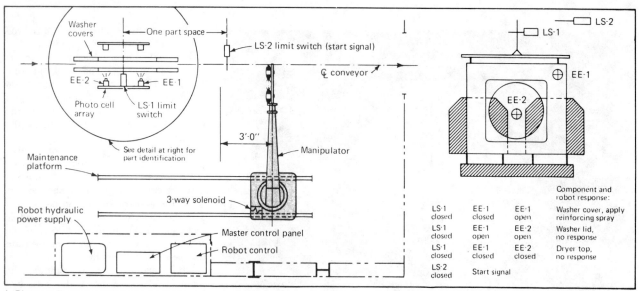

LS-1	EE-1	EE-1	Washer cover, apply
closed	closed	open	reinforcing spray
LS-1	EE-1	EE-2	Washer lid,
closed	open	open	no response
LS-1	EE-1	EE-2	Dryer top,
closed	closed	closed	no response
LS-2	Start signal		
closed			

Component and robot response:

4. Photo-cell array placed one-part space from robot's start-command limit switch identifies washer covers on conveyor line

Robots can also help alleviate hard-core unemployment, almost immediately, as Graham E. Harris Jr, president of EMAC (Oakland, Calif), pointed out.

EMAC, a job shop specializing in painting metal and plastic components for the electronics industry, experienced "tremendous growth" in the past year because of the success of such customers as Apple Computer and Hewlett-Packard and the purchase of two DeVilbiss Trallfas in early '81. Without the robots, according to Harris, the company could never have met the accelerated growth of the industry it serves, which, despite the nation's present hard times, flourishes, thanks largely to its customers' needs for automation.

"Quality painters are hard to find in this industry, and they take long to train," he explained. "One robot does the work of three such painters. The robots got us the business, but their installation required that we hire 18 workers for entry-level positions to supplement each robot—part loaders, wrappers, sanders, touch-up painters, etc. They also freed the company to go after low-volume orders. Short-run parts are more efficiently painted by painters than by robots. The net result was more workers, not less. We had 32 employees in December '80. By midsummer, the number had grown to 80.

"The community surrounding the plant is approximately 90% minority, with very high unemployment, most of which falls in the CETA Title VII, entry-level category. With on-site training, we found that we could hire from this group for many of the robot-interfacing positions, satisfying our labor needs while providing jobs for the hard-core unemployed of our community."

The attitude of workers toward the robots is positive, he said. "Most employees are proud that our company has state-of-the-art equipment, which, over the long term, provides company stability and security. Employees do not seem threatened. They see, on the other hand, a growing company, adding employees because of the robots. If there has been a negative, it's that robots demand more of workers because of the faster line speeds and more-constant production they provide. But this is our problem. We have to train workers properly, give them adequate time for conditioning, and not expect superhuman performance. Which is why we emphasize classroom and production-floor training."

The robots also pleased EPA and OSHA officials, Harris added. "OSHA compliance officers were impressed from the start, not simply because the robots meet California-OSHA requirements but because traditional health concerns with painters are no concern with robots. The EPA voiced its approval early on, too, since reduced paint consumption means fewer paint emissions." Once programmed, the robot repeatedly duplicates the painting sequence exactly. Painters tend to vary paint application between parts and sometimes on the same part. To EMAC, this greater consistency has meant a 15% saving in paint.

In one case, a high-volume run of 4½- x 6- x 8-in. housings for floppy disks, paint consumption was down 20%. And overhead cost—"one of the major cost factors in pricing"—declined 70%.

The company's 40,000-sq-ft plant includes (1) a 1200-ft, variable-speed (0.5-20 ft/sec) conveyor line with five spray booths, the two robots, and a 30- x 44-ft, two-tier gas-baking oven; (2) an 800-ft line with three spray booths and an overhead infrared heating oven; (3)

four spray booths for low-volume work; (4) electric and gas batch ovens; and (5) parts-cleaning facilities.

The robots, which are hydraulically powered by a 5.5-hp motor and have six axes of motion, are equipped with DeVilbiss EPS-513 electrostatic guns. The control center, which consists of a microcomputer and floppy-disk-memory system, permits storing 64 paint programs—any of which can be recalled in half a second. Nearly instant recall is vital, Harris noted, since it enables painting of many different part configurations randomly loaded on the line.

A pulse generator synchronizes robot programming with line speed, which can vary because of random part loading. When the line starts, slows down, speeds up, or stops, so does the robot and, of course, the spray guns. Most part runs are of a single color, but a color change takes just 5-10 min. All that's involved is to open the 10-gal pressurized pot and remove the sleeve, clean it, and put in the new color.

To program the robots, lead painters move the arm of the robot as they would move their own to spray the part. This movement is, of course, recorded in the memory bank. Simple parts take only 15 min or so to program; complex configurations may require 2-3 hr. The painter may alter the program during the course of the run to fine tune the operation further. "Having our lead painters do the programming assures them that the robot is not out to bump them," Harris declared.

"Over the past year, we've experienced less than 1% downtime with the robots. Low downtime is critical to us and to our customers, some of which are stocking only four or five days inventory. If our line stops, so does theirs." ∎

Microcomputers automate welding

Application of microcomputers to achieve flexible welding automation has overcome the limitations in versatility often associated with automated welding

Automated welding has generally tended to offer either of two alternatives: a semiautomatic machine requiring some degree of control by a skilled operator, or a special high-volume station that runs by itself but is very restricted in what it can do. Computer-based welding introduces a third alternative: a high degree of precision and reliability coupled with an inherent flexibility in handling a great variety of welding programs for many different workpieces.

Weigh the alternatives

Any consideration of computerized welding for a particular production environment, however, must weigh its benefits against expectations of higher initial cost as well as some increased operating expenses. Some of these benefits may be unrelated to the performance of the actual system.

For example, a main benefit of a new computer-based welding system, initially developed for high-volume copper cladding, or overlaying, of steel cylinders, is that one operator can be expected to handle as many as three cladding (welding) stations, and the stations can be set up and monitored by operators who are neither welding experts nor computer specialists. Also, the microcomputers and other computer hardware in the system provide the digital-control versatility of a large computer at the cost of conventional programmable controllers or hardwired logic systems.

The computer-based welding machines in question are the result of a joint venture by Arcair Co (Lancaster, Ohio) a specialist in automated welding equipment, and Copeland & Roland Inc (Dublin, Ohio), a specialist in adapting digital computers into industrial processes. The machines were originally developed for munitions work, and some nine are now operating in various munitions-production facilities including Picatinny Arsenal (Dover, NJ), Norris

By Gary A. Bogard, systems engineer
Arcair Co, Lancaster, Ohio, and
Michael W. Velten, project engineer
Copeland & Roland, Dublin, Ohio

The cladding station functions like a welding lathe with automatic load and unload features. The part rotates, and a welding torch oscillates to generate cladding ring

Microcomputers automate welding

Automatic arc-length control is achieved through closed circuit TV system that monitors arc for computer control. Camera is in oblong sheetmetal container

Industries (Vernon, Calif), and Chamberlain Mfg Corp (Scranton, Pa).

Although the initial application dealt with high-volume cladding of cylindrical shapes, the overall system can be applied in many welding or cladding operations on any shape and size of workpiece.

Copper cladding is designed to create a soft layer over a harder material. Conversely, cladding a relatively soft material with a hard layer is used to produce such characteristics as improved abrasion-, corrosion-, or impact-resistance. Equipment in which cladding is commonly used includes refractory vessels, nuclear containers and valves, mixing and crushing rolls, paper-slurry valves, and earthmoving shovels.

In the original Arcair cladding machine, circumferential copper bands are overlaid on steel cylinders that are eventually turned into ammunition shells. The length and diameter ranges of the workpiece that can be handled depend only on the capacity of the mechanical equipment. The computer control system permits laying down any number of bands in any width or thickness.

In essence, the cladding station functions like a welding lathe with automatic load and unload features. As the part rotates in the lathe, a welding torch

Block diagram for computer-automated cladding system

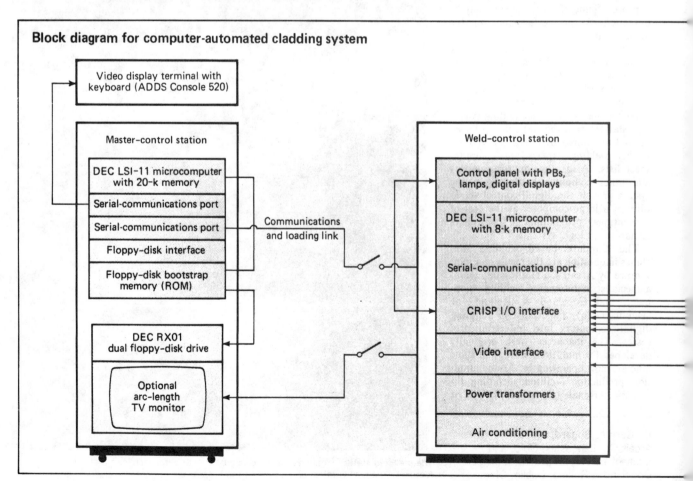

Video display terminal with keyboard (ADDS Console 520)

Master-control station

DEC LSI-11 microcomputer with 20-k memory

Serial-communications port

Serial-communications port

Floppy-disk interface

Floppy-disk bootstrap memory (ROM)

DEC RX01 dual floppy-disk drive

Optional arc-length TV monitor

Communications and loading link

Weld-control station

Control panel with PBs, lamps, digital displays

DEC LSI-11 microcomputer with 8-k memory

Serial-communications port

CRISP I/O interface

Video interface

Power transformers

Air conditioning

oscillates along the part axis to generate the individual rings of cladding material. The machine is loaded from the front and can be fed by hand, magazine, or gravity conveyor. After completion of a cladding cycle, the cylinders are shuttled to the rear of the machine for gravity discharge.

Controlling the deposit

Basically, the GMAW (gas metal-arc welding) process, in which a continuous consumable electrode wire operates in an externally supplied shield-gas mixture, is used to deposit the cladding material. But, for better control over puddle temperature, an auxiliary "cold" wire is run into the puddle as the electrode melts. This wire absorbs some of the heat of the arc plasma and becomes part of the deposit mixture. The resulting hybrid system provides extremely good control over dilution, in which the substrate migrates into the overlay material. Such dilution could result in the need for more than one cladding layer.

Dilution has also been reduced through precise control of the cladding cycle and specifically through an electro-optical arc-length control system, part of the overall computer control system. A closed-circuit TV camera views the arc

and generates a digital signal proportional to the length of the arc. This digital output is, in turn, transmitted to the weld-control computer, a Digital Equipment Corp LSI-11 microcomputer, which then compares the signal with a preset arc-length reference signal and produces an appropriate error signal.

An application program running in the LSI-11 microcomputer analyzes the error signal and then initiates appropriate actions to reduce the signal to zero and thereby correct the arc length.

Corrective actions can consist of adjustments in one or more machine operating parameters: wire feedrate, torch-to-work distance (standoff), power-supply output, workpiece traverse rate, and torch oscillation.

Good overall supervision of the welding process is also achieved with the application of Arcair's feedback-stabilized, heavy-duty welding power supply which helps achieve good weld quality at high welding speeds. To do this, rapid electronic correction of power-line changes is provided by closed-loop, adjustable-slope control of the volt/ampere output characteristics.

The real factor that ensures good overall supervision of the welding process, however, is the coordinated computer-

based control system. A complete Arcair setup includes one or more cladding/welding machines, each with an associated weld-control station; and one master control station for program development.

Controlling the system

The weld-control station uses the DEC LSI-11 microcomputer in conjunction with a Copeland & Roland CRISP computer input/output (I/O) package to control and coordinate all the operating elements of the cladding station. This package includes dc motors for the electrode-wire feed, cold-wire feed, and torch oscillation; workpiece-rotation stepping motor; welding power supply; and arc-length-control TV camera.

The weld-control microcomputer system also monitors the condition of some 20 limit switches involved in loading and unloading the workpiece and in moving the torch and TV camera to the various operating positions. In addition, the microcomputer monitors gas flow and cooling water for the torch and workpiece by processing data from appropriate digital flow meters.

To operate the stepper motor that rotates the workpiece, for example, the weld-control microcomputer provides appropriate stepping pulses and signals to denote clockwise or counterclockwise motion. The pulse rate and direction signals are altered by the computer program that controls the weld schedule to vary the rotation as desired. The computer also provides the necessary signals for manual jog control over workpiece rotation during the setup mode.

The CRISP interface package in the control cabinet sends data from the cladding station to the LSI-11 microcomputer located in the same cabinet. Here the computer welding-control program takes over, and control signals generated by the microcomputer then go back through the CRISP unit to the various electromechanical devices (actuators, solenoids, motors) at the cladding station. The CRISP unit handles all the data transfer in a multiplexing mode via a Digital Equipment Corp DV11 interface at the LSI-11, thereby keeping the computer hardware at a minimum.

Copeland & Roland has also provided a special shop-oriented software that translates English-like programming commands into real-world input/output functions. With it, operator terminology is used to arrive at a complex process profile, consisting of a mixture of time-dependent and position-related functions that make up the weld schedule.

For example, the weld schedule may start with a very slow torch-oscillation rate in order to help form a weld puddle;

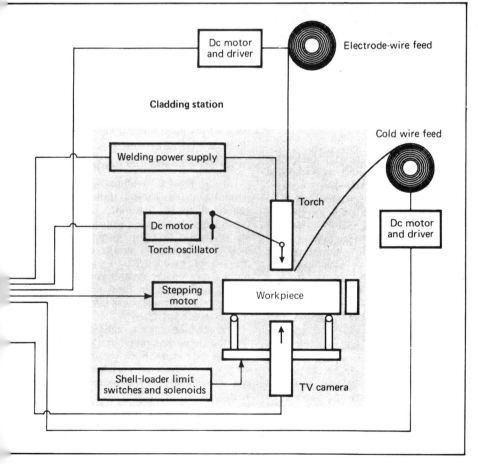

Microcomputers automate welding

Programming is effected by an independent master-control station (lower left in photo) using special operator-oriented commands. Floppy disks store programs

Program development can be achieved with the master-control station operating offline, but, because most programs require a certain amount of empirical tuning, common practice is to develop programs with the master-control station attached to a welding station. In this way, the schedule can be checked out and modified until an optimum program is achieved. This program is then read into the operating-system memory for production operation.

Program can be kept on disk

Once a satisfactory program has been developed, it can be kept on disk storage for future use. It is possible, therefore, to build up a library of programs for different welding or cladding operations. In preparing for production welding, the operator need only transfer the welding program from the floppy disk to the microcomputer in the weld-control station at the machine.

Again, the master-control station, with its dual floppy-disk drive, is used to effect the transfer. Two disks are required: one with the standard RT11 computer-operating-system program, the other with the appropriate weld schedule. Together, they effectively load the weld schedule into the microcomputer.

With the master-control station attached to the machine, the operator may request a display of the complete weld schedule incorporated in the weld-control program. In addition to the weld schedule, the program includes other operating parameters, such as the loading sequence. Most frequently, the CRT is used to display the status of the station during actual operation. Such status information includes both the actual and nominal (as programmed) values of the six basic welding parameters.

Automatic or manual control

During routine welding operations, when the master-control station is not connected to the machine, the weld-control system can be operated in either an automatic or setup mode: from a weld-control program in the computer memory or, manually, by switches and pushbuttons on the control panel. Two digital displays on the front panel indicate workpiece temperature and welding parameters, respectively.

The operator may also choose to override the stored program, altering it with manual data input. Such changes, however, are in effect only as long as the program resides in the control-station computer, and there is no way of transferring the new program to disk storage for subsequent use. Of course, a new program reflecting the changes could be written at the master-control station. ∎

then, as deposition starts, the oscillation rate is increased, and part rotation is initiated. Or it may be desirable to delay certain actions or relate them to the angular rotation of the part. Several of the basic weld parameters can be controlled and coordinated in this way: electrode-wire speed, cold-wire speed, torch-oscillation speed, part-rotation speed and direction, weld voltage, and weld power.

Programming is effected by means of the independent master-control station, which is used initially for program development and subsequently to transfer a satisfactory program, stored on a floppy disk, into the memory of the operating-system computer. The master control station also uses a DEC LSI-11 microcomputer for its programming and editing function.

In addition to the LSI-11, the master-control station comprises a DEC RX01 dual

floppy-disk drive with RT11 computer-operating system, and an ADDS (Applied Digital Systems Inc) Consul 520 video-display terminal. The terminal includes an alphanumeric keyboard for entering data or requesting information for display on the CRT screen. As an optional feature, a separate TV screen can be mounted in the cabinet below the video-display terminal so that the operator can observe a picture of the welding arc, as picked up by the TV camera at the cladding station. This comes in handy during initial setup or for troubleshooting.

The cabinet of the master-control station is provided with wheels so that it can easily be moved around the production floor from one weld-control station to another. Alternatively, it can be located at one fixed location and switched among individual weld-control stations, wherever they are located, by permanent data-transmission lines.

Software brings QA 'up front'

Four basic software packages aim to change quality assurance from a postproduction inspection technique to a statistically controlled management tool for manufacturing planning

In addition to the current, and general, perception that quality should be a prime concern in manufacturing, there is also a belief that contemporary quality-assurance methods are "not keeping pace with advancements in design and machining methods for numerically controlled (NC) machined parts," according to *Quality Assurance in Computer Graphics/Numerically Controlled Processes—Handbook for Aerospace Machined Parts.*

This June 1979 report, compiled under the auspices of the Aerospace Industries Association/Quality Assurance Committee (AIA/QAC), was designed to be a reference volume on the role of QA as it relates to the production of aerospace parts. It was one of a number of sources and stimulants for the development of a quality-assurance-data-management (QADM) system recently introduced by Hansford Mfg Corp (Rochester, NY).

Comprising four basic software packages that run on Hewlett-Packard 1000/45 hardware, the system is intended to bring quality assurance "up front," from post-process inspection to a management-information tool that contributes significant data to manufacturing planning, design, and processes and can communicate with computer-aided design/computer-aided manufacturing (CAD/CAM).

The four packages are a gage history, which provides the software to set up and maintain permanent gage records and recalibration schedules; historical part management, which permits the creation of a database so that histories can be created from measured workpieces; vendor analysis, which permits the user to generate vendor-performance reports via historical record-keeping and inspection reporting; and statistical-analysis software, which gives management the statistical tools necessary to analyze historical results for manufacturing control and planning.

Jobbing showed the need

Hansford does about 40% of its work in the products field, including the manufacture of the Rapid Check line of coordinate measuring machines, the Davis keyseater, a die handler, and the new software system.

The rest of the firm's business involves jobbing and special-machinery building, actually making up a separate Special Machinery/Numerical Controls Division. A sampling of its work includes in-line assembly-inspection machines, pick-and-place components and integrated lines, dial machines, and general NC jobbing for a variety of customers, including Kodak, Xerox, and IBM in the Rochester area.

In fact, the company's work as a general manufacturer had a lot to do with the development of the system. While doing some work for a customer, it was required to establish a gage-calibration system in conformance with Military Specification MIL-C-45662A. The customer also wanted data to be maintained on parts that were contracted out by Hansford to vendors.

Partially in response to this requirement and also to upgrade its QA department generally, Hansford began development of the first component of the system, the gage-calibration package. This software has been operating at the company's manufacturing facilities since January 1980.

Chief Inspector John Richardson runs the software on a Hewlett-Packard (HP) Model 9825 desk-top computer—the package can be used in this stand-alone manner or incorporated in the full-blown HP1000/45 minicomputer hardware with the other three packages. (If upgrading to the full QADM system takes place, this compatible gage package can be transferred to the larger hardware without the data's being manually re-entered.)

The larger hardware consists of the HP processor with 128,000 bytes of memory (expandable), a graphics CRT, 20-million bytes of disk space (10-million fixed, 10-million removable), a 1600-bit-per-in. magnetic tape drive, and a 400-line-per-min printer.

The gage software is prompting, leading inspection personnel through a series of queries that solicit the data required for the file structure. Information that is entered and stored includes gage number (1 to 999,999); gage serial number; gage description; manufacturer of the gage; applicable measurement standard, such as National Bureau of Standards or a secondary source; calibration interval; recalibration source (in-house or farmed out); environmental conditions required for recalibration; and the physical storage location of the gage.

Another file stores the date of recalibration; the inspector; pertinent comments on the gage condition; and the next recalibration due-date.

'If you can read and write . . .'

The prompting software steps Richardson through all the data entries. "I've never worked with computers before; I'm not a programmer by a long shot," he says. "But this is very easy. If you can read and write, you can enter all your data."

He is gradually entering all the gage information from a card file into the system, as he finds time between other inspection functions. Being able to enter and call up data without manual filing procedures is saving him a lot of time.

"I'm the one-man band here. Keeping up a card file with cross-indexing and hand-entry of specs was taking a lot of effort. I could easily spend 1½ days a week on cards in the paper file."

Storage of data is on floppy disk (tape is also available for the HP9825 desk-top model). Each disk can hold 200 gages, with a total system capability of 5000 disks. Each gage entry has room for 12 lines of history, with added space available in a so-called *extend* mode. This is obviously necessary if you're, say, recalibrating a gage every week.

The extend mode consists of a parallel extension disk, also with the capability to hold 200 gages and 12 lines of entry per gage. So a gage history is not actually extended on one disk but is put together as "strings" of 12-line records on these "sister" disks. (With the larger HP1000/45 hardware, extension is automatic without separate disks).

Creating a schedule

Any line can be edited on the calibration package. There is also an update

Software brings QA 'up front'

function. Richardson has found that the intervals necessary between recalibration vary. Generally he checks micrometers every 6-8 weeks or less, gage pins every 6 months, and so forth. (The Mil Spec does not specify *how often* a gage must be checked. What it does say is that a shop has to figure out what needs to be done in its particular circumstances so that its gages are sufficiently in calibration).

Depending on how much traffic an inspection tool sees, the intervals can change. "If a big job comes in, I know they're getting more use than usual. So I'll increase the frequency of recalibration. It also depends on whether I use them or they go out into the shop. Here, if a gage gets dropped, I know it, because I did it. Out in the shop, I can't be sure."

A *delete* function permits a gage and all its extended data to be dropped from the file. The function is equipped with an "idiot-proof" query: after the serial number of the gage is entered and the delete function pressed, the prompt asks again whether the operator wants to delete, just to make sure.

When using the update function, the operator is also asked, after the entry is displayed on a readout, whether the data is correct. There are other error-checking functions as well: for example, a gage can't be entered on Feb 31, an already stored gage can't be entered a second time, etc. Hard-copy printouts of the entire gage directory can be produced at any time.

A *search* function permits Richardson to look at what's due in the future. A certain week can be specified, and the disk will be scanned and everything due on that week printed out. "Just the other

day," Richardson adds, "I entered the week when I'm taking a vacation to see what the workload will be. And, if I find, through an advance search, that a whole slew of recalibrations are coming due in one shot, I can then reschedule some of them to prevent any bottlenecks."

The software can hold dates for a 200-year period. If, say, entries begin in 1980, in 2080, histories could be checked back to the original entry and due-dates until 2180 (actually, until midnight, Dec 31, 2179).

Backup capabilities

So-called "utilities," pieces of software that provide the user with functions outside the normal ones included in the package, are also incorporated in the system. One permits the user to restore damaged tapes.

If a section of tape is destroyed, as much as possible needs to be recovered without data's having to be re-entered, since so much time was initially invested in that process. "If somebody brings a magnetic chuck in here, you're in trouble," Richardson says. A variety of subprograms produce back-up tapes so that a copy can be made and stored and also so that extensions from one particular set of gages to the next can be made.

Richardson is still feeling his way around the system. "With the CMMs, as I got to know the software, I learned to work around certain obstacles. You find lot's of ways to use it that maybe it wasn't designed for . . . a little bit of this, a little bit of that. This will eventually work the same way, I just haven't been able to play with it much yet."

Mike Dickinson, general manager of the Rapid Check Div, adds that "many

firms have, historically, had a shotgun approach to recalibration. A bit of 'well, let's go and recalibrate the darn things.' The problems are obvious—you can be under- or over-calibrated.

"People may not realize that gages can be recalibrated more often than necessary. This is especially crucial if you don't have the facilities in-house and have to send the gages out—that's expensive and time-consuming. You want to adjust to remain in spec, but you don't want to encumber yourself with too many calibrations. This can throw off a QA department. Our system is designed to be very simple but very useful."

Hansford states that the package meets or exceeds the previously mentioned Military Specification MIL-C-45662A in format of record maintenance. The stated purpose of that Mil Spec is to "provide for the establishment and maintenance of a calibration system to control the accuracy of measuring and test equipment used to assure that supplies and services presented to the government for acceptance are in conformance with prescribed technical requirements."

Expanding the package

Having developed the gage-history package, Hansford's software group then began to develop an expanded system designed to bring quality assurance under statistical-control principles to enhance its management-information function.

The historical part-management software essentially serves a record-keeping function, with the data analyzed in the supervisory trend-analysis package to help a user understand what's going on in its manufacturing operations.

The historical software collects information from "communicating" with co-ordinate measuring machines, from keyed-in data from height-gage readings, etc—in other words, dimensional data from workpieces that a company manufactures and inspects.

Its file structure requires the following information: part number; work center; date of inspection; time of inspection; inspector ID; lot size; sample number; and dimensional-data structure.

This information identifies significant aspects of the production process so that, when the trend analysis is performed, it indicates not only how many parts go out of spec but also what the particular reason and location of the problem might be.

Reports and functions of this package include off-line printouts, editing capabilities, plotting routines, scrap reporting, and part-program generation.

The vendor-performance software functions at a similar "record-keeping"

Chief Inspector John Richardson scans a computer printout of QA Dept's gage directory to see which inspection tools are due for recalibration

level. Its file structure requires the part number; name of vendor; date of inspection; inspector ID; lot number; lot size; sample size; samples failed; lot rejected (yes/no); disposition; and comments. The package can generate scrap reports, historical vendor reporting, and lot-acceptance reporting.

Samples prove the lot

As an example, say a lot of 1000 parts is coming in. An inspector would designate a certain sample size, check that amount, and feed the information into the computer. Trend analysis would then give one of a number of possible directives: accept the lot, increase the sample for more certain results, reject the lot.

Obviously, the package is designed to check the quality of a vendor's performance. It may turn out that one jobber brings in unacceptable amounts of certain critical bores oversize and another is holding not-so-critical specs too tight. With the former, a tooling change might be suggested or perhaps the company should route the job to a more precise machine. With the latter, you might not have to pay the premium price being charged for the parts, because such close tolerances aren't really necessary.

Hansford adds that the package also contributes to the "traceability" of components in a company's product, and important consideration with the liability and warranty concerns so prevalent today.

Statistical tools

The trend-analysis package is the supervisory program, providing statistical quality control to the database of information being accumulated by the "record-keeping" software. Its reports and functions include printing deviation reports; 3 Sigma analysis; probability plots; histograms; frequence tables; multi-vary charts; machine-tool capability; precontrol planning; and run-sum planning.

The *3 Sigma analysis* qualifies accuracy by establishing deviations from a number of target dimensions: the data is fed into the computer, and the software prints the analysis.

The technique enables machine-tool builders to assure customers that the product will perform within certain accuracy constraints. Hansford predicated its program on NMTBA specifications for the accuracy of numerically controlled machine tools and has found some of its customers asking for the program to qualify their own machine tools.

The *probability plots* and *histograms* check process performance to indicate whether a particular process or machine

may have capability problems that are interfering with production. Figures 1 and 2 show examples of these. The dimensions refer to a connecting-rod bore radius whose lower tolerance limit (LS) is 0.625,30 in.; the upper specification (US) is 0.625,80 in.

The histogram shows a user how well the process is producing the part. Out of a measured lot, so many will fall into certain "bins": some will be over, some under, and some within range. The histogram gives some indication of how well the work is being done.

The probability plot is used to indicate the percentage of parts below the lower specification and at or above the upper specification. Both are generated from *frequency-table* data, which is composed of the graphic data in tabular form.

Data connected for analysis

Multi-vary charts help to identify *sources* of variation in a process by displaying data from a sample of characteristic measurements. They permit the user to estimate the relative degree to which suspected sources of variation contribute to process performance.

Fig 3 shows a sample multi-vary chart. The part involved (the same connecting rod) has, in fact, two holes that require boring; tolerance is $-0.0000/+0.0005$ in. To isolate within-piece variations, each vertical bar on the chart connects, for one bore, the minimum bore radius measured with the maximum bore radius measured.

The *least-squares-best-fit* (a QA designation based on calculations of the measured data) radius of each part is then connected to the best-fit radius of the next manufactured part to isolate piece-to-piece variation within the process. Groups of five parts are charted together to indicate time-to-time variation.

Time-to-time variation, tracked through this charting technique, could have a variety of uses. For example, if something is going wrong from the first shift to the second—say, productivity is down—isolating the time may reveal that the machine coolant is heating up. Production figures alone won't indicate the cause, but this method pinpoints when and where the problem is occurring.

Information can also be gleaned from the piece-to-piece information charted by the technique. It may be that, between 10 and 11 am (which corresponds to, say, the 5th piece produced on each morning shift), the part is going out of spec.

Following the clue

Investigation based on information from a multi-vary chart might reveal

that, every day at 10 am, material is received at the loading dock and that the machine, located near the dock, experiences a severe temperature change and shrinks just ever so slightly.

Track variance in one piece

The multi-vary charts also provide the information necessary to track excessive dimensional variance within a single piece, as indicated by the length of the vertical bars in the chart.

Once the more powerful software has been used to establish machine capabilities and to ensure that a particular manufacturing process is under control, the precontrol-planning and run-sum control-planning packages can be used. These require less information and work and, typically, are used to check that things are running as before, to make sure that any dimensional drifts do not exceed a certain amount (which will include a smaller band of variation than the part-print allowance and so will indicate a trend before pieces have to be scrapped).

Are things under control?

The trend-analysis software will also print out X-BAR and R-chart reports and graphs to indicate the variability of the process and determine whether a given process is in statistical control. Fig 4 demonstrates the graphs for the connecting-rod radius.

Lot size for the part was 62, and the lot is divided into subgroups of four. Each x and o represents the mean of a particular subgroup of four.

The bottom, R-chart, shows the dimensional range for each subgroup. UCLR stands for the upper control limit; LCLR, the lower control limit. R-BAR is the average *range* of the subgroups. X-DBAR is the average of all the averages of the 15 subgroups.

This software analysis is predicated on the fact that no matter how the individual sizes are distributed, subgroups will be distributed normally, and the upper and lower control limits will be 3-Sigma limits, with three standard deviations contained within the range above and three below.

Statistical law states that 99.27% of the average should fall within this 6-Sigma (three above and below) range. So a point above or below the limits would spark a search for a process or machine reason for the lot's going, statistically speaking, "out of control."

The figure shows two points above and one below the control limits, and so this connecting-rod lot can, in fact, be said to be out of control. Based on scrap-rate permitted and a host of other considerations, it would be the user's decision on

Connecting-rod bore-radius charts

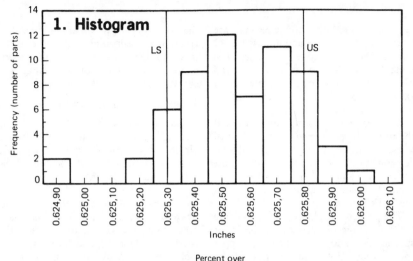

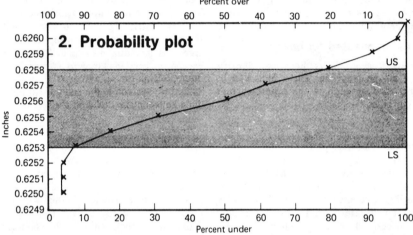

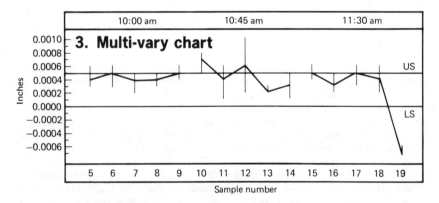

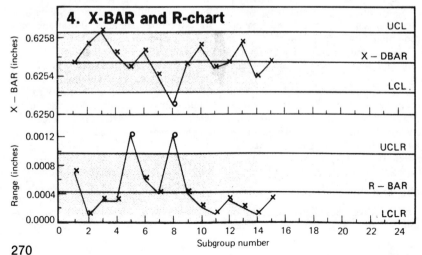

whether to apply further analysis, and at which level, in order to isolate the fault.

The QADM software system, by virtue of the data it accumulates and the analysis it performs, functions essentially as a management-information tool from the vantage point of quality assurance. It provides information that can contribute to a variety of manufacturing decisions:

■ Job estimating—with statistical analysis, a user can begin to understand whether the plant's machines do the work required of them, how fast, whether scrap losses are acceptable, the frequency of tooling changes necessary to maintain tolerances, etc. This information can be compared with job bids or product-development estimates as well as with future quotes.

■ Reduce machine downtime—This can be accomplished in several ways. If a bad lot is discovered through statistical analysis of a sample, it can be pulled out of the production flow before the error is compounded. And the precise fault-isolation capabilities of the system can lessen response time to problem sites.

■ Machine-tool qualification—This would be not so much to check positioning accuracies as much as to check *in-process* accuracy under the various cutting loads specified in a certain manufacturing process. Also, by quantifying the accuracy of the machinery in a shop, a user will be better able to route jobs to the appropriate work stations, rather than relying on gut feelings about a particular machine or the personal knowledge of the foreman (who may leave or retire). Machine-tool-qualification *trends* can also be followed through the course of a machine's life and performance.

■ Personnel—Analysis from these packages could point to problems with particular operators. Hansford stresses that the purpose of this would not be to "go out and beat the worker over the head, but rather to see what can be done to help the employee turn out better parts," states Dickinson. The worker may be misunderstanding certain concepts of fixturing—for example, with cast parts or complicated thin housings, it a screw is tweaked too tightly, the part might be distorted enough that it cannot be machined properly.

■ Manufacturing capability—It follows from these points and the previous dicussion that the purpose of the system is to upgrade a plant's manufacturing capability. By looking at all the points of the process and putting more time and energy into bringing quality assurance up front into all manufacturing decisions, a user, through statistical analysis, should be able to improve its manufacturing operations. ■

Spoken data tracks assembly work

**Workers putting together aerospace electronic components
no longer have to pencil in entries about the work they do**

THE FIRST 15 real-time voice-data-entry (VDE) stations for assembling microelectronic hybrids at Lockheed Missiles & Space Co (LMSC) in Sunnyvale, Calif, saved $400,000 in their first year of operation, more than recovering the $250,000 capital investment for the equipment.

The second installation of ten VDE stations for multilayer printed-circuit-board assembly similarly saved $250,000 within the year, handily covering their $170,000 cost.

More significant in the manufacture of the high-reliability systems for the Trident missile program is the absolute accuracy of the data entry and the immediate availability of the data, declares Leon Lerman, LMSC consulting engineer in electronics manufacturing. To date, they have found no errors in the voice-entered data, he reports.

LMSC is obliged by contract to keep complete records on every step in the manufacture of every component of the Trident missile, a "kind of roadmap" that will enable them to trace any problem back to its source, Lerman explains. "It's data that we never want to use, but, if we do, it has to be accurate," he says.

Before installation of the VDE stations, 68 people were needed to assemble the hybrids, and workers spent about 30% of their time in manual data entry. Employees had to pencil in 112,000 six-digit entries every week, entries that then took six people to key punch into the data bank in the mainframe computer, an IBM 370. The data sheet followed the component through assembly, which meant that the information could not reach the computer until six to nine months after the initial sheet entries.

Now that the hybrid assembly area has 23 VDE stations and a Data General minicomputer, 42 operators can handle the workload, and the six keypunch clerks are no longer needed.

The on-line capability of the VDE system also permits immediate production of management reports. In a few sec-

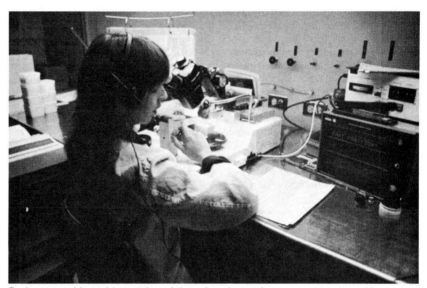

During assembly and inspection of tiny microelectronic components, assembler responds to questions on readout (right) by speaking into headset microphone

onds, the assembly manager can get a one-page-sized report on assembly status and on the requirements for each part for each of the next three months. "Before VDE, the manager had to go through reams of printout paper to get that information," Lerman says.

Lerman believes the LMSC VDE assembly operations are the only real-time manufacturing systems in the country.

The Lockheed program started with a single VDE station in 1977, and Lerman programmed that unit to prove out the concept and ensure that it had a viable system. By late 1978, the company ordered the first 15 production units, and these were fully operational by March 1979. The VDE terminals in the multilayer-board-assembly area were installed in August 1980.

Lerman has been careful to prove out all programming thoroughly on new operations. "If you have a lot of problems when you start using a new piece of equipment, it turns everybody off. If everything goes smoothly, you can get enthusiastic support," he finds.

LMSC management has been very enthusiastic about the program. Eight additional VDEs for the hybrid-chip area

were installed in 1980 and 1981 as additional programs were developed. "We're adding them as fast as we can put them in," says Lerman.

The next installations of VDE terminals will be in inspection areas, Lerman says.

Very natural reaction

"Voice data entry is a natural for inspection, in which both the eyes and hands of the operator are constantly busy," Lerman notes. "To read and voice a word is a natural reaction," he points out. "To read and write something is less direct, and sometimes an inspector reading a micrometer has a problem remembering the reading until it's written down."

Lerman and the LMSC department managers were painstaking in preparing the workers for the shift to VDE and in training them to use the system. "You must always remember that you're dealing with people, not machines," Lerman cautions. "The human factor is tremendously important in making a system work.

"A microphone can be the most intimidating thing in the world," he admits.

Spoken data tracks assembly work

"It's important that the person feel comfortable with the VDE system."

Each operator was trained individually, off the manufacturing floor, and then retrained—again individually—in the assembly area. "It is absolutely essential to train the operators in the same environment in which they will work, at the actual work station," Lerman emphasizes.

When the equipment went in to use, Lerman and department managers met with the operators every morning to get their reactions to the equipment and their suggestions for improvement of the system.

Many of the programming methods in use came from the excellent operator suggestions. At first, for instance, the microelectronic-hybrid program called for the operator to read in the part number and the coordinates for placement of a component. However, the workers recommended that the computer be programmed to carry that information, thus simplifying and speeding the assembly process and improving its accuracy.

In the microelectronic-hybrid assembly area, a clean-room environment, the tiny transistors, capacitors, etc that are thermal-compression-bonded onto substrates are from 0.025 in. to 0.100 in. big, and the operators use tweezers to position them. The work is very delicate; failure rate is about 15% even for these highly skilled operators because of the stringent circuit and performance ratings.

Recognizes speech patterns

The computer leads the operator through each step of the assembly.

First the operator dials his or her number into the computer, and, on the cathode-ray-tube (CRT) screen, the computer greets the operator by name.

Each operator has previously entered a vocabulary of 48 words into the computer by repeating each word ten times. Most are digits or letters of the alphabet, or rather the military phonetics for the letters—able, baker, etc. Or the operator may choose his or her own letter codes.

"Some of the operators use the names of their children," says Lerman. "Some use Spanish or a mixture of English and Spanish." Besides the digits and letter codes, the vocabulary includes such words as *go*, *stop*, *negative*, *ok*, and *help*!

The equipment actually has the capacity to handle 256 different entries—in any words or combinations of words that can be said in a 3-sec period. However, for efficiency, the simplest possible vocabulary is thought to be the best.

The computer program holds the ID number of each chip to be processed and the type and location of each component to be bonded to it. Because the computer asks for verification at each stage, the operator must constantly recheck for accuracy.

When the computer asks a question that can have more than one answer—for example, which manufacturer made a given part?—the question is made multiple choice, and the operator gives only the menu-line number of the correct reply.

At one of the stations in the hybrid-assembly area, the operator periodically removes chips from a batch of hybrids that have been returned as faulty by the Product Assurance Dept. Here a printer was added, so that orders for replacement components can be prepared automatically by voice entry.

At another station, the various components bonded onto the chip are interconnected with two or three ribbon bonds,

---

Computer talks, too

Leon Lerman's group at Lockheed Missiles & Space Co is currently working with a "talk-back" voice-data-entry system and expects to have one in service by the end of 1982 for performing inspections on the receiving dock.

The two-way voiced system is expected to permit significant time savings along with improved accuracy, Lerman says. At present, an inspector in the receiving area works from detailed instructions on a computer printout and must enter the findings manually while moving through the area. Instructions will indicate, for instance, how many of a 100-unit shipment must be inspected, what dimensions are to be checked, and the limits on the number that can be out-of-specification before the shipment can be accepted.

With the talk-back unit, the inspector reads in the numbers identifying the shipment, and the computer then leads him or her step by step through the inspection.

The talk-back unit's diction is flat and uninflected but easily understood, and so Lerman's group is now studying data flow in the receiving-inspection operation in preparation for writing a program. Lerman is working with two programmers—one borrowed from the quality-assurance section—plus one outside consultant.

---

providing double or triple redundancy, and the VDE equipment tallies the bonds as they are installed. Previously, the "ribbon bonds"—30-70 of them—had to be visually counted for verification, a tedious process with a built-in opportunity for error.

One VDE unit is currently being added at an inspection station in the area where three chips from each station must be tested and approved each morning before the equipment can be used for production bonding. This will speed up this preliminary testing and enable operators to get an earlier start.

At two verification stations, where operators view an enlarged image of each assembled chip, zooming in on each segment, the verdict is either "pass" or "fail," and this simple record is manually kept. However, this is also on Lerman's list for conversion to VDE.

The multilayer printed-circuit-board-assembly group handles a more conventional manufacturing operation, and the operator must supply more information to the computer. The operator receives a kit for each board, with the components packed randomly in a tote box.

'Number, please'

The operator must dial in his or her number and voice-enter the part number, vendor, and lot number before the computer indicates where to insert the various components into holes on the board for soldering.

Since a rapport with the microphone is so important, each operator is permitted to choose the most comfortable way to wear or position the instrument. Some use a head band, some wear it on a flexible metal neck brace, and others secure it between the eye-pieces of the microscope on the workstand. However, its position must be consistent; if the position relative to the mouth is changed, it may be necessary to reread in parts of the prelearned vocabulary.

Some humor is even programmed into the computer to make the relationship between machine and operator more personal. If an operator goofs, the machine may chide, "NOW, KATHY, YOU KNOW BETTER." When an operator breaks for lunch, the CRT may flash, "OK, CHRIS, SEE YOU LATER."

Initially, LMSC bought Model T500 VDE units from Threshold Technology (Delran, NJ), but Model 5000 stations were later purchased from Heuristics Inc (Mountain View, Calif). The latter units are compatible with keyboard as well as voice input.

The prices of VDE units have dropped dramatically in the past 18 months, Lerman observed, from $12,500 for the initial units to a current $4,000. ■

CHAPTER X

Computers: The International Scene

CAM: an international comparison

Computer-aided manufacturing is growing in all industrialized nations.
It will lead to largely untended, highly flexible manufacturing systems

THIS ARTICLE is based on a report that is, in a way, the swan song of the Committee on Computer-Aided Manufacturing (COCAM), which was formed at the request of the Air Force Systems Command to review the Air Force program on Integrated Computer-Aided Manufacturing (ICAM) and to advise on the transfer of ICAM technology to all segments of US industry. Now that the ICAM program has matured and is in its implementation phase, COCAM's function is no longer being funded.

To identify useful and promising worldwide developments in computer-aided manufacturing, COCAM invited three authorities to report on the topic. Prof Hiroyuki Yoshikawa, of the Univ of Tokyo, reported on Japan; Prof Keith Rathmill, of the Cranfield Institute of Technology (UK), reported on Western Europe; and Dr Jozsef Hatvany, of the Hungarian Academy of Sciences, coordinated the work and reported on Eastern Europe.

By their own account, the report may, no doubt, be criticized as subjective, disproportionate, inconsistent, and untidy—no attempt having been made to edit each of the regional contributions into a rigid uniform framework. "These faults, however, may also be considered its main strengths, since, as a result, the differences in philosophy and approach of the regions surveyed—while mellowed by much mutual discussion and criticism—nevertheless, come out distinctly," claim the authors. Here is AM's edited version of their report.

The state of the art

Japan

About 70 direct-numerical-control (DNC) systems are now in operation in plants in Japan. The combination of machine tools and computers has become very common, not only in DNC systems but also in computer-numerical-control (CNC) machine tools. Manufacturing automation supported by computers is usually required when a factory manufactures complex products that have short production runs. These products are manufactured in batch-production plants. Therefore, the fact that so many DNC systems are in operation in Japan implies that the need for the automation of batch-production plants is extremely high here.

Automation in mass-production factories is now considerable in many metal working industries, led by watch making. The blanking and machining operations have been almost fully automated, operating untended 24 hours a day, except for monitoring by workers who tour the factory a few times a day. In the assembling area, recently completed lines assemble watches automatically, inspecting and making accuracy adjustments at the final stage of the lines. They still require some workers to watch the system and correct the faults that sometimes occur in the lines. But it seems only a matter of time before the systems become fully automated.

The automobile industry ranks second in automation. Almost all the machining operations have been automated for ten years. Only a few workers are needed at assembly stations to feed the materials into the automated lines. The assembly of such units as engines, has been automated by introducing robots that can transfer, position, and hold parts accurately. But combining automation and accuracy in the final assembly stages remains difficult in this industry.

Roughly speaking, the more that is produced and the simpler the product structure, the easier automation becomes. A typical example of difficult automation is machine-tool production: the production run for each kind is very short, and the structure is complex. Parts manufacturing but not assembly can be easily automated.

NC for short runs

Numerically controlled (NC) machine tools have become popular for the manufacture of complex parts with short production runs, starting in the aircraft industry and followed by other industries. Recently, automatic transfer installations have helped organize NC machines into a unified computer-controlled system.

These flexible manufacturing systems (FMSs) have been applied in many fields and have spread rapidly. This phenomenon shows that the need for automation in the field of batch production is extremely high (Fig 1). However, the design principle, or concept, of the FMS has not yet been fixed completely but is still being developed.

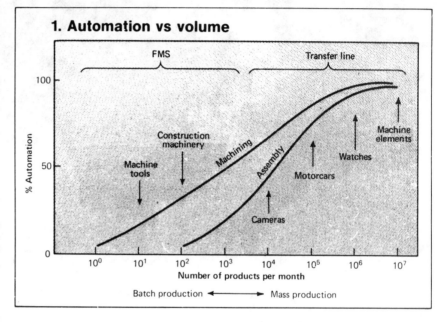

1. Automation vs volume

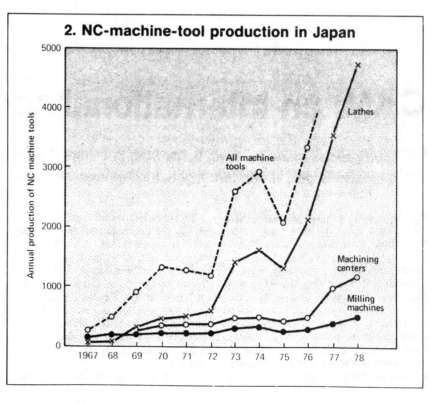

2. NC-machine-tool production in Japan

The first stage of automation in batch-production manufacture was implemented with NC machines. At this stage, NC milling machines are the most important application, but NC has spread to other applications, especially lathes. Fig 2 shows the increase in production of NC machines in Japan since 1967. The NC installations have been equipped with machine tools for such tasks as turning, milling, drilling, boring, and grinding. Machining centers featuring NC appeared from the outset. It is worth noting that the rate of increase of machining centers is considerably higher than that of any other machine tools except lathes. The machine shop might consist of only NC lathes and machining centers in the future, which would provide very high flexibility at a comparatively low cost. There is evidence of a clear tendency for the industry to look for higher flexibility in the production systems.

The trends of percentage increase of NC installations are shown in Fig 3. Of lathes produced in 1978, 21.7% by number, 52.4 percent by value, were equipped with NC. It is probable that almost all machine tools will be equipped with NC in the future.

DNC came in 1968

In Japan, the first DNC system was installed in 1968 at a National Railway vehicle-parts-repair factory. It consists of seven NC lathes controlled by a computer that prepares the schedule for machining with these lathes. This schedule can be changed via control panels on the machine tools. The main merits of this system are that documents, such as drawings, order forms, routing sheets, etc, are eliminated and that manual control tasks are virtually dispensed with.

Transfer and loading are difficult

Automating the process itself is fairly easy in a mechanized factory: such operations as turning, milling, and drilling are easily controlled by NC. On the other hand, supplementary jobs, such as the transfer of parts and the loading and unloading of parts, cannot be automated easily, for technological and economical reasons. The first generation of DNC systems were not equipped with automatic transfer from a loader, requiring human effort in conjunction with automated machine tools.

The second generation of DNC is distinguished by the installation of supplementary equipment. For example, an FMS that manufactures valve bodies started operating in 1972 and it consists of ten stations—specially designed NC machines—linked by transferring equipment, a floating-pallet system for standardized pallets. It resembles a transfer

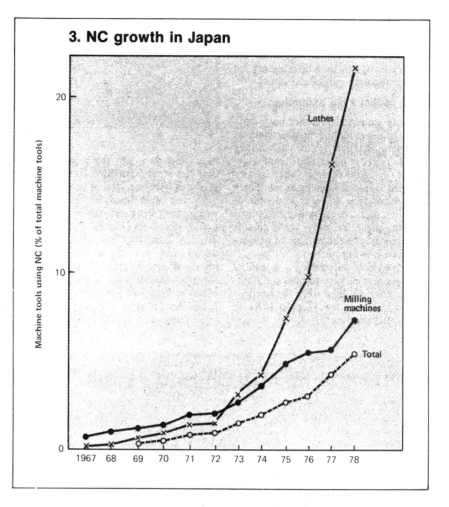

3. NC growth in Japan

line in a mass-production factory. The plant has 10,000 m² of working space, and the line's theoretical capacity is 4000 valve bodies a month.

The valves, intended for a wide variety of applications, may control air, water, steam, or other chemical substances, with a wide variety of flow requirements. The valves may operate at temperatures ranging from −200C to +700C and at pressures of up to 4000 kg/cm². The connecting flanges may have to meet the standards of different countries. This variety means that this line must handle valve bodies in weights from 15 to 250 kg in many different shapes and such different materials as cast iron, cast steel, or stainless steel.

A valve-body casting is first clamped to the pallet, which is then released to the transfer system and advances to a gaging station, where probes confirm that the casting is the stated size and is properly positioned. Next, the pallet advances to a three-spindle mill, a rough-boring machine, and a rough-facing machine.

Tool wear is calculated, and necessary compensations are made. To give machining lines more flexibility in handling the products to be manufactured, the trans-

fer installations in such a system could be replaced by industrial robots. An example of one such system, which began operation in 1974, consists of eight lathes, each with a workpiece feeder and a machine-tool controller. The robot loads and unloads the workpieces and transfers them between lathes.

When one of the lathes reaches the final stage of a machining process, the robot approaches the lathe and waits. After machining is completed, the robot unloads the workpiece and places it on the work feeder, from which it picks up another workpiece and loads it on the lathe.

The robot's hand plays a most important role in improving flexibility. The robot has nine degrees of freedom in motion, with an accuracy of ±1 mm. The hand has three fingers, which act as chuck jaws on workpieces of different shapes. It rotates the workpieces without disturbing other equipment. The robot operates at 45 m/min and the rotations are at about 50 deg/second. The robot is driven by hydraulic motors with encoders, and the hand is driven by stepping motors. Driving signals are usually produced in the computer by a teaching system. A worker manually operates the

CAM: an international comparison

robot through a robot-operating panel, and the motion is stored in the computer. Afterwards, the system can call the motion data at any time by assigning the name of the data taught and stored.

Some recent FMS examples

Nearly untended factories have been rather common in the mass-production metalworking industries for quite a long time. In the case of flexible manufacturing, it is only recently that nearly untended factories have emerged. These systems are very different in degree of flexibility, and the accompanying tables indicate how flexibility requirements vary according to the number of product kinds and lot sizes.

If the level of automation is measured as the number of work stations per worker, automation is high when the flexibility requirement is low (Fig 4). In these cases, workers primarily monitor the sys-

tem, which is almost the same as in the case of a mass-production factory, which produces only one kind of product.

On the other hand, as the flexibility requirement increases, the level of automation decreases (Fig 5). The system at Toshiba Tungalloy has just been introduced and can be expected to be improved considerably in the future. For the most flexible lines, a certain number of workers are still needed, especially for palletizing, loading and unloading, and monitoring. The application of robots is

expected to turn such systems into nearly untended factories.

Night-shift operation is untended

In many factories, systems operate in two or three shifts. Recently, there has been a remarkable trend to operate systems untended in night shifts. Fanuc has built a new factory in Fuji following this trend. Of the plant's 29 cell-like work stations seven are equipped with robots, and 22 have automatic pallet-changers and a pallet-storage system. The work

4. Automation level for low flexibility

	No. of product kinds	Average lot size	No. of stations per worker
Mitsubishi Electric Co	4	300	9
Brother Co	6	50	11
Yanmar Diesel Co	10	3	4

6. Flexible manufacturing systems (FMS) in Japan

Company	No. of machines	No. of machining centers	No. of lathes	No. of product kinds	Average lot size	Product amount, pieces/year	Automatic loaders	Automatic transfer	Computer (controller)	Core memory (K)	Connection	Auxiliary memory (K)	Input	Output	Language	No. of part-programs
1.	8	—	8	—	—	—	8	R	—	—	—	—	—	TY	APT	—
2.	5	5	—	20	200	72,000	5	C	F/To	8	D	512	TY	TY	APT	—
3.	2	2	—	30	20	72,000	0	M	F/Ko	8	B	262	—	—	Fapt III	—
4.	2	2	—	10	50	3,500	2	C	NOVA	32	B D	256	TY	TY CD	TAPROS	25
5.	2	2	—	30	3	6,000	2	C	NOVA	12	D	128	TY	TY GR	TAPROS	200
6.	12	12	—	20	5	15,000	9	C	NOVA	32	D	1,000	TY	TY CD	TAPROS	500
7.	4	4	—	20	3	1,000	4	C	IBM-7	40	B	4,800	TY	TY CD	APT	50
8.	8	8	—	10	3	1,560	8	C	F/Ko	12	D	1,048	TY	TY	APT	—
9.	5	5	—	5	300	18,000	4	C	Prog Cont	—	—	—	—	—	—	—
10.	2	2	—	25	200	20,000	2	C	Intel	8	μp	—	—	—	—	—
11.	9	7	2	—	—	—	3	—	—	—	—	—	—	—	—	—
12.	2	2	—	23	55	8,000	2	C	NOVA	32	B	1,200	TY	TY CD	APT TAPROS	65
13.	22	22	—	6	50	35,000	6	C	TOSBAC 40C	48	μp	2,400	TY	TY	—	—
14.	10	4	6	50	16	14,000	7	C	FACOM	32	D	—	TY	TY CD	KOMA/TSU	700
15.	6	4	2	3,600	5	—	—	—	—	—	—	—	—	—	—	—
16.	5	5	*	9	20	2,500	5	C	FACOM	24	B	256	TY	TY	NIT	40
17.	2	2	—	225	45	15,000	2	C	NOVA	40	B	4,800	TY	TY	APT	—
18.	9	9	—	4	300	40,000	9	C	Prog CNC	—	—	—	—	—	—	—
19.	3	3	—	10	3	1,000	3	C	NOVA	48	B	4,800	TY	TY	TAPROS	50
20.	9	9	—	1,500	5	72,000	0	M	NOVA	48	B	1,200	TY	TY GR	TAPROS	2,000
21.	29	22	7	—	—	—		C,R	FANUC	—	μp	—	—	—	—	—
22.	25	4	1	—	—	—	5	R	FANUC	—	μp	—	—	—	—	—

Notes: A = automatic; B = BTR (behind tape reader); C = conveyor; CD = character display; D = direct; Dlg = dialog; Gr = graphic display; μP = microprocessor; M = manual; R = robot; TY = automatic typewriter; * = supported by government

5. Automation level for high flexibility

	No. of product kinds	Average lot size	No. of stations per worker
Toshiba Tungalloy Co	3600	5	0.8
Toyoda Machinery Co	1500	5	2.3
Komatsu	106	16	1.2

stations are connected by untended vehicles, which are guided electromagnetically or optically.

The plant has two automatic warehouses, one for material and another for finished parts and subassemblies. The vehicles transport material from the warehouse to the untended machining stations. Robots or automatic pallet-changers load materials onto the stations from the vehicles. Finished parts are transferred again automatically by the vehicles to the second warehouse.

The plant has an assembly floor, where workers work during the day. Transportation between the parts warehouse and this floor is also by untended vehicles. In the daytime, 19 employees work around the machining stations, mainly for palletizing, and 63 work in the assembly section.

At night, however, there is only one worker in the plant. The assembly floor is closed, and the machining floor operates without human effort. Every station is equipped with a monitoring device with TV camera, and the one worker monitors all the working stations from the control room. This worker observes the working status of stations through the camera, without touring the factory. The monitoring device also records the spindle-motor current, calculating the cutting force and time in order to judge the cutting conditions.

Many Japanese machine-tool manufacturers have recently completed commercial systems with monitoring devices that can operate nearly untended night shifts. Toshiba Machinery Co, Toyoda Machine Works Co, Makino Co, Yamazaki Iron Works Co, and Niigata Iron Works Co are the leaders in this area.

Control of flexible machining systems has been changing rapidly. Hierarchical computer systems are becoming the most important method for FMS control. For example, Brother Co has equipped its CNC units with 4K-byte memory, and all NC information necessary for one cycle of operations is transferred from the central computer to 22 machine tools during batch changeover. This system has lightened the burden on the central computer, increasing the total reliability of the manufacturing system.

The aforementioned Fanuc system has a similar concept. Its CNC units, with four 256K-bit bubble memories, have enough capacity to store all the NC programs to be used during that day.

Just-in-time production

When the number of product kinds increases or the lot size decreases, the burden upon scheduling becomes tremendously heavy. There are quite a few theories of optimal scheduling, but, unfortunately, they are still too simple and cannot be practically applied. Improvement of the flexibility of FMSs can help to solve this problem. The "just-in-time" production method eliminates the burden of scheduling. In this case, the lot size can be basically thought of as one unit. Besides eliminating the scheduling burden, this method decreases the inventory of materials and finished parts, thus reducing costs considerably. This concept is now being adopted in quite a few factories.

Robotics open new phase

The introduction of robots into FMSs has opened a new phase in their development. At the beginning of this phase, robots were mounted on a frame structure designed specially for the specific machine-tool layout. Many robot manufacturers developed various robots that have been successfully applied to welding and painting, but Fanuc has developed one that is suitably applied to load and unload work for machining. This robot

Precision process						Labor factors					Operation and cost				
Sequence of part manufacturing	Selection of work station	Selection of tool	Cutting condition	Planning (weekly)	Scheduling (daily)	No. of workers, day	No. of machines per worker	No. of workers, night	Software	No. of workers in conventional system	Working time (hr/day)	Uptime/total time (%)	System cost* ($ million)	Software cost ($ million)	Company
M	A	M	M	M	M	2	2.5	2	1	22	16	90	1.3	0.1	1.
M	M	M	M	a	a	4	0.5	—	1	4	10	60	0.15	—	2
—	—	—	—	—	—	—	—	—	—	—	—	—	—	—	3.
M	Dig	M	A	M	M	1	2	1	1	12	18	80	0.75	0.1	4.
M	A	M	M	M	M	1	2	0	1	5	20	95	0.6	0.01	5.
M	M	M	A	M	M	5	2.4	5	4	40	20	90	7.5	0.75	6.
M	M	M	M	M	M	2	2	—	2	16	16	85	2.5	0.1	7.
M	M	M	M	M	M	2	4	2	—	10	14	90	1.7	—	8.
—	—	—	—	—	—	2	2.5	2	1	20	18	95	0.75	0.005	9.
—	—	—	—	—	—	1	2	1	1	10	20	95	—	—	10.
M	M	M	M	M	M	—	—	—	—	—	—	—	—	—	11.
M	M	M	A	M	M	1	2	0	1	10	20	95	1.15	0.08	12.
M	M	M	M	M	M	2	11	—	3	24	8	85	1.45	—	13.
A	Dig	A	A	A	A	4	2.5	—	2	10	16	100	—	—	14.
—	—	—	—	—	—	16	0.8	—	—	70	—	—	2.5*	—	15.
M	M	M	M	A	A	3	1.7	—	1	6	16	—	—	—	16.
M	M	M	A	M	M	2	1	—	2	6	9	50	0.63	—	17.
—	—	—	—	—	—	1	9	1	—	26	16	90	2.0	0.03	18.
M	M	M	A	M	M	1	3	1	1	10	20	95	1.2	0.05	19.
M	M	M	A	M	M	4	2.3	4	2	18	18	50	1.0	0.025	20.
—	—	—	—	—	—	19	1.5	1	—	100	24(?)	—	—	—	21.
—	—	—	—	—	—	—	—	—	—	—	24	—	—	—	22.

has been used successfully in Fanuc factories, serving workpieces to several machine tools located on the periphery of a circle around it.

Such a system has higher flexibility than frame-structure types, and its entire system structure can be changed more easily. A successful example is an FMS in the Niigata Iron Works. In the new Fanuc plant in Fuji, seven robots perform load/unload operations for machining stations. Products of this plant are wire-EDM machines and robots. In essence, robots are manufacturing robots in this plant.

The introduction of robots into the mechanical-assembly function of flexible manufacturing is not yet economical. But many engineers believe that the situation is changing very quickly and that only one more step is needed to realize this potential. Some companies have developed prototypes of commercial systems, which will be discussed later in this report.

In order to evaluate the quantitative aspects of FMS proliferation in Japan, sample statistics have been assembled about machine-tool configurations, loading and transferring equipment, control computers, languages, and economic results of the systems that are presently running at factories of different industries. Twenty-seven systems were selected from about 70 systems as typical cases, and questionnaires were sent to companies using them. Of these, 20 replied, and some information is available for two other companies (Fig 6). The results may be summarized as follows:

■ The number of machine tools composing the system varies from 2 to 29. The average is 7.32.

■ In most cases, the machine tools are machining centers.

■ The number of product kinds is very widely distributed, the maximum being 3600 and the minimum 4.

■ The average lot size varies from 3 to 300. There seems to be some relationship between the number of product kinds and the lot size. One extreme is found in the system of Toyoda Machinery, where the number of product kinds is 1500 and the lot size is 5. Another extreme is found at Mitsubishi Heavy Industry, with 4 and 300, respectively. The ratio of these parameters (the number of product kinds/lot size) can be used to specify the flexibility required.

■ Almost all systems are installed with automatic loaders using pallets and conveyors. Fanuc uses robots for this purpose but only for turning operations.

■ In most systems, minicomputers are used. The core memory size ranges between 8K and 48K.

■ Input/output devices are mainly typewriters, some graphic displays for output. Character displays are usually installed.

■ For control-system software, most factories usually use assemblers. Part-programs, however, are written in APT or similar company-developed languages.

■ The number of part-programs prepared ranges between 25 and 2000.

■ Most companies replied that automatic decision-making in process planning—regarding sequence of part manufacturing, selection of work stations, selection of tools, etc—is a problem for the future. These are now being developed.

■ The effect of these systems upon labor productivity is remarkable. In the case of Mitsubishi, where flexibility, as defined above, is very low, 26 workers were replaced by 1. On the other hand at Komatsu, where flexibility is high, the reduction was from 10 workers to 8.

■ The cost of the system varies from $0.15- to $7.5-million. The cost for software seems very low, approximately 10% of the hardware cost.

Western Europe

Although any estimates of industrial investment in CAD/CAM within Western Europe tends to be based on a large proportion of large companies, the data in Fig 7 is thought to be generally representative. A move toward an increasing number of stand-alone systems seems to be continuing. About 55% of the increasing number of Western European companies using interactive graphics for CAD/CAM have minicomputer-based, stand-alone systems; the remaining companies have graphics terminals served by main-frame computers. The movement to fully integrated engineering-database systems has not been increasing at the rate expected a few years ago (Fig 8).

The distribution of the activities for which West European industry is currently using its CAD/CAM systems is shown in Fig 9. Evidence suggests a continuing trend toward use of an increasing part of the computing budget for CAD/CAM instead of predominantly accounting or other business systems. Currently, however, it is estimated that approximately 75% of industrial computer users spend more on business systems than on engineering or CAD/CAM systems.

The labor-productivity ratios achievable with CAD/CAM systems are crucial to their justification. Some examples of typical productivity ratios currently being achieved are indicated in Fig 10. These figures are considered to be reasonably conservative. Reduced hardware costs—along with software developments in modeling, dimensioning, and annotation—will provide for general ongoing

7. CAD/CAM spending in Western Europe

Industry type	Percent of investment
Mechanical engineering	35%
Aerospace/military	30
Electronics/electrical engineering	20
Architectural/civil engineering	10
Others	5

8. Database integration in Western Europe

Level of integration	Percent of companies
Operating genuine engineering-database systems	15%
Activity working toward a database system	50
No real activity toward integrated systems	35

9. CAD/CAM applications in Western Europe

CAD/CAM activity	Percent of companies
Engineering-design analysis	50%
Automated drafting	50
NC-tape preparation	40
Production-control- and shop-floor-data collection	30
Process control and materials handling	20
Automated inspection	5
Automated process planning	5

10. Typical productivity ratios, W Europe

CAD/CAM application	Ratio
Simple design and drafting with dimensioning	4.5:1
Complex designs with dimensioning	2.5:1
Manufacturing-information production in NC tapes	3.5:1

11. FMS developments in Western Europe

Location	Machine tools	Components	Comments
Heidelberger Druckmaschinen AG Heidelberg, FRG	9 machines	Prismatic—printing-machine side frames	Long-established (1973) system now subject to extensions. Fully integrated system with palletized work and conveyor handling
Heller FRG	2 machining centers	Prismatic—machine-tool components	Fully integrated system developed by Heller, has storage rack and stacker work handling
Motoren Turbinen Union (MTU) FRG	5 machines 1 working station	Prismatic—four types of cylinder head	This fully integrated system features low component variety and has four conveyors and one stacker to handle palletized parts
Messerschmitt—Bölkow-Blohm (MBB) FRG	25 multispindle machines	Prismatic—aircraft components	One of the most impressive systems. Has DEMAC automatic tool-monitoring and -supply system
VFW-Fokker FRG	6 machines	Prismatic—aircraft components	Machines parts for Tornado aircraft. Now fully integrated system with palletized parts handling. Developed from previous, simpler DNC system
Zahnradfabrik-Friedrichschafen FRG	—	Rotational—gear wheels	System has overhead conveyor with loading by robot
Mirlees Blackstone England	Based on 400 KTM machining center	Prismatic—diesel-engine components	Small system proven at National Engineering and featuring automated palletized parts handling
Normalair Garrett England	2 KTM machining centers	Complex prismatic parts	Compact system features high flexibility in terms of tool variety
'600' Machine Tool Group England	10 machine tools, including CNC & automatic machines 9 Fanuc robots	Rotational—machine-tool components	Leading British system has sophisticated four-track conveyor and palletized workpiece handling, with 9 Fanuc robots and computer-assisted scheduling
Sulzer Bros Switzerland	Progressive DNC control of up to 30 NC machines	Various—company produces high-speed weaving machinery	One of the largest Swiss companies, Sulzer has experienced problems in attracting skilled labor
ASEA Ac Motor Plant Sweden	Robot-integrated manufacturing cells	Motor shafts and end plates	Large-batch-size work. The cells are operated both day and night with minimal supervision
BT Handling Systems Sweden	20 hardwired NC and CNC machines	Various—company produces materials-handling equipment	Parts, materials, tools, NC tapes, and inspection gages delivered to work stations by automatic warehouse stacker crane

improvements in CAD/CAM-system productivity.

FMS and robots go together

The Federal Republic of Germany (FRG) has a highly coordinated and well financed government project for CAD/CAM research, development, and implementation. In most other Western European countries, most meaningful work on FMS research and development is a result of commercial interests supported by government funding. The high capital costs associated with FMS developments ensure that they still tend to be monopolized by the larger industrial companies.

The nations leading in FMS development tend to occupy similar positions in robot implementation. The FRG and Sweden are well represented in this field, the UK and other European countries have developed industrial systems more slowly (Fig 11).

It is estimated that, including manufacturer's prototypes and advanced academic research systems, the total number of flexible manufacturing systems currently in existence in Western Europe is approximately 25. Of interest is the number of FMS developments currently cloaked in commercial security. It is a fact that major companies with considerable practical experience of in-house

DNC/FMS installations are strictly limiting publicity of their developments.

The work on modular materials handling systems in the Federal Republic of Germany—Institut für Produktionstechnik und Automatisierung (IPA), Stuttgart—and the concept of expandable FMS systems promoted by KTM Ltd are indications of growing concern for modularity and economy in FMS hardware. Program simulation, swarf and coolant control, part sensing, and tool-wear monitoring are aspects of work directed toward the further removal of human operators from the machining system. Operating flexible machining systems with limited attendance during a night

CAM: an international comparison

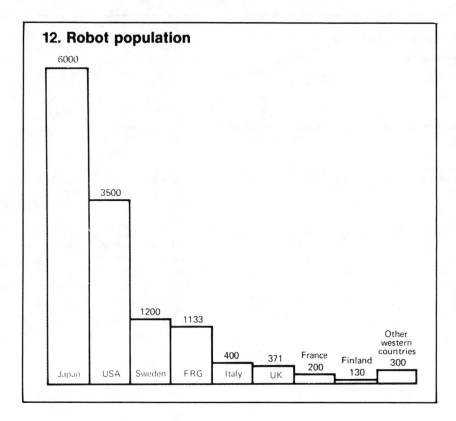

12. Robot population

```
6000  Japan
3500  USA
1200  Sweden
1133  FRG
400   Italy
371   UK
200   France
130   Finland
300   Other western countries
```

13. Robot distribution in UK and FRG

Application	UK No.	UK %	FRG No.	FRG %
Surface treatment	69	18.5	155	13.7
Spot welding	59	15.9	339	29.9
Arc welding	48	12.9	138	12.2
Grinding, drilling, etc	4	1.1	5	0.4
Assembly	5	1.4	44	3.9
Press tools	21	5.7	28	2.5
Diecasting	33	8.9	56	4.9
Injection molding	54	14.6		
Machine tools	39	10.5	113	10.0
Manipulation (investment casting, metal pouring, etc)	10	2.7	34	3.0
Inspection, test	3	0.8	—	—
Palletizing, packaging	16	4.3	—	—
Handling, general	—	—	170	15.0
Research	—	—	17	1.5
Others (unspecified)	10	2.7	34	3.0
TOTAL	371	100%	1133	100%

Trends in robot applications

The best source available on trends in robot use within Western Europe to date is the British Robot Assn (BRA). Data released in February 1981, based on an accurate definition of what constitutes an industrial robot, indicates the distribution of robots by nation (Fig 12).

The total number of robots currently in use in Western Europe is thought to be approaching 4000, with Sweden and the FRG the unquestionable leaders in terms of number of robots in use. Italy's 400 robots are concentrated almost exclusively in the factories of three main users — Fiat, Olivetti, and Alfa-Romeo. On the other hand, nearly all the robots in the UK, with the exception of two spot-welding lines in the automotive industry, have been installed singly or in pairs. An estimated 140 to 180 robots are being used in the UK.

The BRA predicts a 30% growth rate in the UK robot population during 1981.

UK companies that have purchased robots during the last two or three years appear prominently on the list of those most likely to purchase further robots.

Data comparing robot use in the UK and the FRG according to application indicate a remarkable similarity between the countries (Fig 13). Spot-welding and paint-spraying robots are clearly predominant. General handling, machine loading, and arc welding are the next most popular applications.

A popular belief is that arc-welding applications will increase in the relatively near future, with recent improvements in robot technology in this hitherto highly skilled work. Assembly, especially in the electronic-circuit-board industry, and machine-tool loading are generally thought to be other major growth areas.

Although there are differences between countries, the FRG is representative of much of Western Europe in that it currently imports nearly 50% of its industrial robots. Western Europe as a whole imports some 46% of its robots; the US, by comparison, imports approximately 50%. The Japanese import only 4% of their industrial robots. These figures clearly reflect on the strength of the indigenous robot-manufacturing capabilities of the nations concerned.

Increasing commitment

Generally, the rate at which Western European countries are increasing their commitment to CAD/CAM, both industrially and in research, is visibly increasing. Spinoff from the past decade's work in developing CAD systems is now reaching the process and building industries.

Furthermore, improvements in the reliability and modularity of parts-producing systems are being complemented by increased labor costs and a growing shortage of skilled workers. Social and economic factors stimulate a continuing acceleration of CAD/CAM applications.

A major limiting factor is the inertia of society generally and of educational establishments in particular in accommodating the rapid changes that inevitably come. For example, university courses require more frequent updating and more interdisciplinary work.

Industry currently seems to lack turnkey-system suppliers. Unless great strides are soon made toward modularity and interface standardization, the level of expertise required to design and assemble large CAD/CAM systems could severely limit their proliferation.

The drive to adopt CAD/CAM technology seems to be firmly rooted in large market-loading companies. Such companies — given their capital resources, the availability of the technology, and the

shift is clearly a feature of many of the systems that are currently being designed.

rapidly increasing costs of both direct and indirect labor—regard CAD/CAM as the natural and only solution.

User interfaces have received much consideration recently. Reduced computer-processing costs coupled with valuable user feedback has led to a clear improvement in the user interface. More-recent CAM developments indicate the value of systems that do not require high levels of operator training. And awareness of the role of software appears to be inducing companies pioneering CAM to contribute to technology transfer.

The role of the financially smaller company has brought recognition of the widespread need for government inducements to raise the level of technology in these companies.

A feature of more-recent industrial developments is the movement toward more-comprehensive rather than elemental systems. There is, then, evidence that both horizontal and vertical integration is taking place in current CAM systems.

A distinct increase in the industrial use of computer aids in part-programming, process planning, and system simulation is discernible. As NC-machining and -inspection operations continue to improve in number and quality, engineering drawings, as traditionally known, are beginning to disappear. Despite advanced modeling software, the productivity of CAD/CAM systems is still inversely proportional to drawing complexity. For this reason, all-embracing CAD/CAM systems continue to be uneconomic in even the larger companies producing highly complex products. Computer-automated materials handling is fast becoming a vital CAM growth area in application and research.

The number of robot users and producers in Western Europe is increasing rapidly. Commercial competition, especially in the simpler, lower-cost end of the industrial-robot market, is continuing to reduce robot-equipment costs.

Eastern Europe

Intensive work on the development and introduction of CAM systems in Eastern Europe was begun in the early '70s in the German Democratic Republic (GDR) and the Soviet Union. Czechoslovakia and Hungary entered into pilot projects on a relatively large scale in the mid-'70s, followed later by Bulgaria, Poland, Rumania, and Yugoslavia.

Until the mid-'70s, the philosophy leading to major government investments in CAM projects in Eastern Europe was based on continued rapid industrial expansion and a grave shortage of labor.

These factors have since been considerably modified by changes in world trade and international market conditions. The initial trend toward establishment of large systems has, therefore, given way in most of the European countries to an increased emphasis on smaller but more-sophisticated systems.

USSR: 3 generations of FMS

The United Research & Development Institute for Machine Tools (ENIMS) of Moscow, with the participation of other organizations, has developed three generations of computer-controlled FMSs. The first AU-1 system (1971) was superseded in 1976 by the ASV-20 in machining rotary parts (up to 250 mm dia and up to 750 mm long).

The prototype of this system, installed in the Stankokonstrukciya machine-tool factory, had four lathes with stepping-motor slide drives, two lathes with dc servos, three vertical turret drills, one vertical milling machine, one 3D milling machine and a 3D measuring machine. The control computer is an M6000; part-programming is done on a Minsk 32.

In the period up to 1976, ENIMS developed a range of flexible manufacturing systems for machining prismatic parts in the range of 250- to 1600-mm cubes. The purpose of this project was to develop a typical system with standardized modules that could be applied in a wide range of manufacturing situations. The spindle ends, tool grippers, and servos of all the machines in the range are uniform; they all have the same standardized CNC controls with programmable-logic controller (PLC) interfaces and adaptive-control-sensor input.

The systems can be assembled at three different levels of automation: manual workpiece transfer and storage, automatic storage, and fully automatic storage, transport, and gripping. The systems have computer-based part-programming, production control, machining, finishing, cleaning, and measuring stations. There are supplementary work places for marking, tool preparation, and fixture assembly. The productivity of these systems has been three or four times greater than that of previous systems. Since their capacity is generally difficult to exploit within a single factory, they have been established on a regional basis.

The most recent Soviet metalcutting system to be developed is the API. This is a new integrated FMS for the machining of box-shaped parts ranging from 120 x 120 x 120 mm to 500 x 500 x 500 mm at the Stankostroenie factory, Moscow. It is based on six multioperation CNC machine tools, a central control computer, and an automatic part-handling and -storage system.

The system also contains an NC measuring machine, a blank-preparation section, an assembly section for general-purpose fixtures, and a tooling section for storage, assembly, and calibration of cutting tools. It is provided with a central production-control and dispatcher system and a computer-aided process-planning and part-program-editing system.

ENIMS has also developed a DNC system of EDM machine tools. The system includes EDM machines and automatic part-handling and -storage devices with simple local controllers, a central process-control computer, and a central production-control computer. All the digital systems are interconnected through a common bus.

There has been a considerable effort in the USSR to introduce CAD and computer-aided process-planning systems in the manufacturing industries. The research and development center for this project is the Institute of Technical Cybernetics (ITK) in Minsk, which has tested and applied its results primarily in the Minsk factory for automatic manufacturing systems.

In designing gearboxes for machine tools, the system automatically positions the spindles and shafts within the gearbox, selects bearings, checks on interference of parts, and performs calculations of strength. The system generates complete design documentation sufficient for manufacturing and assembly.

An automatic process-planning system for that optimizes plans for rotational parts performs the following tasks:

- Classification and grouping of parts.
- Selection of form and size of blank.
- Process routing.
- Designation of job-shops.
- Operation planning, including machine-tool selection, fixture selection, and tool-operation sequencing.
- Selection of cutting, auxiliary, and measuring tools.
- Rate fixing.
- Documentation (process route sheets, drawings, setup plans, etc).

The Moscow machine-tool factory (Ordzhonikidze) has developed an automatic process-planning system for gears, shafts, and disk-type parts. It performs the following functions:

- Blank design.
- Process routing.
- Rate fixing.
- Designation of job-shops.
- Selecton of machine tools, fixtures, and tools.
- Rate fixing.

About 25% of new process plans are developed by this system.

An automatic system for design of blanking dies was developed by ITK

CAM: an international comparison

Minsk. This system is given the description of the part, the part layout, and type of the blanking die and performs the following functions:

- Geometric processing.
- Calculation of thrust force and center of application.
- Design of the upper die and punch.
- Design of the whole die, including design of guides, strip clamping, advancing, and part removal.
- Documentation.

An automatic design system for fixtures for drilling planar parts was developed by ITK Minsk. Part geometry and machining operations are described for the system, which automatically designs the required fixtures and performs process planning and part-programming for production of the new fixture. It also generates all the documentation required (including drawings), as well as NC tapes. This system is extensively used by industry.

GDR had FMS in '72

The machine-tool industry of the German Democratic Republic launched an ambitious government project in the late '60s, producing first, highly automated flexible manufacturing systems, which began operation by 1972. This program has since been continued, and four more systems were commissioned in 1972, 1973, and 1977. The earlier systems of the ROTA and PRISMA-1 types have been extensively described in the literature. The main characteristics of the more recent ones are as follows:

- PRISMA 2, VEB WZM-Kombinat Fritz Hechert (Karl-Marx-Stadt). Commissioned in 1972, this integrated system was intended to manufacture prismatic parts for milling machines in the range of 1000 x 1000 x 1600 mm. It consists of seven universal machining centers, one qualifying machine, and two measuring machines for quality control. The machines are controlled by two process computers in the behind-the-tape-reader (BTR) mode (16K core) and DNC/CNC (48K core) mode, respectively. Parts are transported on linear-drive air-cushion pallets. The system produces about 4000 pieces of 14 kinds annually in small to medium lot sizes.

- FZ 200 VEB WZM-Fabrik, Hermann Matern (Zerbst). This system produces 60- to 200-mm-dia spur gears for production lathes. Started in 1973, it consists of five chucking lathes, three internal and surface grinders, one broaching machine, three automatic gear-hobbing machines, one power burnishing machine, six gear-generating grinders, and two KRS 4201 (16K-core) process computers. Part transport is palletized. The capacity of the system is 180,000 spur gears/year in 200 different kinds and a maximum lot size of 400.

- PC3 VEB Kombinat Umformtechnik, (Erfurt). This system was established for machining welded prismatic parts with dimensions of more than 1000 mm and a maximum weight of 24,000 kg. The system consists of five vertical boring and milling machines and one process computer. The parts are transported by a pallet-exchange system controlled by the process computer. System capacity is 1200 parts of 100 various kinds.

System developers were SKODA, Plzen (Czechoslovakia), and Forschungszentrum des WZM-Baus, Karl-Marx-Stadt (GDR).

The GDR has also made considerable progress in the widespread industrial introduction of computer-based process-planning and production-planning methods. The programs RATIBERT, RTU, the AUTOTECH series, and such CAD/CAM programs as their auto-body press-tool design and manufacturing system and the CAD/CAM system for extruder-worm bushings have been widely publicized.

Modest Czech software aims

The Czechoslovak machine-tool industry, in the framework of a government project for the years 1974-1977, implemented six different types of flexible manufacturing systems (Fig 14). These systems produce a wide variety of parts in batch sizes ranging from 10 to 100 pieces for box-shaped parts and from 20 to 200 parts for rotating parts.

A very complete range of standardized pallets, modular fixture devices, tool exchangers, and part-storage and -retrieval machinery has been developed, enabling groups of machine tools to be readily assembled into systems. On the other hand, the software systems used in

---

14. FMS in Czechoslovakia

System type	Size of machined parts (mm)
For nonrotary parts	
IVU 200	up to 250 x 250 x 250
IVU 400	from 100 x 100[2] up to 400 x 400 x 600[1] up to 630 x 630
IVU 800	up to 400 x 400[2] up to 800 x 800
IVU 1250	from 400 x 400 up to 1250 x 1250[2]
SKODA—NC-N	from 800 x 800 up to 3500 x 2240 x 2000[3]
For rotary parts	
IVU 320	diameter 320 x 320 flange type

[1] Dimensions of the base x height
[2] Dimensions of the base
[3] Mass (weight) of the part up to 20,000 kg

---

15. New DNC projects in Hungary

Factory	Type of parts	No. of machines
Csepel (machine tools)	Box-type castings 600 cu mm	5
EVIG (motors)	Motor housings	4
Szim (machine tools)	Box-type castings	4
HAFE (gearboxes)	Boxes, shafts, and gears	8

Czechoslovakia have so far had rather modest aims and have generally been designed with extensive manual backup facilities.

Czechoslovakia has been an active participant in the international projects of the Council on Mutual Economic Assistance (CMEA) countries for the development of CAD/CAM software, particularly part-programming and cutting-technology-optimization modules. The 3D sculptured-surface program used in the CKD factory (Prague) for NC machining of turbine blades is a familiar example.

Hungary: sophisticated software

Hungary commissioned its first DNC system, consisting of a minicomputer, two lathes, and a robot, in 1973. This system is still in production and has served as the basis for subsequent work. A government project for the years 1975-1980 provided financial backing for implementation of four more DNC-based manufacturing systems (Fig 15).

Of these systems, the first two are in operation, and the third and fourth are expected to become operative this year. The Hungarian systems have been designed with relatively sophisticated software—especially the Csepel system, in which dual minicomputers with a graphic display and a remote data link provide computer-aided design of parts, computer-based NC programming (using the EXAPT system), graphic program checking, process planning, on-line scheduling and production control, tool scheduling, and fixture design.

The sophistication and complexity of these systems has, on the one hand, led to considerable implementation delays but on the other hand, has spurred advanced work on CAD systems.

A fifth system, comprising four lathes, four machining centers, two robots, and a measuring machine, has been implemented jointly by Budapest Technical Univ and two research institutes to accelerate the development and testing of CAD/CAM software.

Hungary has played an active role in

cooperative CMEA projects for CAM-software development, particularly in generative process planning and in NC programming. An interactive graphics-based blanking-die-design and -manufacturing facility using NC wire-EDM has been in operation since 1977.

The country has also developed a small range of simple robots, of which several hundred a year are exported.

Bulgaria: wide range of robots

Bulgaria's major contribution to the manufacturing-automation projects of the Socialist countries has been in robotics. The Bulgarian automation industry has developed a relatively wide range of robots and manipulators with load capacities between 2.5 and 63 kg, which are also extensively used in the FMS projects of the GDR and the USSR.

The first Bulgarian flexible manufacturing system, built for the machining of rotary parts, comprises four lathes and two robots, all under DNC control. A system for the machining of boxlike parts, having four machining centers and a palletized workpiece-transfer system, has also been developed. These systems operate in BTR modes, using Fanuc-licensed Bulgarian NC to operate the machine tools.

The latest and most ambitious Bulgarian CAM project has been the establishment of a system consisting of four NC cylindrical-grinding machines for the manufacture of electric-motor shafts, with workpiece transfer by four PIRIN-type overhead robots. The grinding machines have hydrostatic bearings, a freon cooling system, electrohydraulic stepping-motor drives, and a laser-interferometer measuring device.

Poland: mainly machining cells

A government-sponsored project in Poland led to the development by the Design & Research Center for Machine Tools (CBKO) of three flexible manufacturing systems (Fig 16). The number of machine tools in the first system, the KOR-1, has recently been reduced to two machining centers, suggesting that the Polish project has been directed primarily toward what are essentially machining cells.

In 1980, three manufacturing systems of the KOR-1 type were ordered by Polish machine-tool factories and will be delivered in 1981 (the systems being limited to two machining centers in each). Prototype systems TOR-1 and TOR-1M are being transferred to factories for pilot exploitation. In 1980, a GDR ROTA spur-gear-machining system was purchased by the construction-machinery factory Stalowa Wola but is not in operation yet.

The Polish automation industry has also had plans to enter robot manufacture at the high end of the scale. It bought a manufacturing license from the Swedish ASEA for this purpose; however, this project has not yet yielded a marketable product.

On the other hand, Poland uses more NC machine tools than any other country in Eastern Europe, except the USSR. Various computer-based programming systems are used, including EXAPT and some Polish-developed, fully automatic design and manufacturing programs for such products as spur gears.

The Polish construction-machinery industry (BUMAR) and the shipyards (for example, Gdansk) are extensive users of CAD methods; in the latter, these methods are linked directly to manufacture (NC flame cutting). The aircraft industry is increasingly using sophisticated three-dimensional design and NC programming.

DNC in Rumania

The Bucharest Research & Development Institute for Automation (IPA-TCT) has recently commissioned the first DNC system in Rumania. The control computer of this system is a FELIX C-32 (Rumanian under French license), which controls seven machine tools in a BTR mode. The local control units are from different manufactures: AEG, General Electric, Tesla, and Sperry Vickers. Workpiece programming is done on a larger computer outside the system, with the IFAPT (French) set of programs.

Yugoslavia develops FMS

Prof Peklenik, Ljubljana Univ, is in the process of developing a flexible manufacturing system over the next two years. His starting point is two CNC machines—an Index turning center with Bosch CNC and a Cincinnati Milacron 15HC machining center with Acramatic CNC. These are running two shifts a day and soon will be running three shifts per day, machining parts to help local industry evaluate numerical control for its operations and to become familiar with NC technology.

Peklenik's department carries out much actual production, testing, and analysis work for industry in its student-

run labs, receiving sufficient income to make these labs essentially self-supporting. The work done on these machines is used to develop machinability data, tool-wear and -breakage data, and data on other performance parameters.

Within about a year, three more CNC machines will be added to the group; then DNC will be implemented, followed by automated work transfer and handling, including robots and automatic tool flow. Finally, in about five years, two flexible manufacturing systems—one for parts of rotation and one for prismatic parts—are expected to be operating almost fully automatically around the clock at the university, working and developing data for industry.

Modular design for FMS work stations has been the focus of recent work. To provide industry—especially machine-tool companies—with a generic approach to the design of flexible-manufacturing-system work stations, Peklenik and associates have developed designs for a set of basic machine-tool modules or building blocks from which any desired type of special-purpose work station can be constructed.

Each module has appropriate microprocessors built in. What is unique about these modules however, is that they are not made of cast iron or steel (although certain active elements, such as ways, lead-screw nuts, and clamping surfaces are made from these materials) but are built up from a few basic cells, almost honeycomb in nature, made from lightweight composite materal. The researchers have patented this concept.

Much government funding

Intensive work, backed by considerable government funds, has been carried out in all the Socialist countries toward the development of CAM production and utilization (Fig 17).

The Soviet Union has striven primarily to develop a range of standardized systems that could then be widely applied in Soviet industry. Although no figures are currently available on the number of application sites in the USSR, a relatively good qualitative picture of the situation can be gained from the October 1980 resolution of the Central Committee of the Communist Party and from Premier Leonid Brezhnev's report to the 26th Congress.

Both of these documents have urged more-rapid dissemination of computer-based automation techniques in Soviet industry and have specifically indicated the need to engage the services of defense-sector engineers with appropriate experience to help in this task. The step is significant as a radical departure from the traditional Soviet policy of

16. FMS in Poland

System	Type of parts	No. of machines
KOR-1 (1977)	Box-shaped	5
TOR-1 (1979)	Shafts	3
TOR-1M (1978)	Shafts	2

CAM: an international comparison

strict separation of the civilian and military sectors.

The German Democratic Republic and Czechoslovakia, both with highly developed engineering industries, have been motivated both by internal considerations (particularly the shortage of labor) and by their positions as major machine-tool-export nations to undertake their national projects. Hungary, which has a smaller machine-tool industry but one that is oriented in large measure toward specialization in sophisticated systems for Western export, has also sought to develop a potential in computer systems.

Bulgaria, with dynamically developing machine-tool, robot, and computer industries, has also been motivated mainly by export considerations, while Poland's flexible-manufacturing-system projects were part of her highly intensive industrial-investment program.

Shift toward smaller systems

Although the motivations and emphases have thus differed somewhat, the basic factors of industrial expansion and a long-term shortage of skilled workers were (and, to quite a large extent, continue to be) common to these countries. Recent changes in the economic environment have, however, tended to shift attention toward smaller but more intensively productive systems. The most difficult problem that has emerged in the course of introducing CAM techniques in the countries of Eastern Europe has been the establishment of satisfactory interfaces with the existing industrial environment.

After much deliberation, it was decided during the 1970s not to establish a single, joint, international development project for CAM for the Socialist countries. However, a very intensive exchange of information was maintained, and many bilateral cooperative arrangements were made (for example, GDR use of Bulgarian robots, joint GDR-Czechoslovak development of PC-3 system, and Hungarian use of Czechoslovak pallet and fixture systems).

Several software systems, including a modular NC-programming system, were also jointly developed. Recently, a series of annual symposia has been organized for the exchange of FMS experiences (Karlovy Vary, Odessa), and work has commenced on the international standardization of machine and control interface characteristics and control schematics.

Summing the state of the art

The regional surveys have shown on the one hand that Japan has a considerable lead over Europe. On the other hand, both Western and Eastern Europe, with roughly equal levels of computer-assisted manufacturing automation, are making very considerable (mostly government-backed and coordinated) efforts to accelerate their CAM progress.

The taxonomy of computer-assisted manufacturing systems can be divided into four categories:

■ Flexible manufacturing systems, which were invented and first developed in Europe and the USA, were first applied on a commercial scale in Japan, where some 40 such systems are now in operation. Western and Eastern Europe (each being a region with about three times the population and twice the mechanical-engineering output of Japan) currently have about 25 systems operating in each region.

Currently installed recent Japanese systems are also much more ambitious than most of their European counterparts. Control- and transport-system developments in all three regions have led toward the development of distributed systems, comprising software- and systems-engineering-linked groups of relatively small machining cells. In Japan, these developments are based on fairly clear-cut and well-founded theoretical principles, elaborated as a result of government-backed cooperative research projects; in Europe, similar solutions have tended to emerge as *ad hoc* responses to market and financial pressures.

■ Computer-aided process planning has been an area in which the European region has been better able to keep up. Based on work at such classical centers of metalcutting science as Aachen (FRG), Dresden (GDR), and Minsk and Moscow (USSR), several computer-based programs for such activities as part classification, process-sequence determination, machine-tool and cutting-tool choice, and cutting-value determination have been developed and are widely used.

Although Japan has not excelled in this sphere, the country has been quick to adapt and use US and European results, while concentrating its own efforts on the development of entirely novel technologies (for instance, laser-beam machining).

■ Computer-aided scheduling differs considerably in the three regions because of divergences in the general levels of industrial organization and discipline. In Japan, it has been found possible to abandon batch manufacture in favor of making parts as and when required for assembly, thus reducing buffer stocks to practically zero. Western Europe (particularly the FRG) has been able to

17. CAM in the Socialist countries

| Country | FMS developed for | | No. of sites |
	Rotary parts	Nonrotary parts	
USSR	1971 AU-1*	1976 ASK-1	
	1976 ASV-20	1976 ASK-2	
		1976 ASK-3	NA
		1979 AP-1	
		1979 EDM	
GDR	1971 ROTA*	1971 PRISMA-1*	
	1973 FZ 200	1972 PRISMA-2	5
		1977 PC-3	
Czechoslovakia	IVV 320	IVU 200	
		IVU 400	
		IVU 800	6
		IVU 1250	
		SKODA-NC-N	
Hungary	1973 DNC-73	1980 IGYR-630	
		1979 FIG	
		1981 DIAGON-500	5
		1982 HAFE	
		1978 BME	
Bulgaria	1976 ZMM	1977 ZMM	3
	1979 SSHO		
Poland	1978 TOR-1M	1977 KOR-1	5
	1979 TOR-1		
Rumania		1979 FELIX	1

*obsolete   NA = not available

introduce adequate "classical" scheduling, while, in Eastern Europe, the present status of market and distribution methods has made this possible only in limited cases.

- Robotics is perhaps, at this time, the most dynamically developing system component of computer-based automation in all three regions, with Japan's lead ratio again roughly the same as in FMSs: more than twice as many robots as in Western and Eastern Europe together. It is generally accepted in all three regions that computer-aided manufacturing systems are the only way that nations that are relatively short of highly skilled machining personnel can remain or become competitive in a world market that requires consistently high quality and the ability to switch products and even product ranges at very short notice.

It is this realization, with its obvious commercial and defense corollaries, that has prompted most of the governments surveyed to invest heavily in their national CAM projects. Examples of this are the Japanese, the West German, and the French national projects and the relevant Soviet Party Congress decisions.

Development trends

Japan

The complex structure of machine tools requires the solution of problems concerned primarily with the optimum layout of units with different functions. For example, a machining head and an assembling head may be located close enough to each other that machined parts need not be transferred to another position for assembly. A second concern is simultaneous processing: for example, a part may be drilled on one side while being milled on another side with multiple tools. New design principles for machine tools need to be devised to accommodate these concerns.

The central organization doing research on this subject is the Research Assn for Flexible Manufacturing System Complex Provided with Laser (AM-Feb'81,p98). As part of this so-called National Project, the Toshiba Machinery Co has built an experimental complex unit for machining operations, and the Toyoda Machinery Co has built one for assembly. Classification of the concept was worked out in the preliminary Method for Unmanned Manufacturing (MUM) project. The fundamental problem of eliminating the transfer equipment was solved by developing a technique for transferring a workpiece directly from chuck to chuck ("kissing technique").

Integration depends on software

Integration of a manufacturing system is closely related to the complexity of its hardware. In Japan, however, the main concern is software. Research on the optimum data structure of products, the development of data-management systems, and the standardization of engineering databases are the most important concerns.

The National Project aims at integrating the hardware of various processes. There are three sections in the experimental plant, which will be commissioned in 1984 in the Tsukuba area: the material-processing section, the machining-assembly-inspection section, and the laser section.

Software integration is the central concern among researchers in universities and institutes. Since 1972, a research group of Hokkaido Univ has been developing an integrated system called TIPS. Recently, Prof Okino, leader of this group, has become interested in developing a unit-combining design method that will improve the integrity of design and manufacturing.

Kobe Univ, too, has long done esearch on the integrated software CIMS/PRO, which performs such functions as geometric modeling, process planning for machining, and associating further engineering information, such as tolerance and surface roughness, to the geometric model.

The Manufacturing Laboratory of Tokyo Univ recently began to develop integrated software that can be applied for designing, machining, and inspection. GEOMAP, a geometrical-modeling system developed by Hosaka and Kimura, has been successfully applied for this purpose. Hosaka's method for sculptured surfaces was used, and the project's current goal is total automation of production of mold cavities. Geometrical design of product forms will produce all necessary data to operate a five-axis NC machining center for cavity production, considering such technological factors as thermal deformation of die systems.

Another group at Tokyo Univ, the Design Laboratory, is developing a system called HIMADES for designing complex machines as well as individual parts. Only the process of combining primitives is allowed in this system (no union, no intersection), thus reducing computing time drastically. It has become possible to easily handle many mechanical parts to be assembled into a machine. Original and modified design of machines with complicated structures, as well as process planning of their assembly, has become possible with this system.

Machine communication needed

In addition to the database and its management, input output devices are also very important for the comfort of the people working with a manufacturing system. Unfortunately, the level of these facilities is not satisfactory. For example, generating a product model with an uncomplicated shape takes too much time in a computer. More-efficient languages, such as a general-purpose machine-design language, are expected to be developed.

Not much research is being done on the fundamental problems of worker-machine communication in CAM. A mathematical model proposed for the human thinking process in design may be useful for constructing CAD systems but is not very efficient for CAM.

Some techniques are being developed in industry. A voice-input system for giving commands to a manufacturing system has been developed by Nippon Electric Co, and a handwriting-input system has been investigated by the Institute of Space & Aeronautics Research at Tokyo Univ. Raster-scan color graphics manufactured by Seiko-sha has become commercially available and has been used successfully in machine design, process planning, and NC programming.

Electronics will rule

There is a trend in mechanical equipment to replace complicated mechanical components with electronics, especially microprocessors. Statistics show that this tendency is most eminent in cash registers, of which 98% of production had become electronic by 1981. Watches are second, of which 60% are electronic.

Machine tools are also part of the leading group. Microprocessor-equipped machine tools have been developed successfully by many of the machine-tool builders. The sophistication of this technique can be expected to proceed without difficulty in the future.

In the DNC systems or FMSs currently in use, BTR types are still found even among newly built systems. This seems to be because the systems were transformed into FMSS from conventional NC machines by retrofitting the controllers. Needless to say, the new systems will be controlled by hierarchical computer systems including host computers and intelligent terminals. The replacement of mechanisms by electronics will become more extensive, reducing system cost and lightening the software burden.

Untended shop needs diagnostics

Substantial technical problems seem to have been solved for operating an untended factory experimentally. But the very difficult problem of systems failure hampers the application of the results in practical production. In a conventional factory, any abnormal phenomenon is checked and removed by workers, even if they are not professional maintenance people, before it develops into a large-scale accident involving other system parts and producing a disaster, either economically or physically. The most necessary development here is the automation of diagnosis and repair.

Nearly untended factories have already appeared, especially on the night shift. But it is still very difficult to replace the last worker who monitors the system when it is engaged in flexible production. There is much research on the automation of system diagnosis.

Monitoring of machining status by observing current in the spindle motor is the most popular method for running systems; its reliability, however is not high enough. The use of pattern-recognition techniques for analyzing the current has been reported successful at Tokyo Univ. Acoustic emission for detecting tool breakage seems very promising at Kobe Univ, Kyoto Univ and Keio Univ. Generally, recognition of the need for automation of diagnostics and repair seems to be growing rapidly.

A recently initiated national project is aimed at developing inspection and repair robots to operate in the containment vessels of nuclear plants. Technology transfers are expected from this project to manufacturing because of the common researchers between them. For example, Prof Takamo, of Tokyo Univ

Mechanism Laboratory, is a member of this project and has designed a mobile robot to be used for diagnosis of the untended factory.

The level of automation of assembly is still low, as far as flexible manufacturing is concerned. Pioneering work was done by Hitachi Co, which had developed a system with eight TV "eyes" and artificial intelligence. It was not used practically, but techniques developed through this project have successfully automated production at Hitachi, which recently unveiled a commercially available double-armed assembly robot.

A practical and very sophisticated double-armed gate-type robot has been developed by Nippon Electric Co. Many universities and institutes are developing new robots, some intended to apply to flexible assembly. Yamanashi Univ, for instance is developing a system called an assembly center. Flexible assembly is likely to be untended in the near future, with robots equipped with computers and artificial-intelligence-type software.

Metamorphism holds promise

Highly advanced unit-changeable machine tools, called "metamorphic," are one of the promising techniques to improve the flexibility of manufacturing systems. The metamorphic system will provide the ultimate in metalworking-factory flexibility.

Conventionally, the process provides flexibility by selecting the equipment used, transferring the work from station to station. With metamorphism, however, a machine tool itself may change for different tasks, eliminating the need to transfer workpieces and facilitating process planning by obviating equipment selection.

Much research is needed to make this technique practical. For example, automatic alignment, contact rigidity, and the methodology for optimum combination of units are necessary. Research to develop practical metamorphic systems indicate that the rigidity of such structures is a most serious problem.

Which way flexibility?

Clarification of the concept of "flexibility" is needed. Group technology will provide a more systematic approach to considerations of flexibility in a manufacturing system and will help to establish some of the structural parameters for such a system.

It is necessary to evaluate flexibility quantitatively for the further improvement of flexible manufacturing systems, which will be applied in more and more diversified areas. Such evaluation may indicate the right direction for development, especially for applications in non-

mass-production manufacturing. This problem is discussed frequently at meetings and conferences, but little systematic research has been done. In the National Project, a working group has been organized to establish a quantitative method to evaluate flexibility.

Western Europe

Apart from somewhat special cases in the aerospace industry, CAD/CAM has tended to be very much more CAD than CAM to date. Companies that have initiated CAD or CAD/CAM systems now seem set to extend their systems capabilities toward on-line transfer of data from design to the machine shop. Hargreaves is known to have already extensively tested a BTR-linked laser cutting machine, and developments appear likely to include initial use of a manually operated coded data link via an intelligent terminal at the machine tool. This is thought to reflect a general trend.

A modular approach to CAM software is given general support, if varying interpretation, by those working in the field. The UK's Production Engineering Research Assn (PERA), which is currently developing a series of CAM modules to complement its automated detail-drawing system, is working toward the development of low-cost package-based systems to tackle engineering activities:

- Process routing
- Machine and tool selection
- Detailed operations planning
- NC-tape generation
- Estimating and rate fixing.

More-sophisticated systems are also under development at such places as the Computer Aided Design Centre (Cambridge, UK), where the complexities of form, solid geometry, and general variety continue to offer a challenge to researchers seeking more-comprehensive and efficient algorithms. Increasing R&D is going into creation of computer-simulation facilities for design and operational planning of manufacturing facilities.

Large simulation-language-based models of a logical nature have proved effective but costly. Currently, work is under way to develop low-cost, interactive microprocessor-based models based on closed-loop queueing theory to assist in the early stages of a manufacturing-system-design study. Work like that by Dr Sackett, Bath Univ, on the development of cost-model-based computer-aided process selection and planning is indicative of the future availability of low-cost computer assistance for this purpose.

In Belgium, work being carried out by

Prof Peters, Univ of Leuven, is also central to ongoing research and development. Work on stand-alone CAD/CAM software modules capable of subsequent integration and on family-of-parts based interactive NC-program generation is expected to have particular relevance to industrial CAM developments in the next five years. Predictably perhaps, as the capital requirements of the technology increase, greater emphasis is being placed on software analysis and engineering as a means of reducing total system costs.

Robotics R&D high

In recent years, the level of research into robotics has been extremely high in Western Europe and is still rising. The FRG has the largest robotics-research program; relevant work includes the project at IPA Stuttgart involving automatic assembly in small-batch production. Gripper-changing time has been reduced by flexible grippers with more than one gripper mounted on one arm. This work, which involved investigations into special gripper-changing flanges, has also been concerned with the future implications of multiarm working.

Other extremely pertinent work, being carried out under Prof H.J. Warneke at IPA Stuttgart, is the study of standardized low-cost microprocessor-controlled handling systems. The work at Stuttgart, in general, reflects the belief that future manufacturing systems will be composed increasingly of standardized, computer-controlled handling modules.

Typical of similar work throughout Western Europe is the Swedish Linkoping Univ's study of the use of robots in cellular manufacture and the Swedish Aeronautical Research Institute's (FFA) comparative investigations of universal and multihead grippers. Interestingly, the latter work suggests that comprehensive knowledge of materials technology is required in gripper design. In particular, the study indicates that fast-curing elastic foams and rubbers are important to the fast, economic construction of customized grippers.

In Switzerland, at the Federal Institute of Technology at Lausanne (EPFL), work representative of that being directed at improving robot performance is under way. The ultimate aim of the Mechanical Engineering Dept at EPFL is to produce an advanced general-purpose, six-degrees-of-freedom robot to match human performance in terms of speed and accuracy in assembling small mechanisms.

At the Brown Boveri Research Centre, a prototype robot vision system under development incorporates a commercial TV camera for the recognition of randomly oriented objects of different shape on a moving conveyor belt.

There is currently considerable interest in this field of R&D within Western Europe, with another example of such work being carried out by the Philips Research Laboratories at Redhill, UK. The Philips laboratory is carrying out a major project on parts orientation under visual control. Two cameras examine parts on a table against models held in memory within the computer system.

Work on mobile robots is under way in Toulouse, France, at Laboratoire d'Automatique et d'Analyse des Systèmes (LAAS), where the autonomous HILARE robot is being developed. Recent work on HILARE has included an image-processing system combining input from a video camera providing information about two-dimensional space with that from a laser telemeter providing information about the third dimension.

Robot vision systems continue to be of mainstream research interest to both industry and university. At Warwick Univ, UK, Dr Mike Larcombe is collaborating with a major materials-handling-equipment manufacturer on development of autonomously controlled robot trucks. Such work is seen to be fairly typical of much Western European interest in converting the extensive research on mobile robots into commercial hardware.

At the Polytechnic of Milan, considerable work is being carried out on development of languages and software with a proposal that the Stanford Research Institute-derived (USA) languages AI, POINTY, and SAIL should be extended. In another project, a multipurpose assembly language (MAL) similar to BASIC has been developed.

In the UK, the Cranfield Robots & Automation Group (CRAG) is working on a variety of industrially linked research projects, including development of an advanced prehensile hand for robot assembly tasks, analysis of operational requirements and technical-development constraints in the robot assembly of small mechanisms, and the development of standards in robot control languages. While CRAG's heavy industrial involvements are not typical of other universities throughout Western Europe, there is now an indisputable movement toward far more applied research and industrial project collaboration within the university system. The West German technical universities are considered by many as the model in this respect.

In general, a wide variety of work is being carried out in the field of robotics with emphasis on modular, low-cost, high-performance robots with well-developed sensing capabilities. The stimulus provided by robotics research is clearly becoming closely linked with computer-automated assembly. Flexible automated assembly cells linked to FMS capabilities seem to be the logical outcome of much of current research and development.

FMS standardization an aim

Within the British Automated Small-batch Production (ASP) project, current R&D is centered less on creating untended machining cells in laboratory conditions and more on encouraging five or six "intermediate" industrial projects over the next five years. An increased emphasis on software has been injected into this program, with greater thought being put into ensuring compatibility between the design, manufacture, and management-control functions.

Increasing attention is being given to the study of automated work handling as part of untended machining systems. The work at Zahnradfabrik (FRG) in which a prototype handling device with hydraulic drives and three degrees of freedom transfers palletized workpieces within a deburring and heat-treatment cell, is an example.

Other ZF work in this area includes development of a full production system in which similar production cells are to be linked by an overhead conveyor which also links into adjoining systems. Positioning, testing, work/tool preparation, and changing will be accommodated, and computer control will be responsible for overall material flow. Such work is directed at merging the disciplines of DNC, robotics, and computer-controlled handling systems to form truly integrated production systems.

Much of the work on FMS being carried out in Western Europe appears to be directed toward gradual or evolutionary development of the technology, with efforts to standardize or modularize hardware and software at the earliest opportunity. It is increasingly evident, however, that great variety exists within the quickly growing number of FMS installations. Currently, a major objective of West European countries appears to be that of establishing a sufficient number of different FMS applications to demonstrate the fundamental concepts and technical implications of FMS from practical experience.

Eastern Europe

Most of the government and industrial organizations of Eastern Europe have emphasized CAM development in their current five-year plans (starting January

CAM: an international comparison

1981). The basic considerations of these plans are these:

■ Computers. During the previous five-year period, the Socialist countries have created a large and viable computer industry, with efficient mass production on an international scale of at least two full ranges (ESVM, ESMVM) of compatible computers. They have created semiconductor and other component industries, which are leading to a rapid closing of the "technology gap" in this area, manifested by the present availability of several low-cost, highly reliable microprocessor chips. Gradually, an efficient international installation, maintenance, and software-support organization (NOTO) as emerged, permitting a rapid penetration of computer technology into the manufacturing industries.

■ Standardization. The past period of independent, partly experimental developments in the Socialist countries has, through a series of information exchanges, joint projects, and mutual purchases, initiated a marked process of module and subsystem standardization. This process is most advanced in the Soviet Union, but such other items as the Czechoslovak pallet system, the Bulgarian manipulators and robots for rotary parts, the jointly developed modular programming system for NC machine tools, and the Hungarian CRT dispays have also become *de facto* standard system components. Implementation of systems with "off-the-shelf" systems components, therefore, is increasingly feasible.

Complete turnkey systems for certain universal tasks (transmission or die design and manufacture, for example) are also becoming available. Thus, investment decisions on CAD/CAM systems are moving out of the realm of R&D financing and into the production arena.

■ Numerical-control units. These units are now in mass production in the Soviet Union, and full ranges of microprocessor-based CNC units are readily available for all types of machine tools in the Socialist countries. The consequent proliferation of NC machine tools has led to the widespread introduction of computer-based NC prgramming and the emergence of electronically oriented cadres of experts in industry.

■ Integration. The developments of the previous five years have created a sound background for the integration of CAD, process-planning, scheduling, manufacturing, and quality-control subsystems into high-level integrated systems. Many of the specific system components have been developed, tested, and introduced into industrial practice over recent years, and a set of CAD/CAM program monitors, database systems, and problem-oriented language code/decoders

has been jointly developed to enable these to be easily merged into consistent holisms.

■ Manpower. Skilled machining operators, particularly, will continue to be scarce and increasingly expensive in all of Eastern Europe. At the same time, national economics are under mounting pressure to accelerate the introduction of new products and shorten the innovation cycle. These and other considerations (for example, energy and space saving) add up to an almost universally accepted rationale for investments in flexible and labor-saving manufacturing systems.

Range of joint developments

Acting on these considerations, the countries of Eastern Europe are both jointly and severally engaged in a wide range of CAM developments. Intensive research in the Soviet Union is concentrated on the architecture, operating systems, and databases of hierarchically structured multiprocessor systems. This is coordinated by the Cybernetic Centre of the Ukrainian Academy of Sciences (Kiev). The Institute of Technical Cybernetics at Minsk has launched projects for turnkey CAD systems of typical part and assembly categories, for automatic process planning based on group technology, and for generative process planning, including computer-aided tooling and fixture design. While, on the one hand, stepping up proliferation of CAM systems in industry and devoting extensive R&D resources toward its medium-term goals, the Soviet Union is also funding two major long-term projects: theory of engineering design, system science; and theory of production processes and process planning.

Development plans in the GDR are, on the basis of the experience gained in the previous period, directed primarily at improving the cost/benefit ratios of CAM systems. Particular attention is being devoted to finding a simpler solution for parts transport and to improving the level of organization. The aim of the latter activity is to make FMS-type shops competitive with other types of investment by lowering quality-control costs, improving delivery-time accuracy, improving working conditions, cutting down on paperwork, automatically updating records, and improving the overall information flow.

Apart from plans to introduce FMS into a considerable number of additional factories during the years up to 1985, the GDR machine-tool industry is also developing single- or two-machine stand-alone machining cells, designed to be integrated with subsequent manufacturing systems. The main feature of these cells is a high machining-time/aux-

iliary-time ratio—for example, by permitting machining on five sides in a single clamping position. Other development projects include tool monitoring, machines designed around maintenance criteria, and automated troubleshooting. The further consolidation and expansion of computer-based process planning is also a priority goal.

The research institutes of Czechoslovakia are developing a new generation of production systems, especially for machining, on a higher level of automation of the technological and production processes. These flexible machining system are built on "untended-factory" principles. Six production systems of this type are now being built, three of them for box-shaped parts with maximum dimensions of 400 mm and 800 mm and three for rotating parts with diameters ranging from 20 to 80 mm produced from bars. Three further systems will be specialized for shafts, flanges, and parts produced on vertical lathes.

The CAM-development philosophy in Hungary is also based on a three-tier principle:

■ Developingly high automated NC machine tools suitable for insertion into CAM system.

■ Creating small groups of NC machine tools—technological cells, often equipped with industrial robots.

■ Creating more units of production and control technology on the workshop level.

The combination of these higher-level production systems will enable the creation of production systems in the plants and factories for stand-alone but integratable untended machining cells. At the same time, considerable research resources are being devoted to the development of turnkey systems with microprocessor-based, stand-alone graphic CAD work stations for the design and process planning associated with a broad range of mechanical-engineering products. Combined with the technologically intelligent CNC units now under development, these systems will constitute turnkey CAD/CAM facilities.

Other projects include some industrial applications for previously developed intelligent robots with vision, the expansion of advanced CAD techniques for the design and documentation of CAD/CAM systems, and work on computer-aided maintenance techniques.

Poland does not at this point contemplate further work on FMS development but plans to concentrate on the dissemination of existing computer-aided process-planning and NC-programming methods. The CAD/CAM systems in shipbuilding are, however, expected to be updated.

In Bulgaria, development work on new robot types is proceeding, and four more flexible manufacturing systems are to be built (three for a Bulgarian gear company, one for the GDR). A major effort will be devoted to the proliferation of (mostly minicomputer-based) CAM software in the engineering industry.

In Yugoslavia, a number of plants (such as Litostroj of Ljubljana, Prvomaiska of Zagreb, and Ivo Lola Ribar of Belgrade) are planning to develop CAM systems. CAD/CAM research has two excellent university bases—Ljubljana with Prof Peklenik and Belgrade with Prof Milacic. They have formed an 18-member CAD/CAM research association of universities and companies, which has successfully disseminated NC-programming and process-planning systems.

Summing the developments

Although development trends in the various regions have not been found to be uniform, certain tendencies appear to be universal.

- The proliferation of computer-aided manufacturing methods of all levels has entered a new period of increased acceleration. Although, in Japan, this is manifested primarily in the adaption of very bold and far-reaching projects, in Europe, it is of a more evolutionary character with emphasis on the development of autonomous machining cells that can be integrated into larger systems.

- Electronic control hardware is no longer as central to CAM development projects as it was earlier. Mini- and micro-computers are readily available and adequately reliable. The emphasis has, therefore, shifted toward development of appropriate control software (distributed systems, improved worker-machine communications, etc) and design and development of appropriate mechanical hardware. Machines of a robustness, versatility, and reliability hitherto unknown are having to be developed.

- The flexibility of manufacturing systems is being vastly increased by the appearance of freely routable transport carts and mobile robots for workpiece transfer and the emergence of multirole (ultimately metamorphic) machine tools. These developments permit virtually any workpiece to be machined anywhere at any time.

- Technological process planning—a field in which Europe has been traditionally strong—is assuming a vastly enhanced role, partly as providing automatic links between CAD and CAM, partly as a growing software component of machine-tool-control units. The intelligent controls now emerging need to be told only *what* to manufacture and from what blank. *How* they will machine it, they will determine for themselves. Generative and artificial-intelligence-based

methods are playing an increasingly important role.

- Assembly automation using sophisticated robots with sensory inputs (for example, vision) is being actively pursued in each of the regions.

- Integration of hitherto separate CAD/CAM and quality-control modules into overall systems is today more easily feasible. Efficient commuter-aided techniques are being evolved for orderly, well-designed, and efficient ways of achieving this goal.

- Operation monitoring, early-warning failed detection, localization techniques, and improved maintenance and servicing (diagnostic and repair) technology are all essential for untended night-shift or totally tended operation. They are being rapidly evolved in each of the regions.

Apart from these universally valid points, there are, of course, dissimilarities also. Japanese developments are generally considerably more advanced, Western Europe is paying painstaking attention to the expected financial repercussions of every single step, while an acute shortage of skilled labor is the most important consideration in Eastern Europe. Nevertheless, the outlines of an industrial system incorporating untended factories with metamorphic machine tools is, for one reason at another, accepted by all. Each of the countries surveyed is devoting considerable public resources to fund progress along this path.

Forecast and issues

A deductive procedure was used to forecast the development of computer-aided manufacturing over the next 10 to 15 years. A series of predictions was deduced from a set of hypotheses concerning uncontrollable environmental conditions—such as economics, labor, and social problems—that affect industry. The resulting general predictions can also be considered as design specifications for future systems:

- The future production system must be a resource- and energy-saving system.

- The system must be able to perform highly complicated tasks.

- The system must be able to use the skills of highly qualified people in a satisfying way and be able to communicate with them at an adequate level.

- The system, as a whole, must have high labor productivity.

- The system must satisfy the condition of strict separation of workers and machinery in space and time.

- The system must be highly flexible.

The spacial separation of workers and machines implies that the factory area will be untended. Workers will work in pleasant office-like control rooms and will be mainly concerned with producing information to drive and monitor the untended factory. This can be done through sophisticated software.

The separation in time implies that the factory will continue to operate at night, when no workers are in the control rooms. Self-diagnostic systems that stop the manufacturing system when failures occur are essential for such untended

night-shift operation; self-repairing functions are even preferable.

Future manufacturing systems will be complex, compact structures rather than a series of work stations like those in even highly advanced present-day DNC systems, which depend on transfer equipment, such as pallet conveyors or robots, to move parts from station to station. The complex-structure system will have no such supplementary systems, which will mean savings in equipment and reduced cycle times. Such a structure will also save floor space.

Direct numerical control will still be an efficient way to improve productivity in the future. But, as terminals associated with machine tools become more intelligent through the continuing application of microprocessor technology, the amount of information that needs to be fed to each terminal can be cut down. Consequently, the data-handling burden on the central DNC controller will be decreased, and the labor productivity of the entire system will improve.

Flexibility a central concept

Flexibility will be a central concept of future manufacturing systems. Indeed, it is one of the major reasons that computers are applied to manufacturing. Conventional machine tools, which were originally operated manually, were considerably flexible. Automation was accomplished through sacrifice of this flexibility; automatic lathes and special-purpose transfer lines are typical examples.

The application of numerical control has successfully recovered the flexibility of machine tools without losing the high level of automation, and the combination of NC with computers has made it possible to increase the automation level as a whole. As a result, the flexibility of automatic machine tools has almost reached that of conventional manual machine tools.

In other words, the flexibility achieved through software cannot exceed that of conventional machine tools. The limit of flexibility is determined not by the software but by the machine-tool structure. Therefore, further improvements in flexibility will require changes in machine structure.

Typically, tools and cutters are changed to manufacture components of different shapes. Further flexibility can be achieved by changing the modular components of machine tools themselves. The level of such flexibility can be categorized according to the kind of module to be changed:

- Tools and cutters
- Tool or cutter holders
- Motion-control mechanisms
- Drives
- Motion guides (ways)
- Machine beds

These are degrees of modularity that provide flexibility to the system by changing its hardware, and such a structure may be called metamorphic. The same concept can also be applied to the workholding functions of a machine tool and to chucks and tables and their mounting devices, motion-control mechanisms, drives, motion guides, and machine beds.

Such metamorphic machine tools will constitute one solution to the needs for flexibility greater than that of normal NC machines, which depends solely on tool- and fixturing-changing combined with the flexibility of the software.

Big future for robots

An investigation into the market potential for industrial robots in the Federal Republic of Germany was made by the IPA, which studied a sample of 915 workplaces from 30 companies. Assessing the emergence of robot capabilities beyond the present state of the art, the study predicted that the number of potential applications could rise to include some 35% of the total number of workplaces sampled, suggesting a rapidly increasing robot market that may rise to an annual value $1.2-billion.

CAD/CAM shifts to smaller firms

The virtual monopoly of CAD/CAM systems by the very large companies is now giving way to the increasingly effective use of less sophisticated lower-cost packages by smaller companies. Most of the first large systems were implemented on very cursory financial considerations, a practice in sharp contradiction to the financial practices of most Western (and some Eastern) European countries.

One of the reasons for a certain amount of caution regarding CAM by European manufacturing industries is that it necessitates capital spending in an area that has traditionally been labor-intensive, requiring little capital expenditure. In Japan, industrial financing is based on far more long-term considerations with a full appreciation of the gains that can, in due course, reward a risk-taking strategy.

In countries with centrally planned economies, the economic justification for CAD/CAM investment is usually in terms of resource-saving. In the GDR, for instance, the projects presently under way are expected to increase production by 132-457%, reduce floor area by 30-58%, and shorten production time by 20-62%.

Currently, larger companies' greater commercial pressures, capital resources, and in-house expertise are tending to motivate them to lead in the application of CAM. However, the trend to smaller, lower-cost package systems should enable small and medium-size companies to take a steadily increasing share of the total number of applications.

Generally, it is expected that larger companies will continue to lead in developing comprehensive computer-integrated systems of increasing scale and sophistication. As the larger companies extend and link their systems, the smaller firms should install increasing numbers of CAM packages of limited scope but with potentially high returns on investments. Two-dimensional drafting/NC-tape-preparation and process-planning packages are expected to be particularly important in even small companies' increasing use of CAM during the next five years (Fig 18).

An inevitable direction

In certain areas, such as the development of FMSs, there is general agreement that progress toward the entirely untended factory will be gradual and evolutionary. In practice, few experts envisage FMS developments' putting people out of work or even directly displacing workers of any kind. Rather, there is general agreement that the drive toward this technology is inevitable in the evolution of manufacturing and that, for numerous commercial and political reasons, its full implementation will be sooner rather than later.

As highly automated manufacturing systems proliferate over the next decade, they are expected, for some time, to form elements of otherwise quite conventional industrial structures. In this way, their increasing cost-effectiveness should permit such developments to make a real contribution to the overall competitiveness of the current companies and to provide a positive social role in improving employees' working conditions and job security.

Considerable evidence from CAM applications to date supports the view that the rate at which progress is made

---

COCAM and the Academy

The Committee on Computer-Aided Manufacturing (COCAM) has operated under the auspices of the National Research Council, which is the operating arm of the National Academy of Sciences. The council was established in 1916 to associate the broad community of science and technology with the academy's purpose of furthering knowledge and of advising the federal government.

COCAM work has been funded by the US Air Force. Funding ended Oct 31, 1981.

The National Research Council continues its work on manufacturing through its Manufacturing Studies Board, established in May 1980 to examine leading manufacturing issues for policy-makers. It encompasses many aspects of manufacturing, including productivity, technology, innovation, related basic sciences, human and organizational behavior, governmental policies, social and economic change, and international competition.

18. Estimated distribution

		No. of employees in company		
		1-99	100-499	500+
CAD/CAM applications	Now	2%	8%	50%
	Within 5 to 10 years	15%	35%	90%
DNC/FMS applications	Now	0%	4%	65%
	Within 5 to 10 years	10%	25%	96%
Industrial-robotics applications	Now	5%	12%	45%
	Within 5 to 10 years	20%	35%	83%

toward untended manufacture depends on a combination of the "push" of economic opportunity and the "pull" of diminishing traditional skills.

New skills needed

One broad feature of the CAM developments to date has been the necessity for industrial employees, at all levels, to accommodate change in their roles. This trend looks certain to continue and is already having its effects. The German technical universities are now running engineering courses with a major CAD/CAM content, and the need for innovation is being reflected in the UK by more multidisciplinary courses and new, extended first-degree courses in engineering manufacture. The French government is concerned about the speed with which their universities can create new courses with an appropriate CAD/CAM content and has recently doubled higher-education resources devoted to computer science.

In Japan, "Precision Engineering" departments of universities and colleges have taught manufacturing technology for a long time. During the past ten years, these departments have become most advanced from the viewpoint of computer applications. Almost all the Precision Engineering Departments have started CAD and CAM undergraduate courses. In the University of Tokyo, for example, 30% of graduate students are engaged in CAD/CAM research projects.

The leading Soviet universities have received large investment funds towards the purchase of sufficient computer hardware (mostly minis) to give mechanical-engineering students adequate hands-on experience. Universities in the GDR, Hungary, Yugoslavia, and Czechoslovakia have established experimental (and teaching) CAD/CAM workshops.

Clearly, some areas of manual work will be affected more quickly than others. For highly skilled machine operators, the current trend is to acquire the skills needed for technical support, perhaps NC-tape preparation.

Support staff in the form of maintenance personnel seems to be affected in two ways. First, the expansion of microelectronic hardware and more-sophisticated control systems on the shop floor is creating a positive demand for the retraining of staff on an ongoing basis. Second, the sophistication of advanced automation is tending toward a modular replacement of systems elements, which will, in certain respects, simplify the maintenance electrician's job.

One possibility, in the case of an ill-conceived CAM development, is that computer assistance means that the tasks left for people are reduced in status and interest. In most CAD/CAM systems, however, removing the monotony of drafting, calculating, and detailing frees the engineers' time for the most creative, true design, and judgmental aspects of the work.

In parts machining, the advent of CNC and DNC promotes the skilled person to a technical-support role and creates a demand for efficient palletization, transportation, quality checking, and swarf removal. Current trends indicate that such work can be arranged to provide for an unstructured service role that compares favorably with the service work required for conventional manufacturing systems. The discipline of high automation coupled with reducing costs is, however, likely to encourage progressive automation of such support services.

Beyond the skilled machine workers, there is also a very clear shortage of the technically qualified people, especially engineers, required to design, implement, and support CAM systems. A recent survey in the UK indicates that the shortage of engineers in the robotics field extends to the three following areas:

- Too few engineers within firms.
- Too few entering the profession through universities and technical colleges.
- Too few involved in applications studies prior to equipment purchase.

Similar shortages have been singled out by the GDR, Czechoslovak, and Hungarian industries as being the most important limiting factor in the proliferation of CAD/CAM systems.

Computer science will help

Recent results of computer-science research will contribute significantly to the development and proliferation of CAM systems. The most important of these results are in the following areas:

- Artificial intelligence
- Database technology
- Very-high-level programming languages
- Operating systems and networks
- Computer graphics
- System analysis and design.

Artificial-intelligence research will, in the next few years, provide not only the software for visual pattern recognition in robotics and graphics input or speech recognition and synthesis for vocal communication but also the situation-recognition and decision-making apparatus necessary for failure detection, diagnosis, and the automatic establishment of recovery strategies.

Database technology, particularly the development of minicomputer-based, distributed, and relational databases, will help both to distribute and to integrate CAM systems.

Very-high-level programming languages, such as PASCAL and, more recently, ADA not only will speed programming and make programs more easily transportable but will also provide automatic documentation, permitting on-site program maintenance and enhancement.

New, smaller, and more efficient operating systems are permitting easier use of computer-based systems by people whose expertise lies more in the application field. Networking research, particularly on distributed processing, is laying the foundation for highly resilient, self-configuring, heterarchical systems.

Computer graphics is moving to the shop floor. Control units and maintenance equipment are already communicating graphically with operators, reducing paperwork, and enhancing efficiency. (One joint US-Hungarian project, SMART, has the demonstrated ability to guide medium-skill personnel through the maintenance and repair of highly complex equipment, using a new graphic technique: the logical zoom.)

Enhanced techniques of computer-aided-systems analysis and design are helping to reduce drastically the require-

CAM: an international comparison

ment of skilled personnel in the design and implementation of CAM systems. Computer-hardware developments will also continue to play an important role.

New technologies expected

Traditional metalcutting is a technology that has, in many respects, been pushed to its limits. The appearance of new technologies is already helping, in many cases, to formulate front-edge projects for CAM.

In Japan, laser machining is a central theme of the present phase of the untended-factory project. In the Soviet Union, a flexible manufacturing system has been based on electrical-discharge machining. New evolving technologies for sheetmetal cutting, forming, and welding are based on plasma, electron-beam, and water-jet techniques.

It is obviously very difficult to forecast which of these technologies (or one still undiscovered) will provide opportunities for a new breakthrough, but the world-wide expectation of some such phenomenon is widespread. From the point of view of computer and control technology, for instance, any technique that allows direct, in-process sensing is better than the present chip-making environment, for it will allow more-reliable, optimally regulated process control.

The most important systems trend is the move away from hardware-linked systems toward far more flexible and modular system-linked ones. The essence of this development is that the earlier rigid-track workpiece-transport systems are being replaced by computer-controlled robots (or robot-cars) that navigate freely in the workshop. At the same time, the advent of microprocessors has made it economically and technically possible to constitute largely autonomous cells, capable of long periods of stand-alone operation. These are nevertheless linked to other computers, by which they can be interrogated and which they can in turn interrogate and inform. This kind of system substitutes "nerve-type control" for "muscle-type control" and will be the major factor in the evolution of the new hierarchical and later heter-archical systems.

Another major trend is undoubtedly toward more-compact and low-cost systems, which may, however, be regarded as prospective modules of the former ones. Suppliers of CAD/CAM systems, having established a limited market of large-scale companies, are now concentrating on developing the much larger potential of the medium-sized company. This represents a major growth area with existing users expanding their systems and with intense commercial competition providing increasingly powerful low-cost

stand-alone systems for first-time users. Later, these systems can be linked to form larger systems.

Hardware, software will change

Standardization and modularization are thought to be key elements of future hardware prospects. Modular machine tools, robots, and handling systems will emerge, facilitating the design and implementation of automated manufacturing systems in addition to further reducing costs.

Current work on vision, rangefinding, tactile, and other sensors is expected to lead to intelligent, adaptive robots within five years. With the developments in sensors and control systems, an increasing number of lower-cost robots will become available for repetitive tasks, including some simple assembly tasks.

Color-graphics displays currently entering the popular market are expected to become more widespread as costs reduce. Overall, it may be assumed that the present trend toward a drastic reduction in the hardware-cost component of CAM (including FMS) will continue. Electronic hardware will become a triviality in these systems; the emphasis will shift back to mechanical design (at a much higher level) and to software and, particularly, systems development. Already, Fanuc has a numerical-control unit on one chip. Single-chip robot contols, process planners, etc can also be expected.

The development of CAM software will move away from its present "computer" orientation toward a "technology" orientation. In other words, the operating systems, monitoring problem-oriented languages and processors, natural-language communications, and question-and-answer systems of tomorrow's computers will eliminate the need for architects or users of CAM systems to speak computerese or to learn about the internal workings of computer systems. Instead, they will communicate in their own language, in that of technology, or, toward the end of the century, increasingly in that of logical *science*.

A new, highly dynamic period of CAM has begun in all the industrialized countries of the world. By the turn of this century, the extent to which CAM principles are applied will determine the status of a nation's industries.

The new factory that is emerging will be largely untended, have high operating reliability, and be almost as flexible in its capabilities as the skilled workers with their hand tools. It will supervise, monitor, schedule, diagnose, and repair itself, adapting its own configuration and capabilities to the task at hand.

The path to this factory is dual: partly bottom-up, partly top-down. The bottom-up approach is through the construction of increasingly sophisticated machining cells flexibly linked to one another mainly by software. These cells, which allow untended night-shift operation, are in themselves competitive products. The top-down approach requires the thoughtful and bold development of the overall system of the future factory and its testing through experimentation.

The governments of almost all industrially developed nations have recognized these trends and are giving them active guidance and support. No single nation has the resources to develop the factory of the future alone. Those whose work is the most advanced have been the first to recognize this and act upon it. ∎

INDEX

298